second edition

Authors

FRANK EBOS, Senior Author
Faculty of Education
University of Toronto

BOB ROBINSON
Mathematics Consultant
Hamilton Board of Education

BOB TUCK
Mathematics Consultant
Nipissing Board of Education

Reviewer Consultants

MARY CROWLEY,
Department of Education,
Dalhousie University,
Halifax, Nova Scotia.

ART JORGENSEN,
Jubilee Junior High School,
Edson, Alberta.

BILL KOKOSKIN,
Handsworth Secondary School,
North Vancouver, British Columbia.

MAXINE STINKA,
Canora Composite High School,
Canora, Saskatchewan.

BOB WELLS,
Co-ordinator, Mathematics and Science,
Avalon Consolidated School Board,
St. John's, Newfoundland.

NELSON CANADA

© Nelson Canada, A Division of International
Thomson Limited, 1984

Published in 1984 by
Nelson Canada,
A Division of International Thomson Limited
1120 Birchmount Road
Scarborough, Ontario

ISBN 0-17-601741-0

Canadian Cataloguing in Publication Data

Ebos, Frank, 1939–
    Math is/2

Includes index.
ISBN 0-17-601741-0

1. Mathematics — 1961–   — Juvenile literature.
I. Robinson, Bob, 1936–   II. Tuck, Bob, 1941–
III. Title.

QA107.E47 1984   510   C84-098013-2

The authors wish to express their thanks to Ruta Demery,
Sheila Bassett, Maggie Cheverie, Frank Zsigo, Sarah
Haggard, Rob McPhail, Andrew Clowes, Peter McBride,
and Bill Allan.

The authors gratefully acknowledge the advice and
assistance of Rose Mary Ebos, Jeff MacNabb, Helen
Murphy, Barbara DeCarlo, Mary Pratte, Gaye Beckwith,
Carol Crowther, Carolyne Dunvre, Allan Ford, Don Fraser,
Keith Hill, Elizabeth Lees, Anna Majorins, Doug Potter,
Ron Shepherd, June Thauvette, George Wolaszczyk,
Peter Walpole

Technical Art: Frank Zsigo

Metric Commission Canada has granted permission for use of
the National Symbol for Metric Conversion.

Printed and bound in Canada.
        BP 89109

Photo Credits

p.1 City T.V., Toronto; Ontario Hydro **p.4** NASA **p.6** Rose Mary
Ebos **p.8** Canadian National Exhibition Archives **p.9** Canada
Wide/Shane Harvey **p.19** Arjen Verkaik, Skyart Productions
p.21 Air Canada **p.23** Tourism British Columbia **p.25** NFB
Phototheque ONF **p.29** Ont. Min. of Tourism and Recreation
p.30 MICOM SYSTEMS Inc **p.36** Robert Stocks **p.37** Ont. Min.
of Transp. and Communications; Frank Ebos **p.46** PA 48680/
Public Archives Canada **p.51** Bruce Bassett **p.52** Dr. N.G.
Dengler, Dept. of Botany, U. of Toronto **p.61** Robert Stocks;
Bob Tuck **p.62** Robert Stocks **p.63** Electronics Today
International **pp.68, 71** Robert Stocks **p.75** Athlete Information
Bureau; Rose Mary Ebos **p.78** Robert Stocks; Henry's, Toronto
p.80 Daoust Lalonde Inc.; Robert Stocks **p.81** Ont. Min. of
Natural Resources, Wildlife Branch **p.83** Burger King Canada
Inc **p.93** Athlete Information Bureau **pp.103, 107** Frank Ebos
p.108 Canadian Football League **p.111** Athlete Information
Bureau **p.115** Miller Services Ltd **p.117** Rose Mary Ebos **p.119**
Screenad Ltd.; Dept. of Development, Govt. of Newfoundland
and Labrador **p.120** Paul Kaufhold **p.125** Frank Ebos **p.128**
Toronto Public Library **p.131** Rose Mary Ebos **p.132** Athlete
Information Bureau **p.133** Athlete Information Bureau **p.133**
Miller Services Ltd.; Banting and Best Institute, U. of Toronto
p.138 Tourism British Columbia **p.139** Robert Stocks **p.142**
Frank Ebos **p.146** Robert Stocks **p.147** Imperial Oil Ltd; Paul
Kaufhold **p.149** Robert Stocks; Paul Kaufhold **p.150** Robert
Stocks **p.151** Paul Kaufhold **p.155** Rose Mary Ebos **p.159**
Travel Manitoba **p.162** Frank Ebos **p.165** Ontario Hydro **p.171**
Rose Mary Ebos **p.174** Miller Services Ltd **pp.176, 177, 185**
Frank Ebos **p.190** DeHavilland Aircraft of Canada Ltd **p.193**
Athlete Information Bureau; The Toronto Stock Exchange;
Miller Services Ltd; Atmospheric Environment Service,
Environment Canada **p.194** Athlete Information Bureau **p.197**
Robert Stocks **p.200** Miller Services Ltd **p.202** Rose Mary
Ebos **p.205** Motorola Semiconductors; Ont. Min. of Natural
Resources, Wildlife Branch; The Goodyear Tire and Rubber
Company **p.207** Robert Stocks **p.208** Athlete Information
Bureau **p.209** Miller Services Ltd **p.211** Air Canada; Athlete
Information Bureau; Miller Services Ltd **p.215** NASA **p.216**
Robert Stocks **p.217** Athlete Information Bureau **p.218** Robert
Stocks **p.219** Robert Stocks; NFB Phototheque ONF **pp.225,
226** Robert Stocks **p.236** Metropolitan Toronto Roads and
Traffic Dept. **pp. 242, 244** Robert Stocks **p.251** Soccer News
Magazine **p.262** PA 30803/Public Archives Canada **p.275**
(Top) Robert Stocks; (Bottom) Frank Ebos **p.276** Robert Stocks
p.282 Hitachi (HSC) Canada Inc.; Sound Canada **p.283** Robert
Stocks **p.296** NFB Phototheque ONF **p.301** Travel Alberta
p.305 Netherlands National Tourist Office **p.306** Canadian
National Exhibition Archives; Ont. Min. of Tourism and
Recreation **p.307** Travel Manitoba **p.309** PA 87770/Public
Archives Canada **p.313** Atmospheric Environment Service,
Environment Canada **p.322** Ont. Min. of Tourism and
Recreation **p.327** Paul Kaufhold **p.328** Athlete Information
Bureau **p.350** United Press Canada Ltd **p.354** Dr. F. Doane,
Dept. of Microbiology, U. of Toronto **p.365** Rose Mary Ebos;
Metro Toronto Zoo **p.386** Frank Ebos

p.131 Trident Gum Wrapper courtesy of Adams Brands Inc.
p.189 Thoreau MacDonald, *Hawk at Evening,* 1937, oil on
        canvas, 51.1 × 76.5 cm, Art Gallery of Hamilton, Gift of
        William Colgate Esq. 1954, Cat. No. 54.87.1

Contents

5 working with geometries and constructions

6 applications with ratios, rates, and percent

7 solving problems: data and diagrams

8 fractions: operations and applications

9 integers: addition and subtraction

10 integers: skills with all operations

11 applications: geometries and their relations

12 problem-solving: using equations to solve problems

using Math Is/2

These pages explain how *Math is/2* is organized. They tell you what to look for in each lesson and in every chapter.

Lesson Features

Identifying the lesson
- Look for the lesson number and title.

Teaching
- The lesson begins with the information you need to learn. Look for pictures and photos that illustrate uses of mathematics. New words are printed in **bold type**.
- Examples and Solutions guide you step-by-step through new material.
- Always read the hints and helps printed in special red type.

Exercise
- **Each lesson gives you lots of practice:**

A These questions let you practice the skills and concepts of the lesson. Many of these questions can be done with your teacher and the class.

B These questions give you practice with what you have learned. There are also lots of problems to solve.

C These questions provide an extra challenge, or may involve another approach.

Applications
These sections show how mathematics is a part of the everyday world. You will solve some problems and learn some interesting facts.

6.9 using percent: comparisons

Your understanding of percents can help you make comparisons. For example, the results of a survey are shown.

Survey Question.

		Survey results		
		yes	no	total
Would you like to take a space shuttle ride to the moon?	Bow City	70	55	125
	Cranbrook	22	18	40

Space Shuttle Challenger prepares to touch down after completing its mission carrying the first five-member crew including the first woman astronaut, Sally Ride.

The results are hard to compare because the totals are different. To compare the results, you can use a percent.

$$\frac{\text{number of yes answers}}{\text{total number of answers}}$$

Bow City: $\frac{70}{125} = 0.56 = 56\%$

Cranbrook: $\frac{22}{40} = 0.55 = 55\%$

You could also use your skills with proportion to find the percent.

$\frac{22}{40} = \frac{\square}{100}$ or $\frac{11}{20} = \frac{\square}{100}$

$\frac{55}{100} = \frac{\square}{100}$ Thus $\frac{22}{40} = 55\%$.

When the results are expressed as percents, you can easily compare them.

3.6 exercise

A In these questions, read carefully. Watch the symbols and follow the instructions.

1 Calculate. Watch the symbols. Read carefully!

(a) 3.6 + 4.8

(b) 19.6 − 3.8

(c) 4.9 × 3.8

(d) 10.4 ÷ 4

(e) 28.92 − 12.79

(f) 7.92 × 4.3

(g) 311.4 ÷ 9

(h) 14.26 + 3.96

(i) 8.3 × 9.62

(j) 36.031 − 12.087

(k) 4.608 + 13.396

(l) 15.36 ÷ 16

(m) (16.8)²

(n) 106.536 ÷ 23

2 (a) Find the sum of the following.
   12.39   489   381.4   13.2

(b) Add 26.98 to the sum of 498.73 and 291.64.

(c) Subtract 1.498 from 28.91.

3 (a) Add 129.9 to the sum of 36.3 and 1234.5
   ... m 36.34.

B Remember to look for clues to solve each of the following problems. Round your answers to 1 decimal place or to the nearest cent.

6 Iron is an essential part of hemoglobin in the blood. Twelve helpings of spinach have 50.4 mg of iron. How much iron is in one helping of spinach?

7 The height of a building is 106.9 m. The tower on the building is 16.6 m. Calculate the combined height.

8 The tide at Charlottetown already rose 1.36 m. At the same time, the tide at Truro rose 4 times as high. How high was the tide at Truro?

9 The original price of a friendship ring was $39.65. The recent selling price was $33.95. By how much had the price dropped?

10 At Gander International Airport, the total precipitation during 12 d was 37 mm. Wh... the average precip...

---

applications: designs with regular polygons

Each of the designs shown were constructed from a regular polygon. A **regular polygon** is a polygon that has all angles congruent and all sides congruent.

The following exercise provides the basis for constructing regular polygons as well as designs based on regular polygons. Remember: One complete rotation is 360°.

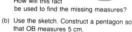

14 An equilateral triangle is inscribed (drawn) in a circle with centre O as shown.

(a) ∠COB is called a **central angle**. Name two other central angles in this diagram.

(b) Measure the central angles ∠AOB, ∠AOC, and ∠BOC. What do you notice?

(c) Explain why ∠AOB + ∠AOC + ∠BOC = 360°.

(d) Why are △AOC, △AOB, △BOC congruent?

(e) What is the measure of ∠AOC?

15 A square is inscribed in a circle as shown.

16 Bradley drew this sketch to help him construct a regular pentagon.

(a) Why is ∠BOA = 72°? How will this fact be used to find the missing measures?

(b) Use the sketch. Construct a pentagon so that OB measures 5 cm.

17 (a) Draw a sketch to show how to construct a regular hexagon.

(b) Use a circle with radius 8.5 cm and construct the hexagon.

18 (a) Use a circle with radius 10 cm. Construct a copy of

Reviews and Tests

These sections review or test skills and concepts *after* every chapter:

- **Skills Quiz**
- **Practice and Problems: A Chapter Review**
- **Test for Practice**

These sections help you review and practise skills from *earlier* chapters:

- **Maintaining Skills**
- **Looking Back: A Cumulative Review**

Problem Solving Features

There are lots of opportunities to learn and practise problem-solving skills — not just in the lessons, but also in special sections based on particular aspects of problem solving:

Solving Problems

Lessons in every chapter give you new problem-solving skills like *deciding which skill to use, looking at patterns, reading carefully, and other strategies.*

- *Problem solving: puzzlers* in every chapter give you a chance to do different types of problems and introduce you to interesting aspects of mathematics. Some show new ways to practice your skills.

- There are also *problem solving: strategy, research, history*.

- *Calculator tips* give you practice with your calculator.

- *Computer tips* will help you learn about Micro computers.

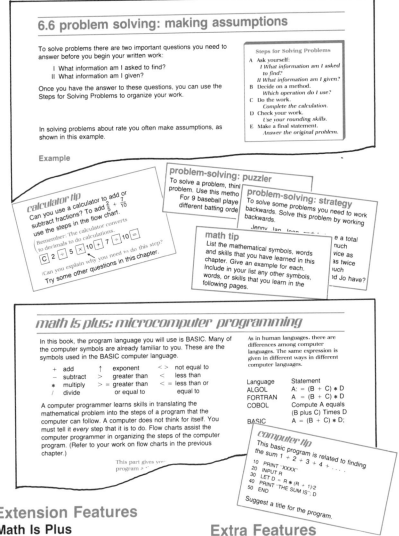

Extension Features

Math Is Plus

These features at the end of most chapters explore a wide range of ideas and enrichment, including calculators, micro computers, probability, coded messages, tangrams and so on.

Math Tips

Do you like learning shortcuts? Are you interested in who "invented" mathematics? *Math Tips* are for you! They are in every chapter.

Extra Features

Math Is/2 includes lots of other special features:

Skills Inventory

Use it to review basic skills from your earlier work in mathematics.

Math Is Glossary

A math dictionary you can use appears in the back of this book.

skills inventories

No matter what you do, you need to practise the basic skills. Using the basic skills quickly and accurately will help you to check answers or to estimate whether answers are reasonable.

The skills inventories are provided to help you develop speed and accuracy. You have used these skills in your earlier work. Use a chart and complete it each time you try each skills inventory.

Skills inventory number				
Date tried				
How many correct				
Time taken				

1 skills inventory: basic skills

4 + 2	8 × 7	7 − 2	28 ÷ 4
2 × 5	17 − 9	15 ÷ 3	8 × 4
54 ÷ 6	5 + 3	3 + 7	14 − 5
6 − 3	2 × 8	35 ÷ 5	5 × 1
6 × 2	9 ÷ 3	8 × 0	9 + 6
16 ÷ 4	8 + 4	42 ÷ 6	9 × 5
8 + 0	5 × 4	12 − 5	3 × 7
4 × 3	6 + 4	16 − 7	72 ÷ 9
4 × 6	27 ÷ 9	6 + 7	32 ÷ 4
8 + 2	8 × 2	30 ÷ 6	7 × 7
11 − 7	9 + 9	7 × 6	9 + 3
7 × 8	3 × 6	24 ÷ 3	8 + 9
48 ÷ 6	7 + 3	72 ÷ 8	14 − 8
6 + 9	12 − 7	7 + 6	5 × 8
18 ÷ 3	4 × 6	7 × 2	13 − 4
4 × 7	35 ÷ 7	9 × 6	10 − 4
6 × 5	13 − 8	3 × 8	16 − 8
3 × 4	8 + 7	8 × 8	4 + 5
5 + 5	24 ÷ 8	5 × 5	30 − 5
9 × 3	7 × 3	36 ÷ 6	14 − 6
18 ÷ 2	63 ÷ 7	7 + 8	6 × 8
12 − 6	40 ÷ 8	7 + 7	36 ÷ 9
4 × 9	9 + 7	45 ÷ 5	11 − 9

2 skills inventory: add, subtract

35 +2	42 −3	14 +2	45 +4	44 −7	53 +4
33 −2	26 +6	46 +3	32 −2	52 −6	74 −5
73 +3	66 −2	39 +5	78 −8	64 +3	24 +4
21 −5	89 +9	32 −5	28 +2	46 −1	16 +7
65 +7	19 −1	58 +4	13 −5	57 +7	31 −4
38 +6	75 +5	49 −7	26 +4	48 −6	49 +8
16 −5	62 +6	88 −7	65 +6	52 +8	58 −9
85 +9	24 −9	71 +8	82 +17	35 −3	49 +2
86 +8	15 −8	84 +7	63 −9	77 −3	52 +9

3 skills inventory: 2 digit addition

The better you add mentally, the quicker you can get problems completed. Try only addition questions this time.

22	86	79	26	51
38	13	19	21	49

71	38	36	66	23
30	38	32	28	49

35	67	44	55	31
66	34	38	20	34

35	38	33	56	49
64	25	69	39	10

37	72	46	51	29
45	11	25	36	27

40	27	48	35	27
53	57	30	54	43

4 skills inventory: 2 digit subtraction

These questions involve only subtraction. How many can you do mentally?

91	35	72	69	48
44	19	20	21	39

49	97	56	28	40
38	38	33	19	27

62	72	55	70	63
25	39	10	53	35

21	45	57	60	41
21	26	38	34	20

28	46	39	39	86
28	29	37	28	16

87	67	69	60	93
11	49	69	11	72

25	42	50	96	63
19	23	43	42	54

5 skills inventory: 2 digit multiplication

Find each product.

17	69	88	29	23	25
×1	×2	×5	×7	×5	×6

12	76	90	94	39	10
×7	×1	×3	×1	×3	×6

54	57	47	82	33	70
×9	×5	×2	×8	×8	×4

41	29	14	47	62	91
×6	×5	×8	×3	×9	×8

50	78	57	50	21	89
×7	×3	×4	×2	×7	×6

66	92	41	32	19	78
×3	×4	×2	×5	×4	×4

83	26	85	33	62	50
×7	×2	×2	×9	×6	×5

75	73	46	35	20	52
×8	×4	×7	×1	×9	×3

6 skills inventory: basic facts

Which inventory can you do faster? Time yourself A or B.

A You need to recall multiplication facts all the time including multiplication by 10. Try to do all these multiplication questions quickly.

6 × 8	7 × 9	7 × 8	3 × 8
4 × 7	6 × 7	9 × 6	6 × 6
5 × 6	9 × 9	7 × 6	8 × 5
9 × 5	5 × 7	3 × 7	6 × 4
5 × 5	9 × 8	4 × 9	10 × 12
8 × 7	3 × 3	6 × 3	4 × 4
8 × 4	8 × 6	5 × 9	3 × 9
10 × 11	8 × 8	4 × 5	7 × 7
10 × 9	10 × 10	14 × 10	6 × 9

B Now time yourself to complete these division facts. (Remember, complete the chart. — Can you improve your time tomorrow?)

81 ÷ 9	30 ÷ 5	18 ÷ 6	24 ÷ 4
56 ÷ 8	15 ÷ 3	54 ÷ 6	20 ÷ 5
72 ÷ 8	25 ÷ 5	27 ÷ 3	14 ÷ 2
12 ÷ 2	35 ÷ 7	42 ÷ 6	24 ÷ 8
49 ÷ 7	40 ÷ 5	63 ÷ 9	20 ÷ 4
32 ÷ 4	42 ÷ 7	64 ÷ 8	45 ÷ 9
32 ÷ 8	36 ÷ 6	18 ÷ 9	27 ÷ 9
12 ÷ 4	48 ÷ 6	21 ÷ 3	48 ÷ 8
16 ÷ 4	36 ÷ 4	28 ÷ 7	72 ÷ 9

7 skills inventory: multiplication and division

Watch the symbols. It is important not to do division when you mean to do multiplication. Each of the following requires basic skills with multiplication and division.

7 × 4	72 ÷ 8	3 × 7	21 ÷ 3
42 ÷ 6	9 × 5	6 × 6	36 ÷ 4
2 × 7	5 × 4	25 ÷ 5	48 ÷ 6
28 ÷ 4	45 ÷ 5	2 × 8	7 × 6
3 × 8	6 × 7	56 ÷ 7	49 ÷ 7
36 ÷ 6	4 × 9	6 × 8	64 ÷ 8
8 × 3	27 ÷ 3	2 × 9	16 ÷ 2
8 × 6	9 × 7	15 ÷ 5	3 × 6
56 ÷ 8	6 × 5	8 × 8	63 ÷ 7
4 × 2	14 ÷ 2	54 ÷ 6	6 × 4
10 ÷ 2	7 × 3	9 ÷ 3	12 ÷ 4
40 ÷ 8	7 × 7	35 ÷ 5	5 × 8
5 × 6	42 ÷ 7	7 × 9	35 ÷ 7
7 × 8	72 ÷ 8	81 ÷ 9	6 × 9

8 skills inventory: vocabulary and symbols

The following words have occurred in your earlier work in mathematics. Use an example to illustrate the meaning of each

addend	equation	number line
addition	estimate	odd number
angle	even number	pattern
area	factor	point
bisect	flip	product
centimetre	fraction	quotient
centre	gram	radius
circle	graph	rectangle
cube	greater than	remainder
data	height	right angle
decimal point	inequality	rounded number
degree	intersect	side
diameter	length	slide
difference	less than	square
digit	line	subtract
distance	line segment	sum
divide	litre	triangle
dividend	metre	turn
divisor	multiple	volume
equal	multiply	whole number

+	−	×	÷	=	<
>	≦	≧	△	m	cm
mm	km	t	mL	L	g
kg	°C	h	s	min	d
a	%	≐			

---

math tip

Throughout the year you will see this feature occurring on different pages in your text. They suggest tips for you to improve your mathematics.

▶ One tip you can begin with is to return to these inventories and try them a number of times. Each time record your results in your chart. Try to improve more and more.

▶ The second tip for you is to watch for the math tips as you begin your study of mathematics.

1 whole numbers: applications and steps for solving problems

Vocabulary and Operations, organizational skills, reasonable answers, language of mathematics, variables and subtitution, rounding skills, microcomputer, problem solving skills, solving problems and applications

Many of the most significant advances in our society have been in the field of communications. Many years ago messages took many days and even months to be delivered. Now messages can be sent around the world in a few seconds.

Mathematicians have played an important role in the development of our sophisticated communication. The principles of mathematics and its symbols are important to know.

Many sophisticated changes have taken place in computing. Today, your lives are touched in many ways by the computer. However, in order for you to work intelligently with a computer you need to understand numbers and their operations. You also need to develop your understanding about many concepts in mathematics.

The most important application of your skills in mathematics is to solve problems. In order to solve a problem, in any subject, you must carefully understand the answer to these two questions.
▶ What information am I asked to find?
▶ What information am I given?
In this chapter you will review some essential mathematical skills and learn about some new ones, as well as develop your skills for solving problems and problem-solving.

1.1 understanding numbers: place value

To communicate information concerning quantities you use numbers. The number system you use is formed by using the ten digits

0, 1, 2, 3, 4, 5, 6, 7, 8, 9

Whether you add, subtract, multiply, or divide numbers, you must have a clear understanding of the numbers you work with.

Place value and face value

Each digit of a number has a certain **place value**. The position of a digit in a number tells *which place* the digit is in — the units place, tens place, hundreds place, and so on. For example:

▶ In the number 15, the digit 5 is in the units or ones place.
▶ In the number 2578, the digit 5 is in the hundreds place.

Each digit of a number has a certain **face value**. The actual digit used (0, 1, 2, 3, 4, 5, 6, 7, 8, 9) tells *how many* ones, tens, hundreds, thousands, and so on there are.

▶ In the number 5164, the digit 5 tells you that there are five thousands.
▶ In the number 3982, the digit 3 tells you that there are three thousands.

Numbers can be written in different forms.
▶ **Standard form** is the most common.
6731 is written in standard form.
▶ **Expanded form** is used to describe the meaning of a number.

Standard form	Expanded form
6731	$= 6000 + 700 + 30 + 1$
	$= 6 \times 1000 + 7 \times 100 + 3 \times 10 + 1$
	$= 6 \times 10^3 + 7 \times 10^2 + 3 \times 10 + 1$

Place value charts also help you read and write numbers.

millions			thousands					
hundreds	tens	ones	hundreds	tens	ones	hundreds	tens	ones
10^8	10^7	10^6	10^5	10^4	10^3	10^2	10^1	1
		7	8	4	5	1	6	3

The number 7 845 163 is read as
seven million, eight hundred, forty-five thousand, one hundred, sixty-three.

Numbers You Use

In early times, various symbols were used to write numbers.

Roman Numerals	Egyptian numerals
IV V XV	IIII ∩ ∩∩∩

The number system you use today is called the decimal number system because there are only ten (from the Latin *deca* meaning 'ten') different number symbols (called numerals) ever used: 1, 2, 3, 4, 5, 6, 7, 8, 9, 0. Any number you can imagine can be written without having to invent any other symbols. This number system can show zero, whereas in the Roman and Egyptian systems, there was no symbol for zero.

hundreds place   tens place

thousands place ⟶ 2578 ⟵ ones place

Remember that
10^2 means 10×10 or 100
10^3 means $10 \times 10 \times 10$ or 1000
10^4 means $10 \times 10 \times 10 \times 10$ or 10 000

1.1 exercise

A

1 For each number, what is the
   ▸ face value of the digit 3?
   ▸ place value of the digit 3?

   (a) 379   (b) 3892   (c) 4093

   (d) 57 831   (e) 307 892   (f) 39 050

   (g) 103   (h) 983 758   (i) 73 002

2 Match the expanded form of the number in
  Column 1 with the standard form of the number
  in Column 2.

Column 1		Column 2
(a) $4 \times 100 + 5 \times 10 + 1$	A	4501
(b) $4 \times 1000 + 5 \times 10 + 1$	B	40 510
(c) $4 \times 10\ 000 + 5 \times 100 +$ 1×10	C	40 051
(d) $4 \times 1000 + 5 \times 100 + 1$	D	451
(e) $4 \times 10\ 000 + 5 \times 10 + 1$	E	4051

3 Write each number in expanded form.

   (a) 489   (b) 7809   (c) 1008

   (d) 301 105   (e) 60 231   (f) 204 789

   (g) 360 102   (h) 300   (i) 2 305 678

4 Construct the chart. Place the following
  numbers in your chart. The first number has
  been done for you.

Meaning	?	?	?	?	?	?	?
	10^6	10^5	10^4	10^3	10^2	10^1	1
(a) 3521				3	5	2	1

   (b) 780 456   (c) 346   (d) 47 931

   (e) 1009   (f) 16   (g) 789 123

   (h) 1030   (i) 40 780   (j) 100 543

   (k) 3761   (l) 969 781

5 Write each number in words.

   (a) 709   (b) 1307   (c) 4009

   (d) 10 905   (e) 48 963   (f) 99 009

   (g) 690 321   (h) 15 231 621

6 Write the following numbers in standard form.

   (a) three hundred, forty-five

   (b) two thousand, one hundred, sixteen

   (c) ninety-five thousand, forty

   (d) one million, one hundred thousand, one

   (e) sixty-five thousand, sixty-four

   (f) three thousand, thirty

B

7 Write the following in standard form.

   (a) $5 \times 1000 + 4 \times 100 + 2 \times 10 + 8 \times 1$

   (b) $9 \times 10^3 + 7 \times 10^2 + 3 \times 1$

   (c) $7 \times 10\ 000 + 2 \times 1000 + 8 \times 100$

   (d) $1 \times 10^3 + 5 \times 10$

   (e) $3 \times 10^4 + 4 \times 10^2 + 9 \times 10$

8 Which number in each pair is greater? Give
  reasons for your answer.

   (a) $6 \times 10 + 3 \times 1$ $2 \times 100 + 6 \times 1$

   (b) $9 \times 10 + 6 \times 1$ $8 \times 10 + 9 \times 1$

   (c) $8 \times 100 + 2 \times 1$
       $3 \times 1000 + 1 \times 100$

   (d) $3 \times 10^3 + 4 \times 10^2$
       $8 \times 10^3 + 4 \times 10 + 3 \times 1$

9 Arrange the following from least to greatest.

   (a) 1020, 1002, 1200

   (b) 2310, 2301, 1302, 1320, 1032

10 Replace ◉ by < or >.

   (a) 4 × 100 + 2 × 1 ◉ 420

   (b) 1080 ◉ 1 × 10 + 8 × 1

   (c) 4 × 10² + 5 × 10 ◉ 405

   (d) 6 × 1000 + 3 × 100 + 4 × 10 ◉ 6349

   (e) 90 799 ◉ 9 × 10⁵ + 8 × 10

   (f) 8 × 10⁴ + 9 × 10³ + 7 × 10² ◉ 89 750

11 On a cheque, the number of dollars is written in words.

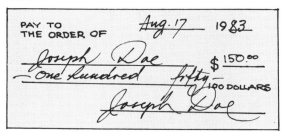

Write each of the following amounts in words.

   (a) $156   (b) $2410   (c) $1048

   (d) $348   (e) $7800   (f) $1005

   (g) $4050   (h) $9001   (i) $3598

12 Write the numbers in the following in standard form.

   (a) Skylab fell on its thirty-four thousand, nine hundred, eighty-first orbit of the earth.

   (b) Lake Superior is about six hundred, thirteen kilometres long.

   (c) The distance from Halifax to Vancouver is six thousand, fifteen kilometres.

   (d) In 1980 Bob Thompson of the Winnipeg Blue Bombers was one of the heaviest football players with a mass of one hundred, thirty-two kilograms.

   (e) The largest garage can hold nine thousand, two hundred, fifty-three cars.

   (f) The greatest advance sale for a record was a Beatles' song, with an amount of two million, one hundred thousand records.

13 The numbers used to describe facts about your solar system are large. Write a number in standard form for each of the following.

   (a) The diameter of the sun is one million, three hundred ninety-two thousand kilometres.

   (b) Jupiter is seven hundred seventy-seven million, nine hundred fifty thousand kilometres from earth.

   (c) The distance across the rings of Saturn is two hundred seventy-three thousand, five hundred kilometres.

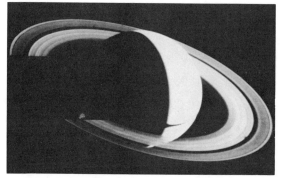

C

14 Did you know that the first colour photograph was shown in 1862? Use the digits of this date to write all the different numbers you can. Then arrange them in order from least to greatest.

calculator tip

Throughout your work in mathematics, a calculator can be useful to have. However, as you probably know, different calculators have different features. Throughout this book, read the calculator tips and try them. But always refer to the manual that comes with your calculator. The manual will give you information about the particular features of your calculator. Each of these numbers occur on the calculator. What is the face value and place value of each digit 5?

   4853   2895   6593   1005
   59 643   503 961   5 106 034

applications: numbers for computers

If you order some item from a catalogue, the item has a catalogue number. Numbers are used in combination with letters to provide a method of ordering items using a computer.

T **Gendron Foldaway Table Tennis.** Folds in half for play-back practice; folds in two for storage. metal skirt and folding tubular legs for easy set-up.
966-549 . . . . **$78.88**

/ These numbers are used to provide a code for ordering the item.

15 Each Canadian can obtain a social insurance number, (S.I.N.).

SOCIAL INSURANCE NUMBER   NUMERO D'ASSURANCE SOCIALE

CANADA
421 817 313
JOSEPH DOE
Joseph Doe

(a) How many persons in your class have a social insurance number?

(b) Who has the greatest S.I.N.?

(c) Who has the least S.I.N.?

(d) Arrange the social insurance numbers in order from least to greatest.

(e) How does a person go about getting a social insurance number?

16 Use the S.I.N.s obtained in the previous question.

(a) How many S.I.N.s have a 5 in the thousands place?

(b) How many S.I.N.s have a 0 in the millions place?

(c) Create a question of your own based on the S.I.N.s.

17 Serial numbers are often used for purposes of identification.

(a) Make a list of items that require a serial number: bicycles, cars, . . .

(b) For each item in your list in (a), obtain a sample of the type of serial number used.

18 Here are 2 ways in which numbers and letters are combined to record items.

Licence plates	Hockey tickets
N22 152	B 1756

(a) Make a list of other items that use letters and numbers to record information.

(b) Provide an example of how numbers and letters are used in (a).

19 Often numbers are used to record secret information. A part of George Hamilton's driver's licence is shown.

H389-40694-10309

He was born March 9 in 1941.

(a) How is the information hidden in the number?

(b) Collect other examples of numbers that hide information.

20 Canada's postal system uses a combination of letters and numbers to identify places.

M3P 1J6

(a) Collect a list of postal codes obtained from letters. Where did the letters come from?

(b) What important information is recorded in each postal code?

1.2 sharpening skills: adding and subtracting

To solve many problems, you need to add or subtract.
List situations that require skills for adding or subtracting.

To add or subtract, you need to use your skills with place value.

Example 1 (a) Add 785 + 861 + 2694

(b) Subtract 4896 − 2398

Solution (a)

```
   785
   861
+ 2694
  4340
```

Think: To add, arrange the numbers in columns according to their place value.

(b)

```
  4896
− 2398
  2498
```

Think: To subtract, arrange the numbers in columns according to their place value.

You need skills with addition or subtraction to calculate how much money you can save. How much money is saved in the photograph?

Remember, you can check subtraction by adding: 2498 + 2398 = 4896.

Every sporting season athletes go through a training camp. They loosen up unused muscles, and sharpen their timing skills. They then use their skills to play the game successfully. In a similar way, as you start your season in mathematics, you practise skills and then apply them to solve problems, as shown in the following example.

To solve any problems, the most important first step is to ask yourself:
I What information am I asked to find?
II What information am I given?
To answer the questions you must read the problem carefully.

Example 2 The Vancouver Sun has a daily circulation of 249 712. The Hamilton Spectator has a circulation of 145 308. How many more newspapers are sold by the Vancouver Sun?

Solution

```
Vancouver Sun        249 712
Hamilton Spectator  − 145 308
                     104 404
```

List the given information.

Subtract to find how many more.

The Vancouver Sun sells 104 404 more newspapers than the Hamilton Spectator.

Make a final statement to answer the problem.

To solve a problem, you must organize your work.

```
Use the given        Decide on a          Do the work to
information.    →     method to use the  →  answer the
                     given information.    question.
```

1.2 exercise

A Before you do the following calculations, try the *skills inventory: addition and subtraction.*

1 Add.

(a) $\begin{array}{r} 45 \\ +34 \end{array}$ (b) $\begin{array}{r} 63 \\ +29 \end{array}$ (c) $\begin{array}{r} 125 \\ +876 \end{array}$

(d) $\begin{array}{r} 789 \\ +\ 65 \end{array}$ (e) $\begin{array}{r} 653 \\ +507 \end{array}$ (f) $\begin{array}{r} 508 \\ +999 \end{array}$

2 Subtract. How can you check your answer?

(a) $\begin{array}{r} 98 \\ -46 \end{array}$ (b) $\begin{array}{r} 54 \\ -46 \end{array}$ (c) $\begin{array}{r} 567 \\ -448 \end{array}$

(d) $\begin{array}{r} 712 \\ -489 \end{array}$ (e) $\begin{array}{r} 650 \\ -448 \end{array}$ (f) $\begin{array}{r} 800 \\ -\ 98 \end{array}$

3 Three possible answers are provided for each question. Which is the correct one?

	A	B	C
(a) 4895 + 756	5641	5651	5551
(b) 4985 + 756	5561	5751	5741
(c) 4985 + 675	5660	5560	5550

4 Calculate.

(a) $\begin{array}{r} 78 \\ +56 \end{array}$ (b) $\begin{array}{r} 64 \\ -49 \end{array}$ (c) $\begin{array}{r} 38 \\ +99 \end{array}$

(d) $\begin{array}{r} 92 \\ -48 \end{array}$ (e) $\begin{array}{r} 48 \\ +52 \end{array}$ (f) $\begin{array}{r} 80 \\ -47 \end{array}$

(g) $\begin{array}{r} 53 \\ -28 \end{array}$ (h) $\begin{array}{r} 84 \\ +87 \end{array}$ (i) $\begin{array}{r} 90 \\ -38 \end{array}$

5 Find the answer.

(a) $\begin{array}{r} 198 \\ +850 \end{array}$ (b) $\begin{array}{r} 890 \\ -455 \end{array}$ (c) $\begin{array}{r} 906 \\ -877 \end{array}$

(d) $\begin{array}{r} 568 \\ +289 \end{array}$ (e) $\begin{array}{r} 700 \\ -499 \end{array}$ (f) $\begin{array}{r} 623 \\ +477 \end{array}$

(g) $\begin{array}{r} 666 \\ +666 \end{array}$ (h) $\begin{array}{r} 800 \\ -488 \end{array}$ (i) $\begin{array}{r} 603 \\ -598 \end{array}$

6 Calculate.

(a) $\begin{array}{r} 708 \\ +296 \end{array}$ (b) $\begin{array}{r} 1991 \\ -\ 879 \end{array}$ (c) $\begin{array}{r} 3691 \\ +2413 \end{array}$

(d) 12 986 + 29 311 + 49 111 − 29 611

(e) 29 361 − 18 760

(f) $\begin{array}{r} 4891 \\ +2389 \end{array}$ (g) $\begin{array}{r} 2396 \\ -1407 \end{array}$ (h) $\begin{array}{r} 4921 \\ -3922 \end{array}$

(i) 444 + 44 + 4 + 4444 + 44 444

(j) (2913 + 4961) − (1321 + 4872)

(k) (48 296 + 28 311) − (19 391 + 31 286)

7 Find the values of ▨.

(a) $\begin{array}{r} 4861 \\ +\ 291 \\ \hline \text{▨} \end{array}$ (b) $\begin{array}{r} 3806 \\ -2981 \\ \hline \text{▨} \end{array}$ (c) $\begin{array}{r} 2819 \\ +\text{▨} \\ \hline 4316 \end{array}$

(d) $\begin{array}{r} 2916 \\ -\text{▨} \\ \hline 1211 \end{array}$ (e) $\begin{array}{r} 4800 \\ -2961 \\ \hline \text{▨} \end{array}$ (f) $\begin{array}{r} \text{▨} \\ -2911 \\ \hline 3191 \end{array}$

(g) $\begin{array}{r} 369 \\ 123 \\ \text{▨} \\ \hline 421 \\ 1132 \end{array}$ (h) $\begin{array}{r} 169 \\ \text{▨} \\ 498 \\ 132 \\ \hline 932 \end{array}$ (i) $\begin{array}{r} 987 \\ 654 \\ 321 \\ \text{▨} \\ \hline 9876 \end{array}$

B

8 Copy and complete the chart for each of the following questions. *Express* the information in your own words. *Then* solve each problem.

I What information are you asked to find?	II What information is given in the problem?

(a) Nerene earned $686 last summer. Jeremey earned $789. Who earned more? How much more?

(b) Calvin collected 1968 kg of newspapers to raise money. Mary collected 3698 kg. How much was collected in all?

continued →

(c) To obtain money for a school trip, $869 was raised. The trip will cost $1983. How much more is needed?

(d) During the vacation, Amber travelled 696 km the first day and 1236 km the next day. How far did she travel in the first two days?

(e) In the first week, a record album sold 23 695 copies. In the next week 28 696 were sold. How many were sold in the two weeks?

(f) The attendance at a soccer game was 11 965. Five minutes before the end of the game there were 9796 people. How many fans left?

(g) Would you believe that a book borrowed in 1823 was returned in 1968? How many years was the book overdue?

9 Energy is given in kilojoules (kJ). A 250 mL glass of chocolate milk has 804 kJ. A 250 mL glass of goat milk has 737 kJ. How many more kilojoules are in a glass of chocolate milk? (Have you ever tasted goat's milk?)

10 The record distance for riding a roller coaster at one time is 16 777 km. The distance between Canada's most easterly and westerly points is 5189 km. How much further was the roller coaster ride?

11 The mass of the elephants in an African exhibit is 29 462 kg. The mass of the hippopotami in the African exhibit is 17 965 kg. Which is heavier? By how much?

12 One day, three Canadian newspapers sold the following amounts.

Calgary Herald	136 456
Halifax Chronicle Herald	72 803
Saskatoon Star Phoenix	54 369

(a) Which newspaper sold the least? the most?

(b) How many papers were sold in all?

(c) How many more Calgary newspapers were sold than Halifax newspapers?

C

13 The number of visitors recorded for each tour is shown.

Tour Package A
Cathedral Grove   12 483
Columbia Ice Fields   6 986

Tour Package B
Mackenzie Delta   16 900
Yukon River   4 696

Which tour package had more people? How many more?

problem-solving: puzzler

There are only 10 chairs in a square room. They are to be placed so that the same number is along each wall. How would you do it?

problem-solving: strategy

To solve some problems, you need to list the possibilities and find the one that works. Try pennies, nickels, dimes, and so on.

There are 13 coins in the jar. The value of the coins is a half dollar. What are the coins?

1.3 rounding off: is my answer reasonable?

Have you ever wondered after you have completed a question whether your answer is correct? To find out, you can do the question again or you can check whether *your answer is reasonable*.

About three million is an example of an **approximate** or **rounded number**. Approximate numbers are found by rounding off. Using your understanding of face value and place value, you can see how to round off numbers to the nearest ten.

Terry Fox raised about three million dollars for Cancer Research during his famous Marathon of Hope run across Canada.

481
482
483
484
} {Look at the ones column. All the digits in the ones column are less than 5.} Round off to 480.

485
486
487
488
489
} {Look at the ones column. All the digits in the ones column are greater than or equal to 5.} Round off to 490.

The skills for rounding off apply to greater numbers.

Example 1   Round each number as indicated.
(a) 4783 to the nearest 100   (b) 15 504 to the nearest 1000

Solution   (a) 4783 ≐ 4800

To round to the nearest 100, look at the tens digit.

(b) 15 504 ≐ 16 000

To round to the nearest 1000, look at the hundreds digit.

Once you learn your skills with rounding off, you can check whether the answer to a problem is reasonable, as shown in the next example.

Example 2   The number of visitors at each exhibit of the zoo are given: African Pavilion   16 183
                                 Reptile Pavilion   9 864

Which pavilion had more visitors? How many more?

Solution

		Check:	
Visitors: African Pavilion	16 183	Rounds to	16 000
Visitors: Reptile Pavilion	9 864	Rounds to	10 000
Subtract	6 319	about	6 000

There were 6319 more visitors at the African Pavilion.

The answer is reasonable.

To check whether the answer was reasonable, you *estimated* the answer using calculations with rounded numbers.
To check whether the answer is *correct*, you either need to do the calculations again, or check using another operation.

Remember: Skills with rounding off help you check whether an answer is reasonable. To check whether it is absolutely correct, you need to either redo the question or do the question in a different way.

```
  16 183      To check the       9 864
 −  9 864     answer, add.      + 6 319
   6 319                         16 183    ✔ Answer is correct.
```

1.3 exercise

A Skills with rounded numbers are important in checking answers.

1 Which place value do you check to round to the nearest

(a) 10?   (b) 100?   (c) 1000?

(d) 10 000?   (e) 100 000?   (f) 1 000 000?

2 Which digit was checked to round each number?

(a) 39 to the nearest 10 is 40.

(b) 124 to the nearest 10 is 120.

(c) 124 to the nearest 100 is 100.

(d) 395 to the nearest 10 is 400.

(e) 395 to the nearest 100 is 400.

(f) 43 587 to the nearest 10 is 43 590.

(g) 43 587 to the nearest 100 is 43 600.

(h) 43 587 to the nearest 1000 is 44 000.

(i) 555 555 to the nearest 100 is 555 600.

(j) 555 555 to the nearest 10 000 is 560 000.

(k) 555 555 to the nearest 1000 is 556 000.

3 Round each number to the nearest ten.

(a) 48   (b) 43   (c) 45

(d) 171   (e) 175   (f) 179

(g) 105   (h) 107   (i) 101

4 Round each number to the nearest hundred.

(a) 258   (b) 248   (c) 298

(d) 1483   (e) 1453   (f) 1433

(g) 5555   (h) 5055   (i) 5505

5 Round each to the nearest ten thousand.

(a) 55 625   (b) 58 625   (c) 53 625

(d) 87 536   (e) 85 736   (f) 81 736

(g) 135 468 (h) 105 468 (i) 195 468

6 Round to the accuracy indicated.

(a) 158 to the nearest 10.

(b) 17 685 to the nearest 10.

(c) 17 685 to the nearest 10 000.

(d) 8555 to the nearest 100.

(e) 8555 to the nearest 1000.

(f) 1 525 785 to the nearest 10 000.

(g) 1 525 785 to the nearest 1000.

(h) 1 525 785 to the nearest 100 000.

7 (a) Round 89 595 to the nearest
       (i) 10 000   (ii) 1000

   (b) What do you notice about your results?

8 (a) Round 999 595 to the nearest
       (i) 10 000   (ii) 1000   (iii) 100 000

   (b) What do you notice about your results?

B

9 Each year the average Canadian spends 10 930 min reading books. Round the number to the nearest

(a) 100 (b) 1000

10 The attendance at the Grey Cup game was 53 692. Round off the number to the nearest

(a) 10 (b) 100 (c) 1000

11 The following numbers have been rounded off. To what accuracy has each been rounded?

(a) The asteroid has a diameter of about 960 km.

(b) There are about 5 500 different languages spoken on earth.

(c) There are about 2 000 000 comets.

(d) Canada has a population of about 24 316 000.

(e) The human brain contains about 10 000 000 000 nerve cells.

12 Round the following to the accuracy indicated.

(a) The largest paper cup held 2154 L of lemonade. (nearest 10 L)

(b) The record for high kicks is 8491. (nearest 100)

(c) The attendance at the game was 15 658. (nearest 100)

(d) The longest book was 4959 pages long. (nearest 100)

(e) The most number of responses to a radio show were 388 299 calls. (nearest 1000)

13 For each calculation, estimate the answer. Then calculate.

(a) 696
    +312

(b) 894
    −429

(c) 3469
    − 875

(d) 8692
    + 365

(e) 9436
    −2189

(f) 6931
    +9876

(g) 28 931
    −14 861

(h) 36 834
    + 9 821

(i) 48 932
    +26 132

14 Questions are shown with 3 estimates. Use rounding skills to choose the most reasonable estimate.

	A	B	C
(a) 89 436 + 10 683	79 000	100 000	89 000
(b) 35 875 − 11 785	48 000	26 000	24 000
(c) 74 655 − 2458	73 000	7300	730 000
(d) 15 254 + 44 766	58 000	60 000	6000

15 For each question, three estimates are given. Which estimate is reasonable?

(a) Lake Nyasa, the deepest lake in Africa, is 1620 m deep. In Canada, The Great Slave Lake is 614 m deep. How much deeper is Lake Nyasa?

A 100 m B 1000 m C 2200 m

(b) During this year Eliza scored 6983 points. She scored 4213 points last year. How many more points did she score this year?
A 300 points B 11 000 points C 3000 points

(c) The mint produced 61 350 one-dollar bills and 38 475 five-dollar bills. How many bills were produced in all?

A 20 000 B 100 000 C 10 000

16 There are 2369 km of paved roads and 6118 km of gravel roads.

(a) About how many kilometres of roads are there in all?

(b) Exactly how many kilometres of roads are there?

17 A whale was tracked 3696 km from the Antarctic to South Africa. A great bull seal travelled 6382 km from Alaska to Mexico.

(a) About how much further did the bull seal travel?

(b) Exactly how much further did the bull seal go?

1.4 vocabulary and operations: whole numbers

To communicate with others, words have been developed to convey a certain meaning. Similarly in mathematics, to be able to talk about the operations of addition, subtraction, and so on, a special vocabulary has been developed.

To do mathematics and solve problems you need to understand the vocabulary. A list of some important words with their meanings is shown.

In addition

$$
\begin{array}{r}
45 \\
+34 \\
\hline
79 \\
\end{array}
$$
(sum)

In subtraction

$$
\begin{array}{r}
89 \\
-15 \\
\hline
74 \\
\end{array}
$$
(difference)

In multiplication

$$
\begin{array}{r}
48 \\
\times 7 \\
\hline
336 \\
\end{array}
$$
(factors) (product)

In division

$$
\begin{array}{r}
408 \\
73 \overline{)29\ 795} \\
29\ 2 \\
\hline
59 \\
0 \\
\hline
595 \\
584 \\
\hline
11 \\
\end{array}
$$
divisor — 73)29 795 (quotient, dividend, remainder

(There are other forms of writing the division operation.
$29\ 795 \div 73$ $\dfrac{29\ 795}{73}$

Often to solve a problem in mathematics, you need to translate carefully and follow instructions accurately.

Example 1   Subtract 497 from the sum of 48 and 568.

Solution   Find the sum.

$$
\begin{array}{r}
568 \\
+\ 48 \\
\hline
616 \\
\end{array}
$$

Subtract from the sum.

$$
\begin{array}{r}
616 \\
-497 \\
\hline
119 \\
\end{array}
$$

Once you have practised skills with numbers, you apply them to solve problems.

Example 2   Lorna was one of 8 people who won a prize of $6000. The prize was shared equally. How much did each person receive?

Solution   Total amount of prize $6000
Shared among 8 people
Each person's share $6000 \div 8 = $750
Thus, each person received $750.

(Remember, to solve a problem, read carefully to answer these two questions:
I   What information am I asked to find?
II What information am I given?

1.4 exercise

A

1 Find each product.

(a) $\begin{array}{r} 32 \\ \times\ 3 \\ \hline \end{array}$ (b) $\begin{array}{r} 48 \\ \times\ 8 \\ \hline \end{array}$ (c) $\begin{array}{r} 86 \\ \times\ 7 \\ \hline \end{array}$

(d) $\begin{array}{r} 480 \\ \times\ 6 \\ \hline \end{array}$ (e) $\begin{array}{r} 206 \\ \times\ 5 \\ \hline \end{array}$ (f) $\begin{array}{r} 330 \\ \times\ 9 \\ \hline \end{array}$

(g) $\begin{array}{r} 3869 \\ \times\ 5 \\ \hline \end{array}$ (h) $\begin{array}{r} 4821 \\ \times\ 9 \\ \hline \end{array}$ (i) $\begin{array}{r} 6926 \\ \times\ 7 \\ \hline \end{array}$

2 Estimate each product. Then calculate.

(a) $\begin{array}{r} 76 \\ \times 28 \\ \hline \end{array}$ (b) $\begin{array}{r} 39 \\ \times 35 \\ \hline \end{array}$ (c) $\begin{array}{r} 43 \\ \times 24 \\ \hline \end{array}$

(d) $\begin{array}{r} 133 \\ \times\ 59 \\ \hline \end{array}$ (e) $\begin{array}{r} 362 \\ \times\ 98 \\ \hline \end{array}$ (f) $\begin{array}{r} 672 \\ \times\ 78 \\ \hline \end{array}$

(g) $\begin{array}{r} 210 \\ \times 617 \\ \hline \end{array}$ (h) $\begin{array}{r} 359 \\ \times 215 \\ \hline \end{array}$ (i) $\begin{array}{r} 334 \\ \times 648 \\ \hline \end{array}$

3 Multiply. $\left(\begin{array}{l}\text{Check whether your answer}\\\text{is reasonable by rounding.}\end{array}\right)$

(a) $\begin{array}{r} 168 \\ \times\ 23 \\ \hline \end{array}$ (b) $\begin{array}{r} 213 \\ \times\ 59 \\ \hline \end{array}$ (c) $\begin{array}{r} 625 \\ \times\ 26 \\ \hline \end{array}$

(d) $\begin{array}{r} 312 \\ \times 416 \\ \hline \end{array}$ (e) $\begin{array}{r} 406 \\ \times 203 \\ \hline \end{array}$ (f) $\begin{array}{r} 589 \\ \times 915 \\ \hline \end{array}$

(g) $\begin{array}{r} 6196 \\ \times\ 28 \\ \hline \end{array}$ (h) $\begin{array}{r} 2096 \\ \times\ 36 \\ \hline \end{array}$ (i) $\begin{array}{r} 8603 \\ \times\ 49 \\ \hline \end{array}$

(j) $\begin{array}{r} 2968 \\ \times\ 318 \\ \hline \end{array}$ (k) $\begin{array}{r} 1693 \\ \times\ 203 \\ \hline \end{array}$ (l) $\begin{array}{r} 8049 \\ \times\ 682 \\ \hline \end{array}$

4 Divide. How many can you do mentally?

(a) $\frac{168}{3}$ (b) $\frac{636}{6}$ (c) $\frac{560}{5}$

(d) $\frac{816}{6}$ (e) $\frac{1001}{7}$ (f) $\frac{840}{30}$

(g) $\frac{2520}{60}$ (h) $\frac{3040}{80}$ (i) $\frac{6210}{90}$

5 Estimate each quotient. Then calculate.

(a) $520 \div 8$ (b) $2024 \div 4$

(c) $426 \div 71$ (d) $504 \div 63$

(e) $1008 \div 36$ (f) $5928 \div 76$

(g) $1596 \div 21$ (h) $7912 \div 92$

6 Divide. Record each remainder.

(a) $\frac{1092}{28}$ (b) $\frac{3318}{42}$ (c) $\frac{3125}{65}$

(d) $\frac{3569}{83}$ (e) $\frac{5549}{76}$ (f) $\frac{7480}{96}$

(g) $\frac{7578}{176}$ (h) $\frac{8268}{212}$ (i) $\frac{7314}{386}$

7 Divide. $\left(\begin{array}{l}\text{Check whether your answer}\\\text{is reasonable.}\end{array}\right)$

(a) $8\overline{)1512}$ (b) $9\overline{)1809}$

(c) $36\overline{)1044}$ (d) $96\overline{)2688}$

(e) $41\overline{)3362}$ (f) $54\overline{)9882}$

(g) $96\overline{)30\ 336}$ (h) $69\overline{)21\ 804}$

(i) $286\overline{)9438}$ (j) $319\overline{)8932}$

(k) $489\overline{)42\ 054}$ (l) $564\overline{)464\ 172}$

8 In each question the number 36 is used in different places. Use an appropriate word from the list to describe its use.

sum	quotient
factor	divisor
product	dividend
numerator	denominator
difference	remainder

(a) $18 + 18 = 36$ (b) $36 \div 2 = 18$

(c) $25 \times 36 = 900$ (d) $108 - 72 = 36$

(e) $48 - 12 = 36$ (f) $864 = 24 \times 36$

(g) $36 = 9 \times 4$ (h) $432 \div 36 = 12$

(i) $\frac{36}{37}$ (j) $\frac{23}{36}$

(k) $1512 \div 42 = 36$ (l) $3456 \div 36 = 96$

B In any questions you try, be sure to read the instructions carefully!

9 Find the value of ■ in each question. Use an appropriate word to describe each use of ■.

(a) $136 - 94 = $ ■ (b) $426 + 291 = $ ■

(c) $448 \div 16 = $ ■ (d) $23 \times 41 = $ ■

(e) $4 \times $ ■ $ = 36$ (f) $36 \div $ ■ $ = 3$

(g) ■ $= 17 \times 36$ (h) $291 - 189 = $ ■

(i) $48 = 6 \times $ ■ (j) ■ $= 700 \div 35$

(k) $560 \div 28 = $ ■ (l) $3 \times $ ■ $ = 27$

(m) $197 + 216 = $ ■ (n) $2 \times 2 \times $ ■ $ = 12$

(o) $672 \div 28 = $ ■ (p) $2 \times $ ■ $ \times $ ■ $ = 8$

(q) $29 \times 31 = $ ■ (r) $100 = 10 \times $ ■

(s) $1000 = 10 \times $ ■ $ \times 10$

(t) $1892 \div 44 = $ ■

10 Multiply. What is special about these questions?

(a) $\begin{array}{r} 2970 \\ \times\ \ 36 \\ \hline \end{array}$ (b) $\begin{array}{r} 1485 \\ \times\ \ 72 \\ \hline \end{array}$ (c) $\begin{array}{r} 495 \\ \times 216 \\ \hline \end{array}$

11 Divide. What is special about these questions?

(a) $\frac{4432}{123}$ (b) $\frac{7440}{169}$ (c) $\frac{20\ 026}{426}$

Try these problems. Be sure to write a final statement to answer your questions. After you do these questions, ask yourself, "How did I organize my solution?"

12 The average person spends about $29 at the fair. How much was spent if 4963 persons visited the fair?

13 A major disaster almost occurred in Mississauga, Ontario, when railway cars overturned and deadly gas was released. If the entire city of 256 070 had to be moved, how many buses were needed? Each bus holds 48 persons sitting and 12 persons standing.

14 A local gardening firm delivers loam to customers. The total supply is 650 m³ of loam. Each truck load delivers 6 m³. How many deliveries could be made?

15 The amount of bacteria in a culture doubles every 2 h. There are 300 bacteria in the container. How many bacteria would there be after 12 h?

16 To calculate the distance you travel on a trip you can use the relationship.

$$\left(\begin{array}{c}\text{distance} \\ \text{travelled}\end{array}\right) = \left(\begin{array}{c}\text{speed} \\ \text{driven}\end{array}\right) \times \left(\begin{array}{c}\text{time} \\ \text{taken}\end{array}\right)$$

(a) James drove at the speed of 80 km/h. How far did he go in 4 h?

(b) Martha drove her bicycle at a speed of 15 km/h. During her trip she drove the bicycle 38 h. How far did she travel by bicycle?

(c) The average speed of the elephant is 26 km/h. How far would the elephant run in 12 h?

C

17 A space probe travels 52 000 km every hour. How long would the space probe take to reach the planet Pluto? Pluto at its furthest distance from Earth is 7 473 000 000 km.

Look for other Calculator Tips.

calculator tip

Calculators may have different appearances, but the principles for using each kind are similar. Before you do any work with a calculator, push C to clear it. This is your *first* step.

problem-solving: puzzler

I am the only 2-digit odd composite number less than 20. Who am I?

1.5 organizing your work: steps for solving problems

In sports, practices and game plans are needed before each game. But, the end results are achieved through the application of the players' skills. When you practise a sport, you often repeat the same successful steps or procedures over and over again.

To solve a problem in mathematics, you also repeat the same steps over and over again. The most important first step is to understand the problem by asking yourself:

    I What information am I asked to find?
    II What information am I given?

Once you know the answers to the previous two questions you need to organize your thinking to solve the problem. The *Steps for Solving Problems* may help you do so. Examine the following problem to see where each step occurs.

> **Steps for Solving Problems**
>
> A Ask yourself:
>   *I What information am I asked to find?*
>   *II What information am I given?*
> B Decide on a method.
>   *Which operation do I use?*
> C Do the work.
>   *Complete the calculation.*
> D Check your work.
>   *Use your rounding skills.*
> E Make a final statement.
>   *Answer the original problem.*

Example   Trina earned $295 in June, $394 in July, and $318 in August.
What was the total amount she earned?

Solution   Her earnings were $295, $394, $318.

Add to find the total.

$$
\begin{array}{rl}
\$\ 295 & \text{about } \$300 \\
394 & \text{about } 400 \\
+318 & \text{about } +300 \\
\hline
\$1007 & \text{about } \$1000
\end{array}
$$

Check whether your answer is reasonable.

Trina's total earnings were $1007.

Remember: Always write a final statement.

1.5 exercise

A For each problem, copy and complete the chart before you do any calculation. Then solve each problem.

I What information am I asked to find?	II What information am I given?

1 In each row of an orchard, there are 24 trees. There are 38 rows. How many trees are there?

2 During one season, 1215 boxes of strawberries were sold. Each crate holds 27 boxes. How many crates were sold?

3 The Computer Club announced that it had increased its membership by 12 persons. If there were 28 members originally, what is the total membership now?

4 Last year 865 students attended Highland Senior School. This year there are 935. By how much did the enrolment increase?

5 The longest frisbee throw is 150 m. The longest recorded distance for throwing a fresh egg (without breaking it, of course) is 105 m. Which is farther? By how much?

B Remember to organize your solution, refer to the *Steps for Solving Problems.*

6 Susan, Bill and Harry collected 128 pop bottles. If they divided the bottles evenly among themselves, how many did each get? How many were left over?

7 At a weather station, a balloon is released every 6 h, day and night. How many balloons are released in a year (not a leap year)?

8 Which is longer? By how much?

(a) A wire fence that encloses the main sheep areas in Queensland, Australia is 5530 km long.

(b) The distance (east-west) across Canada is 6157 km.

9 Supports for a wire fence are placed every 3 m. If the total length of the fence is 198 m, calculate how many posts are needed.

10 At the Arctic Circle, some unusual conditions occur. For example, in Northern Finland, there are 1752 h of constant daylight. How many days is this?

11 During the Hope-a-thon, the following amounts were collected: Mon.—$23, Tues.—$96, Wed.—$83, Thurs.—$115, Fri.—$165. Find the total amount collected.

12 A machine makes 150 cookies every minute. About 36 cookies are placed in a box. How many boxes of cookies would be filled during an 8 h shift?

13 A group of partners withdrew $4488 from its account. It then shared the amount equally between 8 people. If each person pays $12 back into the account, how much does each person keep?

14 The largest snake was reported to be an Anaconda which had a length of 11 m (to the nearest metre). Is this longer or shorter than your classroom? By how much?

15 The Decathlon is an event in the Olympic Games.

The decathlon consists of 10 events completed on 2 consecutive days. Do you know what the 10 events are? One of them is shown on the stamp.

In one of the Olympic Games, Bruce Jenner won the Decathlon with 8618 points. Avilov of the U.S.S.R. received 8369 points, and Kratscher of West Germany received 8411 points.

(a) What were the total points scored?

(b) What was the average?

(c) Which athlete was above average? below average?

16 The Trans-Canada Highway is the longest paved road in the world. The amount of highway in each province is shown in the chart.

Province	Distance (km)
Nfld.	892
P.E.I.	114
N.S.	512
N.B.	628
Que.	644
Ont.	2338
Man.	497
Sask.	653
Alta.	454
B.C.	914
Nat. Parks	225

(a) What is the total length of the Trans-Canada Highway?

(b) What is the average length of the highway in each Province?

C

17 Refer to the chart for the Trans-Canada Highway in the previous question.

(a) Based on the information in the chart, create two questions. Write a solution for each question you create.

(b) Then have another person solve your problems. Compare your solutions. How are your solutions alike? How are they different?

applications: travelling in Canada

A chart is a useful way of showing much information in a compact way. The chart at the bottom of the page shows the distances, in kilometres, between various places in Canada.

Check whether your answer is reasonable.

18 How far is it from Thunder Bay to

(a) Victoria?   (b) Saskatoon?

(c) Quebec City?   (d) Saint John?

19 Which trip is longer: A or B?

A   Saskatoon to Quebec City

B   Regina to Saint John

20 (a) How much further is Vancouver from Toronto than from Regina?

(b) How much shorter is Ottawa from Halifax than from Edmonton?

21 (a) You have travelled half way from St. John's to Vancouver. About how far have you gone?

(b) Use the chart. Which of the cities in part (a) do you live nearest to?

22 (a) Estimate which round trip is longer, A or B?

A: Winnipeg to Edmonton to Ottawa to Winnipeg
B: Calgary to Hamilton to Ottawa to Calgary

(b) Calculate your answer in (a). How close were you?

23 Refer to the chart.

(a) List any cities that you have not used in any of your calculations.

(b) Create a question based on the information in the chart. Use the cities you recorded in (a).

	Calgary	Edmonton	Halifax	Hamilton	Montreal	Ottawa	Quebec City	Regina	Saint John	St. John's	Saskatoon	Thunder Bay	Toronto	Vancouver	Victoria	Winnipeg
Calgary	x	299	4973	3502	3743	3553	4014	764	4664	6344	620	2050	3434	1057	1162	1336
Edmonton	299	x	5013	3523	3764	3574	4035	785	4704	6384	528	2071	3455	1244	1349	1357
Halifax	4973	5013	x	1856	1249	1439	982	4228	309	1989	4485	2942	1489	6050	6154	3656
Hamilton	3502	3523	1856	x	607	467	877	2737	1547	3227	2995	1452	68	4559	4664	2166
Montreal	3743	3764	1249	607	x	190	270	2979	940	2620	3236	1693	539	4801	4905	2408
Ottawa	3553	3574	1439	467	190	x	460	2789	1130	2810	3046	1503	399	4611	4715	2218
Quebec City	4014	4035	982	877	270	460	x	3249	673	2353	3507	1963	809	5071	5176	2678
Regina	764	785	4228	2737	2979	2789	3249	x	3919	5519	257	1286	2670	1822	1926	571
Saint John	4664	4704	309	1547	940	1130	673	3919	x	1727	4176	2633	1479	5741	5845	3347
St. John's	6344	6384	1989	3227	2620	2810	2353	5519	1727	x	5856	4313	3159	7421	7525	5027
Saskatoon	620	528	4485	2995	3236	3046	3507	257	4176	5856	x	1543	2927	1677	1782	829
Thunder Bay	2050	2071	2942	1452	1693	1503	1963	1286	2633	4313	1543	x	1384	3108	3212	715
Toronto	3434	3455	1489	68	539	399	809	2670	1479	3159	2927	1384	x	4492	4596	2099
Vancouver	1057	1244	6050	4559	4801	4611	5071	1822	5741	7421	1677	3108	4492	x	105	2232
Victoria	1162	1349	6154	4664	4905	4715	5176	1926	5845	7525	1782	3212	4596	105	x	2337
Winnipeg	1336	1357	3656	2166	2408	2218	2678	571	3347	5027	829	715	2099	2232	2337	x

1.6 solving problems: looking for clues

Detectives solve mysteries by looking for clues. Solving problems is in some ways different than solving mysteries. However, the need to look for clues is the same. To solve a problem you need to decide on a method. (Refer to the Steps for Solving Problems.) Clues in the problem might suggest a method to use. For example:

The clue you find	→	increased by	fewer
The method you might use	→	add	subtract

A partial list of word clues is shown in the chart. These word clues usually indicate a certain operation. Copy the chart and leave additional space. As you find other words that suggest the operations, add them to your list.

In every section in this book, you will find aspects of problem-solving. However, on special pages, such as this one, certain aspects of problem-solving are summarized and dealt with in detail. Make a list of the problem-solving skills you learn

Clue word	Operation
increased by, more, added to, plus, total, sum, gain, altogether . . .	addition
decreased by, less, minus, reduce, fewer, exceed, deduct, difference, how much more . . .	subtraction
multiply, product, times, doubled, total, in all . . .	multiplication
share, give evenly, divide, distribute . . .	division

1.6 exercise

A For problems 1 to 7.
  ▶ Read the problem carefully:
    I What am I asked to find?
    II What information am I given?
  ▶ Find a clue word. Decide on what operation you likely will use.
  ▶ Then solve the problem.

1 Terri's salary increased by $22. If her original salary was $225, find her total salary now.

2 Dwayne distributed the 450 sheets of paper evenly into 9 sections of his binder. How many pages were put in each section?

3 Donna doubled her weekly running distance. If she ran 38 km last week, how many kilometres did she run this week?

4 By how many metres did Brent's climb of 537 m on Saturday exceed his climb of 468 m on Friday?

5 The Centennials scored 45 points in their first game, 58 in the second, and 53 in the third. How many points were scored altogether in the three games?

6 Brian drove 685 km on Saturday and 486 km on Sunday. How many kilometres did he drive in all?

7 The average cost of a college football game ticket is $5. If the total season receipts are $47 710, how many persons attended?

B 8 Alan made three car models each worth $12 and four plane models each worth $17. Find the total value of the models.

9 Freida scored 6 more points in game 2 than in game 1. If the total points of the two games was 36, find the points scored in each game.

10 At one time the world's most expensive cow was owned by a Canadian. The cost of the cow was $236 000. If 8 persons shared the cost, what was each person's share?

11 Western Canada's first field of wheat was in Saskatchewan's Carrot River Valley. If the seeding took place in 1754, how many years ago was that?

12 Coloured Bristol board sells for 25¢ per sheet, and white sells for 22¢ per sheet. Find the total cost of 2 yellow, 3 blue, and 4 white sheets.

13 The yield from 15 rows of corn with 25 plants per row, was 3000 cobs. How many cobs on the average were there on each plant?

14 The world's largest wiener was brought into the Olympic stadium. It was equivalent to 2063 ordinary wieners. An ordinary wiener is about 38 g. What was the mass of the world's largest wiener?

15 The first Trans-Canada flight took 45 h of flying time. The journey actually lasted 11 d. How much time was spent not flying?

16 Francis won a $20 000 lottery. $4220 was spent, and then the balance was divided evenly between the family of four. Find each person's share.

17 The fastest speaking broadcaster in the world is Jerry Wilmot, a former Canadian hockey commentator. He spoke about 280 words a minute. The average hockey game lasts about 2 h 45 min. How many words would he speak if he spoke continuously?

18 Would you believe that someone has estimated that there are about 105 flashes of lightning every second on earth.

(a) Estimate how many flashes there are in a year.

(b) Calculate how many there are. How do your answers compare?

19 CHAM radio station played the following number of records during September.

Week 1   312   Week 3   169
Week 2   236   Week 4   412

In which part of the month were more records played: first two weeks or last two weeks?

20 The attendance at the first home game of the Calgary Stampeders was 21 650. At the last game only 14 369 fans paid. How many more fans attended the first game?

calculator tip

Does your calculator have a repeat feature for multiplication and division? Try these.

C 3 × 2 = = = ←

If your calculator has a repeat feature for multiplication, then the answer is 24.

C 16 ÷ 2 = = = ←

If your calculator has a repeat feature for division, then the answer is 2.

problem-solving: language of mathematics

To solve a problem in mathematics, you must clearly understand the meanings of the words of mathematics. As well as the symbols. Two words that occur frequently are shown. To learn the language of mathematics look for similarities, such as following.

| equation | equality symbol | meaning | inequation | inequality symbol | meaning |

$8 + 9 \overset{\downarrow}{=} 17$ 8 plus 9 equals 17 $8 + 9 \overset{\downarrow}{<} 18$ 8 plus 9 is less than 18

Equations and inequations together are referred to as **number sentences**.

21 Translate the following into symbols.

  (a) Five added to eight is equal to thirteen.

  (b) Six multiplied by nine is greater than eleven.

  (c) Twenty-four divided by eight is less than five.

22 Write an equation or inequation for each of the following.

  (a) The sum of 14 and 12 is 26.

  (b) The sum of 26 and 13 is less than 40.

  (c) The difference of 48 and 16 is greater than 10.

  (d) The product of 12 and 16 is greater than 100.

  (e) The quotient when 1440 is divided by 45 is 32.

23 For each question
  ▶ write each equation using symbols.
  ▶ find the value of ☐.

  (a) Five times 12 is equal to ☐.

  (b) Eight minus ☐ is equal to 2.

  (c) The sum of 46 and 96 is ☐.

  (d) Eighty divided by ☐ is 20.

  (e) The product of 23 and 14 is ☐.

24 Write a number sentence, using all the symbols given in each set. The first one has been done.

  (a) $\{4, 8, 12, =, +\}$ $4 + 8 = 12$

  (b) $\{6, 5, 30, =, \times\}$ (c) $\{4, 12, 3, =, \div\}$

  (d) $\{8, 12, 20, +, =\}$ (e) $\{6, 8, 48, =, \div\}$

  (f) $\{4, 10, 30, <, \times\}$ (g) $\{7, 4, 9, \times, <\}$

25 Calculate. Read carefully.

  (a) Find the sum of 489 and 283.

  (b) What is the sum of 286 and 983?

  (c) Find the product of 23 and 48.

  (d) Find the quotient for $899 \div 29$.

  (e) What is the quotient when 1230 is divided by 41?

26 Follow these instructions.

  A Subtract the sum of 491 and 261 from 841.

  B Divide the product of 44 and 25 by 55.

  C Multiply the sum of 296 and 381 by 43.

  D Divide the sum of 324 and 432 by 36.

  E Find the remainder when the sum of 486 and 985 is divided by 83.

  Now add your answers in A to E.

1.7 what's the order?

In calculating an expression in mathematics, there are certain rules that need to be followed.

Different values are possible for the expression $3 \times 4 - 6 \div 2$. However, to obtain the *correct* value for the expression, the calculations must be done in a particular order.

In landing, the pilot must follow a certain procedure. Each step must be performed in the right order to land the plane safely.

> **Rules for the Order of Operations**
>
> ▶ Perform the operations in brackets ( ) first.
>
> ▶ Do multiplication or division in the order they appear, left to right.
>
> ▶ Then do addition or subtraction in the order they appear, left to right.

Thus, $3 \times 4 - 6 \div 2 = 12 - 3$
$= 9$

$\left(\begin{array}{l}\text{Do the calculations.}\\\text{Use the rules for the}\\\text{order of operations.}\end{array}\right.$

The rules for the order of operations are also used to obtain the answer in the following example. Which rule is used at each step shown by (?)?

Example 1 Calculate $4 \times 5 - (6 + 9) \div 3$

Solution

$4 \times 5 - (6 + 9) \div 3$
$= 4 \times 5 - 15 \div 3$ (?)
$= 20 - 15 \div 3$ (?)
$= 20 - 5$ (?)
$= 15$

$\left(\begin{array}{l}\text{Be sure to record the original}\\\text{expression each time as the}\\\text{first step of your solution.}\end{array}\right.$

To compute the following expression, apply the rules for the order of operations to the numerator and denominator of the expression.

Example 2 Compute $\dfrac{4 + 5 \times 2}{10 \div 2 + 2}$

Solution

$\dfrac{4 + 5 \times 2}{10 \div 2 + 2} = \dfrac{4 + 10}{5 + 2}$

$= \dfrac{14}{7}$

$= 2$

$\left(\begin{array}{l}\text{Remember: A fraction can be}\\\text{used to indicate division.}\\\dfrac{14}{7}\text{ can mean } 14 \div 7.\end{array}\right.$

1.7 exercise

A

1 Calculate.

   (a) $5 - (3 + 2)$ (b) $14 - 9 \div 3$

   (c) $16 \div 8 \div 2$ (d) $(3 + 2) \times 4$

   (e) $8 \div 4 + 2$ (f) $8 \div 2 \times 4$

   (g) $3 \times 4 \div 6$ (h) $25 - 6 \times 3$

2 Find the value of each expression.

   (a) $16 + 4 - 2$ (b) $16 - 4 + 2$

   (c) $16 \div 4 + 2$ (d) $16 + 4 \div 2$

   (e) $16 \times 4 - 2$ (f) $16 - 4 \times 2$

   How are the above questions alike? How are they different?

3 (a) Calculate each pair.

     (i) $5 \times (3 \times 2)$ $(5 \times 3) \times 2$

     (ii) $8 \times (6 \times 8)$ $(8 \times 6) \times 8$

     (iii) $12 \times (14 \times 8)$ $(12 \times 14) \times 8$

   (b) What do you notice about each pair of answers?

4 (a) Calculate each pair.

     (i) $18 \div (6 \div 3)$ $(18 \div 6) \div 3$

     (ii) $(64 \div 8) \div 4$ $64 \div (8 \div 4)$

     (iii) $45 \div (3 \div 3)$ $(45 \div 3) \div 3$

   (b) What do you notice about each pair of answers?

5 Calculate. Why do the answers for each pair differ?

   (a) $6 \times 5 + 4$ $6 \times (5 + 4)$

   (b) $8 \div 4 + 4$ $8 \div (4 + 4)$

   (c) $32 \div 8 \div 4$ $32 \div (8 \div 4)$

   (d) $8 + 3 \times 5$ $(8 + 3) \times 5$

6 Calculate.

   (a) $3 \times (5 + 2)$ (b) $3 \times (5 - 2)$

   (c) $8 \div (6 - 2)$ (d) $8 \div (6 + 2)$

   (e) $24 \div (3 \times 4)$ (f) $6 \times (12 \div 3)$

   (g) $6 \times 12 \div 3$ (h) $18 \div (9 \times 2)$

7 Compute each of the following.

   (a) $\frac{5 + 7}{2}$ (b) $\frac{7 - 5}{2}$ (c) $\frac{36 - 6}{10}$

   (d) $\frac{8 + 12}{4 + 1}$ (e) $\frac{8 \times 9}{6 \times 2}$ (f) $\frac{18 \div 3}{12 \div 6}$

B

8 Calculate.

   (a) $\frac{(6 + 7) \times 8}{14 - (8 - 2)}$ (b) $\frac{(14 + 2) \div 2}{8 \div (4 \div 2)}$

   (c) $(16 \div 2) - (8 - 2)$

   (d) $(8 - 6) - (9 - 7)$

   (e) $\frac{20 \div 5 + 6}{8 - (12 - 9)}$ (f) $\frac{36 - (3 \times 6)}{12 - (4 + 2)}$

   (g) $8 \times 2 + 3 \times 6 + 4 \times 2$

   (h) $8 \div 4 + 3 \times 2 - 16 \div 8$

   (i) $(14 - 7)(3 + 7)$ $\left(\begin{array}{l}\text{The multiplication sign} \\ \text{is understood.}\end{array}\right)$

9 Replace ● by $<$, $>$, or $=$.

   (a) $6 + (24 \div 3)$ ● $(6 + 24) \div 3$

   (b) $8 \times 4 + 2$ ● $8 \times (4 + 2)$

   (c) $120 \div 4 + 6$ ● $120 \div (4 + 6)$

   (d) $18 \div 9 \div 2$ ● $16 \div 8 \div 2$

10 Evaluate. Then arrange the answers in order from least to greatest.

   (a) $15 \div 3 \times 5$ (b) $16 \times 4 - 2$

   (c) $16 \times (4 - 2)$ (d) $15 \div (3 \times 5)$

11 Calculate.

(a) $\dfrac{3 \times 4 - 2}{12 \div 3 + 1}$ (b) $\dfrac{16 \div 4 + 14}{8 \div 2 - 1}$

(c) $\dfrac{4 + 5 \times 4}{8 - 3 \times 2}$ (d) $\dfrac{3 \times (1 + 3)}{(8 + 12) \div 5}$

(e) $\dfrac{19 - 3 \times 5}{5 - 3 \div 3}$ (f) $\dfrac{36 \div (5 + 1)}{2 + (8 \div 8)}$

12 Calculate. Which expression has the least value?

A $(19 - 6 \div 2) \div (2 + 2)$

B $\dfrac{16 \div 4 - 3}{(8 + 4) \div 12}$ C $\dfrac{8 + 4}{8 - 4} + \dfrac{8 + 38}{21 + 2}$

13 For each expression, place brackets to obtain the value. The first one is done for you.

	Expression	Value
(a)	$36 \div 4 + 2$ $36 \div (4 + 2)$	6
(b)	$16 - 16 \div 4$	0
(c)	$8 + 45 \div 9 - 6$	23
(d)	$27 + 15 \div 3$	14
(e)	$2 \times 4 + 2$	12
(f)	$8 - 3 \div 3 + 1 \times 0$	0

14 The graveyard of the Atlantic is found off Nova Scotia. It is ringed by sand bars and often hidden by fog. The only known nesting area of the Ipswich Sparrow is found here. To find the name of this place write the answers for the following in order from least to greatest.

N $2 \times (4 + 2)$ E $24 - 3 \times (5 + 1)$

A $(9 \times 3) - (8 \times 2)$ S $(16 \div 4) + (25 \div 5)$

D $(26 + 13) \div 3$ B $\dfrac{25 \div 5 - 3}{4 \times 4 - 15}$

I $28 - 3 \times 7$ A $\dfrac{8 + 32 \div 4}{4 \times 4}$

L $2 \times 4 + 2$ S $(8 + 4 \times 3 - 1) \times 0$

L $(15 - 6 \div 2) \div 4$

15 To win a trip to Cathedral Grove you need to answer the skill testing question. Find the sum of the answers to each of the following.

A $3 \times (4 + 2)$ D $3 \times 4 + 2$

B $3 \times (4 - 2)$ E $3 \times (4 \div 2)$

C $3 \times 4 \div 2$ F $8 + 4 \div 2$

Cathedral Grove is found on the western slopes of Vancouver Island. The high rainfall and relatively mild climate create an exceptionally lush forest setting. Your trip will let you camp for a week and sleep among the red cedars, hemlocks, and Douglas firs.

16 (a) The magic number of the magic square is 75. Find the missing values.

?	$3 + 24 \div 8 - 1$	?
?	?	?
$5 \times (6 \div 3 \times 2)$	?	$\dfrac{4 + 4 \times 4}{8 \div 2 - 2}$

(b) Both of the following expressions have the same value.

$\dfrac{6 + 5 \times 2}{9 - 3 \div 3} = 2$ $\dfrac{6 + 6 \times 2}{9 \div 3 + 6} = 2$

Create an expression for each value you find in (a) for the magic square.

1.8 solving problems: more than one step

Many of the problems you have solved required only one operation. You found the solution in one step. However, to solve some problems, more than one operation is required, as shown in the following example.

Example On a computer game, Dwayne scored an average of 15 250 points every 5 min. How many points could he score in 45 min?

Solution Number of points in 5 min   15 250 points

Number of points in 1 min $\frac{15\,250}{5}$ or 3050 points

Number of points in 45 min 45×3050

or 137 250 points

Dwayne could score 137 250 points in 45 min.

It is important that when more than one operation occurs in a problem you should check whether your answer is reasonable after each calculation. An error made in the first step will affect your final answer.

Check your work with a calculator.

1.8 exercise

B For each of the following questions:
  ▶ Decide how many steps are needed to solve each problem.
  ▶ Then solve each problem.

1 The Youth cabin cost $16 485 to build. It cost another $8465 to build the bunks. What was the total cost?

2 By how much does the area of Lake Superior (82 362 km²) exceed the sum of the areas of Lake Huron (59 596 km²) and Lake Ontario (19 477 km²)?

3 In a shipment of oranges, 670 boxes were received. Each box had 64 oranges. How many oranges in all were received?

4 From the concert $1051 was collected. Adult receipts totalled $625. Find the number of students that attended. Each student ticket cost $3.

5 One year a record made $60 450 for a store. In the next year, the record made $8 695 less. How much was made that year?

6 A gas tank holds 455 L. In the first week 183 L of gas were used. If at the end of the second week there were 126 L left, how much gas was used the second week?

7 In a container of plain yogurt there are 628 kJ. How many kilojoules (kJ) would be in a case containing 48 containers?

8 One of the largest planes is the Boeing 747 Jet which carries 365 passengers. All 11 800 persons in St. Albert, Alberta want to go to St. John's, Newfoundland to celebrate the 400th Anniversary. How many round trips would the 747 Jet need to make?

Solve each of the following problems. Be sure to organize your work. Refer to the *Steps for Solving Problems.*

9 During the 3 summer months, the receipts for the Roller Derby are shown.
June $6890   July $8972   August $7650
Including the receipts for September, the total amount collected was $30 692. How much was collected in September?

10 During the Christmas rush, each bag contains about 175 pieces of mail. Of the 175 pieces, about 20 are packages. If there are 35 bags of mail to be sorted, how many pieces are not packages?

11 Forty-eight cases each hold 72 seedlings. How many rows of 54 trees each can be planted in an orchard?

12 In building an end glass wall in a pool, 8 sheets of glass with area 19 m² each were used. If 3 m² was removed for fittings, find the total area of glass used.

13 Did you know that on the average you breathe about 15 times each minute while you are sleeping. Suppose you sleep 8 h each day. How many breaths in all will you take during one year of sleeping?

14 Larry removed 175 g of flour before putting equal amounts in each of 18 jars. If there was 4675 g of flour to start with, then how much flour was in each jar?

15 At Gander International Airport there is a weather station that determines the amount of bright sunshine each month.

Jan.	73 h	May	155 h	Sept.	145 h
Feb.	85 h	June	169 h	Oct.	112 h
Mar.	102 h	July	202 h	Nov.	62 h
April	119 h	Aug.	180 h	Dec.	60 h

(a) What is the average amount of sunshine each month?
(b) Which months are above the average? Which are below?

16 On a tract of land of 913 ha, there are 85 ha of woodland and 765 ha of cultivated land. The remainder is water. How many hectares are water?

17 Jennifer raises worms for bait. At the start of the season she estimated that she had 6900 worms. She picked 2540 worms that summer and sold 8485 worms. How many worms did she have left?

18 During her trip in North America, Loretta travelled 12 465 km in all. She travelled 7825 km in Canada.

(a) How much did she travel in other parts of North America?
(b) Suggest other parts of North America in which Loretta travelled.

C

19 On a computer disk there are 256 bytes per sector, about 19 sectors per track, and 35 tracks per disk. About how many bytes are found on each disk?

calculators and patterns

You can use your calculator to investigate patterns with numbers.

Check whether your answer is reasonable. Use your rounding skills.

20 (a) Find these products.
$11 \times 11 = \square$ $111 \times 111 = \square$

(b) Use your answers in (a) to predict the product, $1111 \times 1111 = \square$. Check your answer.

21 (a) Calculate each of the following.
$1 \times 8 + 1 = \square$
$12 \times 8 + 2 = \square$
$123 \times 8 + 3 = \square$

(b) Use your answers in (a). Predict the answer to
$1234 \times 8 + 4 = \square$
$12\,345 \times 8 + 5 = \square$
Use your calculator to check your prediction.

22 (a) Calculate each of the following.
$5 \times 5 = \square$ $55 \times 5 = \square$
$555 \times 5 = \square$ $5555 \times 5 = \square$

(b) Use your answers in (a). Predict the answers for
$55\,555 \times 5 = \square$ $555\,555 \times 5 = \square$
Use your calculator to check your prediction.

23 (a) Calculate each of the following.
$7 \times 9 = \square$
$77 \times 99 = \square$
$777 \times 999 = \square$

(b) Use your answers in (a). Predict the answer for $7777 \times 9999 = \square$. Use your calculator to check your answer.

(c) Can you use your calculator to find $77\,777 \times 99\,999$? Why or why not?

24 (a) Calculate each of the following.
$3 \times 3 - 2 \times 2 = \square$ $4 \times 4 - 3 \times 3 = \square$
$5 \times 5 - 4 \times 4 = \square$ $6 \times 6 - 5 \times 5 = \square$

(b) Study your answers in (a). Do you see any pattern between the questions and their answers. Use your pattern to predict the answers for
$7 \times 7 - 6 \times 6 = \square$
$16 \times 16 - 15 \times 15 = \square$
$50 \times 50 - 49 \times 49 = \square$
$100 \times 100 - 99 \times 99 = \square$
Check your answers with a calculator.

25 (a) Calculate the products in each box.

A	B
$18 \times 297 = \square$	$23 \times 149 = \square$
$27 \times 198 = \square$	$63 \times 158 = \square$

(b) Study the questions and the answers in each box. The answers in Box B are not like the answers in Box A. What is so special about the products and answers in Box A?

(c) When you think you have the answer in (a), find other products that should fit in Box A. Compare your answers with those of others.

problem-solving: puzzler

Study this question carefully. What sum do you get if the question is turned upside down. Create another pair that have the same property.

808
906
619
818
916
<u>609</u>

math tip

► List the mathematical symbols, words and skills that you learned in this chapter.

► Give an example for each.

1.9 symbols and substitution: variables

To solve problems, you often need to translate from English to mathematics. These translated expressions are written using symbols and numerals.

Expression

In symbols

$\Big($ Fifteen increased by a certain number, n. $\qquad$ $\Big($ $15 + n$, where n represents some number

$15 + n$ is called a **variable expression**. Symbols, such as the letter n, are called **variables** or **placeholders**. Often ▢ or other letters such as x, y, b, etc. are used as placeholders.

$\Big($ Remember, each variable represents some number.

If the number n is given a value of 5, it means to replace n by 5 or write $n = 5$.

$$15 + n = 15 + 5 \longleftarrow n = 5$$
$$= 20$$

Variables are combined with the operations $+$, $-$, $\div$, and $\times$ to construct variable expressions.

$$m + 5m, 5y - y, p \div 2, 2 \times a \longleftarrow \text{(usually written as } 2a\text{)}$$

Expressions may contain more than one variable. To evaluate the expression you substitute the numbers for each variable.

$\Big($ Once you substitute for the variable, you use the rules for the order of operations to evaluate the expression.

Example Evaluate
(a) $2m + 3n$
  where $m = 4$, $n = 6$

(b) $(5a + 4b) \div a$
  where $a = 2$, $b = 3$

Solution
(a) $\quad 2m + 3n$
$\quad = 2 \times 4 + 3 \times 6$
$\quad = 8 + 18$
$\quad = 26$

(b) $\quad (5a + 4b) \div a$
$\quad = (5 \times 2 + 4 \times 3) \div 2$
$\quad = (10 + 12) \div 2$
$\quad = 22 \div 2$
$\quad = 11$

Rules for the Order of Operations

▶ Perform the operations in brackets ( ) first.

▶ Then calculate the powers. Namely, find the value of expressions involving exponents.

▶ Then do multiplication or division in the order they appear.

▶ Then do addition or subtraction in the order they appear.

Often a variable may have more than one value. To show this information in a compact way, symbols are used.

$$3s + 4 \qquad s \in \{2, 3, 4\}$$

$\Big($ means s is replaced by the value 2, 3, or 4 to evaluate the expression, $3s + 4$

Substitution is an important skill needed to aid your problem solving. The exercise that follows will provide practice with this skill.

1.9 exercise

A

1. (a) Find the value of $5m$ if m is replaced by 9.

   (b) The value of k is 3. Find the value of $20k$.

   (c) Replace y by 15 in the expression $36 + y$. What is the value of the expression?

   (d) The variable is replaced by 6. Find the value of the expression $3k - 2$.

2. Find the value of each expression if $a = 6$.

   (means to replace a by 6)

   (a) $3 \times a + 2$

   (b) $3 + a \times 2$

   (c) $a \times a$

   (d) $2a + a \times a$

   (e) $25 - a$

   (f) $(25 - a) \times a$

   (g) $5a$

   (h) $3a + 2a$

3. Use $r = 3$. Match the expression with the value.

   (a) $r + 4$ A   8

   (b) $4r$ B   7

   (c) $4r - 4$ C   2

   (d) $6r \div 9$ D   12

4. (a) Find the value of $2 \times t + 3 \times k$ if $t = 2$ and $k = 3$.

   (b) Find the value of $3a + 5$ if $a = 4$.

   (c) Find the value of $6m - 2n$ if $m = 4$ and $n = 3$.

B

5. Find the value of the expression $3p - 4$ for each of the following.

   (a) $p = 3$ (b) $p = 2$ (c) $p = 8$

6. Evaluate each expression.

   (a) $3m + 2$ $m \in \{0, 1, 2\}$

   (b) $2p - 3$ $p \in \{4, 5, 8\}$

   (c) $8 - k$ $k \in \{1, 2, 5\}$

7. For each expression, the value of s is 2 and t is 3. Evaluate each expression.

   (a) $3s - 2t$

   (b) $3t + 2s$

   (c) $5s - 3t$

   (d) $3 \times s \div 2 + t$

   (e) $3t + 4t - 5$

   (f) $\frac{t + s}{t - s}$

   (g) $4st$

   (h) $2t \div s$

8. An expression A is given by $A = 3p + 2q$. Find the value of A for each of the following.

   (a) $p = 2, \quad q = 0$

   (b) $p = 0, \quad q = 3$

   (c) $p = 4, \quad q = 1$

   (d) $p = 1, \quad q = 4$

9. A team receives 2 points for a win and 1 point for a tie. The total number of points won by a team is given by the expression $2w + t$ where w is the number of games won and t is the number of games tied.

   Calculate $2w + t$ for each of the following.

   (a) $w = 12, t = 5$

   (b) $w = 18, t = 8$

   (c) $w = 12, t = 0$

   (d) $w = 0, t = 5$

10. Refer to the expression in the previous question.

    (a) Find the number of points that each team has in the Canadian Football League.

Team	W	L	T
Concordes	12	3	1
B.C. Lions	7	8	1
Argonauts	12	2	2
Tiger Cats	11	3	1
Stampeders	8	6	2

    (b) Which team is highest in the standings?

    (c) Which team is lowest in the standings?

    (d) How many more wins would the Tiger Cats need to be in first place?

11 The cost in dollars of draperies is represented by the expression $8d where d is the length of the drapes in metres. Find the cost of the draperies of each length.

(a) 2 m   (b) 4 m   (c) 8 m   (d) 15 m

12 Michael works as a guide for the Niagara Parks. His earnings in dollars are shown by the expression
  $4t + 10$ (in dollars) where t is the number of hours worked.
Find the amount earned for each time.

(a) $t = 3$ (b) $t = 5$ (c) $t = 10$

13 The number of cents earned each day picking apples is given by the variable expression
  $95n + 135$ where n represents the number of baskets picked.
Find the amount earned, in cents, if

(a) $n = 10$ (b) $n = 15$ (c) $n = 36$

14 Kenneth sells computer programs and earns $300n in dollars where n represents the number of programs. Find the money earned when he sells the following number of programs.

(a) 6   (b) 8   (c) 12   (d) 20

15 The expression $\frac{n(n + 1)}{2}$ has an interesting property. Copy and complete the chart.

	Step 1: Evaluate the expression.	Step 2: Find the sum.
(a)	for $n = 2$	$1 + 2 = ?$
(b)	for $n = 3$	$1 + 2 + 3 = ?$
(c)	for $n = 4$	$1 + 2 + 3 + 4 = ?$
(d)	for $n = 5$	$1 + 2 + 3 + 4 + 5 = ?$

What do you notice about your answers?

C
16 Use the expression in the previous question. Find the sum of each of the following *without* adding.

(a) $1 + 2 + 3 + 4 + 5 + 6 + 7 + 8 + 9 + 10$

(b) $1 + 2 + 3 + \ldots + 25$

(c) $1 + 2 + 3 + \ldots + 50$ These symbols represent the missing numbers.

(d) $1 + 2 + 3 + \ldots + 100$

skills quiz

In playing sports and games, in playing music, and in anything you do, you develop skills through practice. The *Skills Quizzes* throughout this book will help make you a better player with numbers. How many of these questions can you do mentally?

(a) $18 \times 6 \div 3$ (b) 63×25
(c) $1200 \div 400$ (d) $43 + 212 + 57$
(e) 306×49 (f) $1288 \div 23$
(g) $186 + 23 - 86$ (h) $13 + 6 \times 2$
(i) 50×482 (j) $3195 - 2106$
(k) $15 \times (2 + 8) + 6$ (l) 76×25
(m) $660 \div 55$ (n) $15 \times 5 \times 4 \times 2$
(o) $(13 - 3) \times 12$ (p) $6 \times (37 - 37)$
(q) $2990 \div 65$ (r) $4 \times 86 \times 5$
(s) $5 \times (8 + 3) - 6$ (t) $840 \div 24$

1.10 organizing instructions: flow charts

A computer can only do what it is told to do. It can not think for itself. It is programmed to follow a set of instructions, which must follow a logical order.

▶ Flow charts can be used to organize a list of instructions.

To solve a problem, you also need to organize your thinking and the writing of your solution.

▶ Flow charts can again be used to organize your planning and show the order of steps needed to solve a problem, or do a calculation.

These symbols are used to draw a flow chart.

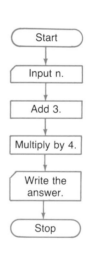

Shows a "start" or "stop" instruction   (START)

Means an "input" instruction | Input 2 |

Shows an "action" or "operation" instruction | Add 3 |

Means an "output" instruction | Write the answer. |

Flow charts tell what steps to follow and in what order. They do so in an easy-to-read 'visual' way.
Read each step in these flow charts. Compare the results.

Example   Use the flow chart and input the given values for $(n + 3) \times 4$.

(a) $n = 5$ (b) $n = 7$

Solution

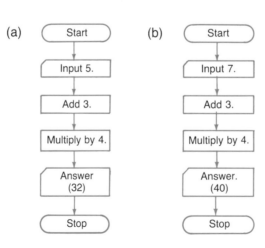

(a)
- Start
- Input 5.
- Add 3.
- Multiply by 4.
- Answer. (32)
- Stop

(b)
- Start
- Input 7.
- Add 3.
- Multiply by 4.
- Answer. (40)
- Stop

- Start
- Input n.
- Add 3.
- Multiply by 4.
- Write the answer.
- Stop

To learn to write instructions for a computer takes a lot of practice. Before you can do this, first you need to learn to organize steps or instructions to calculate the values of expressions. Later, these instructions can be organized for a computer. For example, the flow chart to the right is used to calculate the expression $2n + 4$ for values $n = 0, 2, 4$.

Another symbol used to write this flow chart is called a **decision box**.

To write the values of the expression, you can use a chart. The chart is often called a **table of values**.

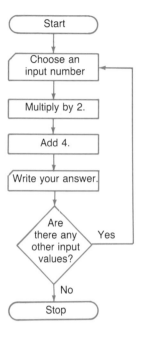

Input Values	Output Values
n	$2n + 4$
0	4
2	8
4	12

Think:
$$2n + 4$$
$$= 2(2) + 4$$
$$= 4 + 4$$
$$= 8$$

1.10 exercise

A

1 (a) The instruction boxes for a flow chart are provided . Use the flow chart to find the output, if the input number is 6.

   (b) Use the flow chart to find the output for each of these numbers.

   12   395
   1028

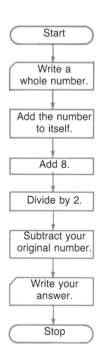

2 (a) Use the input numbers 2, 3, and 4. Follow the instructions of the flow chart.

   (b) Choose input numbers 105, 365, and 496.

   (c) Choose input numbers of your own choice.

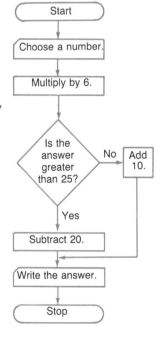

3 (a) Use the flow chart symbols to write a flow chart for the following instructions.

Step 1	Start
Step 2	Write the number 4.
Step 3	Multiply this number by 2.
Step 4	Add 4 to your result.
Step 5	Divide your answer by 2.
Step 6	Subtract 2.
Step 7	Write your answer.
Step 8	Stop.

(b) Work through the flow chart. What is the answer to Step 7?

4 Repeat the list of instructions in the previous question for the following numbers in Step 2. These numbers are called the input.

(a) 48　　　(b) 236　　　(c) 1001

What do you notice about your answers (the output) in Step 7 each time?

B

5 (a) The instructions to multiply 2 numbers on a calculator are shown. Place the instructions in the correct order.

A　press ⊠　　B　Turn calculator on.

C　press ⊟　　D　Enter first number.

E　press Ⓒ　　F　Enter second number.

G　Turn calculator off.

H　Is the answer reasonable?

I　Record the answer.

(b) The instructions to find the average of numbers are shown. Place the instructions in the correct order.

A　Write the answer.　　　D　Add the numbers.

B　Choose the numbers.

C　Start.　　　　　　　　E　Stop.

F　Divide the sum by the number of numbers added.

G　Count how many numbers are added.

6 (a) Write a flow chart to compute the output for $2m - 3$,　$m \in \{2, 3, 4, 5\}$

(b) Construct a chart or table of values to record your values in (a).

7 For each expression:
▶ Construct a flow chart to find the output.
▶ Use a table of values to record the outputs.

(a) $3 + 2y$　　　　$y \in \{5, 10, 15\}$

(b) $2k - 3$　　　　$k \in \{2, 4, 6, 8\}$

8 Suppose you have a combination lock.

(a) Write out a list of instructions to tell someone how to open the lock.

(b) Compare your list of instructions with those of another student. How are your instructions the same? How are they different?

9 (a) You have just arrived at your classroom door. A blindfolded person is with you. What instructions do you need to give this person to go to your place in the classroom?

(b) Write out a list of instructions which will enable a friend of yours to leave the front door of your school and arrive at the front door of your home.

C

10 The instructions to make a phone call are scrambled. Place the list of instructions in the correct order.

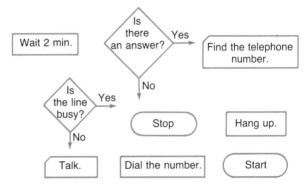

1.11 problem-solving: what information is relevant?

To solve a problem, you need to use the information that is relevant. Very often unnecessary information occurs in a problem. Sometimes you even need to read a text or an encyclopedia to obtain information you require. You need to be able to choose only the information that will help you solve the problem.

Each of the following problems have extra information. Copy and complete the chart.

(For any problem, remember
 to organize your solution.

Steps for Solving Problems

A Ask yourself:
   I *What information am I asked to find?*
   II *What information am I given?*
B Decide on a method.
   Which operation do I use?
C Do the work.
   Complete the calculation.
D Check your work.
   Use your rounding skills.
E Make a final statement.
   Answer the original problem.

Relevant information needed to solve the problem.	Information not needed to solve the problem.

1 This year, the Athletic Club increased its membership by 128 persons. Of these 46 were females. If the membership last year was 438, how many members are there now?

2 A crate of strawberries holds 24 boxes. A shipment had 4625 crates. About 2000 of these are going to Hudson Bay. How many boxes of strawberries are there in all?

3 Jeremy travels 48 km to work each day. He travels 16 km on highway. How far does he travel if he works 220 d in a year?

4 The plane travelled 1065 m on the runway before taking off. The runway is 2500 m long and 320 m wide. How much extra runway did the pilot have?

5 This year, the total number of points scored by the Bengals is 3695 points. About 1620 points were scored on road trips. Last year the Bengals scored 2869 points. By how many points have the Bengals improved?

A chart often contains more information than you need. You need to be able to choose only that information that is relevant to the problem. Use the information in the chart. The attendance at the Gardens is shown for a 12 mon period.

Jan.	4653	May	2196	Sept.	2865
Feb.	3196	June	1896	Oct.	4696
Mar.	6938	July	1283	Nov.	5698
Apr.	5216	Aug.	1492	Dec.	7893

6 Which month had

   (a) the greatest summer attendance?

   (b) the least winter attendance?

7 Last year, the circus was at the Gardens during the months of October, November, and December, and 3695 people saw it. How many persons were in attendance at another event during the time of the circus?

8 (a) List the information that was not used in the chart to answer any questions.

   (b) Use the information in (a) and create a question based on the information. Solve it.

practice and problems: a chapter review

(1.1) 1 What is the place value of the digit 7 in each of the following?

(a) 4576   (b) 13 792

(c) 79 693   (d) 67 892

(e) 476 153   (f) 7 006 863

(g) Write each number above in words.

(h) Write each number above in expanded form.

(1.2) 2 Calculate.

(a)   4783   (b)   3876
      +3128   + 128

(c) 384 + 147 + 803

(d)   4741   (e)   4000
      − 1358   − 857

(1.3) 3 Round each number.

(a) 753 (nearest 10)

(b) 9685 (nearest 100)

(c) 55 460 (nearest 1000)

4 Round the information to the nearest 1000.

(a) The largest active volcano (Mauna Kea) is 4104 m high.

(b) A marathon is 42 195 m long.

(c) Canada has an area of 9 971 875 m².

(1.4) 5 Calculate. Check your answers.

(a)   736   (b)   407
     × 58   ×309

(c)   542   (d) $\frac{2176}{32}$
     ×908

(e) $64\overline{)58\ 048}$ (f) 137 430 ÷ 27

6 Find the remainder.

(a) $\frac{84\ 763}{49}$ (b) $67\overline{)54\ 113}$

(c) 12 359 ÷ 19

(1.5) 7 (a) A can of tuna has a mass of 225 g. Find the mass of 10 cases. Each case has 48 cans.

(b) A container holds 983 mL of cooking sauce. How many portions of 78 mL can be made?

(1.6) 8 The Western Football final had a paid attendance of 59 409 while the Eastern final had a record attendance of 54 530. How many more attended the Western final?

9 Deposits of $1534 and $894 were made into an account with a balance of $12 458. What is the final balance?

(1.7) 10 Calculate.

(a) 5 × 8 − 3   (b) 5 × (8 − 3)

(c) 6 × 10 ÷ 5 + 2(d) 8 ÷ 2 × 4 + 1

(e) $\frac{18 - 2 \times 3}{3 \times 3 - 5}$ (f) $\frac{19 - 3 \times 5}{8 \div 4 \times 2}$

(1.8) 11 (a) The attendance at the last four hockey games was 2847, 2384, 2538, and 2483. Find the average attendance for the games.

(b) The average height of 28 students in one class is 163 cm while the average height of 28 students in another class is 157 cm. Find the average height of all the students.

(1.9) 12 Find the value of each expression. Use $t = 3$ and $n = 7$.

(a) $t + 8$ (b) $n − 4$ (c) $t + n$

(d) $n − t$ (e) $3n − 5$ (f) $4n − 5t$

(1.10) 13 Construct a flow chart.

(a) to obtain the output for $4k − 2$, $k \in \{0, 1, 2, 3\}$.

(b) to send a letter to a foreign country.

test for practice

The questions in this test are not arranged in any special order. An important skill in problem solving is deciding which skill or skills you need to use to solve a problem.

1 What is the place value of each underlined digit?

   (a) 2̲6 972   (b) 183̲ 562   (c) 4 869 0̲53

   (d) Write each number in words.

   (e) Write each number in expanded form.

   (f) Round each number to the nearest 1000.

2 Calculate.

   (a)   5718   (b)   10 418   (c) 481 − 84
         3176   51 414
       + 814   + 3 198   (d) 50 000 − 13 476

   (e) 847 × 98   (f) 908 × 907

3 Find each quotient. Record the remainder.

   (a) 82$\overline{)498\ 806}$ (b) $\frac{31\ 434}{39}$ (c) 80 138 ÷ 57

4 Find the value of each expression.

   (a) 3 × 15 ÷ 5 + 1   (b) 8 ÷ 4 × 2 − 3

5 Evaluate. Use $w = 15$, $x = 4$.

   (a) $w - x$ (b) $61 - w$

   (c) $3w + 14$ (d) $w - 3x$

6 Construct a flow chart to obtain the output:
      $8 + 3y$, $y \in \{0, 1, 2, 3\}$

7 The average person blinks 25 times each minute. How many times would Claudia blink in 45 min?

8 It took 18 containers each with 56 mL to fill a bottle with distilled water. How many 75 mL containers would be needed to fill the same bottle?

9 The largest asteroid, Ceres, has a diameter of 955 km. Pallas and Vesta have diameters of 558 km and 503 km. How much wider is the sum of the diameters of Pallas and Vesta than Ceres?

maintaining skills: basic facts

The foundation of your work in mathematics is based on knowing the basic operations, and being able to do them quickly. To improve your accuracy and speed, practise the following skills several times throughout the year. Make a chart to record your progress.

Date				
Time Taken				
Score				

⎛ Before you begin try the
⎜ "Basic facts" drills in the *Skills Inventory*,
⎝ in the front of this book.

These questions review some basic facts. How quickly can you do them?

Ready. Go!

6 × 9	81 ÷ 9	9 − 6	14 − 7
30 ÷ 5	11 − 9	9 × 9	9 × 3
4 + 9	6 × 8	18 ÷ 6	15 − 6
5 × 6	12 − 4	24 ÷ 4	9 + 5
9 − 5	12 ÷ 4	7 × 9	40 ÷ 5
13 − 5	7 × 6	5 × 5	8 × 7
15 ÷ 3	9 + 8	56 ÷ 8	6 × 6
7 × 8	6 + 8	8 × 5	32 ÷ 4
13 − 8	7 + 9	54 ÷ 6	8 × 8
4 × 5	20 ÷ 5	7 + 5	6 × 3
48 ÷ 6	16 − 7	3 × 8	63 ÷ 9
13 − 9	5 + 9	72 ÷ 8	4 × 4
11 − 6	9 × 5	25 ÷ 5	8 + 7
3 × 6	27 ÷ 3	4 + 7	9 × 4
14 ÷ 2	17 − 8	13 − 6	42 ÷ 7
5 × 7	21 ÷ 3	9 + 3	20 ÷ 4
35 ÷ 7	8 + 3	4 × 7	8 × 4
9 + 7	3 × 7	6 × 4	10 − 6
12 ÷ 2	9 × 8	9 + 2	45 ÷ 9
6 × 7	42 ÷ 6	9 + 9	16 ÷ 4
13 − 4	24 ÷ 8	17 − 9	64 ÷ 8
7 × 7	4 × 9	9 × 6	12 × 6
48 ÷ 8	49 ÷ 7	8 + 4	13 − 7

math is plus: microcomputers

No matter what day of the week you read the newspaper, you will find advertisements for computers. Almost every aspect of your lives is, in some way, affected by a computer. Computers occur in
- ▶ controlling air traffic,   ▶ calculating trends,
- ▶ predicting inventories,   ▶ helping to make scientific discoveries,

Computers have come a long way since they were first invented. As society became more sophisticated in its computing needs, devices were invented to help remove the drudgery of calculations. In the early 1950's there were fewer than 100 computers in the world. Twenty five years later, there were half a million in use; in the home, in your car, at the office, in the schools, in businesses, and even in space, millions and millions of kilometres away. Computers have evolved over the years. Some of the more significant steps in the development of computing devices are as follows.

- ▶ John Napier (1550-1617) invented Napier Bones, and later logarithms, to assist computation skills.

- ▶ Blaise Pascal (1623-1662) and G.W. Leibniz (1646-1716) invented the first calculating machine. Pascal's machine did only addition and subtraction. Leibniz's machine did multiplication and division.

- ▶ Charles Babbage (1833) developed an analytical engine which read information from punched cards.

- ▶ John V. Atansoff (1903) was the first person to design and construct calculating machines using vacuum tubes.

- ▶ The first of the modern computers was ENIAC 1946 (Electronic Numerical Integrator and Computer). The ENIAC occupied a room about 9 m × 9 m and had a mass of 27 000 kg.

- ▶ The invention of silicon chips paved the way to make computers far less bulky. A chip is an integrated circuit that is equivalent to about 100 transistors. With the use of a chip the computer became faster and more compact.

Just as you need to program a washing machine to follow instructions, you also need to program a computer. A program is a sequence of instructions that the computer follows. The programmer gives the instructions to the computer in a specific computer language such as BASIC (Beginners All-Purpose Symbolic Instruction Code)
In this book you will use BASIC as the language of the computer. Throughout the book, various computer tips will suggest programs that relate to the mathematics you learn.

A   Use a newspaper. Collect ads that advertise for people that have had training with a computer.

B   Compile a list of ways that you know computers affect or influence your everyday activities. Include in this list the different ways computers are used.

(In the next chapter, read the *Math Plus*: *"Computer Programming"*

2 patterns and properties: working with numbers

Factors and multiples, divisibility, squares and square roots, exponents, patterns and properties, fractional numbers, rounding skills, computers, problem solving skills, solving problems and applications.

There are patterns in traffic.

By collecting data about the traffic, engineers try to locate highways and interchanges so that traffic will flow as smoothly as possible. Computers are used to sort the data, and patterns are used to help make intelligent decisions for the future.

There are patterns in nature.

There are patterns in numbers. To learn about the properties of numbers, as well as to develop additional skills for solving problems, you need to study patterns about numbers. In this chapter, you will study the answer to these questions and others.

► How are numbers alike?
► What are prime numbers?
► What are some short cuts in computation?
► What is meant by an exponent?

2.1 working with factors and multiples

Often diagrams in mathematics suggest patterns with numbers. As the diagrams show, two types of numbers occur.

▶ For these numbers, you can show different rectangles.
4, 6, 8, 9, 10

▶ For these numbers, you can show only one rectangle.
2, 3, 5, 7

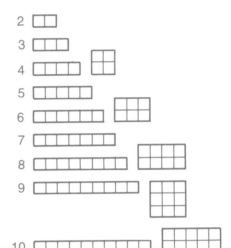

To explore these numbers, you need to know the meanings of special words.
Two numbers 3 and 4 are multiplied.

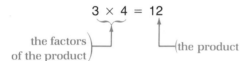

$$3 \times 4 = 12$$

the factors of the product
(the product

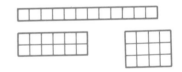

The number 12 can be expressed as factors in different ways.

$$1 \times 12 = 12 \qquad 2 \times 6 = 12 \qquad 3 \times 4 = 12$$

Since 12 has *more than* two different factors, it is called a **composite number**. All the factors of 12 are 1, 2, 3, 4, 6, 12. For the composite number 12, you can show different rectangles.

Since 4 is a factor of 12, then 12 is divisible by 4. To test whether a number is a factor you need only to check whether the number divides evenly.

▶ 4 is a factor of 124.

$$\begin{array}{r} 31 \\ 4\overline{)124} \end{array}$$

Use your calculator to try other numbers.

▶ 4 is not a factor of 125.

$$\begin{array}{r} 31 \\ 4\overline{)125} \\ \underline{124} \\ 1 \end{array}$$
←(remainder

These numbers have *only* two different factors.

$$2 = 1 \times 2 \qquad 3 = 1 \times 3 \qquad 5 = 1 \times 5$$

These numbers are called **prime numbers**. Only one rectangle can be shown for a prime number.

The number 1 has only itself as a factor, $1 = 1 \times 1$. It does not have two different factors. Thus, the number 1 is neither a prime nor a composite number.

A **prime number** is a number with two different factors. (The number itself, and one.)
A **composite number** is a number with more than two different factors.

To find the product of the prime factors of a number, you can use the following methods.

▶ use a factor tree diagram:

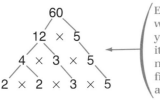

Each time you write a factor, ask yourself whether it is a prime number. If not, find the factors again.

Thus, 60 = 2 × 2 × 3 × 5

▶ use division:

```
2|60
2|30
3|15
  5
```

Thus, 60 = 2 × 2 × 3 × 5

(To find prime factors, the method you use or the starting point may be different, but the prime factors you obtain will always be the same.

Since 2 is a factor of 60, then 60 is a multiple of 2.
Multiples of 2 are 2, 4, 6, 8, . . . , 60, . . .
Multiples of 3 are 3, 6, 9, 12, . . . , 60, . . .

(Note that:
60 is a multiple of 2 and of 3.

(To find the multiples of a number, multiply the number by 1, 2, 3, . . .
Multiples of 3 are
3 × 1   3 × 2   3 × 3   3 × 4   3 × 5 . . .
  3   6   9   12   15   . . .

2.1 exercise

A

1 Which of the following are prime? composite? Give reasons for your answer.

  (a) 2   (b) 7   (c) 10   (d) 19

  (e) 5   (f) 9   (g) 21   (h) 41

  (i) 12   (j) 11   (k) 25   (l) 49

2 Find the missing factors in each of the following.

  (a) ? × 10 = 30   (b) 5 × ? = 35

  (c) 8 × ? = 56   (d) ? × 18 = 72

  (e) ? × 12 = 192   (f) 14 × ? = 84

  (g) 19 × ? = 209   (h) ? × 13 = 364

3 Find the missing prime factors.

  (a) 12 = 2 × ? × 3   (b) 18 = 2 × 3 × ?

  (c) 24 = 2 × ? × ? × 3

  (d) 100 = 2 × ? × 5 × ?

  (e) 128 = 2 × ? × 2 × ? × 2 × ? × 2

4 Write each number as a product of prime factors.

  (a) 50   (b) 48   (c) 30   (d) 81

  (e) 100   (f) 108   (g) 825   (h) 1000

5 Write all the factors for each number.

  (a) 20   (b) 64   (c) 99   (d) 83

  (e) 48   (f) 100   (g) 144   (h) 71

  Which numbers in the above list are prime? How can you tell?

6 (a) Write all the factors of 20.

  (b) Which factors in (a) are prime factors?

7 All the prime factors of each number are shown. What is the number?

  (a) 2, 3, 5   (b) 2, 2, 3, 3

  (c) 2, 2, 3, 5, 5   (d) 2, 3, 5, 5

  (e) 2, 3, 3, 5, 7   (f) 2, 2, 2, 3, 13

8 Which of the following are not multiples of 5?

(a) 20   (b) 25   (c) 72   (d) 75

(e) 100   (f) 105   (g) 552   (h) 635

9 (a) Which of the following are multiples of 4?
       8, 12, 16, 21, 48, 92

   (b) Which of the following are multiples of 5?
       20, 35, 52, 75, 89, 105

   (c) Which of the following are multiples of 7?
       49, 84, 105, 165, 224

B

10 (a) What is the smallest prime factor of each
       number: 10, 21, 55, 154?

   (b) What is the greatest prime factor of each
       number: 60, 56, 99, 234?

11 (a) Two prime factors of a number are 2 and 3.
       What is another factor of the number?

   (b) The prime factors of a number are 3, 5, and
       7. What is another factor of the number?

12 (a) Write the multiples of 3.

   (b) Write the multiples of 4.

   (c) Which multiples are common in (a) and (b)?

   (d) Which of the following are multiples of 3
       and 4: 12, 16, 24, 30, 36, 42, 48?

13 Write each of the following as a product of two
   numbers.

(a) 98   (b) 172   (c) 1008

(d) 616   (e) 900   (f) 1000

14 Write each number as a product of prime
   factors.

(a) 4   (b) 9   (c) 25   (d) 81

(e) 8   (f) 27   (g) 125   (h) 243

(i) 625   (j) 32   (k) 729   (l) 64

(m) How are the above numbers alike? How
    are they different?

15 The prime factors of a number are 2, 2, and 3.

(a) Write *all* the factors of the number.

(b) How can you check your answer in (a)?

16 Each number is shown as a product of prime
   factors. Write *all* the factors for each number.

(a) $2 \times 3 \times 3$ (b) $2 \times 2 \times 3 \times 3$

(c) $2 \times 3 \times 5$ (d) $2 \times 2 \times 3 \times 7$

17 Write the prime factors of each of the following
   numbers.

(a) The first commercial radio broadcast was in
    1922.

(b) The first television cook showed how to
    make an omelette in 1937.

(c) The first woman pilot took to the air in
    1909.

(d) The first fire extinguisher was made in
    1734. It consisted of glass balls and a salt
    solution. To put the fire out, you threw the
    glass balls into the fire.

(e) The first lion tamer lived in England. He
    performed his first act in 1835.

(f) The first motorcycle race was held between
    Paris and Nantes in 1896.

(g) The first parachute opened in 1797. The
    jump was made from a balloon.

C It is important in mathematics to follow
    instructions carefully and exactly.

18 (a) Do the following steps for the number 234.
       Step A: Multiply the number 234 by 7.
       Step B: Multiply the result in A by 11.
       Step C: Multiply the result in B by 13.
       What do you notice about your result?

   (b) Repeat the steps in (a) using the three digit
       number 756. What do you notice about
       your answer?

   (c) Find the product of 7, 11, and 13. Pick any
       three digit number and multiply it by the
       product of 7, 11, and 13. What do you
       notice each time?

2.2 tests for divisibility

In mathematics, look for ways that simplify your work. For example, to find whether a number is a factor of another number, you can divide, and check whether there is a remainder. This is called a divisibility test.

Read the question.	*Use the fact.*	*Do the work.*	
Determine whether 35 is a factor of 1575.	35 is a factor of 1575 if 1575 is divisible by 35.	$\begin{array}{r} 45 \\ 35\overline{)1575} \\ 140\!\downarrow \\ \hline 175 \\ 175 \\ \hline 0 \end{array}$	Each of these statements gives the same information. 35 is a factor of 1575. 1575 is divisible by 35. 1575 is a multiple of 35.

Since the remainder is 0, then 35 is a factor of 1575.

You can also use some simple divisibility tests that you already know.

▶ **divisibility by 2**

If a number is even, it is divisible by 2. These numbers are divisible by 2.

48,　1936,　21 868

▶ **divisibility by 10**

If the last digit is 0, the number is divisible by 10. These numbers are divisible by 10.

110,　4800,　19 630

▶ **divisibility by 5**

If a number ends in 0 or 5, it is divisible by 5. These numbers are divisible by 5.

165,　9655,　26 350

To learn other divisibility tests, try investigations A, B, C, and D.

A: divisibility by 3

Some of these numbers are divisible by 3.

3618	4842	8684
4202	2691	2463

(i) Find the sum of the digits for each of the above numbers. Divide each sum by 3. Which numbers have a sum divisible by 3?

(ii) Which numbers in the above list are divisible by 3? Use division.

(iii) What do you notice about your answers in (i) and (ii)?

(iv) Use your results. Predict which of these numbers are divisible by 3.

8367　　4238　　9633　　11 571

B: divisibility by 9

Some of these numbers are divisible by 9.

1926	8236	92 124
49 624	83 691	20 403

(i) Find the sum of the digits for each of the above numbers. Divide each sum by 9. Which numbers have a sum divisible by 9?

(ii) Which numbers in the above list are divisible by 9? Use division.

(iii) What do you notice about your answers in (i) and (ii)?

(iv) Use your results. Predict which of these numbers are divisible by 9.

441　　8639　　48 213　　96 322

C: divisibility by 4

Some of these numbers are divisible by 4.

6324	4862	9632
38 964	29 443	49 832

(i) Divide the last two digits of the above numbers by 4. For which numbers are the last two digits divisible by 4?

(ii) Which numbers in the above list are divisible by 4? Use division.

(iii) What do you notice about your answers in (i) and (ii)?

(iv) Use your results. Predict which of these numbers are divisible by 4.

2836	9362	9250	82 964

D: divisibility by 8

Some of these numbers are divisible by 8.

8112	49 244	89 656
38 858	96 896	38 784

(i) Divide the last three digits of the above numbers by 8. For which numbers are the last 3 digits divisible by 8?

(ii) Which numbers in the above list are divisible by 8? Use division.

(iii) What do you notice about your answers in (i) and (ii)?

(iv) Use your results. Predict which of these numbers are divisible by 8.

4144	3174	29 672	48 096

2.2 exercise

Based on your results, copy and complete the chart before you begin the exercise.

Number	Divisibility test
2	?
3	?
4	?
5	?
6	Check whether the number is even, and whether it is divisible by 3.
8	?
9	?
10	?

A Use the divisibility tests to answer the questions.

1 Which numbers are divisible by 2?

(a) 336   (b) 441   (c) 2967

(d) 8696   (e) 4963   (f) 3290

2 Which numbers have 5 as a factor?

(a) 6395   (b) 2363   (c) 7940

(d) 2568   (e) 7285   (f) 5190

3 Which numbers are multiples of 10?

(a) 8655   (b) 9600   (c) 4690

(d) 8932   (e) 6960   (f) 8955

4 (a) A number is even. What are possible last digits of the number?

(b) A number is divisible by 5. What are possible last digits of the number?

(c) A number is divisible by 10. What is the last digit of the number?

5 The digits 5, 3, 4, 0 are used to form 4530, which is divisible by 10. Use the digits to form a number:

(a) divisible by 2   (b) divisible by 5

(c) divisible by 2 and 5

B

6 Which numbers are divisible by 3?

(a) 3240   (b) 3538   (c) 4617

(d) 2639   (e) 9486   (f) 5752

7 Which numbers have 4 as a factor?

(a) 1224   (b) 3118   (c) 4664

(d) 26 872   (e) 93 122   (f) 15 196

8 Which numbers are divisible by 8?

(a) 4240   (b) 1930   (c) 2672

(d) 3784   (e) 28 860   (f) 69 992

9 Which numbers are multiples of 9?

(a) 3177   (b) 8723   (c) 13 536

(d) 44 296   (e) 38 655   (f) 56 445

10 (a) Which of the following numbers are

▶ divisible by 2?   ▶ divisible by 3?

| 4692 | 8646 | 6231 | 8064 |
| 82 365 | 42 696 | 13 298 | 28 969 |

(b) Use your results in (a). Which numbers are divisible by both 2 and 3?

(c) Which numbers in the list are divisible by 6?

(d) How are your answers in (b) and (c) related?

11 Which of the numbers are divisible by 6?

(a) 6312   (b) 4563   (c) 1548

(d) 9754   (e) 38 692   (f) 67 986

12 For each division, which answers have a remainder?

(a) 8764 ÷ 2   (b) 4326 ÷ 3

(c) 8901 ÷ 5   (d) 3876 ÷ 8

(e) 48 964 ÷ 4   (f) 28 901 ÷ 2

(g) 36 984 ÷ 8   (h) 21 987 ÷ 9

13 Construct each of the following numbers.

(a) The number has the digits 1, 2, 3, 5, 8 and is divisible by 4.

(b) The number has the digits 1, 3, 6, 8, 9 and is divisible by 6.

14 Copy and complete the chart. (Check your work with a calculator.)

	Number	| Divisible by |							
		2	3	4	5	6	8	9	10
(a)	49 863								
(b)	28 020								
(c)	31 415								
(d)	29 687								
(e)	92 145								
(f)	68 360								

15 There were 1398 persons at the airport waiting for a ride. If 8 persons can fit into each limousine, will there be any cars partly full?

16 Each table at the graduation dance has 6 chairs. There are 469 chairs. Will there be any chairs left over?

17 Each team has the same number of players. There are more than 3, but less than 7 players on each team. If there are 186 players, how many are on each team? There are no extra players.

18 The parks board purchased 423 plants. Each row is to have an equal number of plants. If each row has more than 5, but less than 10 plants, how many are in each row?

C

19 When is a number divisible by 25?

(a) Choose suitable examples of numbers. Construct a divisibility test to determine when a number is divisible by 25.

(b) Check your test in (a). Predict which of the following numbers are divisible by 25.

5275   6430   8525   9650

problem-solving: strategy

To determine whether the following number is a prime, you need to test whether the number is divisible by 2, 3, 5, 7, etc.

One of these numbers is prime! Which one?

22 501   30 031

2.3 greatest common factor and lowest common multiple

To solve this problem you need to use your skills with factors. Jennifer spent 45¢ on packages of beads. Jackie spent 54¢ on beads. Each package cost the same, and each cost more than 5¢. How many packages did they buy?

(To solve the problem, first find the cost of each package.

The factors of 45 are (1), (3), 5, (9), 15, 45

The factors of 54 are (1), 2, (3), 6, (9), 18, 27, 54

(1, 3 and 9 are common factors of 45 and 54.)

(9 is the *greatest* common factor of 45 and 54.)

The price of each package was 9¢.

Jennifer bought 5 packages. (45 ÷ 9 = 5

Jackie bought 6 packages. (54 ÷ 9 = 6

To find the greatest common factor of two numbers you can
- List all the common factors.
- Choose the greatest common factor.

Skills with prime factors can also be used to find the greatest common factor.

- List all the prime factors of each number.

$$45 = 3 \times 3 \times 5$$

$$54 = 2 \times 3 \times 3 \times 3$$

(Multiply the common prime factors.)

- Greatest common factor is 3×3 or 9

(
- The **greatest common factor** of two or more numbers is the greatest number that divides the numbers evenly.
- The **greatest common factor** is the product of the common prime factors of each number.

To understand the meaning of lowest common multiple, you first need to understand the meaning of common multiples.

- List the multiples of 6 and 9.
  Multiples of 6 are 6, 12, (18), 24, 30, (36), 42, 48, (54), . . .

  Multiples of 9 are 9, (18), 27, (36), 45, (54), . . .

- The common multiples of 6 and 9 are 18 36 54 . . .

- Lowest common multiple of 6 and 9 is 18

The skills with the products of prime factors can also be used to find the lowest common multiple.

▶ Write the prime factors of each number.

▶ Lowest common multiple is given by the product

$$6 = 2 \times 3$$
$$9 = 3 \times 3$$
$$2 \times 3 \times 3 \text{ or } 18$$

> The **lowest common multiple** of two or more numbers is the smallest number that has all the prime factors of the numbers.

Example

One downtown bus leaves every 12 min and another leaves every 18 min. After how many minutes do both buses leave at the same time?

Solution

Find the lowest common multiple of 12 and 18.

$$12 = 2 \times 2 \times 3$$
$$18 = 2 \times 3 \times 3$$

Lowest common multiple $= 2 \times 2 \times 3 \times 3$

$$= 36$$

Thus, after 36 min, both buses will leave at the same time.

Often to visualize the solution to a problem, you can record the information.

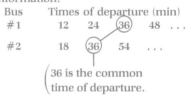

Bus	Times of departure (min)			
#1	12	24	36	48 ...
#2	18	36	54	...

(36 is the common time of departure.

2.3 exercise

A

1 Each number is shown as a product of prime factors. What are the missing numbers?

(a) $18 = 2 \times ? \times ?$

(b) $45 = ? \times 3 \times ?$

(c) $20 = 2 \times ? \times ?$

(d) $16 = ? \times ? \times 2 \times ?$

2 The factors of 12 and 20 are listed.
　　Factors of 12　　1, 2, 3, 4, 6, 12
　　Factors of 20　　1, 2, 4, 5, 10, 20

(a) Which factors are common to 12 and 20?

(b) Which common factor is the greatest?

3 (a) List all the factors of 28.

(b) List all the factors of 8.

(c) List the common factors of 8 and 28.

(d) What is the greatest common factor?

4 Use the prime factors shown. Find the greatest common factor of 36 and 48.
　　$36 = 2 \times 2 \times 3 \times 3$
　　$48 = 2 \times 2 \times 2 \times 2 \times 3$

5 The multiples of 8 and 12 are listed.
　　Multiples of 8　　8, 16, 24, 32, 40, 48, ...
　　Multiples of 12　　12, 24, 36, 48, 60, 72, ...

(a) Which multiples listed are common?

(b) Which is the lowest common multiple?

6 (a) List the multiples of 4.

(b) List the multiples of 6.

(c) Write the lowest common multiple of 4 and 6.

7 Use the prime factors shown. Find the lowest common multiple of 12 and 18.
　　$12 = 2 \times 2 \times 3$　　　$18 = 2 \times 3 \times 3$

B

8 Find the greatest common factor of each pair of numbers.

   (a) 12, 18   (b) 16, 24   (c) 18, 27

   (d) 40, 50   (e) 27, 45   (f) 32, 48

   (g) 36, 27   (h) 60, 45   (i) 35, 56

9 Find the greatest common factor.

   (a) 32, 48, 24   (b) 30, 45, 15

   (c) 12, 18, 24   (d) 36, 54, 72

   (e) 24, 12, 36   (f) 48, 32, 96

10 Find the lowest common multiple for each pair of numbers.

   (a) 3, 4   (b) 2, 3   (c) 5, 10

   (d) 8, 3   (e) 6, 8   (f) 3, 5

   (g) 10, 100   (h) 2, 4   (i) 5, 7

11 Find the lowest common multiple.

   (a) 2, 4, 8   (b) 4, 6, 12

   (c) 6, 9, 12   (d) 3, 6, 4

   (e) 4, 6, 10   (f) 6, 12, 18

12 At lunch, Thomas paid $3.00 for cartons of milk. Sally paid $3.15. Each carton costs the same, but each costs more than 12¢. How many cartons did each person buy?

Cartons of milk have come to replace the familiar milk bottle. The first milk bottles were introduced in 1879. When do you think the last one will be made?

13 Redmond spent 48¢ on packages of stickers. Belinda spent 80¢ on stickers. Each package costs the same, but each costs more than 10¢. How many packages did they each buy?

14 Norman bought 27 tennis balls for the season. Christine bought 21 tennis balls. Each package has the same number of tennis balls. What is the greatest number of tennis balls in each package?

15 Beryl spent $3.50 on grapefruit. Sheldon spent $1.05 on grapefruit. Each grapefruit costs the same, but no less than 25¢.

   (a) How many grapefruits did each person buy?

   (b) What assumption did you make to obtain the answer in (a)?

16 At the supermarket, every 10th customer obtains a free coupon. Every 15th customer obtains a surprise gift. Which customer will obtain a free coupon and a surprise gift?

17 At an inspection station, every 4th vehicle is stopped for a safety check. Every 5th vehicle is stopped for a passenger check. Which vehicle will be stopped for both a passenger and safety check?

C

18 Refer to the chart. Buses leave the depot at the following times. All buses start at the same time.

Bus route	Time of departures
Main Street	Every 8 min
Downtown	Every 15 min
East End	Every 12 min

   (a) When will the next Main Street and East End bus leave at the same time?

   (b) When will the next Downtown and East End bus leave at the same time?

   (c) When will all three buses leave at the same time?

applications: predicting gears

Have you ever thought about the fact that when you change gears on a bicycle you need to pedal faster? Gears are related in special ways and you can use your skills with multiples to predict information about gears. Refer to the gears in the diagram.

After one complete turn of gear A, gear B has made less than a complete turn. How many times will gear A and gear B turn so that the red marks are together again at the starting point S?

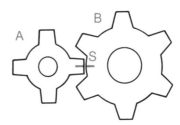

▶ Gear A has 4 teeth. After one complete turn, 4 teeth have passed the starting point S. After two turns, 8 teeth have passed the point S. The pattern is 4, 8, 12, 16, 20, . . .

▶ Gear B has 6 teeth. After one complete turn, 6 teeth have passed the point S. After two turns, 12 teeth have passed the point S. The pattern is 6, 12, 18, 24, 30, . . .

▶ Thus, in order to answer the question about gears A and B, you find the least common multiple

  Gear A   4,   8, ⑫ 16, 20, . . .

  Gear B   6, ⑫ 18, 24, 30, . . .

Thus after 3 turns of gear A and 2 turns of gear B, the red marks will be together again at point S.

---

19 How many turns will each gear make so that the red marks line up again?

(a)

(b)

20 After how many turns of the first gear will both gears be in their original position?

	Number of teeth of first gear	Number of teeth of second gear
(a)	5	10
(b)	6	8
(c)	16	4
(d)	5	7
(e)	100	10

21 Study the three gears in the picture.

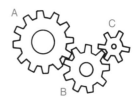

After how many turns of gear B will all three gears return to their original position?

22 After how many turns of the third gear will the three gears return to their original position?

	Number of teeth of first gear	Number of teeth of second gear	Number of teeth of third gear
(a)	9	6	3
(b)	12	4	6
(c)	3	8	4
(d)	8	4	3

2.4 squares and square roots

Your work with multiples and factors can be applied to solve problems about squares and square roots.

The area of the square stamp is 16 cm².

How long is each side?

When a number is multiplied by itself, the result is the square of that number. Since $4 \times 4 = 16$, then 16 is called a **perfect square**.

▶ The square of 2 is
$2 \times 2 = 4$

▶ The square of 3 is
$3 \times 3 = 9$.

Sometimes you might say "3 squared"

To answer the above question about the stamp, you would ask "What number squared gives 16?" The answer is 4.

▶ 4 is called the **principal** or **positive** square root of 16.

To picture square numbers, you can draw dots as shown.

4   9   16

To name the square root of any whole number, first try to find a number which when multiplied by itself is equal to that whole number. For example:

▶ 3 is the square root of 9, since $3 \times 3 = 9$.
▶ 6 is the square root of 36, since $6 \times 6 = 36$.

To find all square roots in this way would be time consuming. You can also use your skills with prime factors, as shown in the example.

(In your later work, you will develop methods to find the square roots of different numbers.

Example   Find the principal square root of 324.

Solution   (To find the square root of 324, write the number as a product of its prime factors.

$324 = 2 \times 2 \times 3 \times 3 \times 3 \times 3$
$= (2 \times 3 \times 3) \times (2 \times 3 \times 3)$
$= 18 \times 18$ (Rearrange the factors.

Thus, the principal square root of 324 is 18.

(In the exercises that follow, you will write, "Find the square root" to mean "Find the principal square root."

The symbol $\sqrt{}$ is used to show the principal or positive square root.

Thus, $\sqrt{324} = 18.$ ◀—— (Read: "The principal or positive square root of 324 is 18."

Does your calculator have a square root key? Read your manual. How does it work? $\boxed{\sqrt{x}}$

2.4 exercise

A

1 Write the square of each number.

(a) 3   (b) 6   (c) 8   (d) 9

2 What is the principal square root of each number?

(a) 16   (b) 25   (c) 100   (d) 64

3 (a) Write all the prime factors of 6.

(b) Find the square of 6.

(c) Write all the prime factors of your answer in (b).

(d) What did you notice about the prime factors in (a) and (c)?

4 (a) Write all the prime factors of 8.

(b) Find the square of 8.

(c) Write all the prime factors of your answer in (b).

(d) What did you notice about the prime factors in (a) and (c)?

5 Write each number as a product of prime factors.

(a) 25   (b) 49   (c) 64   (d) 144

(e) What do you notice about the factors?

6 Match corresponding squares and square roots.

Squares	Square roots
(a) 3×3	A 6
(b) $5 \times 5 \times 3 \times 3$	B 26
(c) $3 \times 3 \times 2 \times 2$	C 3
(d) $2 \times 2 \times 2 \times 2$	D 10
(e) $2 \times 5 \times 2 \times 5$	E 4
(f) 5×5	F 15
(g) $2 \times 13 \times 2 \times 13$	G 5

B

7 Find the square root for each number.

(a) 196   (b) 256   (c) 225   (d) 1600

(e) 900   (f) 324   (g) 400   (h) 1225

8 Evaluate.

(a) $\sqrt{81}$ (b) $\sqrt{169}$ (c) $\sqrt{625}$

(d) $\sqrt{576}$ (e) $\sqrt{1024}$ (f) $\sqrt{1296}$

9 Any square number can be written in the form $100 = 10^2$, $144 = 12^2$, and so on. Find the missing values.

(a) $121 = \blacksquare^2$ (b) $81 = \blacksquare^2$ (c) $225 = \blacksquare^2$

(d) $324 = \blacksquare^2$ (e) $625 = \blacksquare^2$ (f) $441 = \blacksquare^2$

10 What is the area of each square?

(a) ⟵3 cm⟶   (b) ⟵25 mm⟶   (c) ⟵17 m⟶

11 For each square, the area is shown. Find the length of each side.

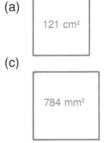

(a) 121 cm²   (b) 484 m²   (c) 784 mm²

12 Find the dimensions of each of the following.

(a) A square carpet has an area of 16 m².

(b) A square piece of property is 625 m².

(c) A square coin is 9 cm².

(d) A square window is 196 cm².

13 (a) The area of the stamp is 324 mm². What are the dimensions?

(b) The area of a square tile is 484 cm². What is the length of each side?

14 The area of a boxing ring is about 36 m².

(a) Find the dimensions of the boxing ring.

(b) What assumption did you make to find your answer in (a)?

15 (a) Wrestling is usually performed on a square surface 144 m². What are the dimensions?

(b) The surface used for karate is a square with an area of 64 m². Find the dimensions of the surface.

(c) Judo is conducted on a square ring 256 m² in area. What are the dimensions of the surface?

16 Ice skating competitions are usually held on a surface made of two squares, that are joined together.

The total area is 1800 m². What are the dimensions of the entire surface?

17 A warehouse has an area of 2940 m². It is subdivided into 15 equal smaller square parts. What are the dimensions of each smaller part?

18 A field has an area of 9720 m². To make more money, a farmer decides to divide the field into 30 equal square plots and rent them. What are the dimensions of each square plot?

Square numbers appear in different ways, as shown in the following questions.

19 (a) Find the value of ■.

$$1 + 3 = \blacksquare$$
$$1 + 3 + 5 = \blacksquare$$
$$1 + 3 + 5 + 7 = \blacksquare$$

(b) What pattern do you see for your values of ■ in (a)?

(c) Use your pattern in (a) to find the sum of

$$1 + 3 + 5 + 7 + 9 = \blacksquare$$
$$1 + 3 + 5 + 7 + 9 + 11 = \blacksquare$$

(d) Complete the pattern for two more steps. Check your work.

20 Use your pattern from Question 19 to predict these sums.

(a) $1 + 3 + 5 + \ldots + 17$

(b) $1 + 3 + 5 + \ldots + 19$

(c) $1 + 3 + 5 + \ldots + 25$

How can you check your prediction?

21 A tricky question!
What is the sum of the first 25 odd numbers?

C

22 (a) Study this pattern. Write two more steps for the pattern.

$$1 \times 1 + 1 = 2 \times 2 - 2$$
$$2 \times 2 + 2 = 3 \times 3 - 3$$
$$3 \times 3 + 3 = \blacksquare$$

(b) Find the values of ■. Use the previous pattern.

$$10 \times 10 + 10 = \blacksquare \times \blacksquare - \blacksquare$$

problem-solving: puzzler

To solve a problem, think of a simpler problem. Use this method to answer this question.
For 9 baseball players, how many different batting orders can you use?

applications: Galileo and falling bodies

You have probably heard of the famous leaning tower of Pisa. It was believed that Galileo used to drop stones off the top of the building to develop a theory about falling bodies. To find the distance, d, in metres, a body falls you can use the rule

$$d = 5 \times t \times t$$

d is in metres ⟵ where t is the time of fall in seconds

Time Fallen	1 s	2 s
Distance Fallen	$d = 5 \times t \times t$ $= 5 \times 1 \times 1$ $= 5$ (in metres)	$d = 5 \times t \times t$ $= 5 \times 2 \times 2$ $= 20$ (in metres)

From the information calculated you can obtain other information.

$$\begin{pmatrix}\text{Distance fallen} \\ \text{in the 2nd second}\end{pmatrix} = \begin{pmatrix}\text{distance fallen} \\ \text{in 2 s}\end{pmatrix} - \begin{pmatrix}\text{distance fallen} \\ \text{in 1 s}\end{pmatrix}$$
$$= 20\ m - 5\ m$$
$$= 15\ m$$

23 A suitcase is dropped from a bridge.

(a) How far will it fall in 4 s?

(b) How far will it fall in 3 s?

(c) Use the information in (a) and (b). Calculate how far the suitcase fell during the 4th second.

24 A ball is dropped from a building 250 m tall. How far will the ball fall

(a) in the 5th second? (b) in the 6th second?

(c) How much further did it fall in (b) than in (a)?

25 The tail section of a jet aircraft fell into the Atlantic Ocean last year. The plane was 3700 m high. How far above the water is the tail section at each of the following times?

(a) 10 s   (b) 20 s   (c) 25 s

(d) 26 s   (e) 27 s   (f) 28 s

26 A skydiver is in a plane at 2500 m. The skydiver must open his parachute at least 500 m from the ground.

(a) Copy and complete the table.

Time of fall	Distance fallen
1 s	?
2 s	?

(b) After how many seconds should the skydiver open his parachute to land safely?

(c) What would happen if the skydiver counted to 23 s and then pulled the ripcord on the parachute?

27 (a) How far does the skydiver travel during the 10th second?

(b) Create one other problem based on the information in Question 26. Write a solution to your problem.

2.5 exponents and powers

In your study of mathematics, you have seen many similarities. For example:

▶ Repeated addition can be written in a more compact way using multiplication.

$$2 + 2 + 2 + 2 + 2$$
$$= 5 \times 2$$

compact form

▶ Similarly, repeated factors can also be written in a compact way.

$$3 \times 3 \times 3 \times 3 = 81$$

$$3^4 = 81$$

4 shows the number of times the factor 3 is repeated.

If a cell divides, you obtain 2 new cells. If a single cell were to divide 40 times, the number needed to show how many cells there were would fill this book.

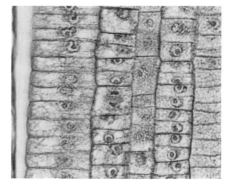

The following mean the same, but are written in a more compact form.

Factors	Exponential Form
$2 \times 2 \times 2 \times 2$	2^4
$5 \times 5 \times 5$	5^3
$3 \times 3 \times 3 \times 3 \times 3$	3^5
$10 \times 10 \times 10 \times 10 \times 10 \times 10$	10^6

Remember, the exponential form means to multiply 2 as a factor 4 times.

When written in exponential form, each part has a special name and meaning.

$$\left(\text{The expression } 3^4 \text{ is called a } \textbf{power} \text{ of 3.}\right) \longrightarrow 3^4$$

4 is called the **exponent**. It is the number of times the factor is repeated.

3 is called the **base**. It is the factor that is repeated.

▶ 4^2 is read as "4 to the exponent 2". It is also sometimes read as "4 squared".
▶ 2^3 is read as "2 to the exponent 3". It is also sometimes read as "2 cubed".

When performing calculations involving more than one operation and exponents, you need to follow the rules for the order of operations, as shown in the example.

Example   Calculate.
(a) $3^2 + 2^3$ (b) $(2^2 - 1)^4 - 6^2 \div 4$

Solution
(a)
$$3^2 + 2^3$$
$$= 3 \times 3 + 2 \times 2 \times 2$$
$$= 9 + 8$$
$$= 17$$

(b)
$$(2^2 - 1)^4 - 6^2 \div 4$$
$$= 3^4 - 6^2 \div 4$$
$$= 81 - 36 \div 4$$
$$= 81 - 9$$
$$= 72$$

Think:
$$2^2 - 1$$
$$= 4 - 1$$
$$= 3$$

2.5 exercise

A In the following exercise, you need to remember the vocabulary.

3^3	exponential or power form
$3 \times 3 \times 3$	expanded form
27	standard form of the number

1 Express each in exponential form.

(a) 3×3 (b) $4 \times 4 \times 4$

(c) $2 \times 2 \times 2 \times 2$ (d) 5×5

(e) $6 \times 6 \times 6$ (f) $9 \times 9 \times 9 \times 9$

(g) $10 \times 10 \times 10 \times 10 \times 10$

(h) $2 \times 2 \times 2 \times 2 \times 2 \times 2 \times 2$

2 What is the base and exponent of each power?

(a) 2^3 (b) 3^4 (c) 4^5 (d) 5^2

(e) 7^5 (f) 6^7 (g) 10^4 (h) 15^2

3 Write the following in symbols. Then evaluate.

(a) 3 squared   (b) 2 cubed

(c) 5 squared   (d) 4 cubed

(e) 3 to the exponent 4

(f) 2 to the exponent 5

4 Write the following in expanded form.

(a) 3^4 (b) 4^3 (c) 2^4 (d) 6^2

(e) 8^3 (f) 10^2 (g) 1^4 (h) 5^4

5 Write each of the following in standard form.

(a) 3^2 (b) 4^3 (c) 2^5

(d) 5^3 (e) 6^4 (f) 8^3

6 Find the missing exponent.

(a) $25 = 5^?$ (b) $100 = 10^?$ (c) $64 = 4^?$

(d) $128 = 2^?$ (e) $81 = 3^?$ (f) $1000 = 10^?$

(g) $625 = 5^?$ (h) $216 = 6^?$ (i) $729 = 3^?$

7 Evaluate.

(a) $3^2 + 3$ (b) $3^3 - 3^2$

(c) $3^2 \times 3$ (d) $3^3 \div 3^2$

8 Find each value.

(a) $10^3 - 10^2$ (b) $10^2 + 10^3$

(c) $10^4 \div 10^2$ (d) $10^3 \times 10^2$

B

Use your calculator to try other numbers.

9 Calculate.

(a) $3^4 - 2^5$ (b) $3^4 - 4^3$

(c) $4^2 + 3^2$ (d) $2^4 - 3^2$

(e) $5^3 + 2$ (f) $8^2 \div 4^3$

(g) $10^3 - 5^3$ (h) $10^3 \div 10^2$

10 Find which has the greater value.

(a) 2^3 or 3^2 (b) 1^2 or 2^1 (c) 10^2 or 2^{10}

(d) 3^4 or 4^3 (e) 4^5 or 5^4 (f) 3^6 or 6^3

(g) 5^3 or 3^5 (h) 2^6 or 6^2 (i) 1^5 or 5^1

11 (a) Which is greater in each pair?

(i) 3 cubed or 2 squared?

(ii) 4 squared or 3 cubed?

(iii) 5 cubed or 11 squared?

(b) Find the sum of 5 squared and 3 cubed.

(c) By how much is 4 cubed larger than 2 squared?

12 Which expression has greater value?

(a) $3^2 + 2$ or $2^2 + 3$

(b) $4^3 \div 2^4$ or $4^2 - 2^4$

(c) $10 + 1^5$ or $10^2 - 1^{100}$

(d) $2^4 + 5$ or $5^2 - 2$

13 Replace ⊙ with $>$, $<$, or $=$ to make each sentence true.

(a) $2^3 ⊙ 3^2$ (b) $4^2 ⊙ 2^4$

(c) $3^2 ⊙ 2 + 5$ (d) $10^2 ⊙ 5^3 - 1$

(e) $5^2 - 2 ⊙ 3^3$ (f) $2^2 + 2^3 + 2 ⊙ 2^5$

(g) $10^3 ÷ 10 ⊙ 10$ (h) $2 + 3^2 ⊙ 3 × 2^2$

14 Evaluate the following.

(a) $2 + 3^2 - 1^3$ (b) $5^2 - (2 + 3^2)$

(c) $(3^3 - 2^4) + 4$ (d) $4 + (2^5 - 3^3)$

(e) $(6 + 1)^2 - 3^3$ (f) $6^2 - (5^2 + 2)$

(g) $10^3 ÷ (10 - 5)^2$ (h) $5 + (10^3 ÷ 10^2)$

15 The magic number of the magic square is 230. Find the missing values.

?	?	?	8^2
?	$2 × 5^2 + 3 × 4$	$7^2 + 3$	?
$7 × 2^3$	?	?	$9^2 - 4^2 - 7$
$8^2 - 1^2$	$7^2 + 3^2 + 2$	?	$2^2 + 7^2$

16 Write each of the following as a product of prime factors using exponents. The first one is done for you.

(a) 24   ($24 = 2 × 2 × 2 × 3$
              $= 2^3 × 3$

(b) 18   (c) 36   (d) 48

(e) 32   (f) 40   (g) 100

(h) 144   (i) 400   (j) 864

17 (a) A page is torn in half. How many pieces are there?

(b) Each part is torn in half again. How many pieces are there?

(c) The pieces are torn again. How many pieces are there now?

(d) How many pieces will there be after you repeat the same steps three more times?

18 Refer to the answers in the previous question.

(a) Copy and complete the chart. Use exponents to show each answer.

The page is torn	There will be
0 times	1 piece
1 time	2 pieces
2 times	2^2 pieces
3 times	?
4 times	?
5 times	?
6 times	?

(b) Continue the chart in (a) 3 more steps. Did you use a calculator to help you?

19 Use $p = 3$, $q = 2$. Find the value of each.

(a) p^2 (b) q^3 (c) $(p + q)^2$

(d) $p + q^2$ (e) $q + p^2$ (f) $p^2 + q^2$

(g) $3p^2 + 2q$ (h) $p^2 + 2q^2$ (i) $3p^3 - 2q^2$

C

20 Use $a = 4$, $b = 5$.

(a) Find the value of $(a + b)^2$.

(b) Find the value of $a^2 + 2ab + b^2$.

(c) What do you notice about your answers in (a) and (b)?

21 Use $m = 6$, $n = 3$.

(a) Find the value of $(m - n)^2$.

(b) Find the value of $m^2 - 2mn + n^2$.

(c) What do you notice about your answers ?

---

computer tip

Try this program. Predict what the output will be. Suggest a title for the program "XX". Use A = 6, B = 8.

```
10  PRINT "XX"
20  INPUT A, B
30  LET C = A + B/2
40  PRINT A, B, C
50  END
```

2.6 patterns with powers

Many mathematical relationships are established by organizing your work and looking for patterns. For example, by organizing your results for multiplying with like bases, you can see a pattern. What pattern can you see in the chart?

> It appears that when multiplying powers with the same base, the sum of the exponents *in the factors* is equal to the exponent *in the product*.

To check this relationship do these calculations.

$$3^2 \times 3^3 = 9 \times 27 \qquad\qquad 3^2 \times 3^3 = 3^{(2 + 3)}$$
$$= 243 \text{ or } 3^5 \qquad\qquad\qquad = 3^5 \text{ or } 243$$
$$\text{Thus, } 3^2 \times 3^3 = 3^5$$

You could think of the pattern for multiplying powers in a different way.

$$3^2 \times 3^3 \text{ means } \underbrace{3 \times 3 \quad \times \quad 3 \times 3 \times 3}$$

3 as a factor 5 times

Thus, $3^2 \times 3^3 = 3^5$.

Multiplying powers with the same base.	
$2^1 \times 2^1 = 4$	$2^2 = 4$
$2^1 \times 2^2 = 2 \times 4$	$2^3 = 8$
$\qquad = 8$	
$2^1 \times 2^3 = 2 \times 8$	$2^4 = 16$
$\qquad = 16$	
$2^2 \times 2^2 = 4 \times 4$	$2^4 = 16$
$\qquad = 16$	
$2^1 \times 2^4 = 2 \times 16$	$2^5 = 32$
$\qquad = 32$	
$2^2 \times 2^3 = 4 \times 8$	$2^5 = 32$
$\qquad = 32$	

A pattern also occurs when you divide powers with like or same bases. Look at the chart. What patterns do you see?

> It appears that when dividing powers with the same bases, the difference in the exponents is equal to the exponent in the quotient.

Do an example to check the relationship.

$$3^5 \div 3^2 = 243 \div 9 \qquad\qquad 3^5 \div 3^2 = 3^{(5 - 2)}$$
$$= 27 \text{ or } 3^3 \qquad\qquad\qquad = 3^3 \text{ or } 27$$
$$\text{Thus, } 3^5 \div 3^2 = 3^3$$

You could think of the pattern for dividing powers in a different way.

$$3^5 \div 3^2 \text{ means } \frac{3 \times 3 \times 3 \times 3 \times 3}{3 \times 3} \text{ simplified to } \frac{3 \times 3 \times 3 \times \overset{1}{3} \times \overset{1}{3}}{\underset{1}{3} \times \underset{1}{3}}$$

Thus, $3^5 \div 3^2 = 3^3$.

Dividing powers with the same base.	
$2^2 \div 2^1 = 4 \div 2$	$2^1 = 2$
$\qquad = 2$	
$2^3 \div 2^1 = 8 \div 2$	$2^2 = 4$
$\qquad = 4$	
$2^4 \div 2 = 16 \div 2$	$2^3 = 8$
$\qquad = 8$	
$2^5 \div 2^2 = 32 \div 4$	$2^3 = 8$
$\qquad = 8$	

You can use these patterns to save work in doing calculations, as follows.

Check whether your answer is reasonable.

Example   Calculate.

(a) $2^8 \div 2^3$

(b) $\dfrac{10^5 \times 10^2}{10^4}$

Solution

(a) $2^8 \div 2^3$
$= 2^5$
$= 32$

Think:
$8 - 3 = 5$

(b) $\dfrac{10^5 \times 10^2}{10^4} = \dfrac{10^7}{10^4}$
$= 10^3$
$= 1000$

Think:
$7 - 4 = 3$

2.6 exercise

A Questions 1 to 7 develop your skills for patterns with powers.

1 (a) Complete the following.
$2^2 \times 2^3 = \square \times 8$
$= \square$

(b) Complete the following.
$2^2 \times 2^3 = 2^{(\square + 3)}$
$= 2^\square$

(c) What do you notice about the results of (a) and (b)?

2 Express each as a single power.

(a) $2^3 \times 2^2$
Think: $2 \times 2 \times 2 \quad \times \quad 2 \times 2$

(b) $3^4 \times 3^2$
Think: $3 \times 3 \times 3 \times 3 \quad \times \quad 3 \times 3$

(c) $2^5 \times 2^3$
Think: $2 \times 2 \times 2 \times 2 \times 2 \quad \times \quad 2 \times 2 \times 2$

(d) $10^4 \times 10^2$
Think: $10 \times 10 \times 10 \times 10 \quad \times \quad 10 \times 10$

3 Find $\square$ in each of the following.

(a) $2^2 \times 2^4 = 2^\square$ (b) $3^4 \times 3^2 = 3^\square$

(c) $4^2 \times 4^5 = 4^\square$ (d) $2^3 \times 2^2 = 2^\square$

4 (a) Complete the following.
$2^5 \div 2^2 = 32 \div \square$
$= \square$

(b) Complete the following.
$2^5 \div 2^2 = 2^{(5 - \square)}$
$= 2^\square$

(c) What do you notice about the results of (a) and (b)?

5 Express each as a single power.

(a) $2^3 \div 2^2$
Think: $\dfrac{2 \times 2 \times 2}{2 \times 2}$

(b) $3^4 \div 3^3$
Think: $\dfrac{3 \times 3 \times 3 \times 3}{3 \times 3 \times 3}$

(c) $2^5 \div 2^3$
Think: $\dfrac{2 \times 2 \times 2 \times 2 \times 2}{2 \times 2 \times 2}$

(d) $10^4 \div 10^3$
Think: $\dfrac{10 \times 10 \times 10 \times 10}{10 \times 10 \times 10}$

6 Find $\square$ in each of the following.

(a) $2^5 \div 2^3 = 2^\square$ (b) $3^5 \div 3^1 = 3^\square$

(c) $4^4 \div 4^1 = 4^\square$ (d) $2^7 \div 2^4 = 2^\square$

7 (a) What is the rule for multiplying powers with the same base?

(b) What is the rule for dividing powers with the same base?

B

8 Match the expression in column A with the result in column B.

	A		B
(a)	$2^3 \times 2^3$		4^6
(b)	$3^4 \times 3^5$		2^2
(c)	$2^5 \div 2^3$		3^5
(d)	$4^4 \times 4^2$		2^6
(e)	$3^7 \div 3^2$		4^2
(f)	$4^4 \div 4^2$		3^9

9 Write each as a single power. Then evaluate.

(a) $2^3 \times 2^4$ (b) $3^4 \times 3^1$ (c) $2^4 \times 2^4$

(d) $3^3 \times 3^4$ (e) $2^5 \times 2^3$ (f) $3^5 \times 3^2$

(g) $10^3 \times 10^2$ (h) $10^4 \times 10^2$ (i) $10^2 \times 10^3$

(j) $2^4 \div 2^1$ (k) $3^7 \div 3^4$ (l) $2^5 \div 2^1$

(m) $3^4 \div 3^2$ (n) $2^7 \div 2^2$ (o) $3^5 \div 3^4$

(p) $10^4 \div 10^2$ (q) $10^3 \div 10$ (r) $10^5 \div 10^3$

10 Replace ◯ with $<$, $>$, or $=$ to make each statement true.

(a) $2^3 \times 2^2$ ◯ 2^1 (b) $3^2 \times 3^3$ ◯ $3^4 \times 3^2$

(c) $3^7 \div 3^4$ ◯ 3^{11} (d) $2^6 \div 2^3$ ◯ 2^3

(e) $2^4 \times 2^2$ ◯ 2^8 (f) $3^4 \times 3^2$ ◯ 3^2

(g) $3^6 \div 3^4$ ◯ 3^2 (h) $2^6 \div 2^2$ ◯ 2^3

11 Copy and complete each chart.

Powers of 2		Powers of 3	
(a)		(b)	

Powers of 2	
$2^1 = 2$	$2^7 = ?$
$2^2 = 4$	$2^8 = ?$
$2^3 = 8$	$2^9 = ?$
$2^4 = ?$	$2^{10} = ?$
$2^5 = ?$	$2^{11} = ?$
$2^6 = ?$	$2^{12} = ?$

Powers of 3	
$3^1 = ?$	$3^6 = ?$
$3^2 = ?$	$3^7 = ?$
$3^3 = ?$	$3^8 = ?$
$3^4 = ?$	$3^9 = ?$
$3^5 = ?$	$3^{10} = ?$

Check your answers in the charts. You need to use the answers in the charts in the following questions.

12 Use only the chart for powers of 2, to calculate each of the following. The first one is done for you.

(a) $1024 \div 32$ $\left(\begin{array}{l} 1024 \div 32 = 2^{10} \div 2^5 \\ \qquad\qquad = 2^5 = 32 \end{array} \right.$

(b) 16×64 (c) $8 \times 32 \times 4$

(d) $2048 \div 16$ (e) $4096 \div 128$

(f) $8 \times 256 \div 32$ (g) $4096 \div 512 \times 8$

13 Use only the chart for powers of 3 to calculate each of the following.

(a) 27×243 (b) $9 \times 81 \times 27$

(c) $6561 \div 27$ (d) $59\,049 \div 6561$

(e) $19\,683 \div 81 \times 9$ (f) $6561 \times 9 \div 81$

(g) $59\,049 \div 243 \times 81$

14 Calculate each of the following. Use only the answers in your charts to do so!

(a) $\dfrac{512 \times 256}{4096}$ (b) $\dfrac{6561 \times 27}{729}$

(c) $59\,049 \div 2187 \times 81$

(d) $\dfrac{512 \times 8 \times 32}{4096}$ (e) $\dfrac{2187 \times 27 \times 243}{59\,049}$

C

15 A hockey coach once used a strange power to make the players play better. Evaluate each power beside the letter. Then match the letter and answer below.

A $2^3 \times 2^2$ G $4^3 \times 4^3$ M $10^3 \times 10^2$ S $2^5 \div 2^5$

B $2^{10} \div 2^2$ H $2^8 \div 2^2$ N $10^7 \div 10^5$ T $4^4 \div 4^2$

C $10^4 \times 10^4$ I $4^3 \times 4^2$ O $10^{10} \times 10^4$ U $10^3 \times 10^3$

D $2^4 \div 2^2$ J $2^4 \times 2^7$ P $2^2 \times 2^2$ V $10^{10} \div 10^2$

E 10×10 K $4^6 \div 4^2$ Q $2^4 \div 2^1$ W $2^4 \times 2^6$

F $2^7 \div 2^6$ L $4^5 \times 4^3$ R $4^2 \times 4^1$ X $2^{12} \div 2^5$

Y $10^2 \times 10^1$ Z $2^4 \times 2^4$

The answer is $\dfrac{?}{2^4}$ $\dfrac{?}{10^3}$ $\dfrac{?}{4^3}$ $\dfrac{?}{2^5}$ $\dfrac{?}{10^5}$ $\dfrac{?}{4^5}$ $\dfrac{?}{2^2}$

problem-solving: puzzler

A drinking glass is a cylinder. It is filled full with cherry pop. How could you share exactly one half of it without measuring?

2.7 properties: whole numbers

Understanding properties of numbers helps you find short cuts for doing calculations. If you add any two whole numbers, the answer is a unique whole number.

$1 + 5 = 6$ $3 + 4 = 7$ $5 + 8 = 13$

By examining the following, it is also true that if you multiply any two whole numbers, the answer is a unique whole number.

$2 \times 5 = 10$ $3 \times 7 = 21$ $8 \times 4 = 32$

Because of the above statements, the set of whole numbers is said to be **closed** with respect to addition and multiplication.

The following illustrate other properties of whole numbers.

Use your calculator to try other numbers.

Commutative
The order in which you add or multiply whole numbers does not affect the answer.

$3 + 4 = 4 + 3$
$4 \times 9 = 9 \times 4$
$5 + 8 = 8 + 5$
$6 \times 8 = 8 \times 6$

Associative
In addition or multiplication, the numbers can be grouped in any order with no change in the answer.

$3 + (4 + 5) = (3 + 4) + 5$
$(2 \times 3) \times 4 = 2 \times (3 \times 4)$
$5 + (7 + 6) = (5 + 7) + 6$
$(5 \times 6) \times 4 = 5 \times (6 \times 4)$

Distributive
The operation of multiplication distributes over the operation of addition.

$3 \times (4 + 5) = 3 \times 4 + 3 \times 5$
$5 \times (6 + 2) = 5 \times 6 + 5 \times 2$
$(4 + 8) \times 7 = 4 \times 7 + 8 \times 7$

properties of 0 and 1

Two important numbers in the whole number system are 0 and 1. They have important properties.

Adding 0: The sum is unchanged by adding 0.
$36 + 0 = 36$ $0 + 68 = 68$ $87 + 0 = 87$

Multiplying by zero: The product is always 0.
$25 \times 0 = 0$ $47 \times 0 = 0$ $0 \times 76 = 0$

Multiplying by 1: The product equals the original number.
$15 \times 1 = 15$ $46 \times 1 = 46$ $1 \times 38 = 38$

Dividing by 1: The quotient equals the original number.
$48 \div 1 = 48$ $96 \div 1 = 96$ $74 \div 1 = 74$

It's impossible!

Can you divide by zero? You have probably heard at one time or another, "You cannot divide by zero!" But why not? To find out why not, find out what happens if you do divide a number by zero.

Use:
If $8 \div 4 = 2$, then $4 \times 2 = 8$

For Zero:
If $8 \div 0 \stackrel{?}{=} \square$, then $0 \times \square \stackrel{?}{=} 8$
But $0 \times \square = 8$ is impossible.
answer : When any number is multiplied by zero, the answer is 0!

Thus: $8 \div 0$ is impossible.

A

1 Find the missing values. Which property, associative, commutative, or distributive, is shown by each?

(a) $45 + ? = 55 + 45$

(b) $25 \times 4 = ? \times 25$

(c) $(388 + 912) + 82 = 388 + (912 + ?)$

(d) $(65 \times 4) \times ? = 65 \times (4 \times 25)$

(e) $7 \times (100 + 3) = 7 \times 100 + ? \times 3$

2 Find the value of each of the following. Which calculations cannot be done?

(a) $15 + 0$ (b) 0×36

(c) $0 + 38$ (d) $220 - 0$

(e) 36×1 (f) $36 \div 1$

(g) $15 \div 1$ (h) $15 \div 0$

(i) $0 \div 85$ (j) $0 \div 800$

(k) $4(9 + 0)$ (l) $5(9 - 0)$

(m) $3(8 \times 0)$ (n) $4(8 \div 0)$

3 (a) Calculate each expression.

     A $(87 \times 25) \times 4$ B $87 \times (25 \times 4)$

(b) What do you notice about your results?

(c) Which is easier to calculate mentally?

4 Calculate each expression. Compare your results. Then determine which expression would be easier to calculate mentally.

         A   B

(a) $(785 + 956) + 44$ $785 + (956 + 44)$

(b) $5 \times 2 \times 87$ $5 \times 87 \times 2$

(c) $(86 \times 25) \times 4$ $86 \times (25 \times 4)$

(d) $234 + (78 + 166)$ $(234 + 166) + 78$

(e) $36 \times (100 + 2)$ $36 \times 100 + 36 \times 2$

B

5 Which of the following are true (T)? false (F)? Give reasons for your answers.

(a) $28 + (4 + 6) \overset{?}{=} (28 + 4) + 6$

(b) $(16 \div 4) \div 2 \overset{?}{=} 16 \div (4 \div 2)$

(c) $36 \times (2 \times 5) \overset{?}{=} (36 \times 2) \times 5$

(d) $28 \times (100 + 2) \overset{?}{=} (28 \times 100) + (28 \times 2)$

(e) $28 \times (100 - 3) \overset{?}{=} (28 \times 100) - (28 \times 3)$

(f) $32 \div (4 + 2) \overset{?}{=} (32 \div 4) + (32 \div 2)$

(g) $(36 - 6) - 2 \overset{?}{=} 36 - (6 - 2)$

(h) Every number is divisible by 1.

(i) Every number has 0 as a factor.

(j) The operation of addition is commutative.

(k) The operation of subtraction is associative.

6 To multiply by 9 mentally, you can use the distributive property.

Calculate: Think:

18×9 $18 \times (10 - 1)$

$= ?$ $= 180 - 18$

                    $= 162$

Calculate each of the following. How many can you do mentally?

(a) 16×9 (b) 23×9 (c) 9×28

(d) 9×32 (e) 45×9 (f) 48×9

(g) 9×53 (h) 9×75 (i) 99×9

7 A similar approach can be used to multiply by 11.

Calculate: Think:

18×11 $18 \times (10 + 1)$

$= ?$ $= 180 + 18$

                    $= 198$

Calculate each of the following.

(a) 16×11 (b) 23×11 (c) 11×28

(d) 11×32 (e) 45×11 (f) 48×11

(g) 11×53 (h) 11×75 (i) 99×11

8 You can use a similar pattern to multiply by 101 or 99.

28×99
$= ?$

Think:
  $28(100 - 1)$
$= 2800 - 28$
$= 2772$

28×101
$= ?$

Think:
  $28(100 + 1)$
$= 2800 + 28$
$= 2828$

Calculate each of the following.

(a) 20×101

(b) 31×99

(c) 36×999

(d) 101×43

(e) 99×50

(f) 999×50

(g) 60×99

(h) 70×101

(i) 999×80

(j) 101×63

(k) 99×83

(l) 23×999

(m) 66×101

(n) 73×99

9 Write each question in another form to help you find the answer mentally.

(a) 15×399

(b) 20×49

(c) 20×499

(d) 30×199

(e) 299×40

(f) 399×45

(g) 699×50

(h) 60×699

(i) 25×299

(j) 36×399

(k) 899×90

(l) 60×799

10 Often skills or properties you learn apply in different ways.

(a) Find the greatest common factor of 14 and 63. Then divide $63 - 14$ by your answer. What do you notice?

(b) Find the greatest common factor of 24 and 72. Divide $72 - 24$ by your answer. What do you notice?

(c) Find the greatest common factor of 126 and 108. Divide $126 - 108$ by their greatest common factor. What do you notice?

(d) Based on your answers in (a) to (c), what result appears to be true?

11 Test your findings from the previous question.
  ▶ Find the greatest common factor.
  ▶ Check whether the difference of the numbers is divisible by the greatest common factor.

(a) 12, 20

(b) 18, 12

(c) 40, 32

(d) 72, 63

(e) 96, 156

(f) 216, 180

C

12 The set of whole numbers is closed for the operation of addition and multiplication. Is the set of whole numbers closed for the operation of

(a) division?

(b) subtraction?

Write an example to illustrate your answers.

13 The set of even whole numbers is
    $\{ 0, 2, 4, 6, 8, \ldots \}$.

(a) For which operation is this set closed:

(i) addition?

(ii) multiplication?

(iii) division?

(iv) subtraction?

(b) Write an example to illustrate your answers.

14 The set of odd whole numbers is
    $\{ 1, 3, 5, 7, 9, \ldots \}$.

(a) For which operation is this set closed?

(b) Write an example to illustrate your answer

computer tip

Try this program. The input is 2 numbers of your choice.

```
10  PRINT "OPERATIONS"
20  INPUT "THE NUMBERS ARE"; A, B
30  LET S = A + B
40  LET D = A − B
50  LET P = A ∗ B
60  LET Q = A/B
70  PRINT "THE ANSWERS ARE"; S, D, P, Q
80  END
```

problem-solving: puzzler
I am the smallest square that becomes a cube when you add me to some other square. Who am I?

2.8 concept of a fraction

Numbers and their applications are an important part of your study of mathematics. You have thus far dealt with whole numbers. But how are numerals used to show parts of a group?

► Fractions can be used to show part of a whole.
To describe the fraction of pieces of cake on the plate:

5 are on the plate   8 pieces in the whole cake

$\frac{5}{8}$ of the cake is on the plate.

$\frac{5}{8}$ (number of equal pieces of cake on the plate
     (number of equal pieces in the whole cake

► Fractions can be used to show part of a group.
To describe the fraction of the group of trophies for bowling:

3 trophies for bowling   5 trophies altogether

$\frac{3}{5}$ of the trophies are for bowling.

$\frac{3}{5}$ (number of bowling trophies
     (number of trophies altogether

► Fractions can be used to label a point on the number line.
To label the number line, divide the line segment between

0 and 1 into 5 equal parts. Mark the fraction $\frac{2}{5}$ by a dot.

In the study of mathematics, symbols are invented to provide information in a compact way. You have already studied many of them. Do you know the exact meaning of each one?

Symbols $<$ $>$ $=$ 2^3 363 $\sqrt{}$

As other mathematical concepts are developed accordingly, additional symbols are invented, as shown by the following.

Common Fractions
You have used fraction symbols to show concepts about parts of a whole. These numerals are called common fractions.

$\frac{1}{2}, \frac{3}{4}, \frac{1}{8}$, and so on

Decimal Fractions
Decimal fractions are symbols also used to show concepts about parts of a whole. You will study these in the next section.

0.5, 0.75, 0.125, and so on

Numbers or Numerals!
Often in the study of mathematics we must be careful to indicate exactly what we mean. For example, a numeral is used to express a number concept. Over the years many types of numerals have been used to show number concepts. Each of the following numerals can be used to record a number for "four".

► Hindu Arabic   ► Egypt
   4 cheerleaders   //// cheerleaders

► Roman   ► Mayan
   Numeral
   IV cheerleaders   ▽ ▽
                         ▽ ▽ cheerleaders

However, in everyday practice, we interchangeably use the words numeral and number. But you know the difference in their meaning.

Example 1   (a) What fraction of the case is full?
                (b) What fraction of the case is empty?

Solution   (a) 7 bottles are in the case.

Thus $\frac{7}{12}$ of the case is full.

            (b) 5 bottles are missing.

Thus $\frac{5}{12}$ of the case is empty.

You often need to interpret positions on the number line.

Example 2   What fractions are shown by the flags on the
number line?

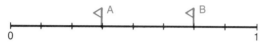

Solution   Since the number line is divided into 8 equal
parts the fractions are in terms of eighths.

Flag A shows $\frac{3}{8}$.   Flag B shows $\frac{6}{8}$.

2.8 exercise

A

1 Write a fraction to show each of the following.

   (a) What fraction of the
chocolate bar is left?

   (b) What fraction of the books are open?

2 What fraction of each diagram is shaded?

   (a)   (b)   (c)

3 Draw a diagram to illustrate each fraction.

   (a) $\frac{1}{4}$ (b) $\frac{2}{3}$ (c) $\frac{3}{5}$

4 What fraction of each beaker is filled? What
fraction of each beaker is empty?

   (a)   (b)   (c)

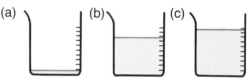

5 Write the fraction shown at each position of the
flag.

   (a)

   (b)

   (c)
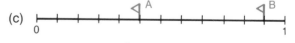

   (d)

B

6 Write a fraction to show the number of logos constructed from

(a) circles   (b) squares

(c) triangles

(d) circles and triangles

(e) squares and triangles

7 Refer to the photograph of the keyboard of a micro computer. Answer the following questions.

Write a fraction to show the number of

(a) letter keys   (b) number keys

(c) symbol/special keys

8 A sketch of a canoe trip is shown. Each sequence shows the distance covered in one day. How much of the trip has been completed after

(a) 1 d?   (b) 2 d?   (c) 5 d?

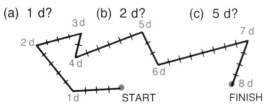

9 From the previous question, how much of the trip has yet to be completed after

(a) 1 d?   (b) 3 d?   (c) 6 d?

10 Out of 1 h of ice hockey practice, the coach practises

     15 min conditioning drills
     30 min on positional hockey
     10 min on defensive hockey
      5 min on strenuous drills

Write a fraction to show the part spent on

(a) conditioning drills   (b) positional hockey

(c) defensive hockey   (d) strenuous drills

11 Do you know whose portraits are on Canadian money? Here is the list.

Person	Denomination
Queen Elizabeth II	$1
Queen Elizabeth II	$2
Sir Wilfred Laurier	$5
Sir John A. MacDonald	$10
Queen Elizabeth II	$20
William Lyon MacKenzie King	$50
Sir Robert Borden	$100
Queen Elizabeth II	$1000

What fraction of the bills uses

(a) Queen Elizabeth II?

(b) a former Prime Minister of Canada?

C

12 Canada has a number of popular historic sites. The ten visited most frequently are listed below.

Historic Site	Number of visitors
Halifax Citadel, N.S.	720 000
Port Beauséjour, N.B.	105 000
Lower Fort Garry, Man.	130 000
Cartier Brebeuf, Que.	100 000
Signal Hill, Nfld.	930 000
Fort George, Ont.	95 000
Alexander Graham Bell Museum, N.S.	210 000
Grand Pré, N.S.	90 000
Citadel Hill, Nfld.	110 000
Fortress of Louisberg, N.S.	300 000

(a) Find the average of the visitors.

(b) What fraction of the historic sites are visited by less than the average?

(c) What fraction of the historic sites are visited by more than the average?

2.9 decimal fractions and place value

In Chapter 1 you learned about place value for whole numbers. These concepts now extend to understanding decimal fractions. Common fractions with the denominators 10, 100, 1000, and so on, can be written as decimal fractions.

Common Fraction	$\frac{3}{10}$	$\frac{45}{100}$	$\frac{4}{100}$	$\frac{365}{1000}$	$\frac{43}{1000}$	$\frac{8}{1000}$
Decimal Fraction	0.3	0.45	0.04	0.365	0.043	0.008

To write any number, the ten digits 0, 1, 2, 3, 4, 5, 6, 7, 8, 9 are used. A decimal point is used as a reference point to separate the whole number part and the fractional part. A whole number is also a decimal numeral, but the decimal point is not included.

Each digit in a decimal numeral has a special *place value*. Each digit also has a *face value* which tells you *how many* ones, tens, tenths, etc. there are. The place value of each digit may be shown in a chart.

In working with decimals, remember how the place values are related.

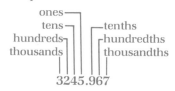

Decimal Number	hundreds	tens	ones	tenths	hundredths	thousandths
496	4	9	6			
36.9		3	6	9		
283.4	2	8	3	4		
2.36			2	3	6	
15.698		1	5	6	9	8

Decimal numbers can be expressed in words.

▶ 496 is read as four hundred ninety-six.

▶ 283.4 is read as two hundred eighty-three and four tenths

▶ 15.698 is read as fifteen and six hundred ninety-eight thousandths.

Writing decimals in expanded form also helps you see the place value of each digit.

$$428.69 = 400 + 20 + 8 + 0.6 + 0.09$$
$$= 400 + 20 + 8 + \frac{6}{10} + \frac{9}{100}$$
$$= 4 \times 10^2 + 2 \times 10 + 8 \times 1 + 6 \times \frac{1}{10} + 9 \times \frac{1}{10^2}$$

You can use your skills with place value to determine which number is greater, as shown in the next example.

Example

In platform diving Eleanor recorded 390.59 points. Martina recorded 390.65 points. Who won the event?

Solution

To compare the numbers, you compare the digits of the same place value.

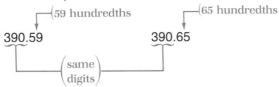

Since, 59 hundredths < 65 hundredths
then, 390.59 < 390.65
Thus, Martina won the platform diving event.

It is important that you learn the skills with place value, since all operations with decimal numbers are based on place value.

2.9 exercise

A

1 For the decimal numeral 48.695

   (a) What is the place value of the 9?

   (b) Which digit is in the tens place?

   (c) Which digit is in the tenths place?

2 For the decimal numeral 4965.381

   (a) Which digit is in the thousandths place?

   (b) Which digit is in the thousands place?

3 Write the place value of each underlined digit.

   (a) 6.9̲4   (b) 7̲5.8   (c) 0.69̲

   (d) 93.201̲   (e) 405.8̲3   (f) 290̲4

   (g) 5.96̲2   (h) 180.9̲6   (i) 485̲3

   (j) 3̲4.818   (k) 96.43̲2   (l) 4̲6 913

4 Write each fraction in decimal form.

   (a) $\frac{5}{10}$ (b) $2\frac{13}{100}$ (c) $\frac{369}{1000}$

   (d) $\frac{49}{1000}$ (e) $2\frac{346}{1000}$ (f) $\frac{6}{100}$

   (g) $6\frac{7}{1000}$ (h) $\frac{67}{1000}$ (i) $\frac{18}{100}$

   (j) $25\frac{16}{100}$ (k) $\frac{5}{1000}$ (l) $2\frac{6}{1000}$

5 Write the following as decimal numerals.

   (a) three tenths

   (b) seventy-three hundredths

   (c) five and eleven hundredths

   (d) six hundredths

   (e) forty-five and eight tenths

   (f) twenty and three thousandths

   (g) two hundred forty-five and fifteen thousandths

   (h) three hundred fifty-three thousands

   (i) three hundred and fifty-three thousandths

6 Write the following in words.

    (a) 0.9   (b) 0.46   (c) 0.013

    (d) 1.8   (e) 1.09   (f) 7.009

    (g) 40.08   (h) 800.007   (i) 9.075

7 Arrange the decimals from least to greatest.

    (a) 35.6   0.365   7.54   5.008   65.9

    (b) 11.1   10.1   111.1   101.101   11.11

8 Write these numbers in decreasing order.

$$\frac{4}{10} \qquad 0.3 \qquad 30 \qquad 40 \qquad \frac{36}{100}$$

$$0.39 \qquad 30.1 \qquad 39.9 \qquad 39\frac{9}{100}$$

B

9 Use the symbols $<$ or $>$ to make each of the following true.

    (a) 7.63 ◯ 6.73   (b) 0.89 ◯ 0.98

    (c) 4.06 ◯ 3.60   (d) 36.25 ◯ 32.65

    (e) 0.816 ◯ 0.861   (f) 3.003 ◯ 2.999

10 Find the missing values of □.

    (a) $246 = 2 \times 10^2 + \square \times 10 + \square \times 1$

    (b) $\square = 4 \times 10^3 + 2 \times 10 + 8 \times 1$

    (c) $0.369 = \square \times \frac{1}{10} + \square \times \frac{1}{100} + \square \times \frac{1}{1000}$

    (d) $5.7\square = \square \times 1 + 7 \times \frac{1}{10} + 2 \times \frac{1}{100}$

    (e) $3\square62 = \square \times 10^3 + 4 \times 10^2 + \square \times 10 + \square \times 1$

    (f) $29.\square4 = \square \times 10 + \square \times 1 + 3 \times \frac{1}{10} + \square \times \frac{1}{100}$

    (g) $4\square3.\square = 4 \times 10^2 + 3 \times 1 + 6 \times \frac{1}{10}$

    (h) $3\square4\square.4 = 3 \times 10^3 + 4 \times 10 + 4 \times \frac{1}{10}$

    (i) $\square = 3 \times 10^2 + 4 \times 10 + 9 \times 1$

    (j) $\square = 9 \times 10^2 + 9 \times \frac{1}{10}$

    (k) $\square = 3 \times 10^3 + 4 \times 10^2 + 9 \times 1 + 4 \times \frac{1}{10^2}$

11 These powers of 10 have been scrambled. Unscramble them and write a decimal numeral. The first one has been done for you.

    (a) $\frac{8}{10} + 4 + \frac{3}{100}$ ⟵ $\left(4 + \frac{8}{10} + \frac{3}{100} = 4.83\right.$

    (b) $5 + \frac{7}{10} + \frac{2}{10^2} + 60$

    (c) $\frac{8}{100} + \frac{5}{10}$

    (d) $\frac{6}{1000} + 90 + 4$

    (e) $3000 + 3 \times 10^2 + \frac{4}{100}$

    (f) $\frac{4}{10} + \frac{3}{1000} + 4000$

    (g) $20 + \frac{1}{10} + \frac{1}{100} + 1$

    (h) $\frac{4}{1000} + 5 \times 10^3 + \frac{3}{100}$

    (i) $\frac{3}{100} + \frac{2}{10} + 5$

12 For each statement, write the decimal numeral in expanded form.

    (a) During the winter, there is darkness for 186 d at the North Pole.

    (b) The elevation of the highest volcano, Antofalla in Argentina, is 6100 m.

    (c) The stratus cloud formation is the closest to the earth at an elevation of 1066 m.

    (d) On July 10, 1960, Roger Woodward, age seven, survived a 50.9 m drop over Niagara Falls.

    (e) On August 10, 1876, Alexander Graham Bell placed the first long distance telephone call between Paris and Brantford, Ontario, a distance of 12.87 km.

    (f) Mount Vesuvius erupted in December, 1631, killing about 4000 people.

    (g) On October 2, 1887, a sturgeon, 3.58 m long, was caught at Ladner, B.C.

(h) The ocean sunfish lays eggs that are 1.27 mm in diameter.

(i) A mass of a male banded louse is 0.004 98 mg.

(j) A dentist, Giovanni Orsemgo, pulled 2 000 744 teeth.

(k) A German shephard's sense of smell is one million times better than yours.

13 (a) At Calabogie Resort 4.68 m of snow fell. At Yellowstone Peaks 4.91 m of snow fell. Which resort received more snow?

(b) For a T.V. poll M*A*S*H received a rating of 18.9. On the same night, To Catch a Cold received a rating of 19.8. Which show had the higher rating?

14 The odometer reading on a car shows the distance travelled.

 (means 9066.9 km

For each pair of readings, which car has travelled further, A or B?

Car A   Car B

(a) 486   843

(b) 28963   29001

(c) 469002   468999

15 The precipitation is shown for 5 cities.

Sydney	139.6 mm
Medicine Hat	23.2 mm
Regina	16.9 mm
Fredericton	96.4 mm
Gander	148.9 mm

(a) Which city had the least amount of precipitation?

(b) Which city had the greatest amount of precipitation?

(c) Arrange the cities in order from least to greatest precipitation.

C

16 The batting average of baseball players is shown as a decimal, to the nearest thousandth.

Player	Batting Average
Moskan	0.563
D'Acquisto	0.286
Seaver	0.556
Fisk	0.289
Hancock	0.287
Wynegar	0.255
Ward	0.463

(a) Which player has the best batting average? (The higher the average, the better the average.)

(b) Arrange the players' batting averages in order from best to worst.

skills quiz

(a) $12 \div 3 + 3$

(b) $12 + 3 \div 3$

(c) $3^2 - 3$

(d) $3^3 - 2^2$

(e) $\dfrac{4^2 + 3^2}{5^2}$

(f) $\dfrac{16 \div 2}{4 + 4}$

(g) $\dfrac{13 + 2}{2 \times 3 - 1}$

(h) $\dfrac{20 + 5 - 9}{13 - 4 - 1}$

(i) $3 + 8 - (2 \times 3)$

(j) $(10 - 5) \times 5 \div 5$

(k) $\dfrac{40 \div 2 + 10}{2 + 16 \div 2}$

(l) $\dfrac{8 + 6 \times 16}{16 - (16 - 4)}$

(m) $\dfrac{(13 + 7) \div 2}{8 + (8 \div 4)}$

(n) $\dfrac{6^2 - 3 \times 6}{12 - (4 + 2)}$

(o) $\dfrac{2 \times 12 + 16 \div 4}{18 - 4}$

(p) $\dfrac{4 \times (13 - 5)}{8 \times 4 \div 4}$

Calculate the value of each of the following expressions for $k = 3$, $x = 5$, and $y = 2$.

(q) $3x + 2y$ (r) $2x - 3k$ (s) $x^2 + y^2$

math tip

List the mathematical symbols, words, and skills that you learned in this chapter. Give an example of each.

2.10 extending concepts: rounding skills

The skills you developed earlier in rounding whole numbers can be extended to rounding decimals.

▶ How are the following the same?

▶ How are they different?

Skills for rounding are useful to obtain approximate answers. About how much would it cost for a case of 48 cartons of milk?

Rounding whole numbers

to the nearest 10

$\left.\begin{array}{l}813\\814\end{array}\right\}$ 810

$\left.\begin{array}{l}815\\817\end{array}\right\}$ 820

to the nearest 100

$\left.\begin{array}{l}8725\\8747\end{array}\right\}$ 8700

$\left.\begin{array}{l}8751\\8783\end{array}\right\}$ 8800

Rounding decimals

to the nearest tenth

$\left.\begin{array}{l}8.13\\8.14\end{array}\right\}$ 8.1

$\left.\begin{array}{l}8.15\\8.17\end{array}\right\}$ 8.2

to the nearest hundredth

$\left.\begin{array}{l}0.8725\\0.8747\end{array}\right\}$ 0.87

$\left.\begin{array}{l}0.8751\\0.8783\end{array}\right\}$ 0.88

The number line shows how these numbers are rounded to the nearest tenth.

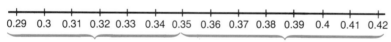

| 0.29 0.3 0.31 0.32 0.33 0.34 0.35 | 0.36 0.37 0.38 0.39 0.4 0.41 0.42 |

These numbers round to 0.3 (to the nearest tenth)

These numbers round to 0.4 (to the nearest tenth)

Example Round the following:

(a) 0.46 to the nearest tenth

(b) 0.735 to the nearest hundredth

Solution (a) 0.46 ≐ 0.5

$\left(\begin{array}{l}\text{rounded to the}\\\text{nearest tenth.}\end{array}\right)$

(b) 0.735 ≐ 0.74

$\left(\begin{array}{l}\text{rounded to the}\\\text{nearest hundredth.}\end{array}\right)$

$\left(\begin{array}{l}\text{The symbol} \doteq \text{means ``is}\\\text{approximately equal to.''}\end{array}\right)$

It is also possible to indicate the accuracy of rounding by stating the number of decimal places.

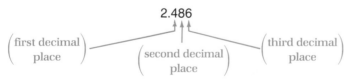

2.486

$\left(\begin{array}{l}\text{first decimal}\\\text{place}\end{array}\right)$ $\left(\begin{array}{l}\text{second decimal}\\\text{place}\end{array}\right)$ $\left(\begin{array}{l}\text{third decimal}\\\text{place}\end{array}\right)$

Remember: These have equivalent meanings.

to the nearest tenth	↔	to the first decimal place
to the nearest hundredth	↔	to the second decimal place
to the nearest thousandth	↔	to the third decimal place

2.10 exercise

A

1 Which digit do you look at to round to the nearest
   (a) tenth?   (b) hundredth?   (c) thousandth?

2 Which digit was checked to round the following?

   (a) 45.9 to the nearest one is 46

   (b) 45.5 to the nearest one is 46

   (c) 45.4 to the nearest one is 45

   (d) 45.69 to the nearest tenth is 45.7

   (e) 45.65 to the nearest tenth is 45.7

   (f) 45.64 to the nearest tenth is 45.6

   (g) 45.639 to the nearest hundredth is 45.64

   (h) 45.635 to the nearest hundredth is 45.64

   (i) 45.634 to the nearest hundredth is 45.63

3 Make up two examples to show you know what the following statements mean.

   (a) Round off to the nearest hundred.

   (b) Round off to the nearest hundredth.

   (c) Round off to the nearest thousand.

   (d) Round off to the nearest thousandth.

   (e) Round off to the nearest ten thousand.

   (f) Round off to the nearest ten thousandth.

4 Round the following to the nearest tenth.

   (a) 0.44   (b) 0.46   (c) 0.45

   (d) 1.72   (e) 1.75   (f) 1.79

5 Round to the nearest hundredth.

   (a) 0.548   (b) 0.545   (c) 0.543

   (d) 2.073   (e) 2.078   (f) 2.075

   (g) 5.555   (h) 5.554   (i) 5.559

6 Round to one decimal place.

   (a) 0.65   (b) 0.63   (c) 0.69

   (d) 9.26   (e) 9.25   (f) 9.22

7 Round to two decimal places.

   (a) 0.788   (b) 0.785   (c) 0.781

   (d) 6.345   (e) 6.347   (f) 6.342

   (g) 6.895   (h) 6.892   (i) 6.899

B

8 Use the decimals in the chart. Choose 2 decimals from the chart that can be rounded to each of the following values.

   (a) 28.4

   (b) 28.8

   (c) 28.75

   (d) 28.35

28.321	28.753
28.343	28.749
28.348	28.758
28.354	28.761
28.438	28.836
28.732	28.853

9 Round each to the accuracy shown.

		nearest tenth	nearest hundredth
(a)	16.235		
(b)	12.896		
(c)	0.169		
(d)	23.832		
(e)	2.936		
(f)	4.968		

10 Round each price to the nearest cent.

   (a) $0.469   (b) $0.373   (c) $0.487

   (d) $12.653   (e) $8.456   (f) $23.319

   (g) $296.316   (h) $182.923   (i) $49.895

11 Write an approximate measure for each of the following.

   (a) 1.45 g   (nearest tenth of a gram)

   (b) 36.558 km (nearest hundredth of kilometre)

   (c) 0.0368 L   (nearest thousandth litre)

   (d) 6.38 cm   (nearest centimetre)

   (e) 3.009 mL   (nearest hundredth millilitre)

   (f) 47.78 m   (nearest tenth metre)

   (g) 3.055 kg   (nearest tenth kilogram)

   (h) 63.895 m   (nearest metre)

   (i) 8.055 L   (nearest hundredth litre)

   (j) 10.055 km (nearest tenth kilometre)

12 Round each measure to one decimal place.

   (a) The smallest lobster is the Cape Lobster which is 9.75 cm long.

   (b) The tallest Christmas tree was 5.525 m tall.

   (c) The shortest snake is 11.749 cm long.

   (d) The widest waterfall is the Khone Falls at 10.72 km.

13 The measurements of each stamp are shown to 2 decimal places. Round each measure to one decimal place.

14 Round each dimension to the nearest centimetre.

   (a) One of the highest bids for Canadian art was $98 000. The dimensions of the canvas were 83.2 cm by 107.9 cm.

   (b) Another high auction price of $41 000 was bid for *Portage Past the Rapids*, a painting by Cornelius Krieghoff. The dimensions of the painting were 46.3 cm by 60.6 cm.

15 Various heights of Canadian buildings are shown in the chart.

Peace Tower, Ottawa	92.3 m
First Canadian Place, Montreal	284.9 m
Lomboard Place, Winnipeg	124.1 m
Canadian National Tower, Edmonton	114.6 m
Toronto Dominion Bank, Toronto	225.4 m
British Columbia Centre, Vancouver	270.9 m
Fenwick Towers, Halifax	91.4 m

   (a) Round the measures to the nearest metre.

   (b) Which is the tallest building in the chart?

   (c) Arrange the buildings in height from least to greatest.

C

16 For a statistics survey, the 10 most popular sports were rated.

Sport	Rating
Curling	5.05
Ice Skating	17.24
Cross Country Skiing	7.94
Swimming	32.83
Ice Hockey	8.43
Tennis	12.96
Downhill Skiing	6.95
Baseball	1.98
Golf	10.83
Bowling	4.31

   (a) Round the ratings to 1 decimal place.

   (b) Which sport was rated the highest?

   (c) Arrange the sports from least to greatest rating.

2.11 problem-solving: more than one answer

There are often problems that have more than one answer. For example, you use coins to buy a chocolate bar in a vending machine. There are different ways of making change for a dollar.

In every section in this book, you will find aspects of problem-solving. However, on special pages, such as this one, certain aspects of problem-solving are summarized and dealt with in detail.

1 Use only 5¢, 10¢, 25¢.
   (a) Write 5 different ways of making change for a dollar bill.
   (b) How many *different* combinations are there, in all, of change for a dollar bill?

2 Use only 5¢, 10¢, 1¢.
   (a) Write 5 different ways of making change for a quarter.
   (b) How many different combinations are there, in all, of change for a quarter?

3 A can of pop costs 55¢. Write 4 combinations of coins that you can use to pay for the pop.

4 Three people arrive at the same ticket window. Peter (P), Quinta (Q), and Rachel (R). One order of buying tickets is P,Q,R, and another is Q,P,R. How many different orders are there?

5 Four people are sitting on a bench; Bert, George, Carole, Mimi.
   (a) Record 4 different ways they can sit on the bench.
   (b) How many different ways, in all, can they sit on the bench?

6 A license plate is shown.

   | LPS 13■ |

   (a) The missing figure is one of the digits 0 to 9. How many different license plates can you make?

(b) On another license plate, the last letter and the last number are missing.

   | LP■ 13■ |

   How many different license plates can you make?
   Questions 7 to 9 are based on the map below.

7 (a) Write two routes that you can take from Edmonton to Winnipeg.

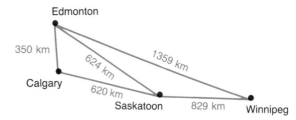

   (b) What is the shortest route in (a)?
   (c) How far is the shortest route from Edmonton to Winnipeg?

8 (a) Write two routes that take you from Calgary to Winnipeg.
   (b) What is the shortest route in (a)?
   (c) How far is the shortest route from Calgary to Winnipeg?

9 (a) Create another question based on the data in the map.
   (b) Solve the problem in (a).

practice and problems: a chapter review

(2.1) **1** Which numbers are prime? composite?

(a) 36   (b) 49   (c) 47   (d) 196

(e) Write each as a product of prime factors.

(2.2) **2** Copy and complete the chart.

Number	Divisible by
	2 3 4 5 6 7 8 9 10

	Number									
(a)	840									
(b)	162									
(c)	312									

(2.3) **3** Find the greatest common factor for each pair.

(a) 12, 24   (b) 36, 80   (c) 30, 75

(2.3) **4** At the hockey game every 18th person was given a puck, while the 12th person was given a team poster. Which persons should receive both a puck and poster?

(2.4) **5** Find the square root of each number.

(a) 64   (b) 144   (c) 324   (d) 1764

6 The area of the square cover of a record is 1024 cm². Find the dimensions of the cover.

(2.5) **7** Evaluate.

(a) $2^3 \times 3^2$ (b) $5^2 \times 2^3$ (c) $3^6 \div 3^3$

(2.7) **8** Calculate the following. What property is shown?

(a) 73×0 (b) $15 + 0$ (c) 18×1

(2.8) **9** Draw a diagram to show each fraction.

(a) $\frac{3}{10}$ (b) $\frac{1}{4}$ (c) $\frac{3}{8}$

(2.9) **10** For each of the underlined digits, what is the face value? place value?

(a) 15.<u>3</u>64   (b) 0.45<u>7</u>   (c) 1.0<u>3</u>5

(d) Write each number in expanded form.

(2.10) (e) Round each number to the nearest tenth.

test for practice

1 Write each number as a product of prime factors.

(a) 48   (b) 72   (c) 108   (d) 720

2 Find the G.C.F. and the L.C.M. of 18 and 30.

3 (a) Find the square of 5 and of 7.

(b) Find the square root of 81 and of 225.

4 Evaluate. Use $t = 5, f = 3$.

(a) t^2 (b) f^3 (c) $f^3 - t^2$

5 Write each as a single power. Then evaluate.

(a) $3^2 \times 3^2$ (b) $5^6 \div 5^3$ (c) $2^3 \times 2^2$

6 Which property is illustrated by each of the following?

(a) $18 \times (62 + 38) = 18 \times 62 + 18 \times 38$

(b) $683 + 317 = 317 + 683$

(c) $37 \times 25 \times 4 = 37 \times (25 \times 4)$

(d) $71 \times 0 = 0$ (e) $83 \times 1 = 81$

7 Draw a diagram to illustrate each fraction.

(a) $\frac{1}{8}$ (b) $\frac{7}{10}$ (c) $\frac{3}{5}$

8 What is the face value and place value of the underlined digits?

(a) 0.3<u>6</u>4   (b) 12.<u>0</u>5   (c) 0.12<u>1</u>

9 Write each fraction in decimal form.

(a) $\frac{27}{100}$ (b) $3\frac{33}{1000}$ (c) $\frac{81}{1000}$

10 Write $5 \times 1 + 3 \times \frac{1}{10} + 8 \times \frac{1}{100}$ in standard form.

11 Copy and complete the chart. Round each number.

	Number	Round to the nearest		
		ten	tenth	hundredth
(a)	48.695			
(b)	35.252			
(c)	93.259			

maintaining skills: computing

This skills quiz is designed to review some of your work in the previous chapters.

(a) $1860 \div 12$

(b) 10^2 (c) $4 \times 4 \times 4 \times 4$

(d) $462 + 361 + 5$ (e) 2^6 (f) $36 + 9 \div 3$

(g) $2^2 + 4 \times 5$ (h) 3^5 (i) $\frac{4005}{45}$

(j) $24 \div 8 + 32 \div 4$ (k) $\frac{9^2 + 1}{26 + 15}$

(l) Which number is divisible by 3?
2986, 4132, 1191, 9145

(m) Calculate the value of $3m + 2n$ where m is 36 and n is 24.

(n) Which numbers are not divisible by 8?
22 924, 12 140, 84 963, 19 696

(o) Multiply the sum of 481 and 296 by 43.

(p) $\frac{25 \div 5 + 6}{18 - (12 - 5)}$ (q) $2^2 + 3^2$

(r) Find the sum $1 + 2 + 3 + 4 + \ldots + 50$.

(s) $(36 + 28)(12 + 14)$

(t) Divide the square of 660 by 33.

(u) Subtract the sum of 365 and 241 from 965.

(v) Find the square root of 1296.

(w) Divide the product of 49 and 48 by 56.

(x) Find the sum $1 + 3 + 5 + \ldots + 19$.

(y) Divide the sum of 395, 296, and 482 by 17.

(z) Find the sum
$1 + 10 + 100 + \ldots + 1\,000\,000$.

problem-solving: strategy

How good are you at following the instructions of a flow chart? Sir Isaac Newton invented a method of finding square roots of numbers. This method is shown in the steps of this flow chart.

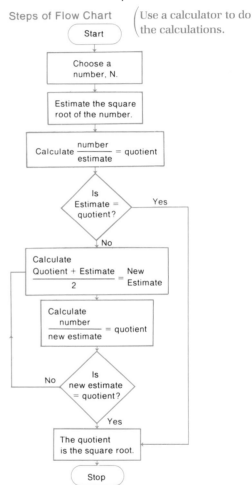

Steps of Flow Chart (Use a calculator to do the calculations.)

A Use the above flow chart to calculate the square root of each of the following to 2 decimal places.
(a) $\sqrt{39}$ (b) $\sqrt{87}$ (c) $\sqrt{93}$
Express your answer to 1 decimal place.

B Use the flow chart. Calculate each square root to 2 decimal places.
(a) $\sqrt{96}$ (b) $\sqrt{296}$ (c) $\sqrt{3.89}$

math is plus: microcomputer programming

In this book, the program language you will use is BASIC. Many of the computer symbols are already familiar to you. These are the symbols used in the BASIC computer language.

+	add	↑	exponent	< >	not equal to
−	subtract	>	greater than	<	less than
*	multiply	> =	greater than	< =	less than or
/	divide		or equal to		equal to

A computer programmer learns skills in translating the mathematical problem into the steps of a program that the computer can follow. A computer does not think for itself. You must tell it *every* step that it is to do. Flow charts assist the computer programmer in organizing the steps of the computer program. (Refer to your work on flow charts in the previous chapter.)

As in human languages, there are differences among computer languages. The same expression is given in different ways in different computer languages.

Language	Statement
ALGOL	A: = (B + C) * D
FORTRAN	A = (B + C) * D
COBOL	Compute A equals (B plus C) Times D
BASIC	A = (B + C) * D;

This part gives your program a title.

Give the computer the values of *m* and *n* you want to use.

Use *m* = 3
n = 4

```
Computer Program
10   PRINT "EVALUATE EXPRESSION"
20   INPUT M, N
30   LET V = 2 * N + 3 * M ↑ 2
40   PRINT "THE VALUE OF THE EXPRESSION IS": V
50   END
```

All computer programs must have an end.

The computer evaluates the expression
* means multiply
↑ means exponent

The computer prints the output.

The value of the expression is 35.

▶ Use the above program as a sample. Write a computer program in BASIC that evaluates these expressions. Try the program. Do a run.

A Evaluate 6*m* − 2*n*.   B Evaluate $x^2 + 3y^2$.

In the *Math Plus: Writing a Program*, you will explore the meaning of some of the computer statements.

Throughout the book look for and try the computer tips.

computer tip

This basic program is related to finding the sum 1 + 2 + 3 + 4 + ...

```
10   PRINT "XXXX"
20   INPUT R
30   LET D = R * (R + 1)/2
40   PRINT "THE SUM IS"; D
50   END
```

Suggest a title for the program.

computer tip

Try the program. Predict what the program is designed to do.

```
10   PRINT "XXXX"
20   INPUT A
30   INPUT B
40   INPUT C
50   LET X = (C − B)/A
60   PRINT "THE ANSWER IS"; X
70   END
```

Write a program to calculate the value of this expression $AB + C^2$.

decimal numbers and applications

Decimals vocabulary and operations, reasonable answers, unit pricing, reading carefully, decimals and common fractions, writing problems, mental calculations, variable expressions, problem solving skills, solving problems and applications

Seldom will a day go by when you won't need to work with decimals in one place or another.

You will use decimals when you want to compare prices in newspaper ads.

Decimals are used to record the times in sporting events.

When you purchase silver tip tetras for your tropical fish aquarium, you will need to use decimals for money.

When you construct a building or a bridge, you need to work accurately with decimals.

Make a list of 10 other places or situations in which you need to know decimals.

In this chapter, you will learn skills with decimals and their operations. The skills you have learned with whole numbers will be extended to skills with decimals.

Throughout the chapter, use a calculator to check your work.

3.1 skills inventory: place value

Often in mathematics, understanding a particular skill will help you understand and learn other skills. For example, skills with operations with decimals depend on your understanding of place value.

In the previous chapter you learned skills with place value, rounding, and comparing decimals. Try the following skills inventory. Then check your answers at the end of page 77.

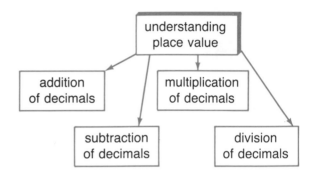

3.1 exercise

1 For each underlined digit, what is the face value? the place value?

   (a) 659   (b) 65.9   (c) 6.59

   (d) 6038   (e) 60.38   (f) 6.038

   (g) 0.905   (h) 90.5   (i) 9050

2 Write each number in expanded form.

   (a) 6845   (b) 684.5   (c) 6.845

   (d) 0.748   (e) 74.8   (f) 7480

   (g) 1.005   (h) 100.5   (i) 20.035

3 Write each as a decimal in standard form.

   (a) $4 \times 100 + 3 \times 10 + 6 \times 1$

   (b) $8 \times 100 + 6 \times 10 + 3 \times 1 + 9 \times \frac{1}{10}$

   (c) $9 \times 10^2 + 5 \times 1 + 9 \times \frac{1}{10}$

   (d) $6 \times 10^2 + 4 \times \frac{1}{10} + 3 \times \frac{1}{10^2} + 5 \times \frac{1}{10^3}$

   (e) $7 \times 10^3 + 9 \times \frac{1}{10^3}$

4 Write each decimal numeral in words.

   (a) 719   (b) 6227   (c) 0.35

   (d) 0.04   (e) 1.36   (f) 0.028

   (g) 100.78   (h) 100.09   (i) 1.006

5 Write each number as a decimal.

   (a) fifty thousand four hundred seventeen

   (b) fifty-one hundredths

   (c) nine hundredths

   (d) thirty-eight thousandths

   (e) two and one tenth

   (f) thirty and twelve hundredths

   (g) six thousand fifty and six hundredths

   (h) ten thousand and six tenths

   (i) eighty-four thousand and eleven thousandths.

6 Replace ○ by the symbols < or >.

   (a) 0.92 ○ 0.93   (b) 0.68 ○ 0.86

   (c) 0.8 ○ 0.08   (d) 2.69 ○ 2.96

   (e) 0.53 ○ 0.503   (f) 0.890 ○ 0.9

   (g) 0.101 ○ 1.01   (h) 0.25 ○ 0.305

7 Which decimal in each of the following has the greatest value?

   (a) 0.04, 0.08, 0.2   (b) 3.02, 3.11, 3.012

   (c) 6.34, 6.43, 6.5   (d) 0.666, 0.680, 0.625

   (e) 1.36, 1.09, 1.41   (f) 0.599, 0.959, 0.995

8 Arrange the numbers in order from the least to the greatest.

(a) 368, 36.8, 0.368

(b) 5.025, 0.525, 0.255, 55.2, 50.52

(c) 1.01, 10.1, 1.001, 1.011

(d) 10.101, 101.01, 1010.1, 1001.1, 1.0101

9 Replace ◯ by the symbols $<$ or $>$.

(a) $2 \times 100 + 7 \times 10 + 5 \times \frac{1}{100}$ ◯ 27.50

(b) 9.87 ◯ $3 \times 10 + 2 \times 1 + 5 \times \frac{1}{10}$

(c) $8 \times 10 + 2 \times \frac{1}{10}$ ◯ 9.8

(d) 0.29 ◯ $3 \times \frac{1}{10} + 3 \times \frac{1}{100}$

10 Round the numbers to the nearest tenth.

(a) 1.78   (b) 1.73   (c) 1.75

(d) 0.555   (e) 0.535   (f) 0.565

11 Round the numbers to the nearest hundredth.

(a) 0.568   (b) 0.565   (c) 0.561

(d) 484.035   (e) 3.552   (f) 12.559

12 Round the numbers to one decimal place.

(a) 0.36   (b) 0.35   (c) 0.31

(d) 21.05   (e) 1.03   (f) 36.06

13 Round the numbers to two decimal places.

(a) 12.055   (b) 12.058   (c) 12.051

(d) 30.009   (e) 8.0095   (f) 0.0081

14 Which of the following can be rounded to 11.8 (to one decimal place)?

(a) 11.760   (b) 11.739   (c) 11.833

(d) 11.860   (e) 11.842   (f) 11.789

(g) 11.851   (h) 11.792   (i) 11.826

15 Round the numbers to the accuracy shown.

(a) 6.9235 (to one decimal place)

(b) 13.4567 (to two decimal places)

(c) 8.6824 (to the nearest tenth)

(d) 19.3436 (to the nearest thousandth)

(e) 16.2193 (to three decimal places)

(f) 7.5518 (to the nearest hundredth)

3.2 adding and subtracting decimals

You often need to use your skills for adding and subtracting decimals to solve problems.

How much does the equipment cost in all? How much more does the camera cost than the equipment bag?

'Extended range' plus telephoto lens
Camera
$39.86

Film
$2.89

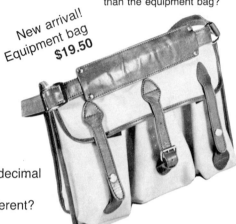

New arrival!
Equipment bag
$19.50

Skills with place value are important to add or subtract decimal numbers.
▶ How are the calculations alike? ▶ How are they different?

| Addition |
| Subtraction |

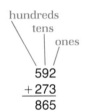
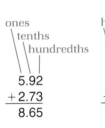
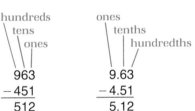

hundreds
tens
ones
```
  592
+ 273
  865
```

ones
tenths
hundredths
```
  5.92
+ 2.73
  8.65
```

hundreds
tens
ones
```
  963
- 451
  512
```

ones
tenths
hundredths
```
  9.63
- 4.51
  5.12
```

To add or subtract decimals, you need to line up digits with the same place value. To do so, you line up the decimal points.

Once you learn skills, you apply them to solve problems. Refer to the steps for solving problems to help you organize your solution.

Example Roma walked 2.5 km on Monday, 3.7 km on Tuesday, and 3.4 km on Wednesday. How far did she walk in all?

To check whether your answer is reasonable, you can use your rounding skills.

Solution

Distance walked		Find the sum
Monday	2.5 km	2.5
Tuesday	3.7 km	3.7
Wednesday	3.4 km	+ 3.4
		9.6

Think: Is my answer reasonable?
round to 3
round to 4
round to 3
estimate 10

The total distance Roma walked is 9.6 km.

The answer is reasonable.

3.2 exercise

A Use your skills with place value to help you add or subtract decimals.

1 Use the results for adding whole numbers. Find the sum of the decimals.

(a)	262	2.62	(b)	348	34.8
	+623	+6.23		+243	+24.3
	885	?		591	?

(c)	983	98.3	(d)	713	7.13
	+748	+74.8		+497	+4.97
	1731	?		1210	?

2 Add.

(a)	64.8	(b)	9.64	(c)	36.7
	+67.8		+8.27		+33.3

(d)	38.6	(e)	56.3	(f)	62.45
	+ 9.7		+18.7		+ 8.60

3 One of the answers given, A or B , is correct. Use your rounding skills to chose the correct one.

	A	B
(a) 4.56 + 75.37	79.93	7.993
(b) 13.4 + 7.59	209.9	20.99
(c) 369.2 + 9.83	37.903	379.03
(d) 65.4 + 14.6	80	8.0

4 Estimate each answer. Then calculate.

(a)	7.78	(b)	10.49	(c)	3.80
	+2.38		+ 2.50		+3.25

(d)	9.86	(e)	19.6	(f)	17.39
	+8.6		+ 9.36		+42.61

5 Calculate.

(a) 4.6 + 3.8

(b) 16.28 + 12.31

(c) 2.96 + 3.82

(d) 12.98 + 4.86

(e) 47.963 + 28.612

(f) 9.826 + 18.919

(g) 12.63 + 2.86 + 14.29

(h) 1.939 + 26.938 + 30.019

6 Add these! (What is the first step you need to do?

(a) 496, 2391, 23 965

(b) 36, 986, 565, 4896, 12, 5

(c) 4.961, 36.92, 48.9, 126.7

(d) 489.32, 1289.6, 489.673

(e) 9.87, 0.443, 92.1, 69.14

(f) 3.998, 13.9, 16.978, 48.9

7 Subtract.

(a)	96.3	(b)	7.45	(c)	6.5
	−38.6		−5.85		−5.9

(d)	3.58	(e)	45.80	(f)	3.80
	−1.70		−38.75		−1.82

8 One of the three answers, A, B, or C, is correct. Use your rounding skills to choose the correct one.

	A	B	C
(a) 26.8 − 8.1	34.9	18.7	1.87
(b) 66.8 − 12.5	7.9	79.3	54.3
(c) 126.9 − 32.8	94.1	49.1	159.7
(d) 12.93 − 1.86	14.79	11.07	1.07

9 Estimate each answer. Then calculate.

(a)	8.96	(b)	32.4	(c)	36.9
	−4.68		− 6.8		−12.8

(d)	15.69	(e)	9.7	(f)	3.8
	− 6.8		−3.48		−1.78

10 Calculate. Check whether your answer is reasonable.

(a) 19.6 − 13.2

(b) 21.6 − 14.8

(c) 6.83 − 4.79

(d) 4.96 − 3.69

(e) 12.86 − 9.67

(f) 29.92 − 13.93

11 Add or subtract. (Did you estimate your answer?)

(a) 6.3 + 4.2
(b) 13.9 − 4.8
(c) 13.6 − 12.2
(d) 9.63 + 4.18
(e) 9.32 + 12.68
(f) 11.296 − 9.213
(g) 6.83 − 1.38
(h) 3.21 + 21.63
(i) 4.8 − 2.36
(j) 12 − 6.93
(k) 16 + 2.68
(l) 5.63 − 5.489

B

12 Estimate each answer. Then calculate.

(a) 23.69
     4.81
     1.96

(b) 29.06
     12.43
     10.08

(c) 123.45
     321.54
     213.45

(d)   49.69
     − 23.06

(e)   130.00
     − 129.54

(f)   269.41
     − 139.41

(g) 1.96 + 3.21 + 12.61
(h) 5.03 + 14.01 + 15.631
(i) 85 + 96.2 + 140 + 0.14
(j) 1200.8 − 491.9
(k) 12 316.9 − 10 219.8
(l) 1964.3 + 1415.8 − 2134.9
(m) 2691.35 + 4432.41 − 1829.96
(n) 123 − 0.38
(o) 23.69 − 9

13 Each cash register tape shows purchases.
▶ Estimate the total purchase.
▶ Then calculate the answer.

(a) 4.84
     0.13
     5.37
     0.60
     2.59

(b) 7.97
     0.48
     1.05
     0.26
     3.09

(c) 0.15
     6.01
     0.29
     3.27
     8.43

14 Which item costs more? How much more?

Estimate first.
Then calculate.

Deluxe Figure Skates. Top quality features like full grain kid leather; PVC moulded heel and outsole; rubber padded tongue; foam insoles; water-repellent counters and Pro' nickel-plated steel blades.
896-19   Price **$38.55**

Snowshoes. Authentic styling, handmade by Canadian Indians. Wood frame, gut netting, adjustable leather harness.
761-23   Price **$43.20**

15 (a) The regular price of an exercise set is $119.29. How much will you save if you buy it on sale for $96.76?

(b) Leona bought *Skylark* for $2.99, and *Deepwater* for $6.25. What was the total cost of the books?

16 (a) The stamp was purchased for $12.65. It was later sold for $28.90. How much money was made?

(b) Terri threw two lawn darts 9.5 m and 10.3 m. Jacky threw her darts 8.7 m and 10.6 m. Who threw their darts the furthest? By how much?

(c) Melody ate an apple with 295.6 kJ of energy and drank a glass of milk with 535.9 kJ. What was the total amount of energy she consumed?

(d) The helicopter hovered 15.4 m above the ground. It then dropped 3.7 m. How high above the ground was the helicopter?

17 The world's tallest orchid is from Malaysia. It grows to a height of 7.6 m. The average height of the roof of a single-story house is about 4.8 m. How much higher is the orchid?

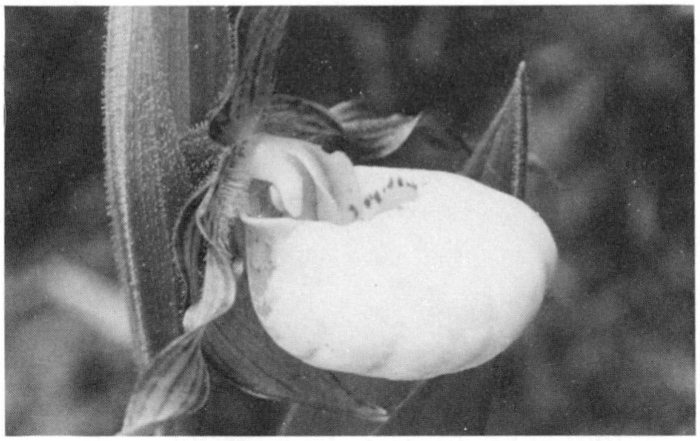

There are over 15 000 different types of orchids in the world. The tallest orchid grows to be almost 8 m tall. Would you believe that, based on today's prices, more than $10 000 was once paid for an orchid.

18 (a) Part of a cash register receipt was torn off. Find the missing value

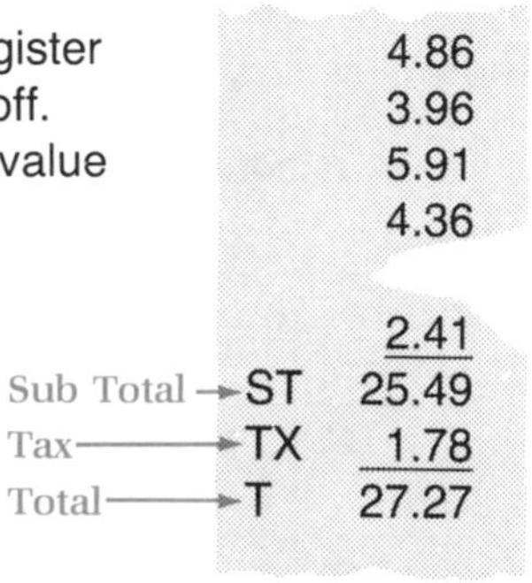
4.86
3.96
5.91
4.36
2.41
Sub Total → ST 25.49
Tax → TX 1.78
Total → T 27.27

Add the tax to the sub total.

Find the missing amounts for these sales receipts.

(b)

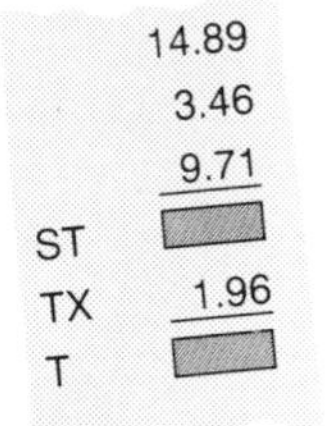
14.89
3.46
9.71
ST
TX 1.96
T

(c)

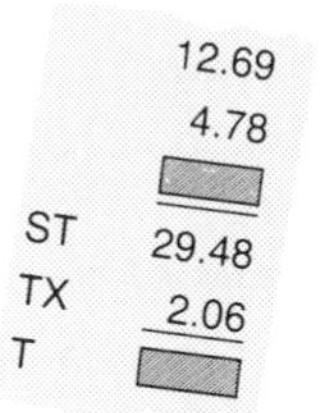
12.69
4.78
ST 29.48
TX 2.06
T

(d)

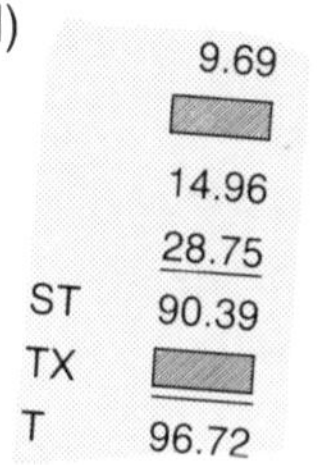
9.69
14.96
28.75
ST 90.39
TX
T 96.72

(e)

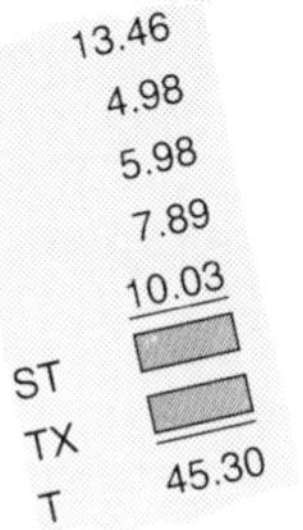
13.46
4.98
5.98
7.89
10.03
ST
TX
T 45.30

19 Merle bought a sweater for $23.65, jeans for $ 8.50 and a belt for $7.95.

(a) What was the total cost?

(b) How much change did she get from $50?

20 (a) A three-sided garden has one side 4.5 m, another side 3.7 m. The total distance around the garden is 11.6 m. Find the length of the third side.

(b) Pierre bought some apples for $3.75, peaches for $2.79 and oranges. The change from a $10 bill was $1.47. Find the cost of the oranges.

(c) In preparing for a beach party, Trina and Sacha bought hot dogs and fixings. The hot dogs cost $15.36 and the fixings, $5.26. If $20.00 was collected, how much more do they need to collect?

C

21 (a) John had $25.00. He bought four Christmas presents, each costing $4.69, $2.89, $11.25 and $4.55. How much money did he have left?

(b) Use the figures in (a) to make up another problem.

Look for other Calculator Tips.

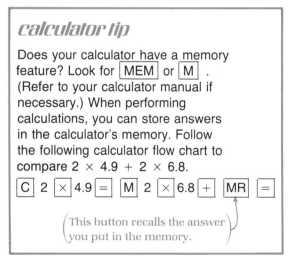

calculator tip

Does your calculator have a memory feature? Look for [MEM] or [M] . (Refer to your calculator manual if necessary.) When performing calculations, you can store answers in the calculator's memory. Follow the following calculator flow chart to compare $2 \times 4.9 + 2 \times 6.8$.

[C] 2 [×] 4.9 [=] [M] 2 [×] 6.8 [+] [MR] [=]

(This button recalls the answer you put in the memory.)

applications: bank accounts and banking

There are many ways you can save money.
If you deposit money into a bank account, you will receive a book to record your transactions.

▶ **deposits** — You place money into your account.
▶ **withdrawals** — You take money out of your account.

The **balance** is the amount of money you have left after you deposit or withdraw money. To obtain your balance you need to add or subtract.

Previous Balance	$469.38
Deposit	$12.25
Balance	$481.63

Previous Balance	$469.38
Withdrawal	$16.50
Balance	$452.88

22 Find the missing entries in each bank account.

(a)
Date	Withdrawal	Deposit	Balance
Nov 3			**166.93
Nov 5	***23.25		?
Nov 10		***26.50	?
Nov 12	***18.95		?
Nov 14		***36.45	?

(b)
Date	Withdrawal	Deposit	Balance
Dec 8			**268.35
Dec 9		?	**337.85
Dec 15	***28.65		?
Dec 16		***36.25	**345.45
Dec 23	?		**331.16

23 When you write a cheque on some accounts, you are making a withdrawal (WD) from your account. The bank may also charge you for each cheque. In your book, the symbol CHQ will occur. Find the missing entries in the bank account.

Date	Item	Withdrawal	Deposit	Balance
Mar 12				**693.25
Mar 14	CHQ	***43.25		?
Mar 18	WD	***12.50		?
Mar 21	CHQ	?		**597.50
Mar 23	DEP		?	**616.86
Mar 24	CHQ	***18.20		?
Mar 25	WD	?		**561.76

24 On some accounts, you receive payment from the bank for letting the bank use your money: Interest (INT) is paid to your account, at certain time periods; end of the month, every 3 mon, and so on. You will be charged 29¢ service charge for writing a cheque. (The symbol used is S/C.) Find the missing entries in the bank account.

Date	Item	Withdrawal	Deposit	Balance
June 8				**436.25
June 10	CHQ	***18.23		?
June 11	CHQ	?		**378.37
June 13	DEP		***45.00	?
June 14	WD	***23.00		?
June 20	CHQ	?		**374.12
June 29	CHQ	***12.50		?
June 30	S/C	?		**360.46
June 30	INT		****1.96	?

calculator tip

In later chapters, you will learn how to calculate the interest on a bank account, as well as learn about different ways of earning interest on your money.

problem-solving: research

To solve some problems, you need to do some research to obtain needed information to answer the problem.

3.3 multiplying with decimals

To solve some problems, you need to use skills with multiplication.

Problem

Michael works at the Pizza King and earns $4.65/h. He worked 12 h last week. How much did he earn?

Multiplication

To find the answer you need to find the product:

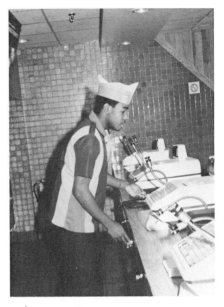

Amount for 1 h $4.65
Multiply to find 4.65
amount for 12 h ×12
930
465
55.80

⎰ Estimate the answer.
⎱ round to 5
round to 10
estimate 50

⎰ Use your estimate to
⎱ place the decimal point.

Michael earned $55.80.

To place the decimal point, you can also use a pattern related to the original number of decimal places.

4.53
×0.6
2.718

⎰ Think:
2 decimal places
1 decimal place
3 decimal places

2.63
× 0.25
0.6575

⎰ Think:
2 decimal places
2 decimal places
4 decimal places

7.8
×0.4
3.12

⎰ Think:
1 decimal place
1 decimal place
2 decimal places

2.08
×0.67
1.3936

⎰ Think:
2 decimal places
2 decimal places
4 decimal places

⎰ Your skill of finding products of
whole numbers, extends to helping
you find products of decimals.
▶ How are they alike?
▶ How are they different?

246   24.6
×4   × 4
984   98.4

Once you learn skills with multiplication, you can apply them to solve problems.

Example   Lace sells at $3.95/m ← means $3.95 per metre
Find the cost of 4.5 m of lace for a fancy tablecloth.

⎰ Check: Is your answer
reasonable?
5 × $4
= $20

Solution   1 m of lace costs $3.95
4.5 m of lace cost 4.5 × $3.95 = $17.775 or
$17.78 (to the nearest cent)

⎰ The answer is
⎱ reasonable.

A This exercise will help you develop skills for multiplying decimal fractions.

1 Find ☐ in each of the following.

(a) 0.7
   × 0.5
    ?

Think:
1 decimal place
1 decimal place
☐ decimal places

(b) 2.37
   × 1.4
    ?

2 decimal places
1 decimal place
☐ decimal places

(c) 14.5
  × 0.36
    ?

1 decimal place
2 decimal places
☐ decimal places

(d) 48.23
  × 0.16
    ?

2 decimal places
2 decimal places
☐ decimal places

Find the product for each of the above.

2 Use each result for the whole numbers to find the product for the decimals.

(a) 36   3.6
  × 9   × 9
  324   ?

(b) 28   2.8
  × 24   × 2.4
  672   ?

(c) 324   3.24
  × 8   × 0.8
  2592   ?

(d) 4869   48.69
  × 36   × 3.6
  175 284   ?

3 For each multiplication question, the digits of the answer are shown. What is the answer after you have correctly placed the decimal point?

(a) 9 × 0.4   (36)
(b) 0.9 × 8.6   (774)
(c) 2.6 × 49.8   (12948)
(d) 2.6 × 4.98   (12948)
(e) 0.2 × 0.3   (6)
(f) 0.3 × 0.46   (138)
(g) 200 × 1.23   (24600)
(h) 1.35 × 0.9   (1215)
(i) 1.909 × 23   (43907)
(j) 4.8 × 16.91   (81168)

4 One of the answers, A or B, is correct. Use your rounding skills to choose the correct one.

	A	B
(a) 4 × 1.36	54.4	5.44
(b) 1.8 × 3.8	6.84	0.684
(c) 6.8 × 2.65	18.02	1.802
(d) 0.8 × 0.365	0.0292	0.292

5 For each question:
▶ Estimate the answer. ▶ Then calculate.

(a)   0.4
  × 0.3

(b)   0.5
  × 0.3

(c)   15
  × 0.4

(d)   0.3
  × 9.0

(e)   4.2
  × 0.5

(f)   0.41
  × 0.2

(g)   0.2
  × 0.3

(h)   2.1
  × 0.04

(i)   0.5
  × 1.2

6 Calculate. Check whether your answer is reasonable.

(a)   2.3
  × 0.5

(b)   7.1
  × 0.4

(c)   4.2
  × 0.7

(d)   0.45
  × 2.3

(e)   0.57
  × 1.38

(f)   46.41
  × 0.5

(g) 4.5 × 1.3   (h) 4.35 × 1.76

B Remember to check whether your answers are reasonable.

7 Find each product and round your answers.

(a) 0.26 × 2.9   (2 decimal places)
(b) 2.9 × 6.8   (1 decimal place)
(c) 16 × 0.39   (nearest tenth)
(d) 2.9 × 8.37   (nearest hundredth)
(e) 0.13 × 0.03   (3 decimal places)
(f) 3.4 × 2.8   (nearest tenth)

8 Estimate each purchase. Then, find the cost of each purchase.

(a) 8 bottles of orange at $0.69 per bottle

(b) 6 rolls of tape at $1.49 per roll

(c) 18 m of wood at $0.54/m

(d) 6.8 kg of syrup at $4.69/kg

(e) 8 jars of pickles

DILL · PLAIN · POLSKI
PICKLES
LARGE 1.5 L JAR
1.49

(f) 12 melons

DIRECT FROM CALIFORNIA
JUMBO SIZE 4's   SELECT YOUR OWN EACH
HONEY DEW MELON **1.29**

9 (a) The Burger Hut pays $4.65/h. Find the total amount paid if Barbara worked 12.5 h last week.

(b) Fifteen employees at Pizza King earned $4.25/h. Find the total amount paid for working 7.5 h.

(c) A cheeseburger costs $1.89. How much will it cost for the team of 32 players to each have a cheeseburger?

10 Did you know that there is soft water and hard water? When you take a bath, the ring around the bathtub is mostly caused by the calcium carbonate in the water.

(a) One litre of hard water contains 0.25 g of calcium carbonate. How much of it is in an average bath of 350 L of water?

(b) Estimate how much calcium carbonate is deposited in a year if you take a bath 3 times a week.

11 Members of a club pay $0.75/d for their dues. Find the total dues for 13 members for 11 d.

12 (a) The greatest crowd to assemble for a tennis match was 30 472 people. The spectators paid $26.80 each on the average. What were the total receipts?

(b) A relay team in Birmingham, England, swam for 168 h, *all underwater*. Each hour they swam 2.67 km. How far did they swim in all?

13 (a) Blue tickets to the Bowie Concert were $16.50 each. There were 1286 persons in the blue section. How much money was collected?

(b) Grey tickets to the concert cost $11.25 each. There were 2160 persons in the grey section. How much money was collected?

(c) What were the total receipts for blue and grey tickets?

14 Two fishing records were set in Canada.
▶ Larry Daunis caught the largest lake trout ever, with a mass of 29.5 kg, in Great Bear Lake.
▶ Ken Fraser caught the largest tuna ever, with a mass of 678.6 kg, at Auld Cove in Nova Scotia.

(a) Estimate which have the greater mass: 100 lake trout, or 4 tuna.

(b) Calculate your answer in (a).

C

15 The cost for admission to the Jungle Show is shown. Find the cost for

ADMISSION	
ADULTS	$7.50
SENIOR CITIZENS	$4.25
STUDENTS	$3.50
CHILDREN	$1.50

(a) 75 adults

(b) 50 senior citizens

(c) 125 students and 360 children

(d) What is the total cost for 75 adults, 50 senior citizens, 125 students and 360 children?

3.4 mental multiplication: is my answer reasonable?

Some skills are useful for checking your work. For example, a calculator saves time by doing tedious computations quickly, but a calculator is not absolutely correct. Errors can occur by pressing the wrong keys or keys in the wrong order. To check your calculations you need to use your skills with rounding. To multiply rounded numbers quickly, look for short cuts. Examine these patterns.

How do the positions of the decimal points change when you multiply by 10, 100, 1000?

Use your calculator to try other numbers.

A
Multiply by 10
10 × 38 = 380
10 × 3.8 = 38
10 × 0.38 = 3.8
10 × 0.038 = 0.38

B
Multiply 100
100 × 4.65 = 465
100 × 46.5 = 4650
100 × 465 = 46 500
100 × 4650 = 465 000

C
Multiply by 1000
1000 × 0.369 = 369
1000 × 3.69 = 3690
1000 × 36.9 = 36 900
1000 × 369 = 369 000

The above patterns suggest the following short cuts for multiplying by powers of 10, namely, 10, 100, 1000.

A
To multiply by 10, the decimal point is moved *one* place to the right.
10 × 0.5 = 5
10 × 0.15 = 1.5
10 × 1.355 = 13.55
10 × 17.46 = 174.6

B
To multiply by 100, the decimal point is moved *two* places to the right.
100 × 0.15 = 15
100 × 1.355 = 135.5
100 × 17.46 = 1746
100 × 0.5 = 50

C
To multiply by 1000, the decimal point is moved *three* places to the right.
1000 × 0.163 = 163
1000 × 2.1 = 2100
1000 × 32.65 = 32 650
1000 × 0.013 = 13

To check whether an answer is reasonable, you use your rounding skills, as well as skills for multiplying by 10, 100, 1000, and so on.

In the following exercise, you extend your skills with rounding to check whether an answer is reasonable.

3.4 exercise

A The skills you learn here will be needed to work with metric units. Learn them well.

1 Multiply each number by 10.

(a) 9.8   (b) 0.73   (c) 1.73

(d) 4.14   (e) 31.45   (f) 10.005

2 Find each product.

(a) 10 × 0.83   (b) 29.6 × 10

(c) 10 × 1.693   (d) 290 × 10

(e) 10 × 48.6   (f) 0.03 × 10

3 Multiply each number by 100.

(a) 0.43   (b) 0.475   (c) 3.17

(d) 17.3   (e) 0.1473   (f) 0.005

(g) 1.001   (h) 0.096   (i) 0.3

4 Multiply.

(a) 100 × 0.83   (b) 46.2 × 100

(c) 100 × 1.639   (d) 390 × 100

(e) 43.29 × 100   (f) 100 × 0.006

5 Multiply each number by 1000.

(a) 0.435   (b) 0.47   (c) 3.17

(d) 0.1003   (e) 1.4756   (f) 0.003

6 Copy and complete the chart.

	Multiply	by 10	by 100	by 1000
(a)	3.82	?	?	?
(b)	43.68	?	?	?
(c)	1.012	?	?	?

7 Calculate. $\left(\begin{array}{l}\text{Remember } 10^2 = 100, \\ \qquad\qquad 10^3 = 1000\end{array}\right.$

(a) 10 × 0.45   (b) 10^2 × 0.45

(c) 10^3 × 0.45   (d) 3.005 × 10

(e) 0.025 × 10^2 (f) 0.025 × 10^3

B Think: When you multiply by a power of 10, move the decimal point to the right, the number of places given by the exponent.

8 Multiply.

(a) 20 × 3.6   (b) 200 × 3.6

$\left(\begin{array}{l}\text{Think: } 20 \times 3.6 \\ \quad = 2 \times 10 \times 3.6 \\ \quad = ?\end{array}\right.$ $\left(\begin{array}{l}\text{Think: } 200 \times 3.6 \\ \quad = 2 \times 100 \times 3.6 \\ \quad = ?\end{array}\right.$

(c) 300 × 4.8   (d) 3000 × 4.8

(e) 50 × 5.6   (f) 500 × 5.6

(g) 8.3 × 60   (h) 8.3 × 600

9 Calculate. (Do as many as you can mentally.)

(a) 200 × 3.4   (b) 4.2 × 2000

(c) 2.1 × 3000   (d) 3.2 × 200

(e) 0.311 × 3000   (f) 1.005 × 200

(g) 3.01 × 20   (h) 3.01 × 2000

(i) 0.223 × 2000   (j) 2.23 × 3000

10 Estimate the answer. Then calculate. (Check with a calculator.)

(a) 29.8 × 9.6   (b) 9.9 × 2.34

(c) 8.9 × 41.53   (d) 98.9 × 1.435

(e) 19.3 × 7.436   (f) 51.04 × 103.1

(g) 23.5 × 49.5   (h) 9.6 × 102.45

(i) 39.8 × 1.96   (j) 98.9 × 4.35

For each of the following problems:
▶ Estimate each answer.
▶ Then calculate the answer.

11 About how many seconds are in

(a) a day?   (b) a week?   (c) a year?

12 Cases of canned soups are stacked 6 high and 28 stacks in a row. There is 48 rows and 24 cans of soup in each case. How many cans of soup are in the warehouse.

13 A page has 65 lines of type. Each line has on the average 59 characters and spaces. How many characters and spaces are there in a book with 512 pages?

math tip

List the mathematical symbols, words, and skills that you learned in this chapter. Give an example of each.

calculator tip

Does your calculator have a square $\boxed{x^2}$ key? Read your manual. How does it work?

3.5 dividing decimals by whole numbers

To divide decimals, you can use your skills with dividing whole numbers. What is the same? What is different?

Example 1   Divide the following.

(a) 0.42 ÷ 7   (b) $\frac{72}{15}$

Solution   (a)  $7\overline{)0.42}$ with 0.06 above

Zeros are written to place digits in their proper place value.

(b)

```
      4.8
 15)72.0
     60
     12 0
     12 0
        0
```

To find the answer, you need to place a zero.

Whole Numbers	Decimals
$\begin{array}{r}14\\ 2\overline{)28}\end{array}$	$\begin{array}{r}1.4\\ 2\overline{)2.8}\end{array}$
$\begin{array}{r}83\\ 3\overline{)249}\end{array}$	$\begin{array}{r}0.83\\ 3\overline{)2.49}\end{array}$
$\begin{array}{r}7\\ 5\overline{)35}\end{array}$	$\begin{array}{r}0.07\\ 5\overline{)0.35}\end{array}$

When you divide a decimal by a whole number, the decimal point in the quotient is placed directly above the decimal point in the dividend.

Once you learn skills, you apply them to solve problems, as shown in the following example.

You can use multiplication to check your answer.
```
  0.06
7)0.42  →  7 × 0.06 = 0.42
```

Example 2   Some of the fastest growing trees occur in Malaysia. A falcata tree grew 81.6 cm in 30 d.
(a) How much did the tree grow in 1 d?
(b) How tall would the tree be in a year?

Solution   (a) In 30 d the tree grew 81.6 cm.
In 1 d the tree grew
81.6 ÷ 30 or 2.72 cm.

(b) In 1 d the tree grows 2.72 cm.
In a year or 365 d, the tree grows
365 × 2.72 cm or 992.8 cm.

Always show your calculations
```
      2.72
30)81.60              2.72
   60                ×3 65
   21 6              13 60
   21 0             163 2
      60             816
      60            992.80
       0
```

3.5 exercise

A   Try to do as many of the following questions as you can mentally.

1 Divide.

(a) $3\overline{)2.7}$ (b) $4\overline{)1.6}$ (c) $5\overline{)3.5}$

(d) $6\overline{)0.48}$ (e) $7\overline{)0.63}$ (f) $8\overline{)0.4}$

2 Find each quotient.

(a) $\frac{3.2}{8}$ (b) $\frac{5.4}{6}$ (c) $\frac{3.5}{7}$

(d) $\frac{0.24}{8}$ (e) $\frac{0.036}{4}$ (f) $\frac{0.18}{3}$

3 Calculate.

(a) 4.5 ÷ 5   (b) 6.4 ÷ 8   (c) 8.1 ÷ 9

(d) 0.45 ÷ 9   (e) 0.4 ÷ 5   (f) 0.042 ÷ 6

4 The digits for each answer are shown. Use an estimate to place the decimal point.

	Question	Digits of answer
(a)	1.25 ÷ 5	25
(b)	10.8 ÷ 8	135
(c)	498.4 ÷ 56	89
(d)	27.95 ÷ 65	43
(e)	1461.6 ÷ 87	168
(f)	456.48 ÷ 36	1268

5 Estimate each answer. Then divide.

(a) 405 ÷ 5   (b) 40.5 ÷ 5   (c) 4.05 ÷ 5

(d) $\frac{3.15}{5}$ (e) $\frac{0.427}{7}$ (f) $\frac{0.378}{9}$

6 Use each ad. Estimate the cost of one item. Express your answer to the nearest tenth of a cent.

(a) Save Energy **Light Bulbs** PKG. OF 4 **$1.19**

(b) Product of New Zealand **Kiwi Fruit** PKG. OF 6 **$1.69**

7 Divide 463.92 by 38. Round your answer

(a) to one decimal place.

(b) to the nearest hundredth.

B The skills you learn for division are needed to solve the problems that follow.

8 Divide the following and round to the accuracy shown.

(a) 132.6 ÷ 52 (nearest tenth)

(b) 2.8998 ÷ 81 (to 3 decimal places)

(c) 76.1941 ÷ 37 (nearest hundredth)

(d) 14.43 ÷ 26 (1 decimal place)

(e) 2.2752 ÷ 18 (nearest thousandth)

(f) 19.4544 ÷ 48 (to 2 decimal places)

(g) 1.9855 ÷ 19 (nearest hundredth)

(h) 415.2336 ÷ 304 (3 decimal places)

9 The total cost of the victory party was $41.25. Find each person's share if 11 people attended?

10 Greg Kennedy followed a diet in which he lost 56.6 kg in 350 d. How many kilograms did he lose each day? Express your answer to 1 decimal place. (Greg's original mass was 412 kg).

11 Jennifer, Lori, and Michael rented a plot of land and grew 28.8 kg of tomatoes. How much is each person's share?

12 (a) The vitamin riboflavin helps to maintain healthy skin and eyes. Six slices of liver have 22.62 mg of riboflavin. How much riboflavin is in 1 slice of liver?

(b) Calcium aids in the maintenance of strong bones and teeth. Four helpings of broccoli contain 633.2 mg of calcium. How much calcium is in 1 helping of broccoli?

13 Johnson Electronics purchased 12 boxes of calculators for $1162.08. Each box contains 12 calculators. What is the store's cost for each calculator?

C

14 Twenty students in a class contributed $17.50 each for the trip expenses. The total amount collected was $34.50 more than needed. How much did the trip actually cost for each student?

applications: comparison shopping and unit prices

To get the best buy when you shop or buy things, you want to compare prices. To compare prices you find the **unit price**. The unit price is the cost of 1 item.

Brand A
Vitamin C
500 tablets
(500 mg each)
$9.79

Brand B
Vitamin C
250 tablets
(500 mg each)
$5.75

Brand C
Vitamin C
100 tablets
(500 mg each)
$2.49

For each package of Vitamin C tablets, calculate $\frac{\text{price}}{\text{number of tablets}}$ to 2 decimal places.

Brand A
500 tablets cost $9.79

1 tablet costs $\frac{979}{500} = 1.96¢$

The unit price is 1.96¢ per tablet.

Brand B
250 tablets cost $5.75

1 tablet costs $\frac{575}{250} = 2.30¢$

The unit price is 2.30¢ per tablet.

Brand C
100 tablets cost $2.49

1 tablet costs $\frac{249}{100} = 2.49¢$

The unit price is 2.49¢ per tablet.

Thus, the best buy is Brand A.

15 Calculate the unit price for each item to 1 decimal place.

(a) 8 peaches cost $1.69.

(b) A box of 4 frozen meat pies costs $3.29.

(c) 24 cans of pop cost $6.99.

16 Calculate the unit price (per gram) for each item. Express your answer to 1 decimal place.

(a) 400 g for $1.19   (b) 362 g for $2.25

(c) 850 g for $16.25 (d) 69 g for $10.50

17 Each of the following are bought in quantity. Calculate how much you save on one item.

(a) Corn is $2.19 per dozen or 25¢ for one.

(b) 5 packages of grape crystals cost $1.96 or 48¢ for one package.

(c) A can of pop is 55¢ or you can buy a case of 24 for $6.89.

(d) 1 submarine sandwich costs $2.49 (with hot peppers) or you can get 12 for $24.50.

18 A package of five chocolate bars costs $1.75. The single price of 1 chocolate bar is 45¢.

(a) How much will you save if you buy the package instead of 5 single bars?

(b) Which is the better buy?

19 Which is the better buy?

(a) Pkg of 8 giant   (b) 2 giant deluxe
    deluxe gift wrap   bows 59¢.
    bows $1.69.

20 Which is the better buy?

A   Ready toothpaste 125 mL $1.29

B   Ivory toothpaste 200 mL $1.99

21 (a) Obtain prices for 3 similar products in a supermarket or convenience store. Calculate the unit price of each product. Which is the best buy?

(b) Repeat (a) above for 2 other types of products.

(c) Is the best buy always the best unit price? Give reasons for your answer.

3.6 problem solving: reading carefully

One of the main reasons for learning skills in mathematics is to apply them to solve problems. Some problems may require the use of more than one skill to obtain the answer. To write a solution, you need to organize your work in some way, such as the steps for solving problems.

In earlier sections, you have learned to look for clues in solving a problem. It is also important to follow *instructions* carefully, and understand the *vocabulary* of mathematics.

> **Steps for Solving Problems**
>
> A Ask yourself:
>   *I What information am I asked to find?*
>   *II What information am I given?*
> B Decide on a method.
>   *Which operation do I use?*
> C Do the work.
>   *Complete the calculation.*
> D Check your work.
>   *Use your rounding skills.*
> E Make a final statement.
>   *Answer the original problem.*

Example 1 Add the product 4.6 × 3.9 to the quotient 56.16 ÷ 12.

Solution

Product	Quotient
4.6 × 3.9	56.16 ÷ 12
= 17.94	= 4.68

$$\begin{array}{r} 3.9 \\ \times\ 4.6 \\ \hline 234 \\ 156 \\ \hline 17.94 \end{array}$$

$$\begin{array}{r} 4.68 \\ 12\overline{)56.16} \\ 48 \\ \hline 8\ 1 \\ 7\ 2 \\ \hline 96 \\ 96 \\ \hline 0 \end{array}$$

Add to find the sum. 17.94
                                4.68
                              22.62

The answer is 22.62.

To solve problems, you must read carefully to answer these two important questions.
  I What am I asked to find?
  II What information am I given?

Example 2 Tracy and Mike walked distances of 2.5 km, 3.4 km, and 1.7 km each day for 3 d. What is the average distance they walked each day? Express your answer to 1 decimal place.

Think:
Find the sum of the distances.
Divide to find the average.

Solution

Total distance walked is 7.6 km.

$$\begin{array}{r} 2.5 \\ 3.4 \\ 1.7 \\ \hline 7.6 \end{array}$$

Number of days walked is 3. Divide to find the average.

$$\frac{7.6}{3} = 2.53$$

Do your calculation to 1 more decimal place than required in your answer. Then round off your answer in your final statement.

The average distance walked is 2.5 km/d.

3.6 exercise

A In these questions, read carefully. Watch the symbols and follow the instructions.

1 Calculate. Watch the symbols. Read carefully!

(a) 3.6 + 4.8　　　　(b) 19.6 − 3.8

(c) 4.9 × 3.8　　　　(d) 10.4 ÷ 4

(e) 28.92 − 12.79　　(f) 7.92 × 4.3

(g) 311.4 ÷ 9　　　　(h) 14.26 + 3.96

(i) 8.3 × 9.62　　　　(j) 36.031 − 12.087

(k) 4.608 + 13.396　(l) 15.36 ÷ 16

(m) $(16.8)^2$　　　　(n) 106.536 ÷ 23

2 (a) Find the sum of the following.
　　　12.39　　489　　381.4　　13.2

(b) Add 26.98 to the sum of 498.73 and 291.64.

(c) Subtract 1.498 from 28.91.

3 (a) Add 129.9 to the sum of 36.3 and 1234.5

(b) Subtract 29.961 from 36.34.

(c) Square the number 1.8.

(d) Subtract the sum of 296.3 and 496.5 from 987.9.

4 (a) Find the product of 9.6 and 3.9.

(b) Multiply 4.93 by 2.6.

(c) Divide 684.8 by 8.

(d) Find the quotient 587.6 ÷ 13.

5 (a) Find the average of the following.
　　　13.9 km　48.9 km　396.4 km　489.6 km

(b) Subtract 8.6 kg from the sum of 3.1 kg and 6.2 kg.

(c) Add the sum of 369.4 m and 681.8 m to the sum of 498.3 m and 1296.9 m.

(d) Subtract the sum of 12.6 L and 9.3 L from 26.6 L.

B Remember to look for clues to solve each of the following problems. Round your answers to 1 decimal place or to the nearest cent.

6 Iron is an essential part of hemoglobin in the blood. Twelve helpings of spinach have 50.4 mg of iron. How much iron is in one helping of spinach?

7 The height of a building is 106.9 m. The tower on the building is 16.6 m. Calculate the combined height.

8 The tide at Charlottetown already rose 1.36 m. At the same time, the tide at Truro rose 4 times as high. How high was the tide at Truro?

9 The original price of a friendship ring was $39.65. The recent selling price was $33.95. By how much had the price dropped?

10 At Gander International Airport, the total precipitation during 12 d was 37 mm. What was the average precipitation for 1 d?

11 Cherrapunji, India holds the record for the greatest amount of rainfall in 12 mon. During that time 26 463 mm of rain fell. How much fell, on average, per month?

12 (a) The total cost of a pair of skates is $14.96. How much change should you get from $20?

(b) Santis wanted to buy a bicycle. The total cost was $69.95. He put $20 down, and paid the rest in 6 equal payments. How much was the amount of each payment?

13 (a) About 40 L of maple sap are required to make 1 L of maple syrup. Calculate how many litres of maple syrup can be made from a 2500 L drum of maple sap.

(b) One litre of maple syrup costs $2.71. Calculate the value of the maple syrup made in (a).

3.7 writing decimals for common fractions

You can write decimals for common fractions. For example, you can think of $\frac{3}{5}$ as $3 \div 5$.

$$\begin{array}{r} 0.6 \\ 5\overline{)3.0} \\ \underline{3.0} \\ 0 \end{array}$$

Thus, $\frac{3}{5} = 0.6$

To compare the performance of players in baseball, you can calculate the value of

$$\frac{\text{number of hits}}{\text{number of times at bat}}$$

	Number of hits	Number of times at bat
Mantle	13	25
Maris	21	40

By writing decimals for common fractions, you can compare them.

For Mantle

$$\frac{13}{25}$$
$$= 0.52$$

$$\begin{array}{r} 0.52 \\ 25\overline{)13.00} \\ \underline{12\ 5} \\ 50 \end{array}$$

For Maris

$$\frac{21}{40}$$
$$= 0.525$$

$$\begin{array}{r} 0.525 \\ 40\overline{)21.000} \\ \underline{20\ 0} \\ 1\ 00 \\ \underline{80} \\ 200 \\ \underline{200} \\ 0 \end{array}$$

Since $0.525 > 0.52$

then $\frac{21}{40} > \frac{13}{25}$.

Thus, Maris has a better record than Mantle.

The decimals for $\frac{13}{25}$ and $\frac{21}{40}$ are called **terminating decimals**. The digits for some decimal equivalents repeat. For example, the decimal equivalent for $\frac{2}{3}$ is calculated.

$$\frac{2}{3} = 0.6666\ldots$$

Since the digits repeat, the decimal equivalent for $\frac{2}{3}$ is called a **repeating decimal**.

Repeating decimals can be written using either one of the following compact forms.

$$\frac{2}{3} = 0.\dot{6} \quad \text{or} \quad 0.\overline{6}$$

The bar extends over the repeating digit or digits.

$$\begin{array}{r} 0.666\ 6\ldots \\ 3\overline{)2.000\ 00\ldots} \\ \underline{1\ 8} \\ 20 \\ \underline{18} \\ 20 \\ \underline{18} \\ 20 \\ \underline{18} \\ 2 \text{ and so on} \end{array}$$

Place zeros as needed to find decimal equivalents.

Example Write decimals for each fraction.

(a) $\frac{5}{9}$ (b) $\frac{7}{11}$

Solution (a) $\frac{5}{9} = 0.5555\ldots$ (b) $\frac{7}{11} = 0.636\,363\ldots$ $\left(\begin{array}{l}\text{The dot appears over the first}\\\text{and last digit that repeats.}\end{array}\right.$

$\frac{5}{9} = 0.\dot{5}$ or $0.\overline{5}$ $\frac{7}{11} = 0.\dot{6}\dot{3}$ or $0.\overline{63}$

To write decimal equivalents for mixed numbers, you find the
decimal equivalent for the fraction part.

$2\frac{1}{4} = 2.25$ $3\frac{7}{11} = 3.\overline{63}$

Use your calculator
to try other numbers.

3.7 exercise

A

1 Match each fraction with its decimal equivalent.

(a) $\frac{1}{10}$ (c) $\frac{1}{25}$ A 0.04 C 0.05

(b) $\frac{1}{100}$ (d) $\frac{1}{20}$ B 0.1 D 0.01

(d) $\frac{5}{4}$ (e) $\frac{23}{25}$ (f) $\frac{7}{8}$

(g) $2\frac{1}{2}$ (h) $1\frac{5}{8}$ (i) $3\frac{3}{4}$

(j) $5\frac{3}{5}$ (k) $4\frac{1}{10}$ (l) $2\frac{3}{20}$

2 Write a decimal equivalent for each fraction.

(a) $\frac{3}{10}$ (b) $\frac{9}{10}$ (c) $\frac{89}{100}$

(d) $\frac{19}{100}$ (e) $\frac{3}{100}$ (f) $\frac{9}{100}$

(g) $\frac{325}{1000}$ (h) $\frac{1}{1000}$ (i) $\frac{12}{10}$

(j) $\frac{125}{100}$ (k) $\frac{235}{1000}$ (l) $\frac{1262}{1000}$

3 Write each decimal in a compact form.

(a) 0.333 . . . (b) 0.7333 . . .

(c) 0.121 212 . . . (d) 0.464 646 . . .

(e) 0.345 345 345 . . . (f) 0.780 780 780 . . .

(g) 1.454 545 . . . (h) 3.456 565 6 . . .

4 Write a decimal for each fraction

(a) $\frac{1}{4}$ (b) $\frac{3}{8}$ (c) $\frac{3}{25}$

5 Write a decimal for each fraction.

(a) $\frac{1}{3}$ (b) $\frac{2}{3}$ (c) $\frac{3}{11}$ (d) $\frac{4}{11}$

(e) $\frac{5}{11}$ (f) $\frac{6}{11}$ (g) $\frac{1}{6}$ (h) $\frac{5}{6}$

(i) $\frac{1}{15}$ (j) $\frac{4}{15}$ (k) $\frac{1}{8}$ (l) $\frac{5}{18}$

(m) $\frac{15}{11}$ (n) $5\frac{3}{20}$ (o) $6\frac{11}{15}$ (p) $7\frac{2}{15}$

6 Write a fraction in lowest terms for each
decimal. The first one has been done for you.

(a) 0.2 $0.2 = \frac{2}{10}$
$= \frac{1}{5}$

(b) 2.5 (c) 0.36 (d) 1.25

(e) 0.08 (f) 2.08 (g) 0.123

(h) 0.045 (i) 2.002 (j) 1.002

7 Round off each decimal equivalent as shown.

(a) $\frac{5}{6}$ (tenth)

(b) $\frac{1}{6}$ (hundredth)

(c) $\frac{1}{3}$ (tenth)

(d) $\frac{2}{3}$ (tenth)

(e) $\frac{2}{7}$ (thousandth)

(f) $\frac{7}{6}$ (hundredth)

(g) $\frac{2}{3}$ (hundredth)

(h) $\frac{4}{7}$ (thousandth)

(i) $\frac{4}{23}$ (tenth)

(j) $\frac{4}{23}$ (thousandth)

(k) $\frac{6}{7}$ (hundredth)

(l) $\frac{2}{13}$ (thousandth)

B

8 For each pair, which is greater?

(a) $\frac{1}{4}, \frac{3}{8}$

(b) $\frac{2}{5}, \frac{3}{10}$

(c) $\frac{7}{12}, \frac{3}{4}$

(d) $\frac{1}{6}, \frac{5}{18}$

(e) $\frac{7}{8}, \frac{5}{6}$

(f) $\frac{3}{2}, \frac{5}{4}$

9 Replace ○ by < or > to make each of the following true.

(a) $\frac{3}{11}$ ○ $\frac{4}{12}$

(b) $\frac{5}{6}$ ○ $\frac{35}{43}$

(c) $\frac{3}{5}$ ○ $\frac{24}{41}$

(d) $\frac{7}{18}$ ○ $\frac{23}{54}$

(e) $\frac{59}{89}$ ○ $\frac{5}{8}$

(f) $\frac{38}{75}$ ○ $\frac{9}{16}$

10 (a) Find a repeating decimal for

$\frac{1}{99}$ $\frac{2}{99}$ $\frac{3}{99}$ $\frac{4}{99}$

(b) Use your results in (a) to predict the repeating decimal for $\frac{5}{99}, \frac{25}{99}, \frac{61}{99}$.

(c) Was your prediction in (b) a good one? How can you check your answer in (b)?

(d) Write the repeating decimal for $\frac{75}{99}, \frac{80}{99}$.

11 At lunch, Arnold ate $\frac{1}{4}$ of the pizza and Tara ate $\frac{3}{8}$. Who ate more?

12 The Bengals played 18 games and won 5. The Blizzards won 8 games and played 21. Who has the better record?

13 After their check points, Sally had finished $\frac{7}{12}$ of the walkathon. Wright had finished $\frac{13}{20}$ of the walkathon. Who had finished more?

C

14 The number of wins for teams in the Canadian Football League are shown. Which team has the best record?

		Games played	Games won
(a)	Vancouver	14	8
(b)	Calgary	9	6
(c)	Toronto	12	9
(d)	Montreal	11	7

skills quiz

Do as many of these as you can mentally.

(a) 49.6 + 23.2

(b) 86.9 − 43.7

(c) 696.4 − 23.9

(d) 0.8 × 4.9

(e) 2.8 × 400

(f) 0.12 × 0.4

(g) 10.9 × 100

(h) 67.56 ÷ 6

(i) 99 × 8

(j) 20 × 101

(k) 75 × 11

(l) 23 × 99

(m) 1000 × 4.965

(n) 192.75 − 25

(o) 98 × 50

(p) 50 × 65

(q) 43.25 × 11.96

(r) 589.688 ÷ 12

(s) 0.943 × 1.23

(t) 995.84 ÷ 38

(u) $\frac{55.174}{11}$

(v) $\frac{4.613 + 7.219}{44 + 23}$

(w) Add 24.96, 32.75, 14.96, and 12.

(x) Subtract 49.85 from 98.74.

(y) Subtract the sum of 149.3 and 2.46 from 296.42.

(z) Subtract 29 415 from the sum of 48 911 and 26 413.   Check your work with a calculator.

3.8 dividing by decimals

To divide 5.65 by 2.5, you first write the question in an equivalent form as follows.

$$\frac{5.65}{2.5} = \frac{5.65}{2.5} \times \frac{10}{10}$$

$$= \frac{5.65 \times 10}{2.5 \times 10}$$

$$= \frac{56.5}{25}$$

Multiplying by $\frac{10}{10}, \frac{100}{100}, \frac{1000}{1000}$, etc. is equivalent to multiplying by 1.

To divide by decimals you use two skills you have already learned.
▶ Dividing a decimal by a whole number.
▶ Understanding equivalent fractions.

Thus, these two questions are equivalent.

$\frac{5.65}{2.5}$ has the same answer as $\frac{56.5}{25}$

$5.65 \div 2.5 = 2.26.$

Divide
```
        2.26
    25)56.50
       50 ↓|
        6 5
        5 0↓
        15 0
        15 0
           0
```

The different ways of writing the same division question are as follows:

$$5.65 \div 2.5 \qquad \frac{5.65}{2.5} \qquad 2.5)\overline{5.65}$$

Example 1 Express each division question with a whole number divisor. Then find the quotient.
(a) $0.0375 \div 0.03$ (b) $4.8 \div 0.35$

Solution (a) $\frac{0.0375}{0.03} = \frac{0.0375}{0.03} \times \frac{100}{100}$

$$= \frac{0.0375 \times 100}{0.03 \times 100}$$

$$= \frac{3.75}{3}$$

$$= 1.25$$

To divide

$0.03)\overline{0.0375}$

use

$$3)\overline{3.75} \quad 1.25$$

(b) $\frac{4.8}{0.35} = \frac{4.8}{0.35} \times \frac{100}{100}$

$$= \frac{480}{35}$$

$$= 13.71$$

(to 2 decimal places)

To divide use

$.35,)\overline{4.80,}$

$35)\overline{480.}$

Once you learn a skill you apply it, and previously learned skills, to solve problems.

Example 2 A heating company receives 151.3 m of ductwork. Each construction site needs 15.5 m of ductwork. How many sites will obtain the material?

Solution Divide to find the answer.

$$\frac{151.3}{15.5} = \frac{151.3}{15.5} \times \frac{10}{10}$$

$$= \frac{1513}{155}$$

$$= 9.8 \quad \text{(to 1 decimal place)}$$

Thus, 9 sites will obtain the material.

```
          9.76 . . .
    155)1513.00
        1395
         1180
         1085
          950
          930
           20 . . .
```

Think:
I   What information am I asked to find?
       Number of sites
II What information am I given?
       Total ductwork — 151.3 m
       Each site needs 15.5 m
    Which operation do I use?
       Divide to find the answer.

A

1 Find each product.

   (a) 1.56×10

   (b) 100×0.456

   (c) 0.456×10

   (d) 10×0.078

   (e) 0.26×100

   (f) 0.457×1000

   (g) 0.3×100

   (h) 0.12×1000

2 Which form of 1 $\left(\frac{10}{10}, \frac{100}{100}, \text{or } \frac{1000}{1000} \right)$ was used to multiply each of the following?

   (a) $\frac{5.6}{0.5} \rightarrow \frac{56}{5}$

   (b) $\frac{0.56}{0.05} \rightarrow \frac{56}{5}$

   (c) $\frac{0.125}{0.25} \rightarrow \frac{12.5}{25}$

   (d) $\frac{1.5}{0.125} \rightarrow \frac{1500}{125}$

   (e) $0.52\overline{)4.5604} \rightarrow 52\overline{)456.04}$

   (f) $1.6\overline{)0.154} \rightarrow 16\overline{)1.54}$

   (g) $0.025\overline{)1.255} \rightarrow 25\overline{)1255}$

   (h) $2.5\overline{)0.2215} \rightarrow 25\overline{)2.215}$

3 Use the appropriate form of 1 to write each question with a whole number divisor.

   (a) $\frac{0.936}{2.6}$

   (b) $\frac{2.5875}{1.125}$

   (c) $\frac{0.0035}{0.14}$

   (d) $0.24\overline{)0.7344}$

   (e) $0.148\overline{)5.3872}$

   (f) $0.113\,75 \div 3.25$

   (g) $9.4208 \div 25.6$

4 For each of the following
   ▶ Write the division question with a whole number divisor.
   ▶ Then divide to find the answer.

   (a) $\frac{0.9}{0.3}$

   (b) $\frac{0.09}{0.3}$

   (c) $\frac{3.6}{0.4}$

   (d) $7.2 \div 0.9$

   (e) $0.48 \div 0.06$

   (f) $0.045 \div 0.009$

   (g) $2.4 \div 0.08$

   (h) $0.5\overline{)0.35}$

   (i) $0.7\overline{)4.9}$

   (j) $0.08\overline{)6.4}$

   (k) $0.6\overline{)0.0054}$

5 For each question, two answers are given. Estimate which one is the correct one. Then check.

		A	B
(a)	$\frac{3.18}{0.6}$	53	5.3
(b)	$2.92 \div 0.08$	36.5	3.65
(c)	$0.007\overline{)0.0245}$	3.5	0.035
(d)	$\frac{0.1005}{0.3}$	3.35	0.335

6 For each division question, estimate your answer first. Then calculate.

   (a) $289.44 \div 6.7$

   (b) $0.672 \div 1.6$

   (c) $2331.2 \div 4.96$

   (d) $0.5746 \div 1.69$

   (e) $\frac{4.944}{0.4}$

   (f) $\frac{701.1}{3.69}$

   (g) $23.4 \div 0.36$

   (h) $726 \div 0.25$

7 Divide. Check whether your answer is reasonable.

   (a) $3.09 \div 1.5$

   (b) $0.014\,95 \div 0.23$

   (c) $61\,488 \div 6.1$

   (d) $0.036\,432 \div 0.72$

   (e) $8.0125 \div 0.25$

   (f) $523.9 \div 0.065$

   (g) $0.887\,88 \div 0.147$

   (h) $13.59 \div 0.045$

8 Divide. Round your answers to 1 decimal place.

   (a) $0.020\,54 \div 0.13$

   (b) $0.498\,15 \div 1.35$

   (c) $0.888 \div 1.6$

   (d) $50.3676 \div 4.08$

   (e) $0.2116 \div 0.46$

   (f) $13.1497 \div 3.67$

   (g) $0.127\,68 \div 0.38$

   (h) $37.7175 \div 1.07$

9 Calculate $29.365 \div 2.864$.

   (a) Write your answer to the first decimal place.

   (b) Write your answer to the nearest hundredth.

10 (a) Find 2.69 ÷ 4.85. Write your answer to the nearest tenth.

(b) Find 2.696 ÷ 4.312. Write your answer to the second decimal place.

11 Find these quotients. Round off each answer to the nearest tenth.

(a) $\frac{286.34}{43.9}$

(b) $\frac{9.672}{1.6}$

(c) $\frac{1038.9}{10.6}$

(d) $\frac{23.312}{4.86}$

(e) 0.5746 ÷ 0.39

(f) 4.943 ÷ 12.39

(g) 7.013 ÷ 2.9

(h) 1461.33 ÷ 23.9

Round off your answers in (i) to (n) to the nearest hundredth.

(i) $\frac{884.69}{213.89}$

(j) $\frac{12.496}{4.68}$

(k) 10.1469 ÷ 0.439

(l) 43.2309 ÷ 0.986

(m) 75 ÷ 0.19

(n) 18.6 ÷ 3.99

B For the following questions, check whether your answers are reasonable. Round your answers to 1 decimal place or to the nearest cent.

12 Find the unit cost (cost of one item) for each purchase.

(a) Hickory smoked **Wieners** 2.3 kg for **$5.86**

(b) Frozen baked **Crumb Apple Pie** 1.5 kg for **$3.69**

(c) Velvet smooth **Macaroni Salad** 5.8 kg for **$6.25**

13 Use the information in the ads. Which is the better buy?

Canadian Mild
Cheddar Cheese

Brand Name
mass 0.65 kg
cost $4.29

No Name
mass 0.44 kg
cost $2.86

14 Steak costs $5.89/kg. How much steak is there if the total cost is $17.92?

15 The Golden Gate Bridge is 1935 m long. Wendy's step is 0.62 m long. How many steps would she take in crossing the bridge?

16 A figurine uses 0.45 kg of clay. How many figurines can be made from 12.75 kg of clay?

17 The longest sausage was 3792 m long. An average size sausage measures 0.136 m. How many average size sausages would be needed to reach the same distance?

18 The cost to make a telephone call from Calgary to Winnipeg is $3.25 for the first 3 min. Each additional minute costs $0.86. How long was a call that cost $7.55?

19 Bologna comes in a piece that is 58 cm long. Two centimetres from each end are not sold. How many slices do you obtain if each slice is 0.2 cm thick?

20 Duck Mountain Provincial Park is on the boundary of Saskatchewan and Manitoba. To visit the sights, Beth drove 6.8 km, 9.8 km, 20.3 km, and 46.8 km. If she took 4.5 h, what was her average speed?

21 To raise money for a charity, 6.85 kg of pistachio nuts were packaged. Each package contained 0.125 kg of nuts.

(a) How many packages were made?

(b) Each package sold for $1.15. How much money was collected?

(c) The bulk pistachio nuts were bought for $4.95/kg. The packaging cost $5.50. How much money was actually made?

C

22 During a regular day of programming, 3 commercials are shown at each break. Each commercial is 0.5 min. How much time is given to commercials if there are 5 breaks every hour for 8 h?

problem-solving: writing problems

You have seen earlier the *same* calculations often occur to solve *different* problems. For example, the same calculation 46.5 ÷ 2.5 is used to solve each seemingly different problem.

Problem A

Jeremy drove his minibike 46.5 km in 2.5 h. What was his average speed?

$$\left(\text{Remember: average speed} = \frac{\text{distance travelled}}{\text{time taken}}\right)$$

Problem B

The area of a large piece of land is 46.5 ha. A developer surveyed the land to make building lots 2.5 ha in size. How many lots will there be?

23 (a) Solve problem A.
   (b) Solve problem B.
   (c) How are the answers in (a) and (b) alike? How are they different?

24 Solve each problem
   (a) On special, a badminton set costs $12.65. The store offers a savings of $3.79. What is the cost of the set?

   (b) The height of the maple tree is 12.65 m. The height of the apple tree is 3.79 m. How much higher is the maple tree?

   (c) How are the answers in (a) and (b) alike? How are they different?

25 Solve each problem. Round to 2 decimal places.

   (a) Refer to the menu. Find the cost for one person.

Dinner for Four
$16.75
4 egg rolls
Sweet & Sour Shrimp
Beef with Tomatoes
Breaded Wings
Chicken & Almonds
Mushroom Fried Rice
Fortune Cookies

   (b) Florence walked 16.75 km in 4 h. How far would she walk in 1 h?

   (c) How are your answers in (a) and (b) alike? How are they different?

26 (a) At the graduation dance, a total of $856.45 was collected. The expenses totalled $650.00. Calculate how much money was left.

   (b) Use the figures in (a) to make up another problem. Solve the problem.

27 (a) During the recent Bucks-for-Bottles pollution drive, the following quantities were collected:

Monday	48.6 kg
Tuesday	96.3 kg
Wednesday	84.4 kg
Thursday	126.7 kg
Friday	153.8 kg

   Calculate the total amount collected.

   (b) Use the figures in (a) to make up another problem. Solve the problem.

28 (a) Create 2 problems for the calculation 4.6 × 3.8.

   (b) Solve the problems in (a). How are the problems alike? How are they different?

29 For each calculation, make up one problem. Have someone solve your problems.

$$\left(\begin{array}{l}\text{Estimate the answer.}\\\text{Then calculate.}\end{array}\right.$$

(a) 52.6
   + 14.9

(b) 145.8
   − 123.9

(c) 4658
   − 3491

(d) $ 1.46
   + 2.95

(e) $ 3.69
   − 1.75

(f) $ 100.00
   − 20.00

(g) 300.15 ÷ 6.9

(h) 9.3 × 2.65

(i) 16.5 × 8.3

(j) 0.672 ÷ 0.24

3.9 mental division: patterns to learn

In an earlier section you learned short cuts for multiplying by powers of 10, namely, 10, 100, 1000, and so on.

To divide by 10, 100, or 1000, you can also use short cuts. Examine these patterns.

How do the positions of the decimal points change when you divide by 10, 100, 1000?

A | Divide by 10
$51.3 \div 10 = 5.13$
$513.4 \div 10 = 51.34$
$5.13 \div 10 = 0.513$

B | Divide by 100
$874.3 \div 100 = 8.743$
$87.43 \div 100 = 0.8743$
$8.743 \div 100 = 0.087\ 43$

C | Divide by 1000
$9786 \div 1000 = 9.786$
$978.6 \div 1000 = 0.9786$
$97.86 \div 1000 = 0.097\ 86$

The above patterns suggest the following short cuts.

A | To divide by 10, the decimal point is moved *one* place to the *left*.
$86.5 \div 10 = 8.65$
$2.35 \div 10 = 0.235$
$0.468 \div 10 = 0.0468$

B | To divide by 100, the decimal point is moved *two* places to the *left*.
$465 \div 100 = 4.65$
$38.5 \div 100 = 0.385$
$4.96 \div 100 = 0.0496$

C | To divide by 1000, the decimal point is moved *three* places to the *left*.
$4693 \div 1000 = 4.693$
$289.6 \div 1000 = 0.2896$
$48.73 \div 1000 = 0.048\ 73$

To check whether an answer is reasonable, you use your rounding skills, and skills for dividing by 10, 100, and 1000.

Use your calculator to try other numbers.

3.9 exercise

A Use the short cuts you have learned to do the questions mentally.

1 Divide each number by 10.

(a) 468   (b) 36.9   (c) 0.129

(d) 1.48   (e) 37.2   (f) 3560

2 Find each quotient.

(a) $362 \div 10$ (b) $36.2 \div 10$

(c) $3.62 \div 10$ (d) $0.362 \div 10$

3 Find the answer if each number is divided by 100.

(a) 814   (b) 7450   (c) 35.2

(d) 6.31   (e) 29.7   (f) 68 900

4 Divide.

(a) $973 \div 100$ (b) $97.3 \div 100$

(c) $9.73 \div 100$ (d) $0.973 \div 100$

5 Divide each number by 1000.

(a) 3880   (b) 10 415   (c) 47.6

(d) 9.25   (e) 36.2   (f) 7130

6 Copy and complete the chart.

	Number	Divide by 10	Divide by 100	Divide by 1000
(a)	48.6	?	0.486	?
(b)	?	38.92	?	0.3892
(c)	?	?	48.5	?
(d)	?	?	?	0.013 69

Questions 7 to 12 investigate a pattern for multiplying and dividing by 0.1, 0.01, and 0.001.

7 Find the missing values in columns A and B.

        A   B

(a) $6243 \times 0.1 = ?$ $6243 \div 10 = ?$

$941.3 \times 0.1 = ?$ $941.3 \div 10 = ?$

$54.68 \times 0.1 = ?$ $54.68 \div 10 = ?$

(b) What do you notice about your answers in columns A and B?

(c) Suggest a rule for multiplying a number by 0.1.

8 Find the missing values in columns C and D.

        C   D

(a) $6243 \times 0.01 = ?$ $6243 \div 100 = ?$

$941.3 \times 0.01 = ?$ $941.3 \div 100 = ?$

$54.68 \times 0.01 = ?$ $54.68 \div 100 = ?$

(b) What do you notice about your answers in columns C and D?

(c) Suggest a rule for multiplying a number by 0.01.

9 Find the missing values in columns E and F.

        E   F

(a) $6243 \times 0.001 = ?$ $6243 \div 1000 = ?$

$941.3 \times 0.001 = ?$ $941.3 \div 1000 = ?$

$54.68 \times 0.001 = ?$ $54.68 \div 1000 = ?$

(b) What do you notice about your answers in columns E and F?

(c) Suggest a rule for multiplying a decimal number by 0.001.

10 Find the missing values.

(a) $42.3 \div 0.1 = ?$ $42.3 \times 10 = ?$

$1.36 \div 0.1 = ?$ $1.36 \times 10 = ?$

(b) Use your results in (a). Suggest a rule for dividing a decimal by 0.1.

11 Find the missing values.

(a) $68.9 \div 0.01 = ?$ $68.9 \times 100 = ?$

$4.86 \div 0.01 = ?$ $4.86 \times 100 = ?$

(b) Use your results in (a). Suggest a rule for dividing a decimal by 0.01.

12 Find the missing values.

(a) $6.86 \div 0.001 = ?$ $6.86 \times 1000 = ?$

$0.489 \div 0.001 = ?$ $0.489 \times 1000 = ?$

(b) Use your results in (a). Suggest a rule for dividing a decimal by 0.001.

Based on the patterns in previous questions, results of each of the following are the same.

If you multiply by		If you divide by
0.1	the same	10
0.01		100
0.001	result occurs	1000

If you divide by		If you multiply by
0.1	the same	10
0.01		100
0.001	result occurs	1000

B

13 Match the operations in columns I and II that will produce the same result.

I	II
(a) multiply by 0.1	(A) divide by 0.1
(b) divide by 100	(B) divide by 100
(c) multiply by 10	(C) divide by 1000
(d) divide by 0.1	(D) divide by 0.001
(e) multiply by 0.001	(E) multiply by 0.01
(f) divide by 0.01	(F) divide by 0.01
(g) multiply by 0.01	(G) divide by 10
(h) multiply by 100	(H) multiply by 0.001
(i) multiply by 1000	(I) multiply by 10
(j) divide by 10	(J) multiply by 100
(k) divide by 1000	(K) multiply by 1000
(l) divide by 0.001	(L) multiply by 0.1

14 Copy and complete the chart.

	c	$c \times 10^2$	$c \div 0.1$	$c \times 0.01$	$c \div 0.01$
(a)	3.6	?	?	?	?
(b)	?	?	425.3	?	?
(c)	?	234.5	?	?	?
(d)	?	?	?	3.267	?
(e)	?	?	?	?	456.2

C

15 Calculate.

(a) 45.1×0.01 (b) $45.1 \div 10$

(c) $0.362 \div 0.01$ (d) 0.784×100

(e) 32.12×0.1 (f) 0.456×10^2

(g) $87.36 \div 0.1$ (h) $3.622 \div 0.01$

(i) 0.23×10^3 (j) $0.236 \div 0.001$

(k) $326.4 \div 10^2$ (l) 964.5×0.001

(m) 2.34×10 (n) $0.345 \div 10$

---

problem-solving: estimates

To check whether an answer is reasonable, you need to use the previous skills you have developed. For each of the following problems:

▶ Estimate each answer.
▶ Then calculate the answer.

16 A bottle has 14.88 mg of important medication. Each dose contains 0.012 mg. How many doses are in the bottle?

17 Last week, 639 students went on a nature hike. Teams of 9 students were organized.

(a) Estimate how many teams there were.

(b) Calculate how many teams there were.

18 A shipment of radios was worth $2070.60.

(a) Each radio cost the dealer $98.60. How many radios were ordered?

(b) The dealer made $23.50 on each radio. How much did the dealer make in all?

19 Sacha liked the ad and decided to buy a minibike.

Minibike Sale
No hidden costs
No interest payments
While they last
$486.50

(a) The weekly payment is $9.40. How many weekly payments of $9.40 will there be?

(b) What is the amount of the last payment?

20 Each case of oranges has about 95 oranges. A train has 4950 cases.

(a) How many oranges are there?

(b) How many dozens of oranges are there?

(c) If each dozen is worth $1.98, what is the value of the shipment?

(d) What assumptions did you make to get your answer in (c)?

3.10 variable expressions and decimals

There are many variable expressions that occur in engineering, business, science.
▶ Often, you calculate important answers to questions, as shown in the photograph.
▶ Variable expressions can be used to show how much you earn.

Bruce works at a pizzeria and is paid $4.63/h. For each hour worked between midnight and 08:00 he is paid $1.12 extra. The total amount, A, he earns in dollars each week is given by

$$A = 4.63\,t + 1.12\,n$$

number of hours worked in all ⟶

number of bonus hours worked from midnight to 08:00

To build this bridge in Vancouver, you need to know how long the bridge will be, how much it will support, how high above the surface of the water it needs to be, and so on.

Example 1   Bruce worked 16 regular hours and 8 bonus hours. Calculate the total earned.

Solution

Total number of hours worked   Bonus hours, 8 h
$16\,h + 8\,h = 24\,h$ Use $n = 8$.

Use $t = 24$.

$A = 4.63\,t + 1.12\,n$

$A = 4.63(24) + 1.12(8)$ (Use the rules for the order of operations.

$\quad = 111.12 + 8.96$

$\quad = 120.08$

The total amount earned was $120.08.

To do calculations, you need to use your rules for the order of operations. Can you explain each step in the following example?

Example 2   Evaluate $\dfrac{a^2 + b^2}{a + b}$, if $a = 1.2$, $b = 3.4$.
Round your answer to 1 decimal place.

Solution

$\dfrac{a^2 + b^2}{a + b} = \dfrac{1.2^2 + 3.4^2}{1.2 + 3.4}$

$\quad = \dfrac{1.44 + 11.56}{4.6}$

$\quad = \dfrac{13}{4.6}$

$\quad = 2.82$ ⟵ (Do your calculations to one extra decimal place.

The required value of the expression is 2.8 (rounded to 1 decimal place).

Rules for the Order of Operations

▶ Perform the operations in brackets ( ) first.

▶ Then calculate the powers. Namely, find the value of expressions involving exponents.

▶ Then do multiplication or division in the order they appear.

▶ Then do addition or subtraction in the order they appear.

3.10 exercises

A Remember to use the rules for the order of operations.

1 Calculate each of the following.

(a) $4.6 + 2.3$ (b) $4.6 - 2.3$

(c) 4.6×2.3 (d) $4.6 \div 2.3$

(e) $(3.8)(2.9)$ (f) $(4.5)^2$

2 Estimate each answer. Then calculate.

(a) $13.6 \div 2.5 - 1.8$ (b) $16.9 \div 1.3 - 9.8$

(c) $24.32 + (6.2)^2$ (d) $19.62 - (3.2)^2$

(e) $(1.2)^2 + 6.34$ (f) $(8.9)^2 - 12.65$

(g) $4.2(7.2 + 3.1)$ (h) $4.2(7.2 - 3.1)$

(i) $7.968 \div (3.2 + 5.1)$

(j) $10.251 \div (8.4 - 6.7)$

3 Which of the following has the greatest value?

(a) $4.7 + 3.5 - 2.8$ (b) $4.7 - 3.5 + 2.8$

(c) $2.5 + 4.6 \times 3.4$ (d) $3.6 \times 9.4 + 11.5$

(e) $3.4 \times 1.2 + 3$ (f) $6.4 \times 1.3 + 3.7$

4 Which of the following has the smallest value?

(a) $5 + 2.7 - 1.8$ (b) $5 - 2.7 + 1.8$

(c) $2.3 \times 4.2 \div 0.7$ (d) $7.14 \div 1.4 \times 2.3$

(e) $9 \div 3.6 \times 2.5$ (f) $3.6 \times 5.2 \div 1.3$

5 Substitute and evaluate if $x = 2.3$, $y = 0.5$. Round your answers to 1 decimal place.

(a) $4x$ (b) $5.2y$ (c) $4x + 2y$

(d) xy (e) x^2 (f) y^2

(g) $2x - y$ (h) $x^2 + y^2$

(i) $x^2 - y^2$ (j) $3x^2$

(k) $2y^2$ (l) $2(x + y)$

B For each of the following, check whether your answers are reasonable.

6 Calculate. Which of the following has the greatest answer?

(a) $2.3 + 5.4 - 3.6$ (b) $3.9 \times 0.34 - 0.6$

(c) $3.5 \times 0.47 + 3.5$ (d) $1.35 \div 0.4 \times 0.3$

(e) $4.15 \div 8.3 + 3.6$ (f) $8.6 - 22.26 \div 4.2$

(g) $(3.5)^2 + 1.58$ (h) $9.4 - (2.8)^2$

(i) $2.6 - (1.3)^2$ (j) $12.5 \div (0.5)^2$

7 Calculate. Which of the following has the smallest answer?

(a) $12 - 2.8^2$ (b) $64.48 \div 5.2 - 8.94$

(c) $6.5 \times 3.6 - 19.45$ (d) $2.958 \div 3.4 + 0.13$

(e) $3.5^2 + 1.5^2$ (f) $6.38 - 3.5 \times 1.8$

(g) $7.2^2 - 5.9^2$ (h) $1.2^2 \div 0.6$

(i) $1.6(3.8 + 4.9)$ (j) $4.8(9.6 - 3.8)$

8 Replace $\bigcirc$ with $>$ or $<$.

(a) $2.1 + 5.6 \times 3.8 \bigcirc 4.8^2$

(b) $33.28 - 6.4 - 0.5 \bigcirc 3.4 \times 6.4 - 5.2$

(c) $(3.7)^2 \bigcirc 5.2(12.4 - 9.8)$

9 Evaluate. Round to 1 decimal place.

(a) $\dfrac{1.3 + 6.4}{4.6}$ (b) $\dfrac{6.3 - 4.8}{1.5}$

(c) $\dfrac{3.4 + 7.5}{7.2 - 6.4}$ (d) $\dfrac{6.2}{1.2 + 3.4}$

10 If $a = 3.1$ and $b = 6.4$, find the value of

(a) ab (b) $a^2 + 0.4b$

(c) $3.4b - a^2$ (d) $a(b - a)$

(e) $ab - a^2$ (f) $a^2 + b^2$

(g) $2a^2 + b^2$ (h) $a^2 + 2b^2$

(i) $b^2 - a^2$ (j) $3b^2 - 2a^2$

11 Use $k = 0.4$ and $d = 3.2$. Which has the greatest value?

(a) $3.6k + 2d$ (b) $d^2 - k^2$

(c) $0.36k + 4.1d$ (d) $d^2 - 6.2k$

12 The length, l, of a rectangle is found by evaluating the expression. Find the length.

$$l = \frac{P - 2w}{2}$$ where P is the perimeter.
w is the width.

Find the length for each.

(a) $P = 36.8$ $w = 6.2$

(b) $P = 24$ $w = 2.8$

(c) $P = 37.5$ $w = 4.7$

(d) $P = 2.5$ $w = 0.28$

13 The amount, A, in dollars, earned is given by
$$A = 5t + 2n$$
where t is the total number of hours worked.
n is the number of bonus hours.

Calculate A for each of the following.

(a) $t = 105$, $n = 6$ (b) $t = 12.75$, $n = 2.5$

(c) $t = 10.25$, $n = 6.5$ (d) $t = 18.5$, $n = 6.25$

14 The total amount of money, T, collected is given by $T = 8.25a + 4.75s$.
where a is the number of adults.
     s is the number of students.

Calculate T for each of the following.

(a) $a = 25$, $s = 50$ (b) $a = 100$, $s = 50$

(c) $a = 120$, $s = 60$ (d) $a = 125$, $s = 45$

C

15 Often in calculations more than one set of brackets may occur.
  ▸ Do the calculation in the inner most brackets first.
  ▸ Then do the remaining calculation.
Calculate each of the following.

(a) $3 [(6.3)^2 - 1.4]$ (b) $[(4.6)^2 - (2.1)^2] \div 2$

(c) $[(9.5)^2 + (3.4)^2] \div 3$ (d) $3 [(4.8)^2 - (3.2)^2]$

practice and problems: a chapter review

(3.1)   1 Replace ○ by $<$ or $>$.

(a) $0.375 \bigcirc 0.357$ (b) $1.013 \bigcirc 1.301$

(3.2)   2 Calculate.

(a) $\begin{array}{r} 4.63 \\ + 1.08 \end{array}$ (b) $\begin{array}{r} 27.36 \\ - 19.8 \end{array}$ (c) $\begin{array}{r} 3.56 \\ \times 0.35 \end{array}$ (d) $\begin{array}{r} 5.06 \\ \times 0.39 \end{array}$

3 The smallest bicycle ever ridden had wheels 5.625 cm wide. The length of a baby finger is about 6 cm. How much longer is the baby finger?

(3.4)   4 Calculate.

(a) 10×0.62 (b) 1000×0.0035

(c) 1.47×10 (d) 3.576×10

5 The smallest book ever written was 0.14 cm long. If the 200 copies sold were laid end to end, find the total length.

(3.5)   6 (a) Round $16.356 \div 16$ to the nearest hundredth.

(b) Round $3.176 \div 8$ to 1 decimal place.

(c) Round $0.9736 \div 19$ to the nearest tenth.

(3.6)   7 (a) Subtract 4.3 from the sum of 0.573 and 3.94.

(b) Divide the product of 5.13 and 2.4 by 9.

(3.7)   8 Write a fraction for each in lowest terms.

(a) 0.8   (b) 1.45   (c) 0.375

(3.8)   9 Divide. Round to the nearest hundredth.

(a) $\frac{12.5}{1.2}$ (b) $\frac{0.263}{0.39}$ (c) $\frac{3.568}{1.3}$

10 Replace ○ by $>$ or $<$.

(3.10)

(a) $5.3 + 2.8 - 4.36 \bigcirc (1.5)^2$

(b) $3.5^2 - 10 \times 0.36 \bigcirc 0.0435 \div 0.01$

test for practice

1 Simplify.

(a) $\begin{array}{r}15.3\\+14.7\end{array}$ (b) $\begin{array}{r}8.36\\+1.6\end{array}$ (c) $\begin{array}{r}7.635\\-1.279\end{array}$ (d) $\begin{array}{r}4.36\\-2.8\end{array}$

(e) $\begin{array}{r}4.3\\\times0.7\end{array}$ (f) $\begin{array}{r}2.45\\\times0.38\end{array}$ (g) $\frac{91.08}{15}$ (h) $\frac{0.0266}{0.19}$

2 Round each to the accuracy shown.

(a) 2.5×1.7 (nearest hundredth)

(b) $(1.6)^2$ (1 decimal place)

(c) $16.43 \div 0.2 - 65.372$ (2 decimal places)

3 Arrange the numbers in order from least to greatest: 0.357, 0.537, 0.0537, 5.307.

4 Replace ○ by < or >.

(a) $0.17 \circ 0.0175$ (b) $4.3 \times 1.8 \circ (3.2)^2$

5 Write the decimal equivalent for each.

(a) $\frac{1}{10}$ (b) $\frac{37}{1000}$ (c) $\frac{7}{8}$

6 Write a fraction in lowest terms for

(a) 0.4   (b) 1.55   (c) 0.625

7 (a) Add 19.3 to the product of 0.3 and 4.57.

(b) Subtract 19.3 from the square of 5.1.

(c) A deck of 52 cards is 2.3 cm thick. How thick is each card?

8 The women's handbow record for archery is 831.15 m while the crossbow record is 1223.83 m. How much further is the crossbow record?

9 The thickest door is 68.57 times thicker than a regular door of 3.5 cm. How thick is the thickest door (to the nearest centimetre)?

10 The average height of 5 students is 158.5 cm. If 6 more students with average height of 163.5 cm join them, find the new average height.

looking back: a cumulative review

1 Without multiplying, decide which of the following is the answer to this product 49.2×15.3.

(a) 7527.6   (b) 752.76   (c) 75.28

2 Calculate.

(a) $\frac{12 + 12 \div 3}{8 \times 2}$ (b) $\frac{4^2 + 2^2}{2^2 + 1}$

(c) $5^2 - 4^2 - 3^2$ (d) $13^2 - 12^2 - 5^2$

(e) $\frac{8 \div 2 + 4 \times 6}{17 - 3}$ (f) $\frac{2 \times (12 - 4)}{2 \times (8 - 4)}$

3 (a) The sum of 46.95, 29.34 and ■ is 149.45. Find ■.

(b) When 782.28 is divided by 36.9, the answer is ■. Find ■.

(c) When 14.732 is subtacted from the sum of 11.261 and ■, the answer is 12.653. Find ■.

4 Use the symbols $+$, $-$, $\times$, or $\div$ for ○ to make a true statement. The first one has been completed for you.

(a) $2 \circ 3 \circ 4 = 10$ $2 \times 3 + 4 = 10$

(b) $2 \circ 3 \circ 4 = 14$ (c) $10 \circ 10 \circ 10 = 11$

(d) $3 \circ 3 \circ 3 = 3$ (e) $4 \circ 2 \circ 2 = 4$

5 The total registration fees for the convention were \$47 310. There were 380 delegates who attended. What was the cost per delegate?

6 The largest bird is the North African ostrich. The mass of one was reported as 156.4 kg. On some of the Indian Ocean islands, the tortoise has a large mass. One specimen had a mass of 148.7 kg. Which had the greater mass? By how much?

4

skills with measurement: applications with perimeter, area, volume

Using metric units, finding perimeter, area, volume, using formulas, triangle, parallelogram, circle, cylinder, patterns for measurement, problem solving skills, solving problems and applications

Everybody is concerned with measurements in one way or another.

When you go camping, you are concerned with how far you will go, how much gas you will use, and how long it will take.

The pilot of the aircraft is concerned with how much runway is available to land the plane.

If you cut the grass you are concerned with how large the lawn is.

If you play a sport, you are concerned with how far away the edge of your playing field is, how high the net is, and how hard you can hit the ball.

Measurement occurs as part of everyday living.

▶ wallpapering a room   ▶ vacuuming

▶ making a dress   ▶ picking apples

▶ wrapping a gift   ▶ buying clothes

Measurement is needed

▶ to build a highway.   ▶ to tile the cafeteria.

▶ to steer a boat.   ▶ to purchase a farm.

In this chapter, you will learn various aspects of measurement:

▶ units of measurement   ▶ applications with measurement

▶ concepts of perimeter, area, and volume   ▶ problem solving with measurement

4.1 measuring length: metric prefixes

Measurement involves comparing. For example, to find how long something is, you compare it to a unit of length. To measure line segment AB you can use the standard unit of measure called a **centimetre**.

By comparing the line segment with a centimetre ruler, you see that AB is 6 cm long. To measure longer lengths, units such as the **metre** or **kilometre** are used.

The base unit of length is the metre. Prefixes are used with the metre to make longer and shorter units. The relationships between different units of length are shown in the table.

The metric system is based on the decimal number system. The prefixes are related by using the powers of 10, namely 10, 100, 1000.

Prefix	Symbol	Prefix with unit of metre	Symbol	Relationship to metre
kilo	k	kilometre	km	1 km = 1000 m
hecto	h	hectometre	hm	1 hm = 100 m
deca	da	decametre	dam	1 dam = 10 m
base unit — metre			m	
deci	d	decimetre	dm	1 m = 10 dm
centi	c	centimetre	cm	1 m = 100 cm
milli	m	millimetre	mm	1 m = 1000 mm

kilo	10^3	1000
hecto	10^2	100
deca	10	10
deci	$\frac{1}{10}$	0.1
centi	$\frac{1}{10^2}$	0.01
milli	$\frac{1}{10^3}$	0.001

Using the relationships above, 4.5 m can be expressed in various units.

4.5 m equals
- 0.0045 km
- 0.045 hm
- 0.45 dam

To write a larger unit as a smaller unit, *multiply* by a power of 10.

- 45 dm
- 450 cm
- 4500 mm

To write a smaller unit as a larger unit *divide* by a power of 10.

The most common prefixes used are these.

kilo	centi	milli
(thousand)	(hundredth)	(thousandth)

If you understand how the various units are related, you can use your arithmetic skills to change from one unit of measure to another.

Example 1   Write 3.5 km as metres.

Solution   1 km = 1000 m

3.5 km = 3.5 × 1000 m $\Big($ Remember: to change a larger unit to

= 3500 m   a smaller unit, you multiply. To write

kilometres as metres, multiply by 1000. $\Big)$

Example 2   Write 350 cm as metres.

Solution   100 cm = 1 m

350 cm = $\frac{350}{100}$ m $\Big($ Remember: to change a smaller unit

= 3.5 m   to a larger unit, you divide. To write

centimetres as metres, divide by 100. $\Big)$

4.1 exercise

A To write metric units, you must remember the chart that relates the prefixes.

1 (a) To write 2.8 cm as millimetres do you multiply or divide by a power of 10?

(b) Complete 2.8 cm = ? mm.

2 (a) To write 285 m as kilometres do you multiply or divide by a power of 10?

(b) Complete 285 m = ? km.

3 In each of the following, decide whether you need to divide or multiply by a power of 10. Then find the answer. Write

(a) 8 cm as millimetres.

(b) 4 km as metres.

(c) 6 m as hectometres.

(d) 49 mm as decimetres.

(e) 12 m as millimetres.

(f) 15 cm as metres.

4 (a) Express 1.5 km in metres.

(b) Express 1.5 m in millimetres.

(c) How do your calculations (a) and (b) compare?

5 (a) Express 230 mm in metres.

(b) Express 230 m in kilometres.

(c) How do your calculations in (a) and (b) compare?

6 For each measure, which measure is reasonable?

(a) The ski run is 1600 km or 1600 m.

(b) The length of the bridge across the St. Lawrence River is 1500 cm or 1.5 km.

(c) The annual precipitation in New Brunswick is about 117 m or 1170 mm.

(d) The length of a bee hummingbird is 5.7 m or 5.7 mm.

(e) Your hand span is about 2 m or 20 cm.

(f) The highest road in the world is at a height of 600 km or 6000 m.

(g) The length of the Trans Canada Highway is 7900 m or 7900 km.

(h) The length of the longest banana split was 2400 mm or 2400 m.

(i) A stamp is 2.4 m long or 2.4 cm long.

(j) The thickness of plywood is 3 mm or 2.5 cm.

(k) The length of the longest traffic jam was 180 m or 180 km.

(l) The length of a brick is 2 m or 20 cm.

B

7 Write each length in millimetres.

(a) 2.3 m   (b) 4.56 m   (c) 0.125 m

(d) 2.3 cm   (e) 4.56 cm   (f) 0.125 cm

(g) 5.2 m   (h) 0.2 m   (i) 0.004 m

8 Write each length in metres.

(a) 12 km   (b) 4.5 km   (c) 0.15 km

(d) 12 cm   (e) 4.5 cm   (f) 0.15 cm

(g) 1250 mm   (h) 125 mm   (i) 12.5 mm

9 Write each length in kilometres.

(a) 1456 m   (b) 2550 m   (c) 357 m

(d) 23 m   (e) 2.3 m   (f) 4000 m

(g) 12 hm   (h) 476 dam   (i) 50 500 cm

10 Copy and complete the chart.

	mm	cm	m
(a)	?	?	165
(b)	469	?	?
(c)	?	142.5	?
(d)	?	?	1.6

11 In the following sentences, express each length in millimetres.

(a) The picture screen is 1.2 m wide.

(b) The newspaper is 0.726 m wide.

(c) The record is 30.1 cm in diameter.

(d) The log is 1.35 m long.

(e) The length of the Canadian dollar bill is 15.2 cm and its width is 0.069 m.

12 (a) The width of a computer diskette is 135 mm. How many centimetres is this?

(b) The width of the screen display on a computer is 19.5 cm. Express the width in millimetres.

(c) The height of a computer is 39.7 cm. How many metres is this?

(d) The take-off board for the long jump is 203 mm wide and 1220 mm long. Express the dimensions in metres.

(e) The longest reef in the world is the Great Barrier Reef in Australia. It is 2 016 000 m long. How many kilometres long is the reef?

13 Estimate and then measure the following line segments. Express each answer to the nearest millimetre.

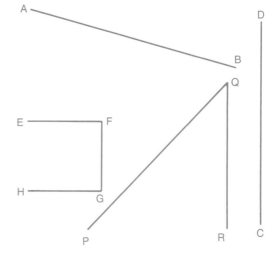

4.2 metric units: area and volume

When you paint a wall or tile a floor, you are interested in calculating area. To measure area, a standard unit is chosen. Then the area of the surface being measured is compared to the standard unit of area.

▶ The square metre is a standard unit of area. The relationships between the units of area can be found by using the relationships between the units of length.

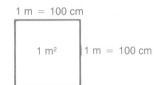

$$1 \text{ m} = 100 \text{ cm}$$
$$1 \text{ m}^2 = 100 \text{ cm} \times 100 \text{ cm}$$
$$= 10 \ 000 \text{ cm}^2$$
Thus, $1 \text{ m}^2 = 10 \ 000 \text{ cm}^2$

The opening ceremonies of the Commonwealth Games (1978) were held in Edmonton. The British Commonwealth is a voluntary association of nations and includes 42 countries, representing about one quarter of the world's population.

Example 1   Write 0.034 m² as square centimetres.

Solution
$$1 \text{ m}^2 = 10 \ 000 \text{ cm}^2$$
$$0.034 \text{ m}^2 = 0.034 \times 10 \ 000 \text{ cm}^2$$
$$= 340 \text{ cm}^2$$
Thus, $0.034 \text{ m}^2 = 340 \text{ cm}^2$

(Remember: to change a larger unit to a smaller unit you multiply.

▶ **Square centimetres** (cm²) are used to measure smaller areas such as the cover of a book, or the top of a desk.

▶ **Square metres** (m²) are used to measure larger areas such as the floor of a classroom, or the schoolyard.

▶ To measure very large areas such as cities, lakes, or countries, the **square kilometre** (km²) is used.

▶ The **hectare** (ha) is used for measuring areas such as farms, or tracks of land. One hectare is the area of a square with each side 100 m.

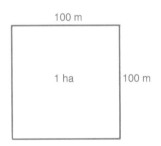

Knowing the relationships between units of length also helps you find relationships between units of volume, or capacity.

A cubic metre is shown.
$$1 \text{ m} = 100 \text{ cm}$$
$$1 \text{ m}^3 = 100 \text{ cm} \times 100 \text{ cm} \times 100 \text{ cm}$$
$$= 1 \ 000 \ 000 \text{ cm}^3$$
Thus, $1 \text{ m}^3 = 1 \ 000 \ 000 \text{ cm}^3$

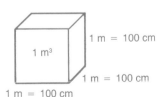

Example 2   Write 2 340 000 cm³ as cubic metres.

Solution   1 000 000 cm³ = 1 m³

2 340 000 cm³ = $\frac{2\,340\,000}{1\,000\,000}$ m³ $\left(\begin{array}{l}\text{Remember: to change a} \\ \text{smaller unit to a larger} \\ \text{unit you divide.}\end{array}\right.$

= 2.34 m³

A unit often used to measure the volume of liquids such as milk, and other substances such as toothpaste, is the litre (L). One litre is equivalent to one cubic decimetre. You apply the prefixes to write smaller or larger units, for example

1 L = 1000 mL

1 L = 10 cm × 10 cm × 10 cm

= 1000 cm³

Thus, 1 mL = 1 cm³

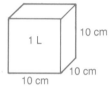

1 cm³ = 1 mL

4.2 exercise

A You can use your knowledge about units of length to find the relationships between the units of area and of volume.

1 Find the values of ■ in the following.

1 cm = ■ mm

1 cm² = ■ mm × ■ mm

= ■ mm²

1 cm = 10 mm

2 Use the results of the previous question to write each area in square millimetres.

(a) 65 cm²   (b) 3.2 cm²   (c) 0.54 cm²

3 Find the values of ■ in the following.

1 m = ■ cm

1 m² = ■ cm × ■ cm

= ■ cm²

1 m = 100 cm

4 Use the results of the previous question to write each area in square centimetres.

(a) 6 m²   (b) 6.2 m²   (c) 0.62 m²

5 Find the values of ■ in the following.

1 cm = ■ mm

1 cm³ = ■ mm × ■ mm × ■ mm

= ■ mm³

6 Use the results of the previous question to write each volume in cubic millimetres.

(a) 73 cm³   (b) 8.5 cm³   (c) 0.36 cm³

7 Draw a diagram to illustrate the relationship between each of the following units of measure.

(a) m², cm²   (b) cm², mm²

(c) m³, dm³   (d) km³, m³

(e) L, dm³   (f) mL, cm³

8 How many

(a) square centimetres are in 1 m²?

(b) square metres are in 1 km²?

(c) hectares are in 1 km²?

(d) cubic centimetres are in 1 m³?

(e) cubic millimetres are in 1 cm³?

(f) cubic metres are in 1 km³?

9 First decide whether you need to multiply or divide. Then choose the proper power of 10 to do each of the following. Write

(a) 85 L as millilitres. (b) 29.3 mL as litres.

(c) 146 kL as hectolitres. (d) 348 L as kilolitres.

Remember, the prefix k means 1000.

B

10 Which measure is more reasonable for each of the following?

(a) The area of the forest is 4.5 m² or 4.5 km².

(b) Joanne ate 400 mL or 400 L of soup.

(c) The microchip is 1 mm² or 1 km².

(d) The first floor of the house is 220 m² or 220 ha.

(e) The toothpaste tube contains 175 mL or 175 L.

(f) A fingernail is about 1.5 cm² or 1.5 mm².

(g) The cup holds about 300 mL or 300 L.

(h) The area of the baseball diamond is about 900 cm² or 900 m².

(i) The dump truck holds 30 m³ or 30 cm³ of sand.

(j) The interior of a lightbulb is about 150 cm³ or 150 m³.

(k) The page of the newspaper is 1 m² or 1 km².

(l) A dollar bill has an area of about 100 cm² or 100 mm².

(m) The refrigerator has a capacity of 1.5 m³ or 1.5 km³.

(n) The bathtub holds 200 L or 200 kL.

(o) The playing card has an area of 50 cm² or 50 m².

11 Find the values of ■ in the following.

(a) 1 cm² = ■ mm² (b) 2.3 cm² = ■ mm²

(c) 1 m² = ■ cm² (d) 6.8 m² = ■ cm²

(e) 1 km² = ■ m² (f) 7.8 km² = ■ m²

12 Find the values of ■ in the following.

(a) 1 cm³ = ■ mm³ (b) 4.5 cm³ = ■ mm³

(c) 1 m³ = ■ cm³ (d) 8.3 m³ = ■ cm³

13 Write each of the following as shown.

(a) 5.3 L in millilitres (b) 4600 mL in litres

(c) 21 dL in litres (d) 2.5 L in millilitres

(e) 0.006 L as millilitres

(f) 56.8 L as millilitres

14 Find the values of ■ in the following.

(a) ■ cm² = 1254.2 mm² (b) 0.35 mm² = ■ cm²

(c) 5.6 L = ■ mL (d) ■ ha = 1289 m²

(e) ■ mL = 4.59 L (f) 6800 mm³ = ■ cm³

(g) 36 mL = ■ cm³ (h) ■ ha = 1235 m²

(i) 1560 m² = ■ km² (j) ■ m² = 45 680 cm²

15 (a) A soft drink can holds 200 mL. How many litres are in a case of 24 cans?

(b) They sold two farms of 50 ha each. How many square kilometres is this?

16 Barry needed to fill an empty vat which holds 0.5 kL of liquid.

(a) How many one litre containers would be needed to fill the vat?

(b) If he could fill and empty 5 L in 30 s, how long would it take him to fill the vat?

17 A metal container has a volume of 13 458 cm³. How many litres of liquid will it hold?

units of mass, time, and temperature

One important nature of mathematics is the similarities that occur. These similarities allow you to look for methods that help you learn information. The same prefixes are used to write units of metric mass, as shown in the chart. The basic unit of mass is the gram (g). The relationships among the most common units of mass are shown in chart A.

A

units	symbols	relationship
kilogram	kg	1 kg = 1000 g
gram	g	
milligram	mg	1 g = 1000 mg
tonne	t	1 t = 1000 kg

The basic unit used to measure temperature is the Celsius degree. In Chart B the common temperatures are shown.

B

Temperature Range	Description
100°C	Boiling water
35°C to 40°C	Very hot
30°C to 35°C	Hot
25°C to 30°C	Very warm
20°C to 25°C	Warm (room temperature)
10°C to 20°C	Cool
0°C to 10°C	Cold
0°C	Freezing (water)
Below 0°C	Below freezing (water)

C

Unit	Symbol	Relationships
Second	s	60 s = 1 min
Minute	min	60 min = 1 h
Hour	h	1 h = 60 min
Day	d	1 d = 24 h
Year	a	1 a = 365 d

18 (a) Write each mass in grams.
   (i) 1 kg   (ii) 2.5 kg   (iii) 0.056 kg

   (b) Write each mass in kilograms.
   (i) 1000 g   (ii) 1260 g   (iii) 236 g

   (c) Write each mass in milligrams.
   (i) 1 g   (ii) 8.5 g   (iii) 0.08 g

19 Find the value of ■ in the following.

   (a) 1 g = ■ mg   (b) 1 kg = ■ g

   (c) 1 g = ■ kg   (d) ■ g = 255 mg

   (e) ■ kg = 236.5 g (f) 2350 mg = ■ g

   (g) 2.6 kg = ■ g   (h) ■ g = 1245 mg

   (i) 3.5 t = ■ kg   (j) 346 kg = ■ t

20 (a) A piece of wood has a mass of 2.5 kg. A rock has a mass of 2276 g. Which has the greater mass and by how much?

   (b) Find the total mass, in grams, of a hamburger. The meat pattie has a mass of 0.125 kg, the bun 45 g and the dressings 2351 mg.

(c) In 1957, Paul Anderson lifted 2 821 500 g in a backlift. How many kilograms is that?

21 How many seconds, in all, are in

   (a) 3 min 5 s?   (b) 6 h 2 min?

   (c) 4.5 h 2.5 min? (d) 3.2 h 3.6 min?

22 The satellite orbits the earth 3 times every 6.5 d. How long does one orbit take to the nearest second?

23 Estimate a suitable temperature for each of the following weather conditions. Justify your answer.

   (a) cloudy skies in September

   (b) a trip by snowmobile

   (c) skating on the pond

   (d) pulling out weeds   (e) raking leaves

   (f) swimming in the irrigation pond

   (g) painting the eavestrough

   (h) buying a valentine card

4.3 suitable units of measure: making decisions

When a space vehicle returns to earth, the astronauts need a very accurate measurement of their position. When planting vegetables, a gardener estimates how far apart to place the plants.

In each case, measurements are made. However, the purpose determines how much accuracy is needed.

▶ When you measure you select a suitable unit of measure. For example, to measure the width of a garage, would you use millimetres, centimetres, or metres?
▶ Then you decide how accurate your measure needs to be. Do you round off to one decimal place, two decimal places, to the nearest centimetre, and so on?

When you measure, you also have a variety of devices from which to choose.

To measure length. . . .

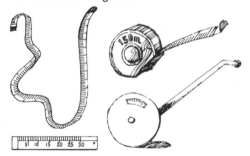

To measure mass. . .

To measure volume. . .

4.3 exercise

A Remember: An important skill is to decide what units are needed in a problem. However, you must also be able to write each measure in smaller or greater units.

1 Change each measure as indicated.

(a) 29.6 m   into centimetres
(b) 1499 g   into kilograms
(c) 486 mm   into centimetres
(d) 49.6 L   into millilitres
(e) 2.9 km   into metres
(f) 2965 mm   into metres
(g) 498 mg   into grams
(h) 369 cm   into millimetres
(i) 15.6 km   into metres

2 Find the missing values. (Remember: You need to know when to use length, area, or volume units.)

(a) 169 cm $=$ ▨ m
(b) ▨ m^2 $=$ 400 cm^2
(c) 1.5 km $=$ ▨ m
(d) ▨ L $=$ 36 mL
(e) ▨ cm^3 $=$ 90 mL
(f) 4.3 m $=$ ▨ cm
(g) 696 mL $=$ ▨ L
(h) ▨ mm^2 $=$ 48 cm^2
(i) ▨ L $=$ 32.2 cm^3
(j) 8.6 ha $=$ ▨ m^2
(k) 93 cm $=$ ▨ mm
(l) ▨ m $=$ 32 km
(m) ▨ m^2 $=$ 46 ha
(n) 16.5 mm^2 $=$ ▨ cm^2
(o) 48 km^2 $=$ ▨ ha
(p) 16.5 L $=$ ▨ mL

B

3 Each question provides different metric measures. Write both measures in the larger unit and find their sum. The first one is done for you.

(a) 3.60 m, 14 cm

14 cm = 0.14 m

Add   3.60 m
        0.14 m
        3.74 m

(b) 434 mL, 8.9 L   (c) 37.2 g, 1.25 kg

(d) 39.6 km, 298 m   (e) 2.8 cm, 3.65 m

(f) 46.9 cm, 23 m   (g) 369 m, 4.96 km

(h) 4.98 g, 469 mg   (i) 269 mm, 4.6 m

(j) 2.3 t, 534 kg   (k) 4.5 kL, 3.6 L

(l) 104 mm, 26.5 cm   (m) 969 L, 3.96 kL

(n) 125 mg, 36 g   (o) 1 L, 96 mL

(p) 235 mL, 4 L   (q) 40.5 kg, 150 g

(r) 2.3 t, 6534 kg   (s) 2 m², 1535 cm²

4 Write the measures that occur in each of the following in the smaller of the two units.

(a) One side of a rectangle measures 46.2 m. The other side measures 3840 cm.

(b) The perimeter of a figure is 4.69 km. One side measures 369 m.

(c) The length of the fence is 136.9 m. The height of the fence is 135 cm.

(d) One side of a stamp measures 48 mm. The other side measures 2.4 cm.

5 Each of the following involves a measurement of length. Which of these units would you use: millimetre, centimetre, metre, kilometre?

(a) The length of an Olympic-sized pool.

(b) The height of the tallest tree ever recorded.

(c) The length of the longest fish.

(d) The total distance of the motor trip last summer.

(e) The width of the tip of a ballpoint pen.

6 For each part:
▶ Choose the most suitable unit.
▶ Change the units to the same measure.
▶ Answer the question using the most suitable unit.

(a) The length of the knitting needle is 0.25 m and the length of the darning needle is 3.5 cm. Find the total length.

(b) Rowena walked 3.5 km and rode 12 500 m. Find the total distance.

(c) The mass of the flour was 1486 g and the butter was 1 kg. Find the total mass.

7 For each of the following, which unit of measure would you most likely need to use?

(a) The length of a roller coaster ride.

(b) The amount of air in your lungs.

(c) The distance from Vancouver to Winnipeg.

(d) The area of postage stamps.

(e) The volume of water in a glass.

(f) The thickness of this paper.

(g) The volume of water used for a shower.

8 For each of these activities, measurement is involved in some way.
▶ List which measurements are most useful.
▶ Decide on a suitable unit of measurement.

For example, when painting a floor you need to know the area of the floor (m²), the width of the brush (cm), the volume of paint needed (L). Anything else?

(a) Baking a pie   (b) Washing a car

(c) Making a glass of uncola

(d) Delivering papers   (e) Playing basketball

(f) Shovelling a walk   (g) Taking a hike

(h) Painting a room   (i) Wrapping a present

(j) Making a pizza   (k) Throwing snowballs

(l) Playing hockey   (m) Swimming a race

4.4 applications with perimeter

The distance around a closed figure is called its **perimeter**.

Example 1   Find the perimeter of each figure.

(a)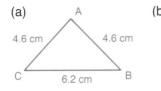

(b)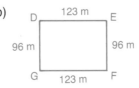

To make a frame for a print of your favorite flower, you need to know the distance around the picture. That is, you need to find the perimeter.

Solution

(a) The distance around is given by
Perimeter = 4.6 cm + 4.6 cm + 6.2 cm
= 15.4 cm
The perimeter is 15.4 cm.

(b) The distance around is given by
Perimeter = 123 m + 96 m + 123 m + 96 m
= 438 m
The perimeter is 438 m.

To solve the following problem, you also need to use your skills with computation.

Example 2

(a) Kirsten keeps her horse in a field 88 m long and 45 m wide. Find the amount of fencing needed to enclose the field.

(b) Find the cost to enclose the field if fencing costs $4.65/m.

Solution

(a) Find the perimeter.⌐(Find the distance around.
Perimeter = 88 m + 45 m + 88 m + 45 m
= 266 m
The perimeter is 266 m.

(b) Calculate the cost. The perimeter is 266 m.
1 m of fencing costs $4.65
266 m of fencing cost 266 × $4.65 or $1236.90
The cost of fencing is $1236.90.

Once you have obtained your answer, remember to check whether your answer is reasonable.

Draw a diagram to help you picture the problem.

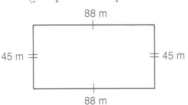

Check your work with a calculator.

4.4 exercise

A Remember, perimeter is the distance around.

1 Find the perimeter of each figure. Each side of a small square represents a metre.

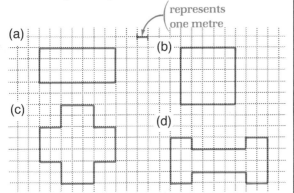

(a) — represents one metre
(b)
(c)
(d)

2 Find the perimeter of each figure.

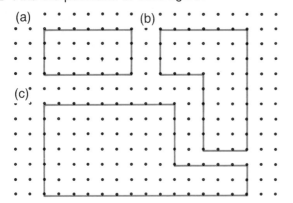

(a) (b) (c)

3 Find the perimeter of each figure.

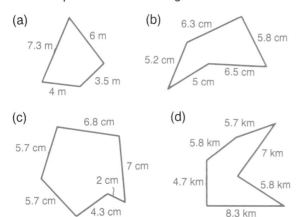

(a) 6 m, 7.3 m, 3.5 m, 4 m
(b) 6.3 cm, 5.8 cm, 5.2 cm, 6.5 cm, 5 cm
(c) 6.8 cm, 5.7 cm, 7 cm, 2 cm, 5.7 cm, 4.3 cm
(d) 5.7 km, 5.8 km, 7 km, 4.7 km, 5.8 km, 8.3 km

4 Use a pattern to calculate the perimeter of each figure.

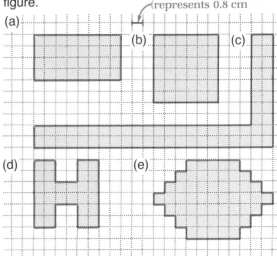

represents 0.8 cm
(a) (b) (c) (d) (e)

5 Copy and complete the chart. Find the perimeter of each rectangle.

	Length	Width	Perimeter
(a)	24 cm	16 cm	?
(b)	3.6 m	2.4 m	?
(c)	44.8 m	32.3 m	?
(d)	8.15 km	2.89 km	?

6 The symbols, a, b, c, are used to refer to the lengths of the sides of a triangle. Find the missing sides.

	a	b	c	Perimeter, P
(a)	48 cm	63 cm	?	163 cm
(b)	?	8.3 m	7.9 m	25.8 m
(c)	2.65 km	?	1.39 km	6.02 km

B

7 Kokanee Glacier Provincial Park in British Columbia is a square. Each side measures 16.1 km. What is the perimeter of the park?

8 One of the largest omelettes ever prepared was cooked in Kitchener, Ontario. The rectangular pan measured 9.1 m by 3.1 m. Calculate the perimeter of the pan.

9 A triangular vegetable garden has two sides that measure 4.6 m and 3.9 m. If the perimeter is 9.5 m, what is the measure of the remaining side?

10 You want to frame the poster. Find the perimeter.

56.2 cm
29.5 cm

11 The dimensions of the Avalon Wilderness Area in Newfoundland are shown.

(a) Estimate the perimeter of the wilderness area.

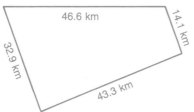
46.6 km
14.1 km
32.9 km
43.3 km

(b) Find the perimeter. How close was your estimate?

The Avalon Wilderness Area is a protected region in which caribou are found. If you want to cast for brook trout in this wilderness area, you will first need to obtain a permit to visit the area.

12 Refer to the diagram.

(a) Find the missing sides.

(b) Find the perimeter.

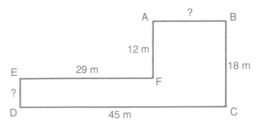
A ? B
12 m
E 29 m
F
18 m
? D 45 m C

13 Find each perimeter.

(a)
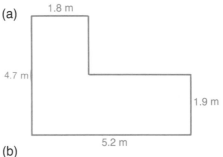
1.8 m
4.7 m
1.9 m
5.2 m

(b)
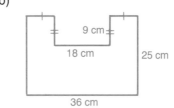
9 cm
18 cm
25 cm
36 cm

14 (a) Estimate which figure has the greatest perimeter. The diagrams are *not* drawn to scale.

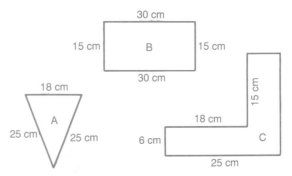
30 cm
15 cm B 15 cm
30 cm
15 cm
18 cm
18 cm
25 cm A 25 cm
6 cm C
25 cm

(b) Find each perimeter. How accurate was your estimate?

15 Estimate each perimeter to the nearest centimetre. Copy and complete the chart. Measure each side to find the perimeter.

Perimeter (estimate)	Perimeter (measure)	Difference

(a)   (b)

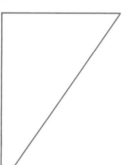   

16 Which has the greater perimeter, A or B?

⎛ Estimate first,
⎝ then measure.

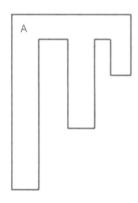

17 (a) Find the perimeter of the stamp.

(b) A square sheet of stamps has 100 stamps. What is the perimeter of the sheet?

⎛ Hint: Use your answer
⎝   in (a) to help you.

3.65 cm

RAS AL KHAIMA 2.50 RIYALS

2.73 cm

18 Eden planted a hedge around her garden. The rectangular garden measures 16.2 m by 12.6 m.

(a) Find the perimeter.

(b) She put a hedge plant every 30 cm. She also put one at each corner. How many plants did she use?

C

19 By using a piece of string, Jean and Frieda measured the distance around this bicycle wheel and found it to be 2 m.

(a) How many turns would the wheel make if the bicycle was driven 100 m?

(b) How many turns would the wheel make if it was driven 1 km?

20 (a) Measure the distance around your bicycle wheel.

(b) How many turns would the wheel make if your bicycle was driven 1 km?

calculator tip

Calculate the perimeter on a calculator. Use the calculator flow chart below.

$P = 2\ell + 2w$
length, 18.2 m
width 9.6 m.

| C | 2 | × | 18.2 | ÷ | 9.6 | + | 2 | × | 9.6 | = |

∠(Why is this step needed?

Use your calculator to obtain answers for the formulas in this section.

4.5 patterns and perimeter

If you repeat the same calculations over and over again, look for a pattern to simplify your work. For example, the measure of each side of the equilateral triangle is shown by s.

Write the perimeter, P.   Simplify the expression.
$$P = s + s + s$$ $$P = 3 \times s$$

The following chart suggests a pattern to find the perimeter of a rectangle.

Length (l)	Width (w)	l + w	Perimeter (P)
12 cm	7 cm	19 cm	38 cm
8 cm	5 cm	13 cm	26 cm
4.5 cm	2.6 cm	7.1 cm	14.2 cm
9.8 cm	4.7 cm	14.5 cm	29 cm

$(2 \times 14.5 = 29)$

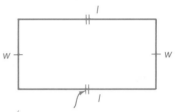

(These marks show segments
with the same measure.)

From the chart you can see that the perimeter of a rectangle can be found by using the formula $P = 2 \times (l + w)$.
This formula is used to find the perimeter of a rectangle in the following problem.

Example   The family pony is kept in a rectangular pen. The dimensions are 9.3 m by 6.4 m. If the fence costs $6.79/m, calculate the cost of fencing the pen.

Solution   **Step 1** Find the perimeter.

$$P = 2 \times (l + w)$$ (length (l)   9.3 m
$$P = 2 \times (9.3 + 6.4)$$ width (w)   6.4 m)
$$= 2 \times (15.7)$$
$$= 31.4$$ The perimeter is 31.4 m

List the given information.
Sketch a diagram.

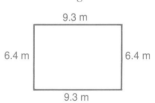

Step 2 Calculate the cost.
1 m costs $6.79
31.4 m cost $6.79 × 31.4 or
$213.21 (to the nearest cent)
The cost of fencing the pen is $213.21.

In the exercise that follows, look for other patterns and formulas that simplify your calculations to find perimeter.

A

1 Find the perimeter of each figure. Use a pattern to help you.

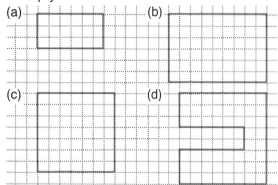

(a) (b)

(c) (d)

2 Find the perimeter of each figure. Use a pattern to simplify your calculation.

—(represents 0.8 cm

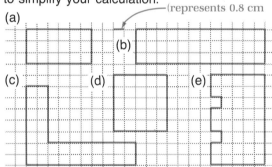

(a)

(b)

(c) (d) (e)

3 Each calculation finds the perimeter of a figure. Match the calculation and the figure.

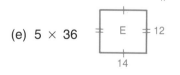

(a) 53 + 36 + 82

(b) 36 + 82 + 53 + 63

(c) 4 × 12

(d) 2 × (14 + 12)

(e) 5 × 36

4 For each rectangle, find the missing values to calculate the perimeter.

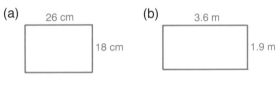

(a) 26 cm 18 cm

(b) 3.6 m 1.9 m

$P = 2 \times (l + w)$
$P = 2 \times (? + ?)$
$= 2 \times ?$
$= ?$

$P = 2 \times (l + w)$
$P = 2 \times (? + ?)$
$= 2 \times ?$
$= ?$

5 Copy and complete the chart. Find the perimeter of each rectangle.

	Length	Width	Perimeter
(a)	13 cm	8 cm	?
(b)	36 m	21 m	?
(c)	1.8 m	1.2 m	?
(d)	5.2 km	3.6 km	?

6 Use the rectangle.
   (a) Find the perimeter by measuring the distance around.

   (b) Find the perimeter by using the formula. Compare your answer to that in (a). What do you notice?

7 Find the perimeter. Estimate, then measure.

(a) (b)

B

8 (a) Develop a formula to find the perimeter, P, of the square.

(b) Use your formula in (a). Find the perimeter of a square with sides 18.2 m each.

9 (a) Develop a formula for the perimeter, P, of the figure shown.

(b) Use your formula in (a). Find the perimeter, P, if s = 12.1 m, n = 8.6 m.

10 Develop a formula to find the perimeter, P, of each figure.

(a)

(b)

(c)

(d)

11 Each figure has different sides that are equal. Develop a formula to find the perimeter, P, of each figure.

(a)

(b)

(c)

(d)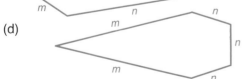

12 A regular polygon is a polygon with all sides and all angles equal. Develop a formula for the perimeter of each regular polygon.

(a) regular hexagon   (b) regular octagon

13 A seal is used along the top of a freezer to keep the cold air in. Find the amount of seal used.

14 A polo field is one of the largest playing fields. Its dimensions are 280 m by 185 m. How far would you walk, in kilometres, around the edge of the field?

15 The largest flag ever had dimensions 125 m by 64 m. People lined up around the perimeter of the flag. Each person needed 50 cm. How many persons were there around the flag?

16 A rectangular tablecloth measures 2.1 m by 3.6 m.

(a) Find the perimeter.

(b) Lace costs $1.69/m. Find the cost of putting lace around the tablecloth. Check whether your answer is reasonable.

17 (a) The perimeter of a square is 324 m. Find the measures of its sides.

(b) The amount of fencing needed for a square field is 48.2 m. Find the measures of the sides.

C

18 The amount of fencing used for an irrigation pond was 400 m. The width of the pond is 40 m less than the length. What are the dimensions of the pond?

problem solving: investigating relationships

The Ancient Greeks discovered a very interesting relationship between the diameter and the circumference of any circle. Complete the following questions, in order, and you will be able to make that same discovery. Your calculator might be useful.

Remember: The parts of a circle.

centre of the circle

This distance is called the diameter.

The distance around the circle is called the circumference.

Distance from the centre to the circumference is the radius.

19 Arnold and Sheila measured the circumference of a can, using a piece of string.
The circumference, C, was 33 cm.
The diameter, d, was 10 cm.
Calculate the value of $C \div d$.
Round off your answer to the nearest tenth.

20 For the bicycle wheel, John and Kathleen made these measurements.
The circumference, C, is 202.1 cm.
The diameter, d, is 64.5 cm.
Calculate the value of $C \div d$.
Round off your answer to the nearest tenth.

21 Compare your answers in Questions 19 and 20. What do you notice?

22 Susan's class made the following measurements of some tops and cans, using a tape measure.
Find the missing values in the following chart

	Measure of circumference C	Measure of diameter d	Calculation $C \div d$
Large can	29.5 cm	9.4 cm	
Small can	10.1 cm	3.2 cm	
Large top	54.9 cm	17.5 cm	
Small top	21.4 cm	6.8 cm	
Blue top	102.1 cm	32.5 cm	
Peach can	23.9 cm	7.6 cm	

What do you notice about your answers for the calculation $C \div d$?

23 (a) Choose any bicycle wheel.
Find the measure of the circumference, C, and the diameter, d.
Calculate the value of $C \div d$. Round off your answer to the nearest tenth.

   (b) What do you notice about your answers in (a) above for $C \div d$?

24 Find circular items. Measure the circumference and diameter. Calculate the value of $C \div d$ to two decimal places.

Circular object	Measure of circumference C	Measure of diameter d	Calculation $C \div d$

What do you notice about your answers for the calculations $C \div d$?

math tip

For circular objects you probably found from your computations that approximately the same answer was obtained for $C \div d$ or $\frac{C}{d}$.

Of course, your calculations depend on how accurate you were. However, if you were careful, your answers should have been *approximately* the same.

Finding an exact value for the ratio $\frac{C}{d}$ has intrigued people for centuries. This ratio is represented by the Greek letter π (pi) and is pronounced the same as the word *pie*.

By using different circles and computing the value $\frac{C}{d}$, you can obtain only an approximate value for π. In your problems that include decimal measures, the approximate value you will use is

$$\pi \doteq 3.14 \qquad \frac{C}{d} = \pi$$

A value of π will be needed to calculate the area of a circle and its perimeter (circumference) in the sections that follow.

4.6 perimeter of a circle: circumference

By completing the experiment in the previous section, you found that the measure of the circumference, C, divided by the measure of the diameter, d, always had a constant value of approximately 3 (or 3.14 to 2 decimal places). The symbol π is used for this constant value. Thus, you can write a formula to calculate the perimeter, or circumference, of a circle.

$$\frac{C}{d} = \pi \quad or \quad C \div d = \pi$$

This relationship can be written as $C = \pi \times d$

measure of the circumference ⌐──────┘ ↑ └──────⌐ measure of the diameter

$$\pi \doteq 3.14$$

The radius, r, and the diameter, d, of a circle are related by d = 2r or d = 2 × r. Therefore, the formula can also be written as $C = \pi \times 2 \times r$ or $C = 2 \times \pi \times r$

You can find the measure of the circumference if you know the measure of the radius or the diameter, as shown in the following example.

How far would you travel for one complete turn of the ride? What is the total distance you travel for 1 ticket?

Example 1   Calculate the circumference of each circle. Express your answer to 1 decimal place.

(a)  16 cm

(b) 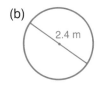 2.4 m

Solution   (a) Use $C = 2 \times \pi \times r$ radius (r), 16 cm

$C \doteq 2 \times 3.14 \times 16$

$\doteq 100.48$

The circumference is 100.5 cm (to 1 decimal place).

Does your calculator have a ⎡π⎤ key? Read your manual. How does it work?

(b) Use $C = \pi \times d$ diameter (d), 2.4 m

$C \doteq 3.14 \times 2.4$

$\doteq 7.536$

The circumference is 7.5 m (to 1 decimal place).

You can use your skills with the circumference to solve problems.

Example 2   The radius of the Ferris wheel in the previous photograph is 16.3 m. How far would you travel in one turn of the wheel? Express your answer to 1 decimal place.

Solution   Use $C = 2\pi r$ ◀——(radius (r), 16.3 m

$C \doteq 2 \times 3.14 \times 16.3$

$\doteq 102.4$ (to 1 decimal place)

The distance travelled in one turn of the Ferris wheel is 102.4 m.

The formulas can also be written as shown.

$C = 2 \times \pi \times r \leftrightarrow C = 2\pi r$

$C = \pi \times d \quad \leftrightarrow C = \pi d$

$\left(\begin{array}{l}\text{The operation of} \\ \text{multiplication is} \\ \text{understood to be here.}\end{array}\right.$

4.6 exercise

A Throughout this exercise use the decimal value 3.14 for π. Decide how you will round off each answer.

1 Find the circumference of each circle.

(a)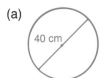
40 cm

(b)
1.6 m

2 Find the circumference of a circle if the diameter is 14.6 m.

3 The radius of a circle is 28.6 cm. Calculate the circumference.

4 The diameter is given for several circles. Calculate the circumference of each circle.

(a) 20 cm   (b) 100 m   (c) 3.6 cm

(d) 14.8 cm   (e) 9.6 m   (f) 712.8 m

(g) 136.9 cm   (h) 461.8 m   (i) 0.75 m

5 The radius is given for several circles. Calculate the circumference of each circle.

(a) 10 cm   (b) 28 cm   (c) 100 cm

(d) 1.5 m   (e) 6.5 m   (f) 12.5 m

(g) 32.6 cm   (h) 16.8 cm   (i) 2.46 cm

6 Copy and complete the table for each circle.

Radius r	Diameter d	Circumference C
340 cm		
	4.8 m	
	18.7 m	

7 (a) Draw a circle with a radius of 9 cm.
   (b) Estimate the circumference.
   (c) Calculate the circumference. How close was your estimate?

8 (a) Draw a circle with diameter 12 cm.
   (b) Estimate the circumference.
   (c) Calculate the circumference. How close was your estimate?

9 Measure each radius. Calculate the circumference of each circle.

A 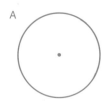   B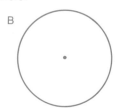

B Use your skills with circumference to solve the following problems.

10 An ordinary basketball has a diameter of about 25 cm. What would be the measure of the circumference?

11 The face off circle at centre ice in hockey has a diameter of 9 m. Find the circumference of the face off circle.

12 Did you know that George Ferris constructed the original Ferris wheel at the midway in Chicago in 1893?

(a) The diameter of the Ferris wheel was 76 m. Calculate the circumference.

(b) The diameter of a Ferris wheel is 28.4 m. Calculate the circumference of the Ferris wheel.

13 Often you don't eat the crust on pizza. For each pizza, estimate the length of pizza you don't eat. Then calculate the length.

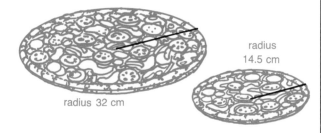

radius 14.5 cm

radius 32 cm

14 The diameter of Marlena's bicycle wheel is 70.5 cm. Calculate how many turns the bicycle wheel will make if she rides the bicycle 1 km.

15 A circular track has a radius of 24.6 m. How many laps would John complete in a 10 km run?

16 Telescopes let us see far into the sky. The largest telescope in the world is in Russia. The circular mirror used in the telescope has a diameter of 600 cm.

(a) Calculate the circumference of the mirror.

(b) Would this mirror fit into your classroom?

17 (a) George measured the diameter of a truck's wheel and found it to be 85.9 cm. Calculate the circumference.

(b) George then measured its circumference and found the value to be 270.5 cm. Why is there a difference in the two answers?

18 A patio umbrella has a diameter 2.5 m.

(a) Calculate the length of fringe needed for the edge of the umbrella.

(b) What is the cost of the fringe at $3.69/m? Check whether your answer is reasonable.

19 How far would you walk to travel around the track?

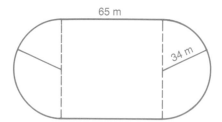

65 m

34 m

20 (a) The diameter of the earth at the equator has been shown to be 12 800 km. Calculate the circumference of the earth at the equator.

(b) The radius of the earth's moon is 1728 km. Calculate the length of the "equator" of the moon.

C

21 To calculate the diameter of a circle when you are given the circumference, use the formula

$$d = \frac{C}{\pi}$$

Calculate the diameter of the circle for each circumference. Round your answer to the nearest centimetre or metre.

(a) 219.9 cm   (b) 502.6 cm

(c) 3.8 m   (d) 11.9 m

22 An aircraft tire turns 115 times in travelling 1 km. What is the diameter of the tire?

4.7 working with area

There are many times you need to use skills with area.
▶ To buy paint for a house, you need to know the area you are painting.
▶ To find the cost of a rug or a carpet, you need to know its size or area.
▶ To wallpaper a room, you need to know the area of the walls.

DO IT YOURSELF

To find the area of a region, a unit of measure is chosen. The number of square units needed to cover the region is called the area of the region. For example, each unit of area shown on the grid represents 1 cm².

A The area of the region is 12 cm².

B The area of the region is 4.5 cm².

C The area of the region is about 13 cm².

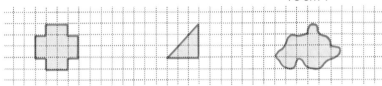

To find the area of an irregular region, such as C, you often need to approximate the area.

To find the area of a rectangular region, you could look for a pattern.

Count the number of square units. The area is 18 m².

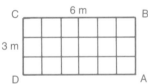

Look for a pattern to find the area:
6 × 3 = 18

length (m)   width (m)   area (m²)

The area is 18 m².

You could calculate the areas of other rectangles by using the relationship shown on the right. This formula, combined with your earlier skills, is used to solve the following problem.

area of rectangle (in square units) → $A = l \times w$ ← measure of width of rectangle

measure of length of rectangle

Example   The dimensions of a rectangular ice rink are 21.5 m by 9.7 m. What is the area for skating? Round your answer to 1 decimal place.

Sketch a diagram to record the information.

Solution $A = l \times w$

$= 21.5 \times 9.7$

length (l), 21.5 m
width (w), 9.7 m

$= 208.55$

The area for skating is 208.6 m².

└─ (Rounded to 1 decimal place)

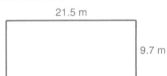
21.5 m
9.7 m

To find the area of some regions, you may need to find the area of its parts. For example, to find the area of the region below, you can simplify your work by first finding the area of A and B.

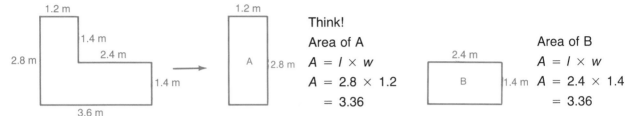

Think!

Area of A	Area of B
$A = l \times w$	$A = l \times w$
$A = 2.8 \times 1.2$	$A = 2.4 \times 1.4$
$= 3.36$	$= 3.36$

To find the area of the entire region add the area of A and B.

Area $= 3.36 \text{ m}^2 + 3.36 \text{ m}^2$

$= 6.72 \text{ m}^2$

The area of the entire region is 6.7 m² to 1 decimal place.

To find the area of a square in the exercise that follows, you use the same formula.

Area of a square

$$A = s \times s$$

measure of each side

Use your calculator. Check your answers for the problems.

4.7 exercise

A In the following exercise be sure to
▶ estimate your answer.
▶ check whether your answer is reasonable.

1 Find the area of each region.

Each square unit represents 1 m².

(a) (b)

(c) (d)

(e)

2 Find the area of each region. represents 1 m²

(a) (b)

(c) (d)

3 For each region:
▶ Estimate its area.
▶ Then find the area.
(a) (b)

4 (a) Find the area of each region. What do you notice about your answers?

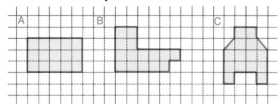

(b) Use your results in (a). Draw 3 different shapes that have an area of 16 cm².

(c) Draw 3 different shapes that have an area of 30 cm².

5 Find the area of each region.

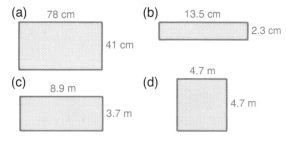

6 Find the area of each region. Round your answers to 1 decimal place.

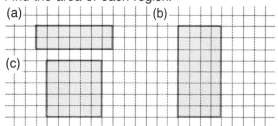

7 For each of the following rectangles, estimate the area, then calculate.
Compare your estimate with the area.

	Length	Width
(a)	12.5 cm	7.3 cm
(b)	37.6 m	12.9 m
(c)	8.76 m	6.3 m
(d)	23.5 cm	15.7 cm
(e)	3.5 m	3.5 m

8 (a) What unit of area would you use to estimate the area of the rectangle below? What is your estimate of the area?

(b) What information do you need to calculate the area of the above rectangle? Find the area.

9 For each of the following rectangles:
► Estimate the area.
► Then calculate the area.

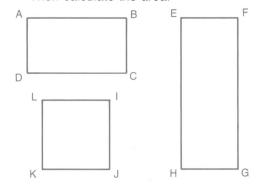

B

10 To find the area of a rectangle, both dimensions need to be expressed in the same units. The dimensions of a rectangle are 6 m by 550 cm.

(a) Write both dimensions as metres. Find the area.

(b) Write both dimensions as centimetres. Find the area.

11 Find the area of a rectangle with dimensions 1.6 km by 860 m.

12 (a) The measures of the sides of a rectangle are 46.2 m and 38.4 m. Find the area to one decimal place.

(b) A side of a square measures 46.9 m. Find the area to the nearest square metre.

13 The measures of the sides of a rectangular field are 102.3 m and 96.2 m. Calculate the area to the nearest tenth.

14 The side of a square measures 263 cm.

(a) Calculate its area.

(b) Write your answer to the nearest square metre.

15 The largest indoor ice rink has measurements 75.2 m by 107.3 m.

(a) Calculate its area.

(b) Each person needs about 20 m² to practise skills. How many persons are on the ice at one time?

16 The cost of sodding an area with grass is $1.65/m². Find the cost of sodding a rectangular backyard 26.3 m by 18.5 m.

17 The width of the flashing is 0.4 m. A litre of aluminum paint covers 9.5 m².

(a) How much paint is needed if the total length of flashing is 29.5 m? You need to apply 2 coats.

(b) What is the cost of the paint at $8.99/L?

18 (a) The area of a rectangle is 9.43 cm². The length is 4.1 cm. Calculate the width.

(b) A rectangle has an area of 804 m². If the width is 24 m, find the length.

19 Complete the chart.

	Sides (m)		Area (m²)	Perimeter (m)
(a)	4.6	4.6		
(b)	3.2		10.24	
(c)		18.6		62.8
(d)	9.6			40.6

20 The perimeter of a square is 486 m. Find its area.

21 The perimeter of a rectangle is 212 m, the width is 48 m.

(a) Find the length of the rectangle.

(b) Find the area of the rectangle.

22 The width of a rectangle is 25.4 m and the area is 825.5 m². Find the length.

23 To enclose a rectangular playground, 420 m of snow fence was used. Find the area, if the length of the playground is 112 m.

24 (a) A grid is placed over the wrapper. Calculate the area.

(b) Find other wrappers. Calculate their areas.

25 (a) A grid is placed over the irregular shaped stamp. Find the area to the nearest square unit. Find the area of other irregular shaped regions.

applications: baseball strike zone

Have you ever played baseball and got a strike? Well, the umpire saw the ball going into your strike zone. A pitcher must throw the ball into the area that lies as shown in the diagram. The shaded area is called the **strike zone**. To calculate the area of the strike zone, you need to know the width and length of the rectangular shape of the strike zone.

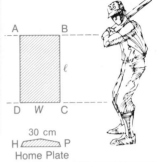

30 cm
Home Plate

26 The strike zones of 3 players are shown. Calculate each area.

(a) (b) (c)

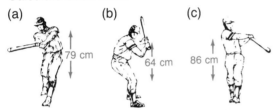

79 cm 64 cm 86 cm

Remember, the width of home plate is 30 cm.

(b) Which player has the greatest strike zone?

27 Calculate the area of each player's strike zone.

(a) (b) (c)

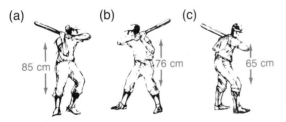

85 cm 76 cm 65 cm

28 For a player, two positions are shown for hitting the ball.

Bunt Position   Home Run Position

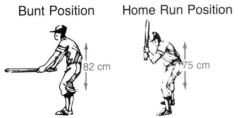

82 cm 75 cm

(a) Calculate the area of each strike zone.

(b) By how much do the strike zone areas differ?

(c) Why is the strike zone in a bunt position greater than in the home run position?

29 The strike zone of a player is 2160 cm². What is the distance between the player's shoulders and knees.

30 Copy and complete the chart.

Player	Distance from shoulder to knees (cm)	Strike zone area (cm²)
Jay Liptay	68	?
Norm Prentice	?	2220
David Wray	83	?
Jeff MacNabb	?	2250

31 Position yourself as you would to bunt the ball.

(a) What is the distance from your shoulder to your knees?

(b) Calculate the area of your strike zone.

(c) Compare the areas of your strike zone for
   ▶ hitting a home run.
   ▶ bunting the ball.
   By how much do they differ?

4.8 patterns: area of a parallelogram

Scientists repeat experiments looking for similarities or patterns in the results.

In mathematics, the same problem-solving technique of looking for patterns is used.

▶ By studying examples of squares and rectangles, you developed formulas to find their perimeters.

▶ Similarly, you developed formulas to find the areas of rectangles and squares.

In both cases, you first looked at numerical examples and noticed patterns. The study of patterns led to the development of a formula. You then used the formula to simplify your calculations.

In the following exercise you will study patterns and develop a formula for finding the area of parallelograms.

Dr. Frederick Banting (right), the discoverer of insulin, is shown with Margery, the first diabetic dog to be treated successfully with insulin, and his assistant Charles Best (left).

To do so, you need to understand the meaning of the terms **base** and **height** of a figure.

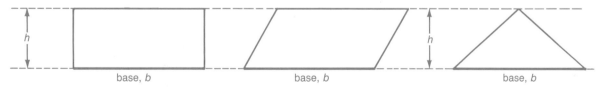

You can also indicate the height within the figure as shown.

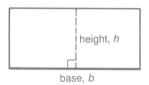
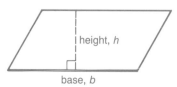
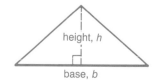

4.8 exercise

A Area of a parallelogram

- ■ represents a unit of area
- ▨ represents $\frac{1}{2}$ unit of area

1 (a) Find the area of each region.

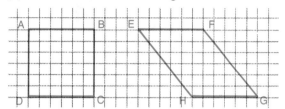

(b) How are the areas of the rectangle and the parallelogram related?

2 Refer to the diagram.

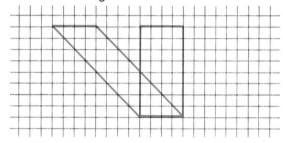

(a) What is the area of the rectangle?

(b) What is the area of the parallelogram?

3 (a) Find the area of the parallelogram ABCD (in square units).

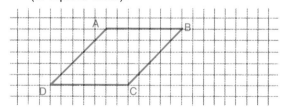

(b) What is the measure of the base? of the height?

(c) Find the product:
    measure of base × *measure of height*

(d) How do your answers in (a) and (c) seem to be related?

4 Copy and complete the chart for these parallelograms. What pattern can you see in your answers?

	Measure of area (A)	Measure of base (b)	Measure of height (h)	Product b × h
fig. 1				
fig. 2				

5 In the diagram, a slide is used to construct a rectangle.

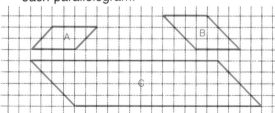

Calculate the area of each region. How do the areas compare?

6 Use squared paper. Draw four parallelograms. For each parallelogram you draw:
  ▶ Construct a related rectangle, as shown in the previous question.
  ▶ Find the area of the parallelogram and the rectangle.

7 Refer to your results in Questions 1 to 6.
  (a) Suggest a formula to calculate the area of a parallelogram.
  (b) Use your formula to calculate the area of each parallelogram.

  (c) Check your results in (b). Find the area of each parallelogram by counting the number of square units.

From your investigations, you found the following formula to calculate the area (A) of a parallelogram

$A = b \times h$

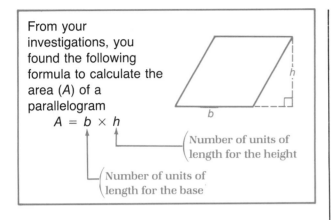

⎛ Number of units of
⎝ length for the height

⎛ Number of units of
⎝ length for the base

B Where needed, round your answers to 1 decimal place.

8 (a) Calculate the area of each parallelogram.

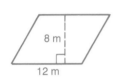

8 m
12 m

12 m
8 m

(b) What do you notice about your answers in (a)? Why is this so?

9 For each parallelogram:
▶ Which is the base? the height?
▶ Calculate the area.

(a)   (b)   (c)

  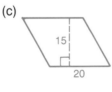

8
12

16
12

15
20

(d)   (e)   (f)

  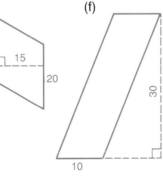

60
40

15
20

30
10

10 For each parallelogram:
▶ Estimate the area.
▶ Then calculate the area.

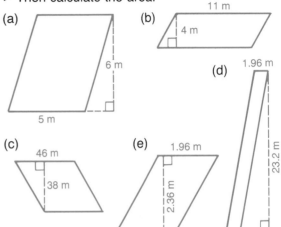

(a)

6 m
5 m

(b) 11 m
4 m

(d) 1.96 m
23.2 m

(c) 46 m
38 m

(e) 1.96 m
2.36 m

11 The height of a parallelogram measures 16 cm and the base is 24 cm. Calculate its area.

12 The base of a parallelogram measures 12.6 cm and the height is 6.8 cm. Calculate the area.

13 (a) A parallelogram has a base that measures 14 cm and a height of 12 cm. Calculate its area.

(b) Calculate the area of a rectangle whose sides measure 14 cm by 12 cm.

(c) What do you notice about your answers in (a) and (b)?

14 Which has the greater area, A or B?
A: A rectangle with dimensions 16.2 m by 8.5 m.
B: A parallelogram with base 16.2 m and height 8.5 m.

15 (a) Estimate which has the greatest area.

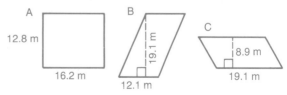

A
12.8 m
16.2 m

B
19.1 m
12.1 m

C
8.9 m
19.1 m

(b) Calculate the areas.

4.9 area of a triangle

In the previous section you developed a formula for the area of a parallelogram by following the steps shown.

In a similar way, you will study patterns and develop a formula for finding the area of a triangle.

Step A You examined numerical cases and looked for a pattern.

Step B You then suggested a formula to find the area of a parallelogram. You tested the formula and found that it was valid.

Step C You applied the formula to solve problems.

4.9 exercise

A Area of a triangle

■ represents a unit of area ◪ represents $\frac{1}{2}$ unit of area

1 (a) Find each area.

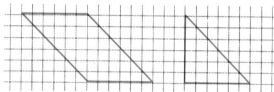

(b) How are the areas of the parallelogram and the triangle related?

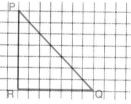

2 (a) Count the squares and half squares. Find the area of the triangle PQR.

(b) What is the measure of its base? height?

(c) Find the product:
measure of base × measure of height

(d) How do the answers in (a) and (c) seem to be related?

3 Draw four triangles on squared paper. Copy and complete the chart for the triangles. How do the answers in the chart seem to be related?

Measure of area (A)	Measure of base (b)	Measure of height (h)	Product b × h

4 For figure 1 and figure 2:

(a) What is the area of ABCD?

(b) Find the area of triangle ACD.

(c) How are the answers in (a) and (b) related?

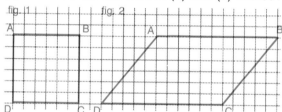

5 Refer to your results in Questions 1 to 4.

(a) Suggest a formula to calculate the area of a triangle.

(b) Use your formula to calculate the area of each triangle.

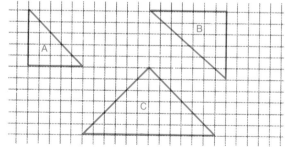

(c) Check your results in (b). Find the area of each triangle by counting the number of square units in each area.

From your investigations on the previous page, you found the following formula:

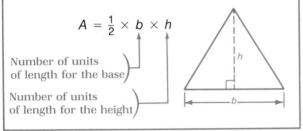

$$A = \tfrac{1}{2} \times b \times h$$

Number of units of length for the base

Number of units of length for the height

B Where needed, round your answers to 1 decimal place.

6 For each triangle:
- ▶ Which is the base? the height?
- ▶ Calculate the area.

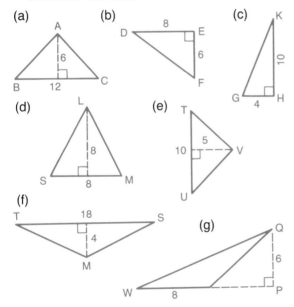

(a)

(b)

(c)

(d)

(e)

(f)

(g)

7 (a) Calculate the area of each triangle.

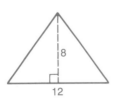 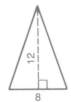

(b) What do you notice about your answers in (a)? Why is this so?

8 For each triangle, calculate the area.

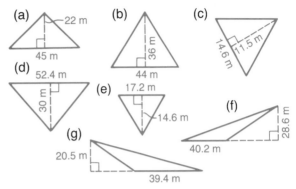

(a)   22 m   45 m
(b)   36 m   44 m
(c)   14.6 m   11.5 m
(d)   52.4 m   30 m
(e)   17.2 m   14.6 m
(f)   40.2 m   28.6 m
(g)   20.5 m   39.4 m

9 For each triangle:
- ▶ Estimate the area.
- ▶ Then calculate the area.

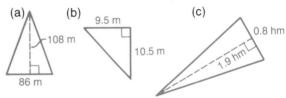

(a)   108 m   86 m
(b)   9.5 m   10.5 m
(c)   0.8 hm   1.9 hm

10 Which has the greater area, A or B?
- A: A triangle with height 16.2 m and base 8.5 m.
- B: A parallelogram with base 16.2 m and height 8.5 m.

11 Estimate which has the greatest area, then calculate.

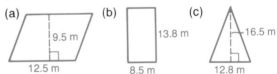

(a)   9.5 m   12.5 m
(b)   13.8 m   8.5 m
(c)   16.5 m   12.8 m

12 Copy and complete the chart.

	Measure of base of triangle	Measure of height of triangle	Area of triangle
(a)	46 cm	28 cm	
(b)	14.3 cm	18.6 cm	
(c)	78.2 cm	12.9 cm	
(d)	6.46 m	8.35 m	
(e)	0.48 m	0.86 m	

13 The measures of the height and base of a triangle are respectively 12.86 m and 8.96 m. Calculate the area to the nearest hundredth.

14 The base of a triangle measures 12 cm. The height is 36 cm. Calculate the area.

15 The height of a triangle measures 16.8 cm and the base is 24.8 cm. Calculate the area.

16 A protected area of land is in the shape of a triangle with base 3.2 km and height 2.6 km.

(a) Calculate its area.

(b) Write the area in hectares.

17 Strathcona Provincial Park on Vancouver Island is approximately in the shape of a triangle, as shown.

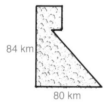

84 km

80 km

Estimate the area;

In Strathcona Park, one of the world's highest waterfalls can be found. The park itself is nestled among spectacular snowcapped peaks that protect the abundant wildlife in this sanctuary.

18 Highway 39 outside of Regina meets the Trans-Canada Highway and Highway 6 as shown. Calculate the area of the tract of land bounded by these highways.

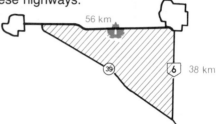

56 km

39   6   38 km

19 Refer to the diagram. The forward sail is called the jib.

(a) Calculate the area of the jib.

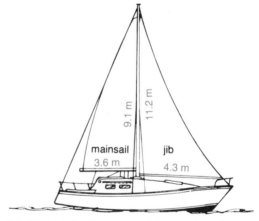

9.1 m   11.2 m

mainsail   jib
3.6 m   4.3 m

(b) Calculate the area of the mainsail.

(c) Which sail has a greater area, the jib or the mainsail? By how much?

(d) The material used in the sail costs $6.95/m². How much is the material in each sail worth?

20 Calculate the area of each stamp. Express your answer to the nearest square millimetre (mm²).

1.4 cm

3.2 cm

1.1 cm

3.4 cm

3.5 cm

5.2 cm

4.10 applications: area of a circle

To find the area of a circular region you can place a grid on the circular region. Then count squares and part squares. The approximate area of the circular region shown is 50 cm².

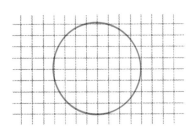

Using a grid to find the area of a circle is time consuming. You will develop a way of finding the area of a circle using a formula. A circle is marked off in sectors, as shown in Step A.
In Step B the semi-circles are separated. From your previous work with the perimeter of a circle, you know the length of the semi-circle is πr units ($\frac{1}{2}$ of the circumference).
The sectors are then separated in Steps C and D.

Step A

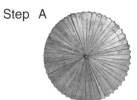

Step B

Step C

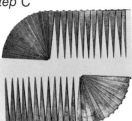

Step D

Fit these sectors together to form a figure that is an approximate rectangle.

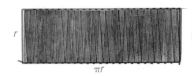

The area of the circle has been arranged as an almost rectangular region. If you increased the numbers of sectors in the circle, the base of the rectangular region would become closer and closer to a straight line.

The area of a rectangle is found by using the product
measure of base × *measure of height*
► base is πr units   ► height is r units

The area of the circle, A, is developed as
$$A = b \times h$$
$$= (\pi \times r) \times r$$
$$= \pi \times r \times r$$

The formula for the area of a circle can be written as
$$A = \pi \times r \times r \quad or \quad A = \pi r^2$$

Exponents are used to write the formula in a compact form.

Example 1   Find the area of each circle. Use $\pi \doteq 3.14$.

(a)
12 cm

(b)
10 m

Round each answer to 1 decimal place.

Solution   (a) Use the formula:

$A = \pi \times r \times r$ $r = 12$
$A \doteq 3.14 \times 12 \times 12$ (in centimetres)

$\doteq 452.16$

The area of the circle is
452.2 cm² (to one decimal place).

(b) Use the formula:

$A = \pi r^2$ $d = 10$ (in metres)
$A \doteq 3.14(5)^2$ $r = 5$ (in metres)

$\doteq 3.14(25)$

$\doteq 78.5$
The area of the circle is
78.5 m² (to one decimal place).

Once you learn the skills for finding the area of a circle, you apply them to solve problems.

Example 2   A helicopter landing platform is circular with a radius of 12.4 m.
(a) Calculate the area.
(b) What is the cost of building the platform at $28.90/m²?

Sketch a diagram to show the information.

Solution   (a) $A = \pi r^2$ $r = 12.4$ (in metres)

$A \doteq 3.14(12.4)^2$

$\doteq 3.14(153.76)$

$\doteq 482.8$

12.4 m

(b) Cost of 1 m² is $28.90.
Cost of the platform is 482.8 × $28.90 or
$13 953.

Remember to check whether your answer is reasonable.
$500 \times 30 = 15\ 000$
$13\ 953 \doteq 15\ 000$

4.10 exercise

A   Throughout the exercise, use $\pi \doteq 3.14$. Round your answers to 1 decimal place.

1 For the circle:

(a) What is the measure of the radius?

(b) Calculate the area of the circle.

20 cm

2 For the circle:

(a) What is the measure of the radius?

(b) Calculate the area of the circle.

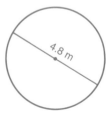
4.8 m

3 Match each calculation with the appropriate circle. Then find the area.

(a) $A \doteq 3.14 \times 10 \times 10$

(b) $A \doteq 3.14 \times 15 \times 15$

(c) $A \doteq 3.14 \times (5)^2$

(d) $A \doteq 3.14 \times (50)^2$

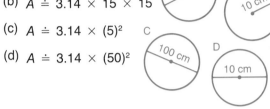

4 Estimate the area of each circle. Then calculate.

(a) radius 10 cm

(b) diameter 12 m

(c) radius 14.6 cm

(d) diameter 6.5 cm

5 The dimensions are shown for each circle. Calculate each area. Check whether your answers are reasonable.

(a) (b) (c)

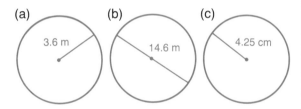

6 Copy and complete the chart.

	Radius	Diameter	Area
(a)	12 cm	?	?
(b)	?	6.8 m	?
(c)	16.5 cm	?	?

7 Refer to the diagram of the circle.

(a) Estimate the area of the circle.

(b) Use the formula. Find the area of the circle.

(c) How do your answers compare?

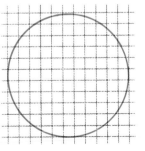

B

8 For each circle:

▶ Measure the diameter to the nearest millimetre.

▶ Then calculate the area of the circle.

(a) (b)

(c)

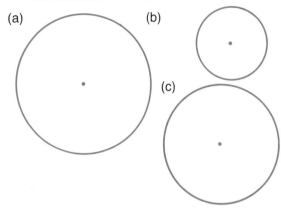

9 (a) Which circle has the greater area? By how much?

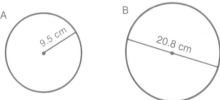

(b) Estimate which has the greater area, A or B.

Square with sides 10 cm   Circle with radius 6 cm

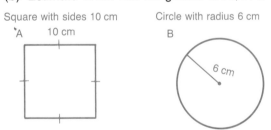

Calculate each area.

10 (a) The discus used in the Olympics is circular. Its radius is about 11 cm. Calculate the area of the discus.

(b) In throwing the discus, an athlete uses a circular area to work up a spin. The diameter of the circle is approximately 2.8 m. Calculate the area of this circular area.

11 An aircraft patrols the sky as shown. The area of observation has a radius of 14.5 km. Calculate the area.

14.5 km

12 The shotput is an Olympic track and field event. The athlete shoots the shotput from a circle 2.1 m in diameter. Calculate the area of the circle.

13 The umbrella has a radius 1.3 m.

   (a) Calculate the area.

   (b) What is the approximate area of each section of the umbrella?

14 (a) Find the area of the top of the pie.

   (b) How many top crusts could be cut from a rectangular sheet of dough 2.5 m by 1.5 m?

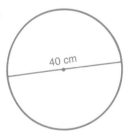
40 cm

15 Calculate the area of each shaded area.

   (a)   (b)   (c)

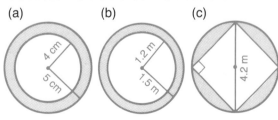
4 cm / 5 cm   1.2 m / 1.5 m   4.2 m

(d)   (e)   (f)

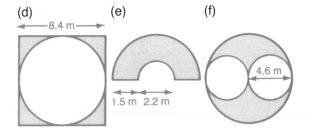
← 8.4 m →
1.5 m 2.2 m
4.6 m

16 The surface markings of a basketball court are shown. Ralph and Debbie measured the distances marked on the diagram.

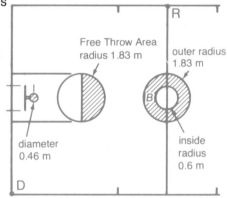
R
Free Throw Area radius 1.83 m
outer radius 1.83 m
B
diameter 0.46 m
inside radius 0.6 m
D

   (a) Calculate the area of the free throw semi-circle.
   (b) Calculate the area of the shaded area at centre court.
   (c) Debbie is standing at D. Her furthest throw with a basketball is 12.2 m. What area can she cover?
   (d) Ralph is standing at R. His furthest throw with a basketball is 11.5 m. What area can be covered?
   (e) Create a problem based on the above information. Write a solution for your problem.

C
17 Before you do any calculations, make an estimate of your answer to the following question.
   Which has the greater area, A or B?
   A: two circles, each with a radius of 5 cm
   B: one circle with a radius 10 cm

18 Two circles each have a radius of 12 cm. Estimate the radius of one circle that has an area equal to the area of the two circles.

4.11 patterns for volume

Containers and packages occur in many different sizes and shapes. The shapes shown have something in common. They are all prisms.

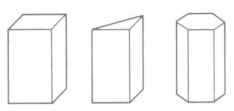

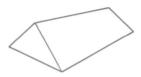

▶ How are the prisms alike?   ▶ How are they different?

Both ends of a prism have the same shape and size. The sides of prisms are always rectangular in shape.

The volume of a solid or a prism is the amount of space the solid occupies. Volume is measured in cubic units such as cubic metres (m³) or cubic centimetres (cm³). The capacity of a container is the amount of substance the container can hold. Capacity is also measured in cubic units, as well as in litres (L).

A rectangular solid is shown as an example of a prism. To find the volume of a rectangular solid you can count the number of cubic units in one layer, then count the number of layers.

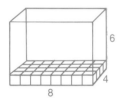

represents 1 cm³

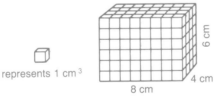

There are 8 × 4 or 32 cubic units in one layer.
There are 6 layers.

Volume is 6 × 32 cm³ or 192 cm³.

Volumes of other rectangular solids are found. Based on the data in the chart, a formula is developed to find its volume.

Length (l)	Width (w)	Height (h)	Volume (V)
6	4	3	72
5	4	4	80
8	5	3	120
8	6	2	96

From the data, the formula suggested is $V = l \times w \times h$.

To count the number of cubic units each time is time consuming. You can also use a pattern or formula to find the volume.

Volume ⟶ $V = l \times w \times h$ ⟵ measure of the height

measure of the length ⤴   measure of the width ⤴

You can think of the formula from a different point of view.

$V = l \times w \times h$

$= B \times h$ ⟵ height of solid / area of the base of the solid

The product $l \times w$ gives the area of the base.

You can use this form of the formula to find the volume of any prism.

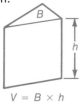 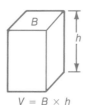 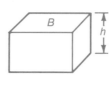

$V = B \times h$ $V = B \times h$ $V = B \times h$ $V = B \times h$

Example

Calculate the volume of each prism. Express your answer to one decimal place.

(To calculate the volume of prisms, the dimensions must be in the same units.)

(a)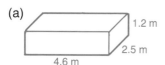

1.2 m
2.5 m
4.6 m

(b)

1.2 m
2.6 m
350 cm

Solution

(a) For a rectangular prism, use

$V = l \times w \times h$

$V = 4.6 \times 2.5 \times 1.2$

$= 13.8$

The volume is 13.8 m³.

(b) For a prism, use

$V = B \times h$

$V = 1.56 \times 3.5$ ◄—(Write 350 cm as 3.5 m.

$= 5.46$

$\left(\begin{array}{l} B = \frac{1}{2} \times 2.6 \times 1.2 \\ = 1.56 \end{array} \right.$

The volume is 5.5 m³ (to one decimal place)

To find the volume of some solids, you may need to think of two prisms. For example,

To find the volume of the solid

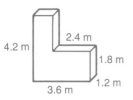

2.4 m
4.2 m
1.8 m
1.2 m
3.6 m

find the volume of A and B

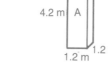

4.2 m   A
1.2 m
1.2 m

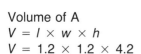

B   1.8 m
1.2 m
2.4 m

Volume of A
$V = l \times w \times h$
$V = 1.2 \times 1.2 \times 4.2$
$= 6.048$

Volume of B
$V = l \times w \times h$
$V = 2.4 \times 1.2 \times 1.8$
$= 5.184$

Total volume
6.048 m³
5.184 m³
11.232 m³

The volume of the solid is 11.2 m³ (to one decimal place).

To find answers to problems about volume and capacity you need to use a relationship you learned earlier.

Remember: 1 L = 1000 cm³ or 1 mL = 1 cm³

4.11 exercise

A Round off your answers to 1 decimal place unless otherwise indicated.

1 Find the volume of each rectangular solid.

(a) represents 1 cm³

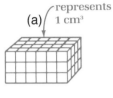

(b)

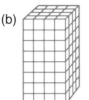

(c)

(d)

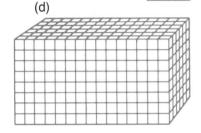

(e)

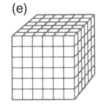

2 For each rectangular solid, calculate its volume.

(a)

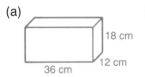

18 cm
36 cm
12 cm

(b)

5.2 m
3.6 m
4.2 m

3 For each of the following:
▶ Estimate the volume.
▶ Then calculate the volume.

(a)

3.6 cm
6.5 cm
4.6 cm

(b)

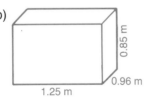

0.85 m
1.25 m
0.96 m

4 For each rectangular solid:
▶ Calculate the area of the base.
▶ Then calculate the volume.

(a)

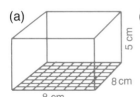

5 cm
8 cm
8 cm

(b)

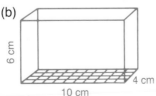

6 cm
10 cm
4 cm

5 The length, width, and height of each box is given.
▶ Estimate the volume. Then calculate.
▶ Check whether your answer is reasonable.

	Measure of width	Measure of height	Measure of length
(a)	14 cm	86 cm	92 cm
(b)	23 m	46 m	28 m
(c)	1.6 cm	2.3 cm	4.5 cm
(d)	4.8 m	9.6 m	9.6 m
(e)	1.39 cm	2.50 cm	4.70 cm
(f)	9.86 m	5.00 m	2.81 m

6 Calculate the volume of each prism.

(a)

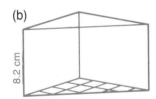

2.3 m

(b)

8.2 cm

7 Calculate the volume of each prism.

	Area of base, *B*	Height, *h*
(a)	46.5 cm²	12.5 cm
(b)	123.2 m²	40.3 m

8 For each prism
▶ Calculate the area of the base.
▶ Then calculate the volume.

(a)

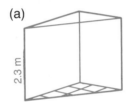

6.5 cm
5.2 cm
12.6 cm

(Check whether your answer is reasonable.

(b)

8.3 m
4.6 m
4.8 m

(c)

4.2 m
3.5 m
12.6 m

(d)

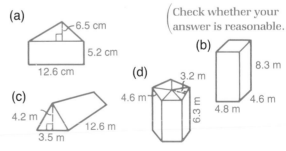

3.2 m
4.6 m
6.3 m

9 The area of the base of a triangular prism is 160 cm². If the height is 20 cm, calculate its volume.

10 The height of a prism is 5.2 m. The base of the prism has an area of 20.6 m². Calculate its volume.

B

11 Each container shows a common item. Find the capacity of each box.

12 Use the dimensions shown for the cereal boxes.

(a) Estimate the volume of each box. Then calculate.

(b) Which box holds more? How much more?

13 Copy and complete the chart for rectangular prisms.

	Length	Width	Height	Volume
(a)	25 cm	15 cm	?	7500 cm³
(b)	1.8 m	?	3.0 m	60.75 m³
(c)	?	3.2 cm	4.5 cm	69.12 cm³

14 The dimensions of a rectangular room are 3.5 m by 4.5 m by 3.1 m.

(a) Calculate its volume.

(b) The cost of heating the air in the room is 1.5¢/m³. Find the cost.

C

15 An aquarium tank is 60.5 cm long, 28.6 cm wide, and 22.3 cm deep.

(a) Calculate how many litres of water the tank will hold when full.

(b) The tank is filled so that the water is 3.8 cm from the top. Calculate how much water is in the tank.

(c) The mass of 1 cm³ (1 mL) of water is 1 g. The mass of the empty tank is 3.65 kg. Calculate the total mass of the aquarium if the tank is filled to within 3.8 cm of the top.

skills quiz

(a) The sides of a square measure 4.6 cm. Find its perimeter.

(b) The base and height of a triangle measure 3.9 cm and 4.8 cm. Find its area.

(c) Find the area of a square whose side measures 9.6 m.

(d) The measures of the width and length of a rectangle are 4.65 m and 12.96 m. Find the perimeter.

(e) Find the area of the rectangle in (d).

(f) The base and height of a parallelogram measure 14.6 m and 12.96 m. Calculate the area.

(g) The sides of a triangle measure 12.69 cm, 18.45 cm, and 14.36 cm. Find the perimeter.

(h) The perimeter of a square is 576 cm. Find the measure of its sides.

(i) The perimeter of a triangle is 146.3 cm. Two sides measure 64.6 cm and 48.9 cm. Find the measure of the third side.

4.12 applications with cylinders

How are the shapes shown alike? How are they different? The shapes shown are cylinders.

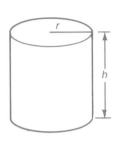

To calculate the volume of a prism you can use the formula:

$$V = B \times h$$

volume ← V

height of prism ← h

area of base ← B

To calculate the volume of a cylinder you use the same concept.

$$V = B \times h$$

volume of cylinder   area of base   height of cylinder

$$V = (\pi \times r \times r) \times h \quad \text{or} \quad V = \pi r^2 \times h$$

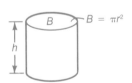

$B = \pi r^2$

The formula is used to calculate the volume of a cylinder in the following example.

Example How much does the can hold? Express your answer to the nearest cubic centimetre.

Solution Use the formula

$$V = \pi \times r \times r \times h$$

$$V \doteq 3.14 \times 4 \times 4 \times 4.5$$

$$\doteq 226.08$$

The can holds 226 cm³ (to the nearest cubic centimetre).

Since 1 cm³ = 1 mL, you could also write:
The can holds 226 mL.

4 cm

4.5 cm

4.12 exercise

A Use the approximate value 3.14 for π.
Decide how you will round off each answer.

1 Calculate the area of the base or top of each
cylinder.

(a)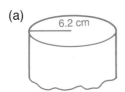
6.2 cm

(b)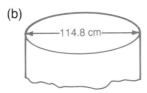
──114.8 cm──

2 The area of the base of each cylinder is shown.
Find the volume.

(a)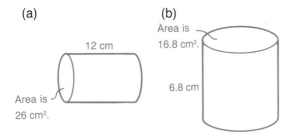

12 cm

Area is
26 cm².

(b)
Area is
16.8 cm².

6.8 cm

3 Copy and complete the chart for each cylinder.

	Area of base	Height	Volume
(a)	4.8 m²	3.2 m	?
(b)	12.6 cm²	8.5 cm	?
(c)	9.6 km²	8.6 km	?

4 For each cylinder, two answers are given for
the volume. Which answer is reasonable,
A or B?

	Radius	Height	A	B
(a)	10 cm	10 cm	31.4 cm³	3140 cm³
(b)	5 cm	10 cm	785 cm³	78 500 cm³
(c)	2 m	5 m	62.8 m³	6.28 m³
(d)	5 m	6 m	47.1 m³	471 m³

5 For each cylinder:
  ▶ Calculate the area of the base.
  ▶ Then calculate the volume.

(a)   (b)   (c)

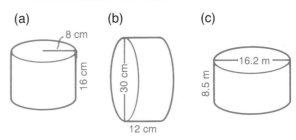

8 cm

16 cm

30 cm

12 cm

16.2 m

8.5 m

6 Various measures are given for cylinders. Copy
and complete the table.

	Radius of base r	Height h	Volume V
(a)	2 cm	7 cm	?
(b)	4 cm	16 cm	?
(c)	4.6 m	3.7 m	?
(d)	4.3 cm	12.6 cm	?

7 For each cylinder:
  ▶ Estimate its volume.
  ▶ Then calculate.

(a)   (b)   (c)

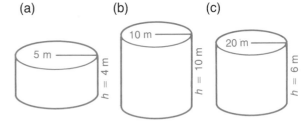

5 m

h = 4 m

10 m

h = 10 m

20 m

h = 6 m

8 (a) The diameter of a cylinder is 18 cm. The
    height is 12 cm. Calculate its volume.

  (b) The height of a can is 16.8 cm. The radius
    of the can is 8.5 cm. Find its volume.

  (c) George measured the height and diameter
    of a can to be 14.6 cm and 10.6 cm
    respectively. Calculate the volume.

B

9 Calculate the capacity of each container.

10 Which can holds more? Before you calculate, estimate your answer.
   A: A can with a radius of 4.2 cm and a height of 12.6 cm.
   B: A can with a diameter of 8.2 cm and a height of 12.8 cm.

11 The dimensions of three cans are shown.

   (a) Estimate which can holds the most.

   (b) Calculate the volume of each can.

   (c) Compare your answers in (a) and (b). How close were you?

12 A well is 12.5 m deep. The width of the well is 75 cm. Calculate the amount of material removed to construct the well.

13 Lisa drinks 6 glasses of water a day. The dimensions of her glass are shown.

   (a) Calculate the volume of water she drinks in a day.

   (b) Calculate the volume of water she drinks in a year.

   (c) What assumptions did you make to find your answers in (a) and in (b)?

   (d) How much of your classroom would this volume of water fill?

14 A juice can has a height of 8 cm. The radius of the base is 5.2 cm.

   (a) How many millilitres of juice will the can hold? Remember, 1 mL = 1 cm³.

   (b) What assumption did you make to find your answer in (a)?

15 The height of an oil drum is 1.8 m. The radius is 58 cm. How many kilolitres of oil will the drum hold? (Remember, 1 kL = 1 m³.)

16 The largest cherry pie was cylindrical in shape with a diameter of 44 m and a depth of 61 cm.

   (a) Calculate the volume of the pie.

   (b) Each person was given a portion of 300 cm³ of pie. How many persons could the pie feed?

   (c) What assumption did you make in finding your answer in (b)?

C

17 Wax candles are made with the dimensions shown. Blocks of wax with dimensions 13.5 cm by 7.5 cm by 7.5 cm are used to make the candles. How many candles can be made from 5 blocks of wax?

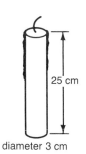

4.13 finding surface area

As a consumer you are concerned about how much a container holds. However, the manufacturer is also concerned with how much material is needed to make each container. The material needed to construct a box in the shape of a cube is shown. The **pattern** or **net** used to make the cube is shown.

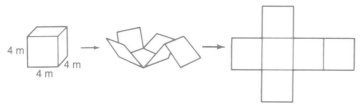

To calculate the surface area of a cube or any prism, you need to calculate the total area of the faces or surfaces.

Area of 1 face $= 16 \text{ m}^2$

Total area $\quad = 6 \times 16 \text{ m}^2$

$\qquad\qquad\;\; = 96 \text{ m}^2$

The surface area of the cube is 96 m^2.

To calculate the surface area of a cylinder you again calculate the total area of the surfaces of the cylinder.

▶ The cylinder shown below is made of three parts: two ends and a curved surface.

▶ The net can be drawn as shown.

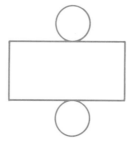

The ends of the cylinder are circular, so you can find the area of each end using the relationship: $A = \pi \times r \times r \quad (A = \pi r^2)$

The distance, C, around the can is the same as the measure of the circumference of the end.

$\qquad C = 2 \times \pi \times r \quad \text{or} \quad C = \pi \times d$

For the curved surface of the can, a rectangular piece is used with measures as shown, where h is the height of the can. The area of the curved surface, A, is given by:

$\qquad A = C \times h$

Example

Find the surface area of the can. Express your answer to the nearest square centimetre.

4 cm

12 cm

Solution

Step 1

Find the area, A, of each end of the can.

$A = \pi \times r \times r$

$A \doteq 3.14 \times 4 \times 4$

$ \doteq 50.24$

Total area of two ends $= 2 \times 50.24$ cm²
$ = 100.48$ cm²

Total surface area of the can is given by
curved surface   301.44 cm²
two ends   100.48 cm²
                401.92 cm²

Thus, the surface area of the cylinder is 402 cm² (to the nearest square centimetre).

Step 2

Find the area of the curved surface.

$C = 2\pi r$

$C \doteq 2 \times 3.14 \times 4$

$ \doteq 25.12$

The area of the curved surface of the can is given by

$C \times h = 25.12 \times 12$
$ = 301.44$

The area of the curved surface is 301.44 cm².

Check your work with a calculator.

4.13 exercise

A ▸ Use 3.14 for π.
  ▸ Decide how to round off each answer.

1 Find the surface area of each net.

(a)

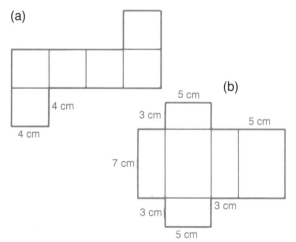
4 cm
4 cm

(b)
5 cm
3 cm
5 cm
7 cm
3 cm
3 cm
5 cm

(c)

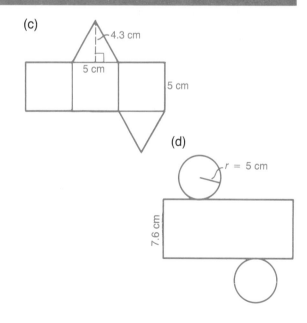
4.3 cm
5 cm
5 cm

(d)
$r = 5$ cm
7.6 cm

2 (a) Draw a net for the following box.

3.8 cm
4.6 cm
6.9 cm

(b) Calculate the surface area of the box.

3 (a) Construct a net for the prism.

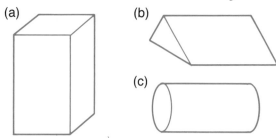

10 cm 8 cm
6 cm
12 cm 10 cm

(b) Calculate the surface area of the prism.

4 Construct a net for each of the following.

(a)

(b)

(c)

B

5 Calculate the surface area for each solid.

(a)

3.6 cm
3.8 cm
3.6 cm

(b)

9.8 cm
12.8 cm
14.6 cm

(c)

1.96 cm
48 cm
55 cm

(d) a rectangular solid with dimensions 3.5 m by 2.5 m by 1.5 m

(e) a cube with sides measuring 40.5 cm

6 Find the surface area of each cylinder.

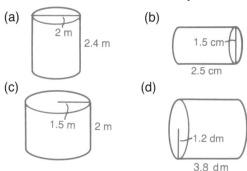

(a)

2 m
2.4 m

(b)

1.5 cm
2.5 cm

(c)

1.5 m
2 m

(d)

1.2 dm
3.8 dm

7 The height of a sealed can is 10 cm. The diameter is 9.4 cm.

(a) Make a sketch of the can and its measurements.

(b) Calculate the surface area.

8 A tomato can is 12.4 cm in height and has a radius of 4.1 cm. Find the area of the label used on the can. (Include 5 cm² used to overlap and glue the label together.)

9 The storage shed shown is made from tin. Calculate the amount of tin used.

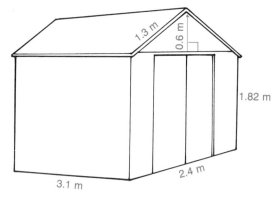

1.3 m
0.6 m
1.82 m
3.1 m
2.4 m

10 Collect various boxes from the store.

(a) Take the necessary measurements and calculate
   ▶ the volume
   ▶ the total surface area of each box.

(b) Compare the volumes. Which type of box is most commonly found?

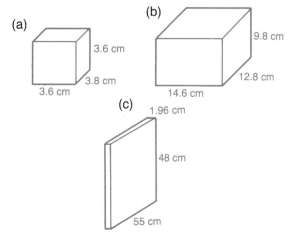

4.14 problem-solving: a strategy

Often methods you develop for finding a known quantity can be used to solve for an unknown quantity. For the circle, you already have a method of determining its area.

From the diagram, count the number of squares.

> Greatest area = 216 square units
> Smallest area = 180 square units

Find the average.

> The area is about $\frac{216 + 180}{2}$ or 198 square units Compare this value to the area from $A = \pi r^2$.

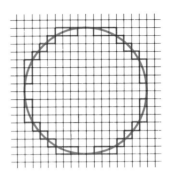

1 For each circle, find the approximate area by counting.

(a) (b)

(c) (d)

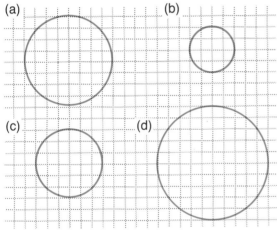

2 Use the data in Question 1. Copy and complete the chart to 1 decimal place.

A Circle	B Area	C Radius	D Calculate area ÷ (radius)^2
(a)	?	?	?
(b)	?	?	?
(c)	?	?	?
(d)	?	?	?

What do you notice about your answers in column D?

3 Find the approximate area of each figure.

(a) (b)

(c)

(d)

(e)

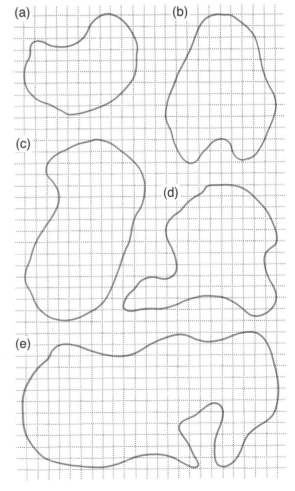

test for practice

1 Find the perimeter of each figure.

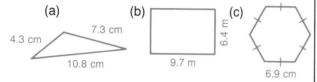

(a) 4.3 cm 7.3 cm 10.8 cm

(b) 9.7 m 6.4 m

(c) 6.9 cm

2 Find the area of each figure.

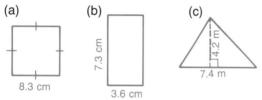

(a) 8.3 cm

(b) 7.3 cm 3.6 cm

(c) 4.2 m 7.4 m

3 Find the volume and surface area of each figure.

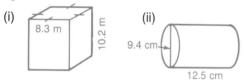

(i) 8.3 m 10.2 m

(ii) 9.4 cm 12.5 cm

4 Find the missing values ■.

(a) $3.5 \text{ m} = ■ \text{ cm}$ (b) $3154 \text{ cm}^2 = ■ \text{ m}^2$

(c) $12\,465 \text{ cm}^3 = ■ \text{ m}^3$ (d) $12.3 \text{ mL} = ■ \text{ cm}^3$

5 Choose a unit to measure

(a) the amount of air in a room.

(b) the surface area of a baseball field.

6 Find each area.

(a) top of a triangular cheese wedge with base 9.7 cm and height 0.063 m.

(b) parallelogram with base 13.6 m and height 236 cm.

(c) circular pitcher's mound with diameter of 2.4 m.

7 A bicycle wheel has radius 0.265 m. Find the circumference of, and the area inside the rim.

maintaining skills: metric

Find the value of ■ in each of the following.

1 (a) $5 \text{ mL} = ■ \text{ L}$ (b) $6 \text{ kg} = ■ \text{ g}$

(c) $■ \text{ km} = 28 \text{ m}$ (d) $7400 \text{ mL} = ■ \text{ L}$

(e) $46 \text{ g} = ■ \text{ mg}$ (f) $■ \text{ m} = 496 \text{ mm}$

(g) $■ \text{ mm} = 48 \text{ cm}$ (h) $1125 \text{ g} = ■ \text{ kg}$

2 (a) $3.2 \text{ m} = ■ \text{ cm}$ (b) $■ \text{ L} = 147 \text{ mL}$

(c) $8.5 \text{ kg} = ■ \text{ g}$ (d) $■ \text{ mm} = 3.6 \text{ cm}$

(e) $■ \text{ mg} = 23 \text{ kg}$ (f) $■ \text{ cm} = 8.4 \text{ m}$

(g) $2916 \text{ m} = ■ \text{ km}$ (h) $8.5 \text{ km} = ■ \text{ m}$

(i) $396 \text{ mg} = ■ \text{ g}$ (j) $■ \text{ g} = 9.6 \text{ kg}$

(k) $200 \text{ mL} = ■ \text{ dL}$ (l) $2500 \text{ mL} = ■ \text{ L}$

(m) $■ \text{ t} = 3000 \text{ kg}$ (n) $0.296 \text{ kg} = ■ \text{ g}$

(o) $650 \text{ mL} = ■ \text{ cL}$ (p) $0.96 \text{ t} = ■ \text{ kg}$

(q) $12 \text{ dm} = ■ \text{ cm}$ (r) $■ \text{ L} = 39.26 \text{ cL}$

(s) $0.36 \text{ t} = ■ \text{ kg}$ (t) $■ \text{ mm} = 23.6 \text{ cm}$

(u) $8654 \text{ mL} = ■ \text{ L}$ (v) $26 \text{ cL} = ■ \text{ L}$

problem-solving: strategy

To solve some problems you need to work backwards. Solve this problem by working backwards.

Jenny, Jan, Jean, and Jo have a total of $150. Jenny had twice as much money as Jan, and Jan has twice as much money as Jean. Jean has twice as much money as Jo. How much money do Jenny, Jan, Jean and Jo have?

math tip

List the mathematical symbols, words and skills that you have learned in this chapter. Give an example for each. Include in your list any other symbols, words, or skills that you learn in the following pages.

5

working with geometries and constructions

Language of geometry, constructions, angles, triangles, working with translations, reflections, rotations, symmetry, concept of congruence, co-ordinate geometry, polyhedra, and perspective, problem solving skills, solving problems and applications

Everywhere you look you see examples of geometry.

Geometry in Architecture

Geometry in Movement

The influence of geometry is all about you. Throughout this chapter you will study different types of geometry, which you call geometries.

▶ In **plane geometry** you will study relations and properties among figures.

▶ In **co-ordinate geometry** you will locate points and figures on the plane.

▶ In **transformational geometry** you will study the properties and applications of translations, reflections and rotations. In a later chapter you will also study size transformation or dilatations.

Geometry in Nature

Throughout the study of geometry, a clear understanding of the **vocabulary** and **concepts** will play an important role in your future work in mathematics. Throughout this chapter continue to collect the meanings of mathematical words. Illustrate their meanings with examples and diagrams.

5.1 language of geometry

To study geometry you need to learn the language of geometry.

Words to know

▶ A **point** shows position and is a "building block" of geometry. Capital letters are used to name points.

▶ Two points, A and B, name a **straight line**. The arrows show that the line extends in each direction. (You will use *line* to mean *straight line*.)

▶ **Line segment** AB is part of a line. It has end points A and B. Its length can be measured. Line segment AB has the same length as line segment CD. Line segment AB is said to be **congruent** to line segment CD.

▶ AB is also part of a line. It is called a **ray**. It starts at an end point A and extends indefinitely in one direction.

▶ An **angle** BAC is constructed from two rays as shown. These rays are often referred to as the **arms** of the angle. When naming an angle the letter at the vertex of the angle is always written in the middle. Two angles are *congruent* if they have equal measures.

To work with geometry, you need to learn the vocabulary and the meaning of symbols.

point • A

A is the vertex

The name of the angle is ∠BAC or ∠CAB

Tools to use

Certain tools for geometry are used to help in your study. For example, a protractor can be used to measure and construct angles. The centre of the protractor is placed at the vertex of the angle. The base line of the protractor lies along one of the rays of the angle.

There are two scales on the protractor to measure or construct angles in different positions. To measure or construct the angle, always start from 0 on the scale.

To measure ∠PQR or construct ∠PQR.

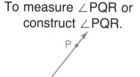

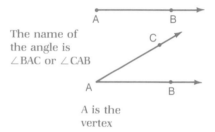

PQ passes through measure showing 52°.

Always measure from the zero.

The measure of ∠PQR = 52°.

Compasses can be used to draw circles.
▶ The **centre** of the circle is at the metal point.
▶ The pencil point is on the circle. The **radius** is the distance between the pencil point and metal point.

5.1 exercise

A

1 Refer to the diagram.
   (a) Name the three lines drawn.

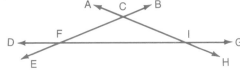

   (b) Name three different angles.
   (c) Name three different line segments and rays.

2 Refer to the diagram. What is the measure of each angle?

   (a) ∠ROF   (b) ∠ROE   (c) ∠ROC

   (d) ∠AOR   (e) ∠BOR   (f) ∠DOR

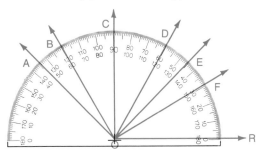

3 Measure the following angles and state which pair of angles is congruent.

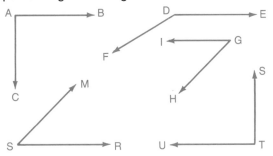

4 Construct each circle

   (a) with radius 6 cm   (b) with radius 4.5 cm

   (c) with diameter 10 cm ⎛ Remember: the radius is
                            ⎝ $\frac{1}{2}$ of the diameter.

B

5 For each angle drawn below:
   ▶ Choose the best estimated measure from those given to the right.
   ▶ Then measure.

   (i)   75°
   (ii) 180°
   (iii) 45°
   (iv) 120°
   (v)   90°
   (vi) 340°

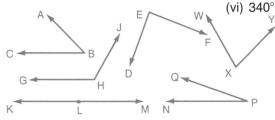

6 Refer to the diagram. Name
   ▶ two pairs of congruent line segments.
   ▶ two pairs of congruent angles.

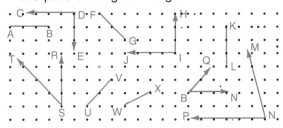

7 Construct an angle for each measure.

   (a) 30°   (b) 90°   (c) 128°   (d) 83°

   (e) 36°   (f) 150°   (g) 210°   (h) 100°

8 (a) Draw an angle that you think measures 90°. Do not use a protractor.

   (b) Measure the angle you drew in (a). How accurate is your estimated angle?

   (c) Repeat the steps in (a) and (b) for 60° and 45° angles.

C

9 For the figure, find and name all the angles that are congruent. Find and name all line segments that are congruent.

copying segments and angles: constructions

You can use a ruler to measure the length of a line segment and a protractor to measure the size of an angle. You can also copy a line segment or an angle *without measuring*. Your tools are a straightedge and compasses. You can use compasses to draw a circle.

Copy line segment AB.   Draw a ray. Mark point C.

Use radius AB and centre C.
Draw an arc to cut the line at D.

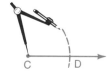

*The line segments AB and CD have the same length. They are said to be **congruent**.*

10 Construct a circle with each radius.

   (a) 5 cm   (b) 6 cm   (c) 4.5 cm

11 (a) Construct a copy of the line segment CD in your notebook.

   (b) Construct a line segment in your notebook that is twice as long as CD.

   (c) Construct a line segment that is 5 times the length of CD.

12 To construct the design, you mark equal line segments and join the points as shown.

   (a) Make a copy of the design.

   (b) Construct a design of your own.

13 (a) Each design is based on equal line segments and circles. Make a copy of each design. The radii of all circles are equal.

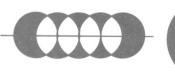

   (b) Construct a design of your own.

14 Copying an angle is a useful construction. The steps Gloria used to make a copy of ∠ABC are shown below. Describe her steps in words.

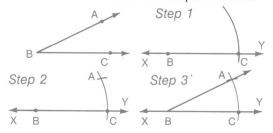

15 Refer to the diagram.

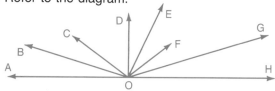

Construct a copy of each diagram in your notebook.
   (a) ∠AOB   (b) ∠AOE   (c) ∠AOG
   (d) ∠GOB   (e) ∠DOE   (f) ∠HOF

16 (a) Draw any angle   ABC.

   (b) Make a copy of the angle.

   (c) Make an angle twice the size as ∠ABC.

   (d) Make a copy of the diagram. Extend BA and EF to meet.

5.2 types of lines: constructions

If you were to look down from a plane, you would see many aspects of geometry:
- lines
- figures
- solids

There are special words you need to know about lines.

Horizontal lines

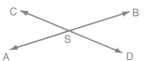

Vertical lines

Intersecting lines

The lines AB and CD intersect at one point S. ∠CSB and ∠ASD are called **vertically opposite angles**.

Perpendicular lines

This symbol shows that the lines are perpendicular.

The lines ST and RV intersect in a special way, ∠RQT = 90°. The lines are said to be perpendicular. You write RV ⊥ ST.

Parallel lines

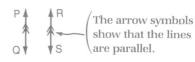

The arrow symbols show that the lines are parallel.

The lines PQ and RS never meet. They are said to be parallel. You write PQ ∥ RS.

You can construct a perpendicular from a point, P, to a line, AB, using a straight edge and compasses. Follow these steps. Can you describe the steps in words?

Step 1

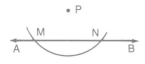

Step 2

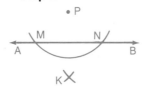

Step 3

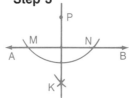

To bisect a line segment, AB, you can also use a straight edge and compasses. Follow these steps. Can you describe the steps in words?

Step 1

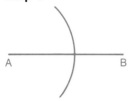

Step 2

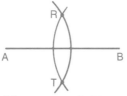

Step 3

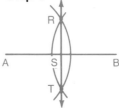

The line RT is called the **perpendicular bisector** or **right bisector** of the segment AB.

∠RSB = 90°   BS = SA

5.2 exercise

A

1 From the diagram, name

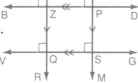

   (a) parallel lines.

   (b) perpendicular lines.

   (c) horizontal lines.

   (d) vertical lines.

2 Describe some objects or places that contain

   (a) parallel line segments.

   (b) perpendicular line segments.

   (c) intersecting line segments.

   (d) horizontal line segments.

   (e) vertical line segments.

3 (a) Trace the diagram containing point S and segment TU.

     • S

    T ——————————— U

   (b) Construct a perpendicular from point S to line segment TU.

B

4 Draw an example of each of the following.

   (a) parallel lines HJ and LP

   (b) perpendicular lines RE and CV

   (c) horizontal line AW

   (d) line XB perpendicular to line AW in (c).

5 (a) Draw any line segment.

   (b) Construct its perpendicular bisector.

   (c) Measure each part of the line segment. (How accurate is your construction?)

6 To find the altitude of a triangle you can construct PS ⊥ RQ or RQ extended.

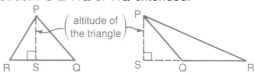

For each triangle

   (a) measure PS   (b) measure RQ

   (c) What is the area of each △PQR?

   (d) What do you notice about your answers?

7 (a) Draw any triangle. Construct an altitude.

   (b) Estimate the measure of the altitude and corresponding base.

   (c) Calculate the area of the triangle.

8 An aircraft is at point P above the surface AD.

   (a) Trace the diagram.

   (b) Construct the altitude from P to AD.   A———————D

   (c) What do you think is meant by the term "the altitude of an aircraft?"

C

9 The device shown can be used to draw parallel line segments.

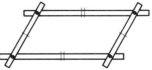

   (a) Examine the properties of the device. Suggest steps to construct parallel lines using a straight edge and compasses.

   (b) Use the method you suggest in (a). Construct a pair of parallel lines.

applications: locating centres

In solving a problem, there is often more than one way of finding the answer.
For an experiment you need to find the centre of the can. How will you do it? The questions that follow will provide you with different methods.

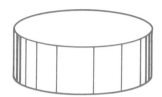

10 (a) Draw a circle with centre O. Label four points on the circumference R, Q, E, and D.

(b) Draw line segment DE. DE is a chord of the circle. Construct the perpendicular bisector of DE.

(c) Draw chord RQ. Construct the perpendicular bisector of chord RQ.

(d) Extend the bisectors in (b) and (c) to meet at T. Measure TR, TQ, TE, and TD. What do you notice?

(e) Use the steps above. Suggest a method for locating the centre of a circle.

11 (a) Trace the base of a coin, jar, or circular garbage can.

(b) Use the method in the previous question to locate the centre of the circle.

12 Part of a circle is shown. Make a copy of the arc. Use the previous method to locate the centre of the circle, then draw the complete circle.

13 (a) Mark three points A, B, C not in a straight line.

(b) Construct the perpendicular bisectors of AB and of BC.

(c) Extend the perpendicular bisectors in (b) to meet at O.

(d) Use O as centre, and radius OA. Draw a circle. What do you notice?

14 Three towns are situated as shown in the diagram.

                     • Belleville

Akron •

             • Caledonia

(a) Trace a copy of the diagram.

(b) How would you locate a site for a watertower to service the three towns? (You want the watertower to be equidistant — the same distance — from each town.)

15 (a) Trace the base of a circular can on a piece of thin paper. Fold the paper so that one half of the circle folds onto the other half. Make another fold in the paper so that one half of the circle folds onto the other half. Mark the point where the two folds intersect.

(b) Use the method in (a). Trace circular objects. Find the centre of each circle.

16 (a) Another method to locate the centre of a circle is to use a piece of transparent plastic. Repeat these steps.

Step 1
Place the plastic so that the circle reflects onto itself, then draw a line.

Step 2
Repeat Step 1, except place the plastic in another position. Draw a line. Mark the point where the two lines intersect.

(b) Use the method in (a). Trace circular objects. Find the centre of each circle.

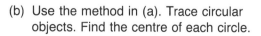

5.3 angles: constructions and language

You can see angles used wherever you look. How are angles used in the photograph?

Angles are classified according to their measures, as shown in the table.

Angle name	Measure of angle
Acute	between 0° and 90°
Right	90°
Obtuse	between 90° and 180°
Straight	180°
Reflex	between 180° and 360°

There are other important words you need to learn to work with angles.

Complementary
The sum of ∠ABC and ∠DEF is 90°. The angles are **complementary**.

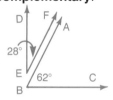

Supplementary
The sum of ∠PQR and ∠STV is 180°. The angles are **supplementary**.

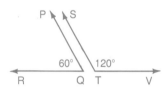

∠CDF and ∠FDE are called **adjacent** angles. Adjacent angles share a common vertex and ray and their interiors do not intersect.

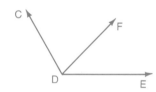

Angles can be **bisected**. The **bisector** of an angle divides an angle in half. The ray BD is called the bisector of ∠ABC since ∠ABD and ∠DBC are congruent. Each is half of ∠ABC.

You can bisect ∠LOM using a straight edge and compasses, as shown in the following diagrams. Can you describe the steps in words?

These marks show that the angles are equal.

Step 1

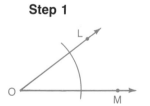

Step 2

Step 3

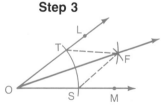

5.3 exercise

A Use the following diagram for Questions 1 to 3.

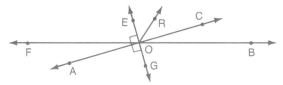

1. Write the names of two angles that are
   (a) complementary.   (b) supplementary.

2. Name two angles that are
   (a) acute   (b) obtuse   (c) right
   (d) straight   (e) reflex

3. Name two angles that are
   (a) adjacent   (b) vertically opposite

4. Classify each of the following angles.
   (a) 123°   (b) 45°   (c) 90°   (d) 94°
   (e) 180°   (f) 300°   (g) 10°   (h) 115°
   (i) 198°   (j) 7°   (k) 70°   (l) 185°

5. For each angle:
   (a) Estimate its size.
   (b) Measure its size.
   (c) Classify it.

6. (a) Trace each angle in the previous question.
   (b) Construct the bisector of each angle.

7. Find the complement of each angle.
   (a) 20°   (b) 50°   (c) 15°   (d) 35°
   (e) 42°   (f) 67°   (g) 10°   (h) 80°

8. Find the supplement of each angle.
   (a) 20°   (b) 150°   (c) 115°   (d) 35°
   (e) 72°   (f) 167°   (g) 112°   (h) 73°

9. (a) Draw an acute angle on a sheet of paper.
   (b) Fold the paper to find the bisector of the angle.
   (c) Repeat steps (a) and (b) for a right angle; obtuse angle; straight angle.

B

10. (a) Draw an acute angle. Construct its bisector.
    (b) Check your results in (a) by measuring.
    (c) Repeat the steps for an obtuse angle.

11. (a) Draw a straight angle and construct its bisector. Check your work.
    (b) Construct an angle whose measure is $\frac{1}{4}$ of the measure of the angle in (a). What is the measure of this angle?

12. Find each missing measure.

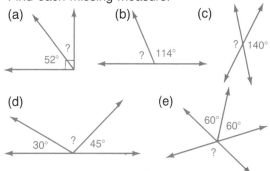

13. To draw each design, angle bisectors were used. Determine the steps used to construct each design; then make a copy of it.

C

14. Make a design of your own based on constructing bisectors of angles.

problem solving: working backwards

You have constructed a perpendicular from a point P
to a line AB. How would you construct a
perpendicular from a point R on the line AB?

You can work backwards and study the diagram and develop the
steps of the construction.

A You want to obtain
this diagram.

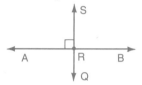

B What information do
you know?

SR ⊥ AB   ∠SRA = 90°
SQ is the bisector of ∠ARB.
∠ARB is a straight angle.

C Use the facts in B to develop
the method. Draw a straight
angle. Bisect the angle to
obtain the perpendicular.

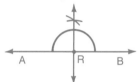

Thus a perpendicular has been constructed at R on line AB.
You have worked backwards to develop the method.

---

15 To construct a perpendicular
at B, you need to
extend the line segment AB.

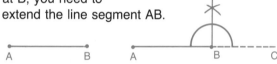

(a) Draw a segment PQ = 5 cm.

(b) Construct a perpendicular to PQ at P.

(c) Construct a perpendicular to PQ at Q.

16 (a) Draw a line segment AB.

(b) At B construct a line segment CB so that
CB ⊥ AB.

(c) Join AC. What type of triangle have you
constructed?

17 The diagram shows the
construction lines to
make ∠FBC = 45°.

(a) What is the
measure of ∠ABF?

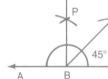

(b) Use the sketch to
construct an angle
that measures 45°;
135°.

18 You can also use paper folding to construct a
perpendicular at a point on a line.

(a) Follow these steps to construct the
perpendicular

Step 1
Draw RS and a point
P on RS.

Step 2
Fold the paper so
that RP lies along
PS.

Step 3
The fold through P is
perpendicular to RS.
PT ⊥ RS

(b) Repeat the steps in (a) for a point Q drawn
on line AB.

math tip
A transparent mirror
can also be used to
construct a
perpendicular.

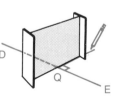

5.4 constructing triangles: using sketches

Storms and high winds can cause heavy damage. To provide strength against the elements, triangular shapes are used in constructing towers and buildings. Triangles can be formed by using 3 line segments. There are also 3 angles in a triangle.

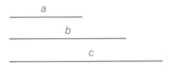

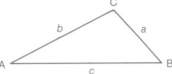

Triangles can be classified according to the measure of their angles.

Acute triangle
All angles are acute.

Right triangle
One angle is 90°.

Obtuse triangle
One angle is obtuse.

Equiangular triangle
All angles are equal.

You can also classify triangles according to the measures of their sides.

Scalene triangle
No sides are equal.

Isosceles triangle
Two sides are equal.

Equilateral triangle
Three sides are equal.

You can use your geometric tools to construct triangles.

Example   Construct △PQR where ∠Q = 90°, PQ = 4 cm, and QR = 4 cm.

(Think: draw and label a sketch of the triangle to plan your construction steps.)

Solution   **Step 1:**
Draw a line. Mark points Q and R so that QR = 4 cm.

Step 2:
Construct ∠Q = 90°.

Step 3:
Mark P so that PQ = 4 cm.

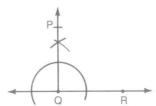

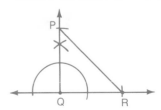

A

1 Measure the sides of each triangle. Classify the triangles.

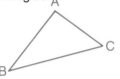

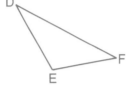

2 Measure the angles of each triangle. Classify each triangle.

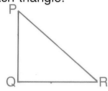

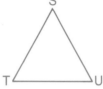

3 Construct the triangles from the given sketches. Measure the remaining parts. Mark the measures on your triangle.

(a)

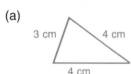

(b)

(c)

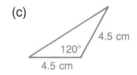

4 (a) Draw an obtuse triangle.

(b) Bisect the obtuse angle.

(c) Bisect the sides.

(d) Repeat steps (a) to (c) for another triangle.

B

5 A triangle has the properties

$\angle H = 35°$ $\angle J = 45°$ HJ = 5 cm

(a) Draw a sketch of the triangle.

(b) Construct the triangle.

(c) Measure the remaining parts.

(d) Why is HJ called a **contained side**?

6 A triangle has these measures:

JK = 5 cm, $\angle K = 90°$,   KL = 6 cm

(a) Draw a sketch of the triangle.

(b) Construct the triangle.

(c) Measure the remaining parts.

(d) Why is $\angle K$ called a **contained angle**?

7 Construct a triangle that has the sides shown.

8 (a) Construct △ABC such that AB = BC = 12 cm and AC = 6 cm.

(b) Construct △ABC so that BC = 3.5 cm, AC = 3 cm, and BA = 2.5 cm.

(c) Construct equilateral △ABC whose sides measure 7 cm.

9 Construct each of the following triangles. Once you have completed the construction, measure the remaining parts.

(a) △DEF, FE = 6.5 cm, $\angle$DFE = 100°, DF = 8.5 cm

(b) △KMN, MN = 10 cm, $\angle$KMN = 55°, $\angle$KNM = 25°

(c) △PQR, $\angle$PRQ = 20°, RQ = 6.5 cm, $\angle$Q is a right angle.

C

10 Construct a triangle with each property. Record the measures of all sides and angles.

(a) isosceles and acute angled

(b) scalene and right angled

(c) equilateral and acute angled

(d) isosceles and right angled

(e) scalene and obtuse angled

problem-solving: which parts are necessary?

A triangle has 6 parts — 3 angles and 3 sides.

▶ Do you need to know information about all the parts to construct the triangle?

▶ If you are given three parts, can you construct a unique (only one) triangle?

In the exercise that follows you will explore some properties about triangles.

11 The three angle measures of △ABC are known. ∠A = 90°, ∠B = 40°, and ∠C = 50°

   (a) Construct △ABC.

   (b) Compare your △ABC with others in the class. What do you notice?

   (c) Can you construct a larger triangle with the same measures for angles? Give reasons for your answer.

12 (a) Construct △SDF so that SD = 4 cm, DF = 3 cm, SF = 2 cm.

   (b) Measure the remaining parts. Compare your answers with other members of your class. Is the triangle unique?

   (c) Repeat (a) and (b) for each of the following triangles.
   △QWG: QW = 3 cm, WG = 4 cm, GQ = 3 cm
   △TYH: TY = 5 cm, YH = 4 cm, TH = 3 cm

   (d) Based on your results, is the following true or false? "If 3 sides of a triangle are known, the triangle, when constructed, is unique".

13 (a) In △ABC, ∠CAB = 45°, AC = 8 cm, AB = 6 cm. Use the sketch. Construct the triangle.

   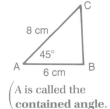

   (A is called the contained angle.

   (b) Make a sketch, then construct, each triangle.
   △ABC: AB = 3 cm, ∠B = 55°, BC = 5 cm
   △VWX: VW = 4 cm, ∠W = 35°, WX = 4 cm

(c) Measure the remaining parts. Compare your answers with other members of your class. Is the triangle unique?

(d) Based on your results, is the following true or false? "If the measures of two sides and the contained angle are known then the triangle is unique".

14 (a) In △ABC, ∠A = 45°, ∠B = 30°. AB = 6 cm. Use the sketch. Construct the triangle.

   (AB is called the contained side.

   (b) Make a sketch of each triangle. Then construct each triangle.
   △GLF: ∠G = 60° ∠L = 55° GL = 4 cm
   △BDR: ∠B = 95° ∠D = 35° DB = 6 cm

   (c) Measure the remaining parts. Compare your answers with other members of your class. Is the triangle unique?

   (d) Based on your results, is the following true or false? "If the measures of two angles and the contained side are known then the triangle is unique".

The investigations you completed were probably similar to the type of thinking the famous mathematician, Euclid, followed when he made the following conclusions about triangles. These conclusions are also based on the work you explored on this page.

▶ **Congruent Triangles SSS:** If three sides of one triangle are congruent to three sides of another triangle, then the triangles are congruent. (Which means the triangle you construct is unique.)

▶ **Congruent Triangles SAS:** If two sides and the contained angle of one triangle are congruent to two sides and the contained angle of another triangle then the triangles are congruent.

▶ **Congruent Triangles ASA:** If two angles and the contained side of one triangle are congruent to two angles and the contained side of another triangle then the triangles are congruent.

5.5 language of polygons: constructions

A **polygon** is any closed figure that is constructed from line segments which do not cross.

Polygons are classified according to the number of sides they have.

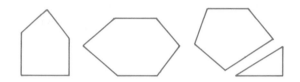

Number of Sides	3	4	5	6	7	8
Name of Polygon	Triangle	Quadrilateral	Pentagon	Hexagon	Septagon	Octagon

Quadrilaterals are polygons with 4 sides. As with triangles, some quadrilaterals have special properties and are given special names.

Square
All sides are equal.
All angles equal 90°.

Rectangle
All angles equal 90°.
Opposite sides are equal.

Parallelogram
Both pairs of opposite sides are parallel.

Rhombus
All sides are equal.

Trapezoid
One pair of opposite sides are parallel.

Kite
Two pairs of adjacent sides are equal.
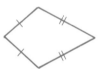

5.5 exercise

A

1 Which polygon is used for each of the following?

2 How many sides does each polygon have?

(a) quadrilateral (b) hexagon (c) pentagon

(d) octagon (e) kite (f) rhombus

3 To construct a square with side measures of 6 cm, a sketch is made. Construct the square.

4 A sketch of a rhombus is shown. Construct a copy of this figure.

5 A sketch of a parallelogram is shown. Construct a copy of the figure in your notebook.

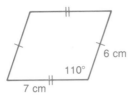

6 Construct a kite with the following measures.

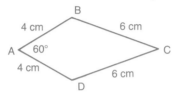

B Be sure to draw a sketch to help you plan the constructions.

7 (a) Construct a square whose sides measure 10 cm.

(b) Construct a rectangle whose sides measure 6 cm and 8 cm.

(c) Construct a rectangle whose sides measure 6.5 cm and 9.5 cm.

(d) Construct a parallelogram whose largest angle is 130° and whose sides measure 9.5 cm and 6.5 cm.

8 The **diagonal** AC of the rectangle is shown.

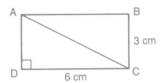

(a) Construct the rectangle.

(b) Measure the 2 diagonals. What do you notice?

9 (a) Construct a rectangle of your own size.

(b) Measure the diagonals. What do you notice?

(c) Repeat steps (a) and (b) for other rectangles.

(d) Use your previous results. What seems to be true about the diagonals of a rectangle?

10 "The diagonals of a square are equal." How would you check whether the statement is true or false?

11 (a) The diagonals of rectangle PQRS intersect at T.

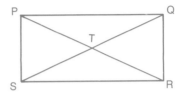

Measure the pairs of line segments, ST, TQ, and PT, TR. What do you notice?

(b) Use another rectangle. Repeat the steps in (a). What do you notice about your measures?

(c) Based on your results, what appears to be true about the intersection point of diagonals of a rectangle?

(d) How would you check whether your statement in (c) is true or false for a square?

C

12 Polygons are drawn with diagonals as shown.

(a) Copy and complete the chart.

Name of polygon	Number of sides	Number of diagonals
Triangle	3	0
Quadrilateral	?	?

(b) What pattern do you see for the number of diagonals?

13 Use the pattern in (b) above to find the number of diagonals in each polygon.

(i) decagon   (10 sides)

(ii) dodecagon   (12 sides)

applications: designs with regular polygons

Each of the designs shown were constructed from a regular polygon. A **regular polygon** is a polygon that has all angles congruent and all sides congruent.

The following exercise provides the basis for constructing regular polygons as well as designs based on regular polygons.
Remember: One complete rotation is 360°.

 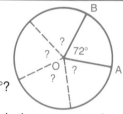

14 An equilateral triangle is inscribed (drawn) in a circle with centre O as shown.

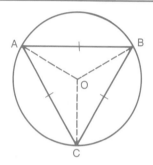

(a) ∠COB is called a **central angle**. Name two other central angles in this diagram.

(b) Measure the central angles ∠AOB, ∠AOC, and ∠BOC. What do you notice?

(c) Explain why ∠AOB + ∠AOC + ∠BOC = 360°.

(d) Why are △AOC, △AOB, △BOC congruent?

(e) What is the measure of ∠AOC?

15 A square is inscribed in a circle as shown.

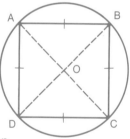

(a) Name the central angles.

(b) Predict the measures of the central angles.

(c) Check your prediction in (b) by measuring the central angles.

(d) Explain why ∠AOB + ∠BOC + ∠COD + ∠DOA = 360°.

(e) Why are △AOD, △AOB, △BOC, △DOC congruent?

(f) What is the measure of ∠AOD?

16 Bradley drew this sketch to help him construct a regular pentagon.

(a) Why is ∠BOA = 72°? How will this fact be used to find the missing measures?

(b) Use the sketch. Construct a pentagon so that OB measures 5 cm.

17 (a) Draw a sketch to show how to construct a regular hexagon.

(b) Use a circle with radius 8.5 cm and construct the hexagon.

18 (a) Use a circle with radius 10 cm. Construct a copy of this design. Hint: Use the steps shown in the previous questions.

(b) Each design is related to a regular polygon. Construct a larger copy of the design.

5.6 constructions with translations

You have probably seen designs that are based on **slides** or **translations**.

A slide is one way of making a translation image. A translation puts square ABCD in a new position called its image position. A translation is shown by a *slide arrow* or *translation arrow*. It shows the direction and distance of the translation.

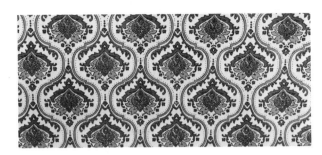

A is the **pre-image** point which corresponds to A′ called the **image** point.

     A′ is read as "A prime."

     A → A′   B → B′

     C → C′   D → D′

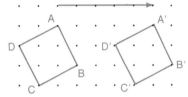

To describe a horizontal or vertical translation, the following symbols are used: R, right   L, left   U, up   D, down

To describe the translation for the square ABCD, you can write it as

               [5R, 0]

5 units right)   (0 units up

To describe a slide of 5 units up with no horizontal slide, you use the symbols [0, 5U].

Example   Find the translation image of △PQS if it undergoes a translation given by [3R, 4D].

Solution   3R means 3 units to the right

                4D means 4 units down

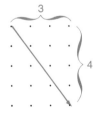

To describe the translation, you often say that △PQS is *mapped onto* △P′Q′S′.

A

1 The pre-image and image are shown. Describe each translation in words.

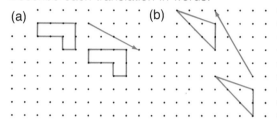

2 Match the translation arrow with the corresponding symbol.

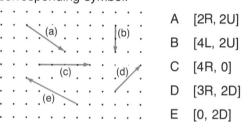

A [2R, 2U]

B [4L, 2U]

C [4R, 0]

D [3R, 2D]

E [0, 2D]

3 Make a copy of each figure. Find the image for each translation.

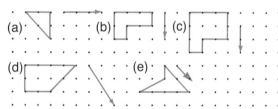

4 For the figure construct the image for each translation.

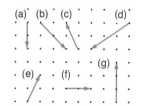

5 Write the symbols to describe each arrow.

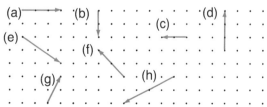

6 Draw translation arrows for each of the following.

(a) [5L, 2U] (b) [3R, 0] (c) [0, 3U]

(d) [4L, 3D] (e) [4R, 3U] (f) [3L, 3U]

B

7 Find the image of the given figure for each translation.

(a) [3L, 0] (b) [0, 2U] (c) [2R, 2D]

(d) [3L, 2U] (e) [4L, 1D] (f) [4R, 1U]

8 Describe the translation that will map the grey figure onto the red figure.

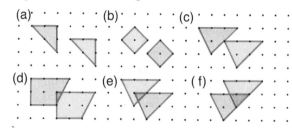

9 (a) Apply the translation [4R, 3D] to △ABC.

(b) Apply the translation [4L, 3U] to the image △A′B′C′. What do you notice?

10 A translation described by [3R, 2D] is applied to a figure. What translation will return the figure to its original position?

11 For each of the following, describe the translation in symbols that will return a figure to its original position.

(a) [5D, 2U] (b) [3R, 0] (c) [0, 2D]

(d) [3L, 3D] (e) [0, 3U] (f) [4L, 0]

(g) [2R, 3U] (h) [2L, 3D] (i) [0, 0]

5.7 language of reflections

There are many creatures and situations that remind us of
reflection.
To find the reflection image of a polygon, a line of reflection is
drawn. For example, the reflection image of △ABC can be shown
in relation to the reflection line, ℓ. A flip, as shown, is one way of
constructing a reflection image.

△ABC is drawn.

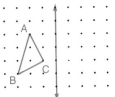

△ABC is "flipped" or reflected in
the line, ℓ.

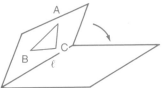

The reflection image of △ABC is
obtained.

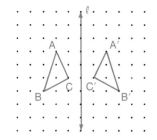

The vertices of the △ABC and its image △A'B'C' are given by the
correspondence:
△ABC ↔ △A'B'C'   A ↔ A'   B ↔ B'   C ↔ C'

By joining each vertex of the original figure and its image point,
you will find
  ▶ AA', BB', CC', are perpendicular to the line of reflection.
  ▶ The line of reflection ℓ bisects each of AA', BB', and CC'

> The line of reflection is the
> perpendicular bisector of the line
> segments joining corresponding
> points of a figure and its image.

You can use the properties of reflection to find reflection images
as shown in the example.

Example   Find the reflection image of △BNH.

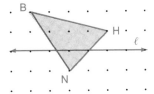

Solution

Step 1: Find the reflection image of each
vertex.

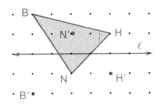

Step 2: Join the points to form the reflected
image.

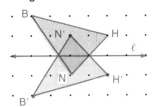

A

1 Use a reflection to read each of the following.

(a) In what year was the first outboard motor used?

(d) Would you believe it was in the year 1896?

2 Construct the reflection of each word.

(a) 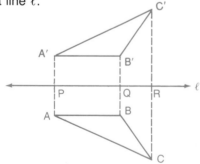 MATH

(b) SMILE

(c) NO WAY

(d) LAST CHANCE

3 The word ambulance is written so that a driver can see it in the rear view mirror. What other important words can you list so that the reflection can be read?

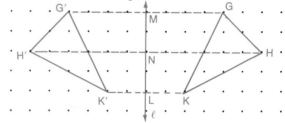

4 The logo is based on a reflection. Find other examples of logos or symbols that are based on a reflection.

5 The image of △ABC is obtained by a reflection about line ℓ.

(a) Measure AP, A′P; BQ, B′Q; CR, C′R. What do you notice about the measures?

(b) Measure ∠APR, ∠BQP, ∠CRQ. What do you notice about your measures?

6 A shape and its image are shown.

(a) What line segments are equal?

(b) Name perpendicular lines.

B

7 Use dot paper to make a copy of △PQR and the reflection line, ℓ. Find the reflection image for △PQR.

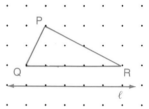

8 Make a copy of the figure and the line of reflection, *m*. Find the reflection image of △STV.

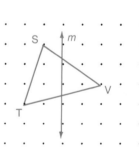

9 Draw the reflection image of each figure.

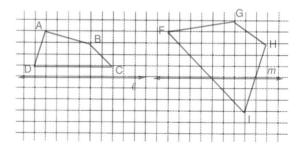

10 Trace each figure and the line of reflection. Construct the reflection image of each figure.

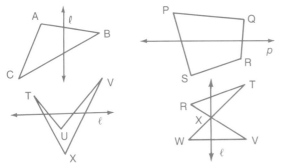

11 Find the reflection image of each design. Use the reflection line, ℓ.

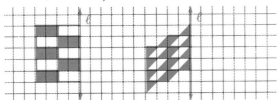

12 (a) The letter A, when flipped in a vertical line of reflection, is still an A. Find other capital letters of the alphabet that have the same property.

A | A

(b) The letter E, when flipped in a horizontal line of reflection, is still an E. Find other capital letters of the alphabet that have the same property.

E
⟵⟶
E

(c) Find capital letters of the alphabet that are the same when flipped in a vertical and horizontal line of reflection.

13 A design, as shown, is obtained by reflecting a figure a number of times. Reflect each of the following to create a design of your own.

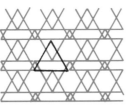

(a) 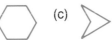 (b) (c)

14 A piece of red plastic can also be used to do those constructions you did in an earlier section.

(a) Draw diagrams of your own to do the following constructions.

I *Bisect an angle:* Place the plastic so that the image of AB lies on AC. Then draw the bisector along the edge of the plastic EF.

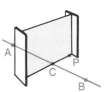

II *Draw a perpendicular to a line:* Place the plastic on the point P so that the image of AC lies on CB. Then CP ⊥ BA.

III *Draw a perpendicular from the line:* Place the plastic on the point P so that the image of AP lies on BP. Then PS ⊥ AB.

(b) Suggest how you would use the red plastic to find the right bisector of a line segment.

C
15 (a) Two reflection lines, m_1 and m_2, are parallel as shown. Predict the image of the figure reflected in line m_1 followed by reflection in line m_2. Then construct the image.

(b) Use other lines $m_1 \parallel m_2$. Find the images of figures of your own reflected in parallel lines m_1 and m_2.

(c) Two reflection lines, p_1 and p_2, are perpendicular as shown. Predict the image of the figure reflected in line p_1 followed by a reflection in line p_2. Then construct the image.

(d) Use other lines $p_1 \perp p_2$. Find the images of figures of your own reflected in perpendicular lines p_1 and p_2.

applications: symmetry and design

Each of these figures shown have a common property. Do you know what it is? Each figure is symmetrical. For each figure there is a line of reflection such that one half of the figure is reflected onto the other half identically. The two parts of the figure are congruent. Each figure is said to have **reflectional** or **line symmetry**. The line of reflection is called the **line of symmetry**.

You can determine how many lines of symmetry a figure has. To find lines of symmetry, you find the lines in which one half of a figure is reflected onto the other half of the figure itself. The rectangle has two lines of symmetry, ℓ_1 and ℓ_2 as shown.

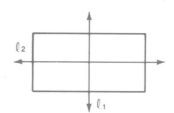

16 How many lines of symmetry does each figure have?

(a) **M** (b)   (c)

17 Symmetry is often used in designs. How many lines of symmetry does each of the figures on the stamp have?

(a)   (b)

18 (a) How many lines of symmetry do each of the following logos have? Use a mirror to help you.

(b) Find logos in the newspaper or telephone directory that have lines of symmetry. Determine the number of lines of symmetry each logo has.

19 How many lines of symmetry does each quadrilateral have?

(a) square (b) parallelogram (c) rhombus

20 Which of the figures have reflectional symmetry? Give reasons for your answer.

(a)   (b)   (c)

21 Squared paper is used to create designs that have symmetry.

(a) How many lines of symmetry does the design have?

(b) Construct a design of your own. How many lines of symmetry does it have?

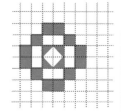

22 A design is shown with 4 lines of symmetry. Construct a design of your own with

(a) 2 lines of symmetry.

(b) 4 lines of symmetry.

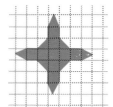

5.8 working with rotations

In the previous section you worked with the transformations of translations and reflections. Another transformation is a **rotation**. In the study of geometry, various skills and concepts related to rotations are important to know.

How do each of these suggest a turn or rotation about a point?

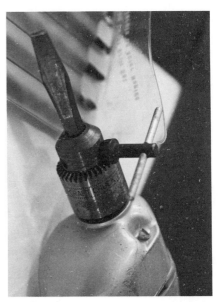

△PQR is rotated about point O, called the **turn centre** or **rotation centre**. The **rotation angle** is the amount and direction of the rotation.

△P′Q′R′ is called the **rotation image**. The rotation angle is 90° clockwise (90° cw), or $\frac{1}{4}$ rotation clockwise.

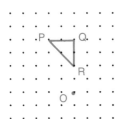

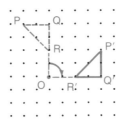

You can find the rotation image of a figure by using a tracing. The above figure is traced and rotated $\frac{1}{4}$ turn ccw (counter clockwise).

Trace the figure as shown.

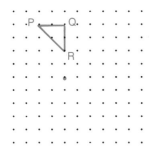

Then rotate the figure. Mark the final position of the rotation image.

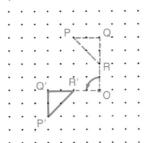

Apart from *understanding* the meaning of each word about rotations, you can ask yourself two important questions to learn the properties of rotations:
▶ What has changed as a result of the rotation?
▶ What has not changed as a result of the rotation?

Two important questions that have helped people develop and extend mathematical concepts and thinking are:
▶ What has changed?
▶ What has not changed?

You will explore the properties of rotations in the exercise.

5.8 exercise

A Questions 1 to 6 explore rotations and their properties.

1 △ABC is rotated to a new position, △A'B'C'.

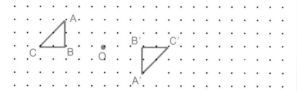

(a) What is the rotation angle? Rotation centre?

(b) Compare the lengths:
OB, OB';   OA, OA';   OC, OC';
AB, A'B';   BC, B'C';   AC, A'C'

(c) Which angles are congruent?

(d) For the rotation, what has changed? What has not changed?

2 The △RTY is rotated 90° clockwise about the turn centre O.

(a) Measure ∠ROR',
∠TOT', ∠YOY'.
What do you notice?

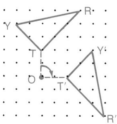

(b) Measure RO, R'O;
TO, T'O; YO, Y'O.
What do you notice?

3 △PQR is shown. Trace the figure on a sheet of paper.

(a) Use a rotation
angle of 180° cw
and centre O. Find
the image △P'Q'R'.

(b) From your diagram:
▶ What has changed?
▶ What has not changed?

4 (a) In the diagram, △PQR has a clockwise sense.

For the previous questions, complete the chart.

	Sense of original figure	Sense of image figure
△PQR		
△ABC		

(b) What do you notice about your answers?

5 For each rotation angle describe
▶ the amount of turn   ▶ the direction of turn

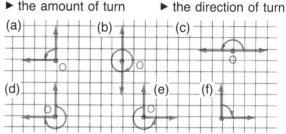

6 For each rotation the original figure and the image are shown. What is the rotation angle?

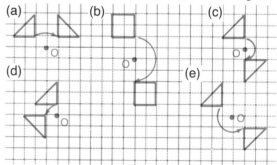

B

7 For each of the following, find the rotation image about the centre O.
For each rotation, what has
▶ changed?   ▶ not changed?

(a)
90° cw

(b)
180° ccw

(c)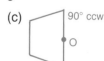
90° ccw

8 For each figure, find the rotation image about the centre O. Use the rotation angle shown.

(a)

(b)

(c)

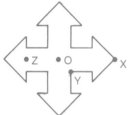

$\frac{1}{4}$ cw $\frac{3}{4}$ cw $\frac{3}{4}$ ccw

9 Make a tracing of the figure. Use each of the following rotation centres to find the rotation image for a rotation angle of 90° cw.

(a) O   (b) X   (c) Y   (d) Z

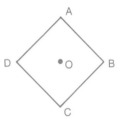

10 Use grid paper. Draw square ABCD as shown with turn centre O. Find the rotation image for each rotation angle.

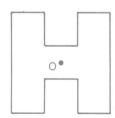

(a) 90° cw   (b) $\frac{1}{2}$ cw   (c) 270° cw

(d) $\frac{1}{4}$ ccw   (e) 180° ccw   (f) $\frac{3}{4}$ ccw

11 Find the rotation image of the letter H. Use the turn centre O. Rotate the figure

(a) $\frac{1}{2}$ cw   (b) $\frac{1}{2}$ ccw

What do you notice?

12 Refer to the previous question. For which letters of the alphabet is the rotation image mapped onto the original figure for a rotation angle of

(a) 90° cw?   (b) 180° ccw?

13 Two congruent triangles can be used as shown to construct special quadrilaterals.

Rotate the scalene triangle 180° cw about O.

A parallelogram is obtained.

Use dot or squared paper to answer the following.

(a) A right triangle is rotated $\frac{1}{2}$ turn about the point O. What figure is obtained?

O is the midpoint of AC.

(b) An isosceles right triangle is rotated $\frac{1}{2}$ turn about O. What figure is obtained?

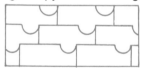

O is the midpoint of AC.

C

14 Congruent figures are used to cover the surface. The pattern is called a tiling design or **tessellation**. Make a larger copy of each design.

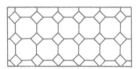

15 Use a translation, reflection, or rotation to create a tiling design of your own.

math tip

So far you have studied 3 transformations: translations, reflections and rotations. Since the original figure and image figure are congruent, they are called **congruence transformations**.

In Chapter 11 you will study another transformation called a dilatation. Dilatations are referred to as **similarity transformations**.

rotational symmetry

A figure has **rotational symmetry** about a point if the rotation image is the original figure itself. The number of times that the figure can be rotated so that it is mapped (placed) onto itself in one complete revolution is called the **order of rotational symmetry**.

The order of rotational symmetry of the figure to the right is 3, since in one complete revolution (360°) the figure maps onto itself 3 times. Rotational symmetry is often called **point symmetry**. To find the order of rotational symmetry, you can use a tracing.

Start with a figure. You want to find its order of rotational symmetry.

Use thin paper. Cover the figure and make a tracing.

Rotate the tracing paper. Match the tracing with the original figure.

16 How many times can each figure be rotated to match its original position?

(a) 　(b) 　(c)

17 Find the order of rotational symmetry of each figure.

(a) 　(b) 　(c)

18 Each of the following figures has rotational symmetry with order greater than 1.
   ► Copy each figure on grid paper.
   ► Mark the rotation centre.
   ► What is the order of rotational symmetry for each figure?

A 　B 　C

19 (a) Each figure is a regular polygon. Find its order of rotational symmetry.

(b) Use your results in (a). What relationship is there between the number of sides of the polygon and the order of rotational symmetry?

20 (a) Which of the following designs have rotational symmetry of order greater than one?

A  B

(b) Which of the above designs have reflectional symmetry? How many lines of symmetry are there?

21 Logos and designs are shown.

(a) Which have reflectional and rotational symmetry?

(b) Which have only rotational symmetry (order greater than one)?

A B C

22 Construct a design that has rotational symmetry of order

(a) three　　(b) four　　(c) six

5.9 problem solving: investigating congruent figures

How can you test whether two figures are congruent or not?

(Congruent figures have the same size and shape.

If two figures are congruent, they can be placed one on top of each other and they match exactly. Earlier you learned that under certain conditions triangles are congruent. To test whether two figures are congruent, you can make a tracing of one figure and see whether it fits exactly on top of the other. Two figures are congruent if you can find a transformation that relates the figures.

To show congruent figures mark the translation arrow, reflection line, or rotation centre and angle.

The figures match.
The figures are congruent.

The figures do not match.
The figures are not congruent.

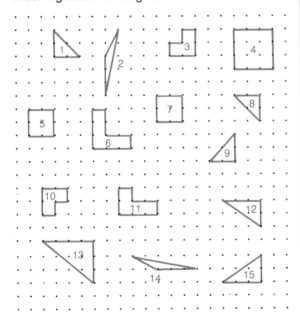

5.9 exercise

1 Decide which figures are congruent. Give reasons for your answer. Use a tracing to test which figures are congruent.

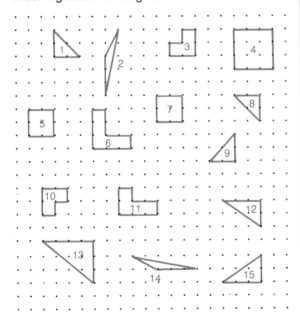

2 Decide which figures are congruent.

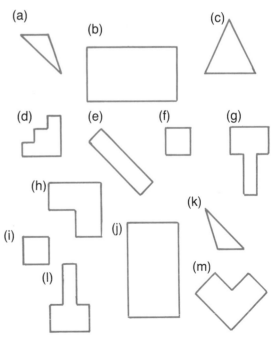

5.10 geometry and grids: co-ordinates

In the previous sections you saw geometries from different points of view. To locate positions, you can use numbers and grids in a very special, but, important way.

Ordered pairs of numbers can be shown on a grid.
To show the position of the ordered pair (2, 4) you can draw two number lines, one horizontal, and one vertical.
The ordered pair (2, 4) is then shown on the grid at the right.

$$\left(\begin{array}{c}\text{This number tells how}\\ \text{far to go horizontally.}\end{array}\right)\overset{(2,\,4)}{\underset{\uparrow\quad\uparrow}{}}\left(\begin{array}{c}\text{This number tells how}\\ \text{far to go vertically.}\end{array}\right)$$

Each ordered pair of numbers can be used to show a point on the grid. The numbers in the ordered pair are used to find the position of the point. These numbers are called the **co-ordinates** of the point.

$$\underset{\text{horizontal co-ordinate}}{\underset{\quad\quad}{}}\overset{(2,\,4)}{\underset{\uparrow\quad\uparrow}{}}\underset{\text{vertical co-ordinate}}{\underset{\quad\quad}{}}$$

The horizontal axis and the vertical axis are sometimes called the co-ordinate axes.
When you mark the point for each ordered pair, you are drawing the graph of the ordered pair or **plotting** the ordered pair.

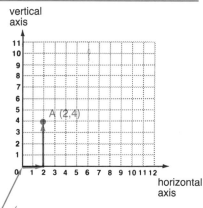

vertical axis

horizontal axis

(The point of intersection of the two number lines is called the origin. Its position is shown by the ordered pair (0, 0).)

(Drawing graphs of ordered pairs is a powerful and important tool in mathematics and in many other subjects.)

5.10 exercise

A

1 Each letter represents an ordered pair. Write the ordered pair for each point.

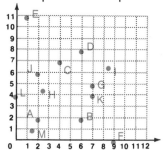

2 Use the diagram in the previous question. Which letter corresponds to each of these points?

  (a) (2, 2)   (b) (6, 8)   (c) (2, 6)

  (d) (1, 11)   (e) (7, 5)   (f) (9, 0)

  (g) (1.5, 1)   (h) (4, 7)   (i) (8.5, 6.5)

3 (a) Plot the following points.
    A(1, 3) B(3, 8) C(7, 6) D(9, 3) E(8, 3)
    F(6, 1) G(0, 5) H(3, 0) I(3, 2)   J(5, 2)
    K(5, 3) L(2, 2) M(4, 6) N(6, 3) P(2, 6)

  (b) Mark these line segments AK, LP, BI, IG, HJ, EF, DC, MN.

  (c) Which line segments in (b) seem to be
     ▶ perpendicular?   ▶ parallel?

  (d) Which line segments in (b) are congruent?

4 On grid paper, draw and label co-ordinate axes from 0 to 8. Plot (mark) the ordered pairs.

C(8, 4), D(4, 8)

(a) How are these ordered pairs the same?

(b) How are they different?

B

5 Refer to the diagram.

(a) What figure would be drawn if you joined the following points in order?

H(3, 11)   J(8, 11)   B(8, 3)   A(3, 3)

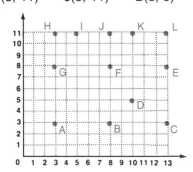

(b) Join the points (3, 3), (8, 8), (13, 8), and (8, 3). What figure have you drawn?

(c) Write the ordered pairs that would name
▶ a square.   ▶ a rectangle.   ▶ a triangle.

(d) Write the ordered pairs for a triangle and a square that have equal areas.

(e) Write the ordered pairs for a rectangle and a parallelogram that have equal areas.

(f) Write the ordered pairs for the triangle with
▶ the largest area.   ▶ the smallest area.

6 (a) Graph the following ordered pairs.
A(3, 3)   B(3, 9)   C(10, 9)   D(10, 3)

(b) Draw the following line segments.
AB   BC   CD   DA

(c) What is the name of this figure?

7 (a) Graph the following ordered pairs.
(1, 5)   (3, 3)   (7, 3)   (9, 5)   (5, 7)

(b) Use a line segment to join all the points.

(c) How many different line segments have you drawn?

8 (a) Graph these points.
A(2, 1)   B(2, 4)   C(2, 6)   D(5, 1)
E(5, 4)   F(5, 6)   G(7, 1)   H(7, 6)
I(10, 6)   J(10, 1)   K(12, 6)   L(14, 6)
M(16, 6)   N(14, 1)

(b) Draw these line segments: AC, DF, BE, CF. What letter have you drawn?

(c) Draw these line segments: HG, HJ, IJ. What did you notice about your answer?

(d) What letter is shown by the remaining points? What word have you spelled?

9 By using ordered pairs you can send a message in code. To find the missing message you will need to follow these instructions. Each question shows a letter. Use line segments.

(a) Join (1, 8) to (1, 12). Join (1, 10) to (3, 10). Join (3, 12) to (3, 8).

(b) Join (5, 8) to (5, 12).

(c) Join (2, 2,) to (2, 6). Join (1, 6) to (3, 6).

(d) Join (4, 2) to (4, 6). Join (4, 4) to (6, 4). Join (6, 2) to (6, 6).

(e) Join (9, 6) to (7, 6) to (7, 2) to (9, 2). Join (7, 4) to (8, 4).

(f) Join (12, 2) to (10, 4) to (12, 4) to (12, 6). Join (12, 6) to (10, 6) to (10, 2).

(g) Join (15, 6) to (13, 6) to (13, 2) to (15, 2). Join (14, 4) to (13, 4).

C

10 Use the type of code in the previous question to make a message of your own. Exchange your coded message with other students and have them decode (solve) your message.

---

computer tip

Use this program to find the area of a circle.

```
10  PRINT "AREA OF A CIRCLE"
20  INPUT "THE RADIUS IS"; R
30  LET A = π * R ↑ 2
40  PRINT "THE AREA IS"; A
50  END
```

5.11 geometry: working in 3 dimensions

You have already learned some of the properties of certain solids, or 3-dimensional objects when you dealt with surface area: cubes, prisms, and cylinders. In your work in geometry, you need to understand certain words.

A **skeleton** of a figure shows the framework or the edges.

To obtain a **shell**, you cover the skeleton with material.

Fill the shell with material to obtain a **solid**.

You obtain the **net** of the cube to construct the shell of the cube.

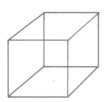   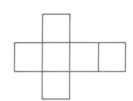

A **polyhedron** is a 3-dimensional object with flat surfaces. (Polyhedra is the plural form.)

These are polyhedra.   These are not!

Certain vocabulary for discussing polyhedra has been developed. Polyhedra with special properties are given special names.

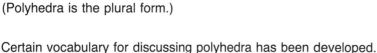

Two **faces** meet at an edge.

Edges meet at **vertices**.

Pyramid

These faces are triangular.

The name of the pyramid is related to its base: square-based pyramid.

Prism

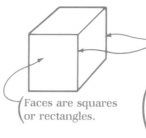

parallel

Faces are squares or rectangles.

The name of the prism is related to its base: square-based prism.

Building language for figures in two dimensions is similar to building language for figures in three dimensions.

2-dimensional shapes
A **line of symmetry** is shown.

3-dimensional shapes
A **plane of symmetry** is shown.

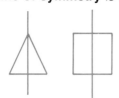 

A line of symmetry acts like a mirror. A plane of symmetry also acts like a mirror. It reflects each half of the shape onto the other half.

5.11 exercise

A

1 For each shape, give an example of an object that has that shape. Give an example of a common object and a not-so-common object.

2 (a) Use the chart.

Skeleton	Shell	Solid

Place each of the following objects into one of the columns of the chart.

match box   cake   coffee mug   bird cage

box   chocolate bar   orange   shoe

barrel   aquarium   glass jar   oil drum

balloon   hydro tower   pail   play pen

(b) Find other objects about you: in your classroom, at home, at the beach, etc. Classify the objects as either skeletons, shells, or solids.

3 (a) Make a list of 3-dimensional objects that have the same shape.

(b) Which 3-dimensional shape occurs most frequently around you?

(c) Which 3-dimensional shape occurs most frequently in nature?

4 From the shell of a prism, a net is obtained.

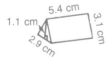

(a) Calculate its surface area.

(b) Make a larger copy of the net. Construct the prism.

5 From the shell of a cylinder, a net is obtained.

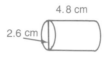 

(a) Calculate its surface area.

(b) Make a larger copy of the net. Construct the cylinder.

B

6 Pipe cleaners and straws are used to make these shapes.

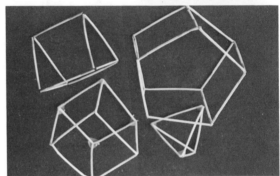

Use pipe cleaners and straws to construct each skeleton.

(a) cube   (b) square based pyramid

(c) rectangular prism   (d) triangular prism

7 For each shape:

(a) Construct its net.

(b) Calculate its surface area.

8 For each polyhedron:
▶ Design a net.
▶ Then construct a shell from your net.

(a) (b) 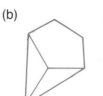 (c)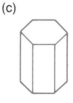

9 The net of a polyhedron is shown. A grid is used to make a larger net.

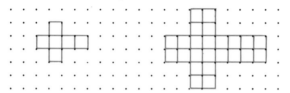

For each of the following:
▶ Make a larger net. ▶ Construct the shell.

(a) (b) (c)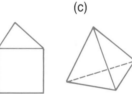

10 Make a larger copy of each net using cardboard.
▶ Construct the shell.
▶ Make suitable measurements to calculate the surface area.

(a) 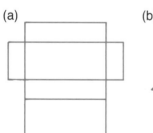 (b)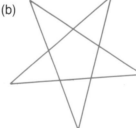

11 (a) What is meant by the term regular polygon?

(b) What do you think is meant by the term regular polyhedron?

12 There are only 5 regular polyhedra. The net for each polyhedron is shown.
▶ Make a larger copy of each net.
▶ Construct each regular polyhedron. Use cardboard.
▶ Each prefix is in Greek. What do you think is its meaning?

Regular tetrahedron

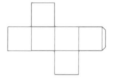

Regular hexahedron

Regular octahedron

Regular dodecahedron

Regular Icosahedron

13 Each net shows 6 faces. Which nets can be used to construct a cube?

(a) (b) (c) (d) (e) (f)

14 A plane cuts the cone. The cross section of the figure is shown.

The cross section is a circle

A plane slices each of the following solids. Draw a diagram to show the cross section.

(a) (b) (c)

15 A plane of symmetry of a cube is shown. How many planes of symmetry does the cube have?

16 How many planes of symmetry does each of the following have?

(a) (b) (c)

17 An axis of symmetry is shown for the cube. If the cube is rotated about the axis of symmetry, a $\frac{1}{4}$ turn, then the cube is mapped onto itself.

(a) For which turns about the axis of symmetry will the cube map onto itself?

(b) How many axes of symmetry does the cube have?

18 How many axes of symmetry does each solid in Question 16 have? Give reasons for your answer.

C

19 (a) Copy and complete the chart. Use these polyhedra.

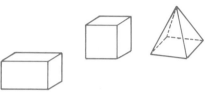

| | (i) | (ii) | (iii) |
Name of polyhedron	Number of vertices, V	Number of faces, F	Number of edges, E

(b) Study the chart. Do you see any patterns that relate the numbers in (i), (ii), and (iii)?

(c) Use any of the other polyhedra you have already constructed. Extend the above chart. Complete (i), (ii), and (iii) for each of these polyhedra.

20 Use the polyhedra in the previous question. Test which of the following relationships are true for all polyhedra.

(a) $V - F = E - 2$ (b) $V - F = E + 2$

(c) $V + F = E + 2$ (d) $V + F + 2 = E$

math tip

The pattern you studied on this page was probably known at least as early as 225 B.C., but no one wrote it down to let others know. René Decartes knew the formula $V + F = E + 2$ was true for polyhedra, but he also failed to record it and let others know. In 1752, Len Euler stated the formula and *wrote it down*. The formula, although officially called the Euler-Descartes formula, is today more commonly called the Euler formula. Next time you want credit, *write it down*.

5.12 perspective: sketching figures

A 3-dimensional shape may appear different, depending on how you look at it.

To describe a solid, usually 3 views are taken, as shown.

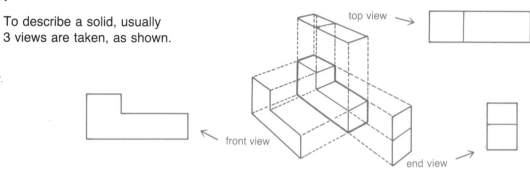

These 3 views are used to provide a clear picture of the 3-dimensional object.

To make an object appear real, an artist will use **perspective**. For example, the road in the photo at the right appears to vanish. To sketch a 3-dimensional object to appear real, **vanishing points** and **parallel lines** are used.

front of house

A vanishing point is drawn.

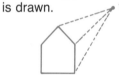

Parallel lines are used to construct the house.

If you change your eye level, the vanishing point appears in a different position.

Looking from below.

Looking straight on.

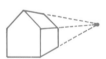

Looking down.

You can use vanishing points to create interesting designs. You could use one of your designs to make a cover for your next project.

You can vary the position of the vanishing point to obtain different effects.

B

1 The front, top, and end views are shown for various solids. Draw the solid that best fits the views.

(a)

(b)

(c)

(d)

 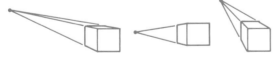

2 You can use dot paper to create some 3-dimensional objects as shown.

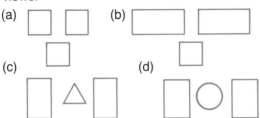

(a) Use dot paper. Create 3-dimensional figures of your own.

(b) For each figure you create, draw a front, top and end view.

3 Use 3 views: front, top, and end, to describe each solid.

(a) (b) (c)

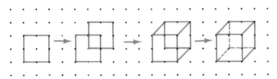

4 The cube is drawn from 3 different points of view.

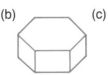

Draw a diagram to show each solid. Use the point of view shown.

(a) (b) (c)

C

5 The painting shows a good example of the use of perspective. Where is the vanishing point?

Find other examples of art, photography, and magazine pictures that use vanishing points.

skills quiz

In this chapter you have met the following words. Give an example or diagram for each word.

right angle	ray	parallel lines
right triangle	kite	scalene triangle
degree	bisector	vertical lines
square	pentagon	obtuse angle
angle	vertex	rectangle
rhombus	hexagon	acute angle
acute triangle	radius	obtuse triangle
congruent	image	line segment
altitude	rotation	polygon
diagonal	diameter	translation
inscribed	symmetry	reflection
prism	skeleton	co-ordinates
perspective	pyramid	shell
rigid	cylinder	net

translation arrow   ordered pair
rotation centre   straight angle
line of symmetry   parallelogram
intersecting lines   contained angle
equiangular triangle   isosceles triangle
supplementary angles   horizontal lines
regular polygon   circumference

5.13 problem solving: guess and test (rigid or not?)

Often to test whether something will work or not you take a guess. For example, an engineer will construct a model of an aircraft or a building and test its properties. This is certainly cheaper and less costly to human lives than to actually build them. For example, you could take a guess as to whether these figures are rigid or not. You could use straws to build them and experiment.

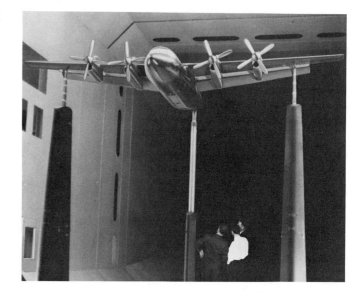

Rigid ✔   Not rigid   Rigid ✔

After you test various figures, you will find that figures that are constructed from triangles are rigid. Others that contain quadrilaterals are not.

1 For each of the diagrams, guess which ones are rigid.

  ▶ Build the figures from straws and pipe cleaners.

  ▶ Test whether your predictions are correct.

(a)   (b)   (c)

(d)   (e)

2 Each of these figures is not rigid. Suggest where a support might be placed so that the figure is rigid.

3 Each of these figures is a 3 dimensional skeleton.
  ▶ Guess which ones are rigid.
  ▶ Build the figures from straws and pipe cleaners. Test whether your predictions are correct.

(a)   (b)   (c)

(d)   (e)   (f)

(g)   (h)

(i)   (j)

          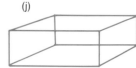

test for practice

1 (a) For the given figure, name a pair of
    (i)   parallel lines
    (ii) perpendicular lines
    (iii) congruent angles
    (iv) congruent line
          segments

    (b) Estimate and measure $\angle ABC$, $\angle BCD$,
         $\angle DTC$.

2 Find the complement of 68°; supplement of 78°.

3 Find the image of each figure.

   (a) Apply the   (b) Reflect $\triangle HGL$
        translation arrow to   about line ℓ.
        $\triangle KPQ$.

   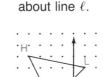   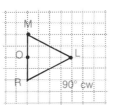

   (c) Apply a rotation to
        $\triangle MLR$ about O.

   (d) For each of (a),
        (b), (c),
        (i) what stays the
             same?
        (ii) what changes?

4 Construct $\triangle ABC$ with $\angle B = 53°$, $\angle C = 28°$,
   $BC = 7$ cm. Classify the type of triangle.

5 (a) Draw a line segment BC. Locate a point A
        so that $AB \perp BC$, and $AB = BC$.
   (b) Bisect $\angle B$.   (c) Find the midpoint of AC.
   (d) What do you notice about the result of the
        constructions in (b) and (c)?

6 (a) A net is shown. Name the
        3 dimensional shape
        for the given net.
   (b) Sketch a top, front, and end view of the shape.

looking back: a cumulative review

1 (a) Find the remainder when 39 854 is
        divided by 489.
   (b) Calculate 3941.63 ÷ 13.62. Round off
        your answer to the nearest tenth.
   (c) Round off 146.98 ÷ 3.69 to the nearest
        hundredth.

2 The base of a prism is a square with side
   measures of 14.2 cm. The height of the
   prism is 12.6 cm. Calculate the volume.

3 The diameter of a dime is about 18 mm. The
   diameter of a quarter is about 24 mm. Which
   would have more value   a kilometre of dimes?
   a kilometre of quarters?

4 (a) Which numbers shown below are
        divisible by 9? by 8?
        2916, 3214, 41 311, 7164, 448, 9111, 21 132
   (b) Which numbers shown above are divisible
        by 9 and by 8? not divisible by 8 or 9?

5 (a) Study this design
        carefully. Make
        suitable measure-
        ments to calculate
        the area of the
        shaded part.

   (b) Construct a copy of the design.

6 The dimensions of a track are shown. The
   ends are circular.
   (a) Calculate the surface area of the track.

   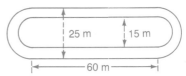

   (b) The school board decided to pour
        asphalt on the track. Calculate the cost if
        the paving company charged $6.75/m² to
        complete the job.

math is plus: writing a computer program

Two terms that you often hear associated with computers are **hardware** and **software**.
► **Hardware** is the equipment you see.
► **Software** is the programs which are written, or the routines and codes which are used, to direct the operation of a computer.
In this math plus you will explore the meaning of the statements you have used in your programs.
Steps A and B will provide you with some additional background to work with computer programs.

The **memory** of the computer is made of cores that can be magnetized. Internally, the computer uses binary numbers, that is numbers that have base 2.
Each binary digit is called a **bit**. A computer word, or **byte**, is composed of 8 bits. To rate the size of a computer's memory, the term **kilobyte** or **K bytes** are used. One kilobyte consists of 2^{10} bytes.

A Computer Expressions
Write each of the expressions in BASIC.

(a) $2p + q$ 　　(b) $4x + 5y$ 　　(c) $2x + 3y^2$

(d) $(p + q)^2$ 　　(e) $\frac{1}{2}(a + b)h$ 　　(f) πR^2

B Computer Instructions
● Each line of a computer program begins with a number. Numbers like 10, 20, 30, . . . are used. The numbers indicate to the computer the order in which it is to carry out the instructions.

● A PRINT line is used to have the computer print the result.
　　20　PRINT "THE ANSWER IS"; N
　　20　PRINT 2↑3

● Every computer program needs to finish with an END statement. This is the last statement in the program.

● In some of the programs you have tried, a LET statement was used. A LET statement is used in different ways.
　　30　LET N = 6
In this case, a value is assigned to the variable N. In the program the computer will assign the value of 6 to N.
　　30　LET V = A/B

In this case, V is calculated once A and B are known.

● To input the values of A and B into the computer program, you use the INPUT statement

　　20　INPUT A, B
If a program is run with the above statement, the computer will display the following. 　? ■
The computer waits for you to input the value for A and then for B.

Type this program into a microcomputer.

This program finds the volume of a cone.

```
10   PRINT "VOLUME OF CONE"
20   INPUT "RADIUS IS"; R
30   INPUT "HEIGHT IS"; H
40   LET V = π * R↑2 * H/3
50   PRINT "VOLUME OF CONE IS"; V
60   END
```

Every type of computer has variations. You should read your instruction booklet carefully. However, in general, once you have typed in the program, you need to give the computer instructions to begin to work. You type in RUN. Then you press the RETURN key. The computer is now ready to accept INPUTS.

(i) Write a program to calculate the area A of a triangle.
Use $A = \frac{1}{2} \times b \times h$ for these values.

b	12	16.2	1.96
h	8	12.6	2.38

(ii) Write a program to calculate the volume of a sphere. Use the formula
$V = \frac{4}{3} \times \pi \times r^3$ where r is the radius and $\pi \doteq 3.14$. Choose different values of the radius.

6 applications with ratios, rates, and percent

Skills with ratios, proportions, scale diagrams, using rates, making assumptions, time-distance-rate, introduction to percent, percent of a number, percents for consumers, interest and sales tax, probability, problem solving skills, solving problems and applications

There are many situations in which you need to compare quantities.

To compare the performance of athletes, times are compared.

To compare the profit and loss of a business, numbers of dollars are compared.

To tell how fast you are travelling, you compare distance and time.

In making weather predictions, data are compared.

To compare quantities, you need to develop skills with **ratio** and **rate**. Throughout your work, look for ways to relate new skills to skills developed previously.

Look for
Puzzlers.

6.1 basic skills with ratios

You often need to compare one quantity with another.

For example, the season record for a school basketball team is shown.

	Cedar Heights
games won	31
games played	46

You can compare the number of games won to the number of games played.

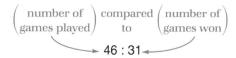

$$\left(\begin{array}{c}\text{number of games}\\\text{won}\end{array}\right) \begin{array}{c}\text{compared}\\\text{to}\end{array} \left(\begin{array}{c}\text{number of games}\\\text{played}\end{array}\right)$$

31 : 46

A **ratio** is a comparison of quantities expressed in the same units.

The above ratio 31 : 46 is read as "31 is compared to 46."
The symbol : means *is compared to*. The numbers 31 and 46 are called the **terms** of the ratio.

In working with ratios, you must know the *order* in which the terms are to be written. For example, 46 : 31 means

$$\left(\begin{array}{c}\text{number of}\\\text{games played}\end{array}\right) \begin{array}{c}\text{compared}\\\text{to}\end{array} \left(\begin{array}{c}\text{number of}\\\text{games won}\end{array}\right)$$

46 : 31

A two term ratio such as 5 : 7 can also be written in fractional form, as $\frac{5}{7}$.

(This is read, "5 is compared to 7".

Example 1 Of the 15 bicycles in the bicycle rack, 11 are ten-speed.

(a) Write a ratio comparing the *number of ten-speeds* to the *number of bicycles*.

(b) Interpret the meaning of the ratio 15 : 11 for the bicycles.

Solution (a)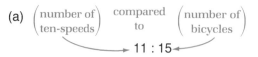

$$\left(\begin{array}{c}\text{number of}\\\text{ten-speeds}\end{array}\right) \begin{array}{c}\text{compared}\\\text{to}\end{array} \left(\begin{array}{c}\text{number of}\\\text{bicycles}\end{array}\right)$$

11 : 15

(b)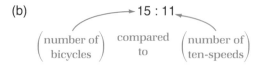

15 : 11

$$\left(\begin{array}{c}\text{number of}\\\text{bicycles}\end{array}\right) \begin{array}{c}\text{compared}\\\text{to}\end{array} \left(\begin{array}{c}\text{number of}\\\text{ten-speeds}\end{array}\right)$$

The order in which the terms of a ratio are written is very important. If you change the order of the terms, you change the meaning of the ratio.

Often in a recipe, you may need to compare more than two ingredients. For example, in a recipe 6 L of flour, 3 L of milk, and 1 L of butter are used. To compare the amount of *flour* to *milk* to *butter*, you could write the three-term ratio:

flour   milk   butter

Example 2 Write a ratio that compares the length to the width to the height of the box.

Solution 200 cm = 2 m
The ratio is   12 : 5 : 2

length   width   height

A ratio compares quantities expressed in the same units. To compare measures, they must be expressed in the same units.

A three-term ratio is a compact way of writing two-term ratios. For example, from the three-term ratio 12 : 5 : 2, you could write these two-term ratios.

Ratio of length to width	Ratio of length to height	Ratio of width to height
12 : 5	12 : 2	5 : 2
length width	length height	width height

Skills with ratios are important in solving problems in which you make comparisons.

6.1 exercise

A

1 Write a ratio to compare the number of

(a) cones to sundaes

(b) milkshakes to cones

(c) sundaes to milkshakes

(d) cones to milkshakes

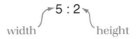

2 Write a ratio to compare the number of

(a) A's to B's

(b) A's to C's

(c) B's to C's

(d) C's to B's

(e) B's to all letters

3 The ratio of nickels to dimes to pennies is 5 : 3 : 7. Write a ratio to compare the number of

(a) nickels to dimes

(b) dimes to pennies

(c) nickels to pennies

(d) pennies to dimes

(e) dimes to nickels

4 From each three-term ratio, write three different two-term ratios.

(a) 1 : 2 : 5   (b) 12 : 7 : 11

(c) 3 : 1 : 8   (d) 15 : 4 : 23

B

5 Write a ratio to compare the lengths of the following line segments.

A   B   C   D   E   F   G   H   I   J

(a) AB : DE

(b) AC : DE

(c) BD : DI

(d) AD : AE

(e) BC : CH

(f) AG : CD

(g) FI : DF

(h) AF : BF

(i) AB : CE : FI

(j) EH : AD : IJ

(k) DF : CD : AE

(l) FJ : BC : AD

6 In a hockey game, the Oilers had 27 shots on goal. The Canucks had 22 shots on goal. Write a ratio to compare the number of shots on goal for the Oilers to the number for the Canucks.

7 Belinda is 119 cm tall and Sharon is 135 cm tall. Write a ratio to compare the height of Belinda to the height of Sharon.

8 In a video game, Tanya scored 11 525 points and Henri scored 9083. Write a ratio to compare Tanya's score to Henri's score.

9 The chart shows the number of games played and goals scored by various hockey players.

	Hickey	Devon	Wedge
games played	45	39	42
goals scored	23	22	25

Write a ratio to compare the number of

(a) goals scored to games played for each player.

(b) games played to goals scored for each player.

(c) games played by Hickey to Devon to Wedge.

(d) goals scored by Hickey to Wedge to Devon.

10 Paul's flight to Ottawa took 45 min. It took him 3 h to bus from his home to the airport. Express as a ratio the length of time spent on the bus compared to the length of time on the plane.

11 This book is 22 cm long, 22 cm wide, and 24 mm thick. Write a ratio to compare

(a) the length to the width

(b) the length to the thickness

(c) the length to the width to the thickness

12 Estimate, and then measure these line segments to the nearest centimetre. Answer the questions that follow.

A ———————————————————— B

C _____ D E _____ F

G ____ H

Write a ratio to compare the lengths of the following line segments.

(a) CD to AB

(b) EF to CD

(c) GH to AB

(d) AB to EF

C

13 There are 15 girls in a group. The ratio of the number of boys to girls is the same as the number of girls to boys for the group. How many boys are there?

14 There are 3 less vans than cars. There are 11 cars in the lot. Write the ratio of the number of vans to cars.

---

problem-solving: research

What a Record! What do you think is the record for each of the following? Choose a suitable unit of measurement for each

▶ The longest banana split ever made.

▶ The diameter of the tightrope used for the earliest crossing of Niagara Falls.

▶ The highest recorded temperature on earth.

▶ The volume of the largest fresh-water lake.

6.2 equivalent ratios and proportions

The label gives the directions for making orange juice from concentrate. You can use a ratio to compare the number of cans of concentrate to the number of cans of water.

For 1 can of concentrate: 1 : 3
                            number of cans   number of cans
                            of concentrate   of water

For 2 cans of concentrate: 2 : 6
                            number cans   number of cans
                            of concentrate   of water

The ratios 1 : 3 and 2 : 6 are called **equivalent ratios**. An equation that shows two ratios are equivalent is called a **proportion**.

$$1 : 3 = 2 : 6$$ (This equation is called a **proportion**.

To obtain equivalent ratios, you multiply both terms by the same number.

Ratio form   Fractional form
$1 : 3 = 2 : 6$ $\frac{1}{3} = \frac{1 \times 2}{3 \times 2} = \frac{2}{6}$
  1×2 3×2

Ratios equivalent to 1 : 3 are shown.

$1 : 3, \ 2 : 6, \ 3 : 9, \ 4 : 12, \ldots \qquad \frac{1}{3}, \frac{2}{6}, \frac{3}{9}, \frac{4}{12}, \ldots$

The ratio 1 : 3 is said to be in the lowest terms since the only common factor of each term is 1.

2 : 6 is not in lowest terms $\frac{2}{6}$ is not in lowest form   (Each term has 2 as a common factor.

Example 1   Express each ratio in lowest terms.

(a) 10 : 45   (b) $\frac{9}{15}$

Solution   (a) $10 : 45 = 2 : 9$ (Divide each term of the ratio by the same number.
                                          (Divide each term by 5.
              $10 \div 5 \quad 45 \div 5$

(b) $\frac{9}{15} = \frac{9 \div 3}{15 \div 3}$ (Divide each term by 3.

   $= \frac{3}{5}$

Once you learn skills with equivalent ratios, you can use them to solve problems.

Example 2   Last winter, for every 2 students that went skiing, 3 went snowshoeing. 96 students went snowshoeing. How many went skiing?

Solution   Use n to represent the number of students that went skiing.

Step 1 $\left(\text{To answer the question,}\atop\text{write the proportion}\right)$

$2 : 3 = n : 96$

or $\dfrac{2}{3} = \dfrac{n}{96}$ ←——— compare

$\dfrac{64}{96} = \dfrac{n}{96}$

Thus, $n = 64$

Last winter, 64 students went skiing.

Step 2 $\left(\text{Write an equivalent}\atop\text{ratio for } \frac{2}{3}.\right)$

$\dfrac{2}{3} = \dfrac{32 \times 2}{32 \times 3}$

$= \dfrac{64}{96}$

Check whether your answer is reasonable.

6.2 exercise

A The exercise that follows reviews and develops the basic skills along with the vocabulary needed to work with ratios.

1 Write at least two equivalent ratios for each of the following.

(a) $1 : 4$ (b) $3 : 7$ (c) $\dfrac{4}{5}$

(d) $2 : 3 : 5$ (e) $\dfrac{5}{6}$ (f) $10 : 6 : 4$

2 Which ratios are equivalent?

(a)	$1 : 2$	$2 : 4$	$2 : 5$	$3 : 6$
(b)	$2 : 3$	$8 : 12$	$6 : 9$	$10 : 12$
(c)	$\dfrac{3}{4}$	$\dfrac{6}{8}$	$\dfrac{9}{15}$	$\dfrac{15}{20}$

3 Write each ratio in lowest terms.

(a) $3 : 6$ (b) $15 : 5$ (c) $2 : 10 : 6$

(d) $4 : 10$ (e) $3 : 6 : 9$ (f) $25 : 100$

(g) $10 : 5 : 10$ (h) $85 : 20$ (i) $8 : 12$

4 Write a ratio in lowest terms for each statement. The first one is done for you.

(a) From a survey, Jean found that 20 out of 25 students walk to school.

$\left(\text{Ratio of }\textit{students who walk to school}\atop{\textit{compared to } \textit{total number of students}}\atop{\text{is } 20 : 25 \text{ or } 4 : 5}\right)$

(b) In a mixture of garden soil there are 4 pails of peat moss to 6 pails of earth.

(c) In Harry's class 3 out of 9 students have brown eyes.

(d) For every 20 g of sugar there are 30 g of flour and 15 g of marshmallows.

(e) There were 12 maples and 16 evergreens in the park.

(f) Twelve boys had blue eyes while 24 boys had brown eyes.

(g) Out of 50 eggs that Brian tested, 16 had slight imperfections.

(h) 6 out of 18 students work after school.

5 For each comparison, write a suitable ratio in lowest terms.

> (Remember: To compare measures they must be expressed in the same units.)

(a) The length of AB is 60 cm. The length of CD is 1.2 m.

(b) The length of XY is 1.4 cm. The length of QR is 28 mm.

(c) It took 2 h to go to the store. It took 30 min to come home.

(d) It took 3 h to fill the pool. The pool was emptied in 25 min.

(e) George jogged 2.5 km in the morning. Of that distance he walked 250 m.

6 For each proportion, write three proportions that have two-term ratios.

(a) $1 : 2 : 3 = 2 : 4 : 6$

(b) $12 : 18 : 9 = 4 : 6 : 3$

(c) $12 : 8 : 20 = 3 : 2 : 5$

(d) $1 : 3 : 2 = 3 : 9 : 6$

(e) $20 : 4 : 20 = 5 : 1 : 5$

(f) $2 : 3 : 5 = 4 : 6 : 10$

(g) $2 : 1 : 5 = 4 : 2 : 10$

(h) $12 : 6 : 3 = 4 : 2 : 1$

B

7 Find the missing terms.

(a) $3 : 6 = k : 12$

> (To solve this proportion, you can also use the fractional form. $\frac{3}{6} = \frac{k}{12}$)

(b) $9 : 12 = 3 : k$ (c) $\frac{25}{k} = \frac{5}{3}$

(d) $\frac{s}{12} = \frac{3}{4}$ (e) $7 : p = 70 : 30$

(f) $\frac{2}{3} = \frac{n}{15}$ (g) $15 : 5 = 45 : s$

(h) $8 : k = 4 : 3$ (i) $6 : 5 = k : 100$

8 In a recent poll the ratio of boys to girls interviewed was $15 : 5$. If 102 boys were interviewed, how many girls would you expect to be interviewed?

9 On the back of a wrapper Jean saw

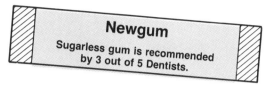

Newgum

Sugarless gum is recommended by 3 out of 5 Dentists.

(a) If 200 dentists were surveyed, how many would you expect to recommend sugarless gum?

(b) How many would you expect to not recommend sugarless gum?

10 Free-range farm eggs are shipped in boxes containing 180 eggs. Anita opened a carton of one dozen of the eggs and found that 2 were brown eggs. How many brown eggs would you expect to find in a full box?

11 Find the missing terms.

(a) $2 : 3 : s = 6 : p : 15$

(b) $k : 2 : 10 = 5 : 1 : w$

(c) $3 : h : m = 9 : 6 : 9$

(d) $6 : 12 : d = a : 4 : 5$

12 In a variety store, the ratio of small bags of plain chips to salt and vinegar chips to ketchup chips is $3 : 4 : 5$.

(a) The store usually sells 72 bags of plain chips in a week. How many bags of salt and vinegar chips do they usually sell?

(b) For the long weekend the store ordered 125 bags of ketchup chips. How many plain chips should they order?

C

13 (a) The ratio of the lengths of MN to OP is $4 : 5$. This ratio does not necessarily tell you how long MN is. Why?

(b) If MN is 12 cm, how long is OP?

6.3 working with scale diagrams

Often it is necessary to draw a diagram of a large area or object on a sheet of paper. To do so, a scale diagram is used. Maps, blueprints, and floor plans are examples of different types of scale diagrams.

To solve problems about scale diagrams, use a ratio to compare the measures on the actual object to the measures on the diagram. For example, a tennis court is shown. To compare the width in the diagram to the actual width of the tennis court, you write a ratio.

The number of centimetres in the width of the *diagram.* ⟩ 2 : 1000 (The number of centimetres in the width of the *actual* tennis court.

(To compare measures you express them in the same units. e.g. write 10 m as 1000 cm

The ratio 2 : 1000 tells you how many times a diagram has been reduced or increased in size from the actual real-life object. The ratio 2:1000 is called the **scale** or the **scale ratio** of the diagram.

4 cm · 2 cm

This diagram represents the tennis court.

The scale is written in lowest terms.

2 : 1000 = 1 : 500 ← (The ratio means that 1 cm on the drawing represents 500 cm measured on the tennis court.

Often for convenience, the scale of a diagram is written in the following form:

    1 cm *represents* 500 cm
             or
    1 cm *represents* 5 m

(If you write the scale in this form you do not need to express both measures in the same unit.

In the following scale diagram, the diagram is enlarged from the actual object.

Example 1   A micro chip is shown enlarged.
               1 cm *represents* 0.5 mm
        Write the scale of the diagram as a ratio.

Solution   1 cm *represents* 0.5 mm
          10 mm *represent* 0.5 mm

measure on the diagram ⟩ 10 : 0.5 (measure on the actual micro chip

    10 : 0.5 = 100 : 5
             = 20 : 1

(Decimals are avoided in writing ratios. Multiply each term by the same number, 10 so that each term in the ratio is a whole number.

The scale of the diagram is 20 : 1.

If you know the scale of a diagram, you can calculate lengths on the actual object, as shown in the next example.

Example 2   A diagram of the flag is drawn using the scale 1 : 75. Find the actual length of the flag.

Solution   By measuring, the length of the flag is 2.3 cm.
Use the scale.
   1 cm represents 75 cm
   2.3 cm represent 2.3 × 75 cm or 172.5 cm
The actual length of the flag is 172.5 cm.

In Chapter 11 you will use your skills again with scale ratios to solve problems.

6.3 exercise

A   Unless indicated otherwise, round your answers to one decimal place.

1   Write each ratio in lowest terms.

   (a) 2 : 6   (b) 5 : 25   (c) 8 : 2

   (d) 25 : 100   (e) 16 : 40   (f) 100 : 25

   (g) 8 : 6   (h) 1000 : 10   (i) 250 : 1000

2   Write the ratios so that each term in the ratio is a whole number. Express each ratio in lowest terms.

   (a) 2 : 1.5   (b) 2.5 : 6   (c) 1.8 : 3

   (d) 1.4 : 2   (e) 10.5 : 5   (f) 2.5 : 10

3   Write each scale as a ratio.

   (a) 1 cm *represents* 6 m

   (b) 1 cm *represents* 10 km

   (c) 1 m *represents* 2.5 km

4   Express each scale in lowest terms.

   (a) 4 : 30   (b) 100 : 10   (c) 1000 : 750

   (d) 4 cm *represents* 100 cm

   (e) 2 cm *represents* 10 m

   (f) 2 cm *represents* 2 mm

5   Write a scale for each of the following.

	Actual distance	Distance on the diagram
(a)	5 km	2.5 cm
(b)	100 cm	10 cm
(c)	2 m	4 cm
(d)	100 cm	2 cm

6   The scale on a map is 1 cm *represents* 12 km. Vince measured a distance of 4 cm on the map. Find the missing values to find the actual distance.
   1 cm *represents* 12 km.
   4 cm *represent* ▢ km.
   The actual distance is ▢ km.

7   The scale on a diagram is 10 : 1. Anna measured a length of 4.5 cm on the diagram. Find the missing values to find the actual length.
   10 cm *represent* 1 cm.
   1 cm *represents* ▢ cm.
   4.5 cm *represent* ▢ cm.
   The actual distance is ▢ cm.

8 The scale on a diagram is shown as 1 : 2.

(a) What does this scale mean?

(b) On the diagram an object measures 2 cm. What is the actual length of the object?

(c) A length on an actual object measures 8 cm. How long would this length be on the diagram?

9 A measurement of 3 cm is made on a diagram. For each scale, calculate the corresponding measure on the actual object.

(a) 1 : 5　　　(b) 1 : 10　　　(c) 1 : 50

(d) 1 : 100　　(e) 1 : 1000　　(f) 1 : 10 000

10 On a diagram, the scale is 1 cm *represents* 2 m. Find the corresponding length on the diagram for each of the following actual lengths.

(a) 6 m　　　(b) 10 m　　　(c) 5 m

(d) 3 m　　　(e) 2.5 m　　　(f) 6.5 m

11 The scale of each diagram is shown. Measure to find the length MN in each diagram. Then use the scale to find the actual length that MN represents.

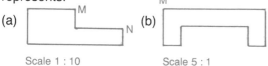

(a) Scale 1 : 10

(b) Scale 5 : 1

B

12 A tower is 20 m high. Calculate its height on a diagram if the scale is 1 : 1000.

13 The diameter of a large circle measures 12 m. Calculate the length of the diameter on a diagram if the scale is 1 : 200.

14 The length of the gym floor is 35 m. Calculate its length in a drawing if a scale of 1 : 650 is used.

15 On a map the scale is 1 cm *represents* 2.5 km. If John drove 45 km, how many centimetres would represent his trip on the map?

16 The scale on a map is 1 : 25 000.

(a) What distance would you walk if the distance measured on the map is 4.5 cm?

(b) Calculate the distance on the map if the actual distance walked is 4.75 km.

17 The actual height of the Douglas Fir shown in the diagram is 160 m. What is the scale of the diagram?

18 The Mackenzie River is 4200 km long. On a map this length measured 28 cm. Find the scale on the map. Express your answer as a ratio.

19 The Fraser River is about 1400 km long. The length measured on a map is 16 cm. Write the scale of the map as a ratio.

20 A scale diagram is shown. Calculate its length.

Scale
2 : 1

21 A photo is also a scale diagram. The scale of the photo is 1 : 190.

Find each of the following.
(a) width of the house
(b) height of the peak

applications : Prairie Provinces

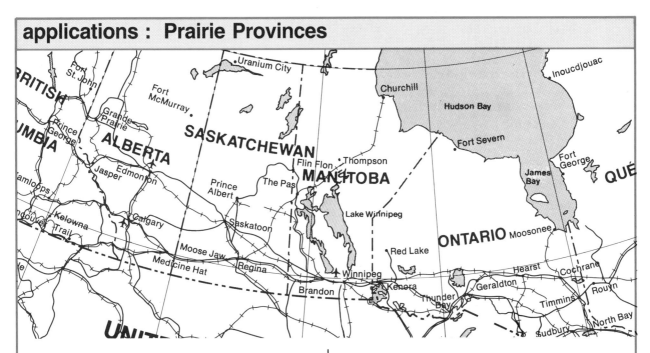

The following questions are based on the map of the Prairie Provinces. Round off your answers to 1 decimal place.

22 (a) The scale of the map is 1 : 19 800 000. What does this mean?

(b) How many kilometres does 1 cm on the map represent?

23 Wayne flew from Edmonton to Calgary.

(a) Find the distance in centimetres between these two cities on the map.

(b) What is the actual distance of the flight?

24 Janice drove from Winnipeg to Regina.

(a) Measure the distance between these two cities on the map.

(b) Calculate the actual distance that your answer to part (a) represents.

25 René took the train from Churchill to Thompson. What was the approximate distance of his journey?

26 Jasper, Alberta is 772 km due west of Saskatoon. How long would this distance be on the map?

27 Flin Flon, Manitoba is 456 km north east of Saskatoon. What length on the map would represent this distance?

28 Michelle is working in Fort McMurray. During her holiday she flew to Prince Albert and then to Edmonton. At the end of her holiday she flew back to Fort McMurray.

(a) Find the total distance of her flights on the map.

(b) Calculate the actual distance she flew.

29 Imagine that you can fly a light plane. Make a flight plan to visit three cities in the Prairie Provinces.

(a) Measure the distance of your flights on the map.

(b) Calculate the actual total distance of your trip.

6.4 how is your accuracy?

Blueprints and diagrams are used in dam or building construction.
An engineer needs to accurately measure lengths on a diagram.
In the following example, if a measurement was inaccurate by
0.1 cm, then the answer would be inaccurate by 2.1 m. Be sure to
measure scale diagrams accurately.

Example   The scale diagram shows a dam
that is part of the Gardiner
Dam project on the South
Saskatchewan River.

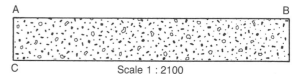

Scale 1 : 2100

Calculate
(a) the width of the dam.   (b) the height of the dam.

Solution   (a) From the diagram,   (b) From the diagram,
length AB measures 7.5 cm.   length AC measures 1.1 cm.
1 cm *represents* 21 m   1 cm *represents* 21 m
7.5 cm *represent* 7.5 × 21 m   1.1 cm *represent* 1.1 × 21 m
            or 157.5 m   or 23.1 m
The width of the dam is 157.5 m.   The height of the dam is 23.1 m.

6.4 exercise

A

1 The scale on a diagram is 1 : 500.

   (a) Ellery measured a length on the diagram to
       be 2.6 cm. What is the actual length on the
       object?

   (b) If he measured the length to be 2.5 cm
       (inaccurately), by how much would the
       answer differ?

2 A map has a scale of 1 : 10 000.

   (a) Phyllis measured the distance between two
       places to be 12.5 cm. How far apart are the
       places actually?

   (b) If she measured the length to be 12.6 cm
       (inaccurately), by how much would the
       answer differ?

3 The scale diagram
   shows the world's
   tallest totem pole,
   which is located at Alert
   Bay, British Columbia.

scale
1 : 976

   (a) Ruby measured the
       height to be 5.4 cm.
       What is the height
       of the pole?

   (b) Glen measured the
       height to be 5.3 cm.
       What is the height
       of the pole?

   (c) By how much do the answers in (a) and
       (b) differ? Who is correct?

B In each diagram or photograph, the scale is given. Make suitable measurements to find the actual lengths.

4 A scale diagram of a billiard table is shown.

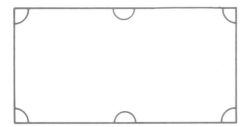

Scale 1 : 50

(a) Measure the length of the playing surface on the diagram.

(b) Use the scale to find the actual length of the playing surface of a pool table.

(c) Use the diagram to find the width of the playing surface.

(d) Use the diagram to find the actual distance from one corner pocket to the opposite corner pocket.

5 A magnified view of a bug is shown.

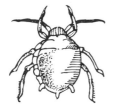

Scale 15 : 1

(a) Calculate the actual length of the body. (Do not include the antennae.)

(b) How wide is the actual bug?

6 A magnified photograph of a microprocessor chip is shown. Calculate the length and the width of the actual chip.   scale 2.5 : 1

7 Calculate the measure of the wing span of the gull.

Scale 1 : 11.2

C

8 The new Goodyear tire is the largest the company has ever built.

What you are looking at is one of the "biggest of the big". There are 6 of these big tires on the "King of the Lode" dump trucks, one of the largest trucks in the world.

Scale 1 : 66

(a) Calculate the measure of the diameter.

(b) Calculate the diameter of the opening of the centre of the tire.

6.5 working with rates: unit rates

In a ratio, the quantities being compared must be expressed in the *same units*. You used a ratio to show these comparisons:

15 m to 10 m   275 to 55
15 : 10 or 3 : 2   25 : 5 or 5 : 1

Sometimes you need to compare quantities that are expressed in *different units*.

A comparison of quantities expressed in different units is called a **rate**. For example, Jennifer jogs at the rate of 10 m in 2 s.

▶ The rate can be expressed in different forms. $\Big\}$ 10 m/2 s $\begin{pmatrix} \text{ten metres per} \\ \text{two seconds} \end{pmatrix}$ $\dfrac{10\ m}{2\ s}$ $\begin{pmatrix} \text{Since a rate shows a comparison of} \\ \text{quantities measured in different} \\ \text{units, the units used must be written} \\ \text{as part of the rate.} \end{pmatrix}$

▶ Equivalent rates can be expressed in lowest terms. $\Big\}$ 5 m/s $\begin{pmatrix} \text{five metres} \\ \text{per second} \end{pmatrix}$ $\dfrac{5\ m}{1\ s}$

Since the second term in the rate 5 m/s is 1, this rate is often called a **unit rate.**

The skills and concepts you learned about ratios extend to rates.

▶ You can express rates in lowest terms by dividing each term by the same number. $\dfrac{150\ km}{5\ h} = \dfrac{30\ km}{1\ h}$ $\begin{pmatrix} \text{Divide each} \\ \text{term by 5.} \end{pmatrix}$

▶ You can write equivalent rates by multiplying each term the same number. $\dfrac{45\ g}{1\ m^2} = \dfrac{450\ g}{10\ m^2}$ $\begin{pmatrix} \text{Multiply each} \\ \text{term by 10.} \end{pmatrix}$

▶ You can also use proportions to solve problems involving rates, as shown in the next example.

Example 1   Wanda picked 15 apples in 2 min. At that rate, how many would she pick in 14 min?

Solution   Let n represent the number of apples picked.
Write the proportion   Write an equivalent ratio.
in fractional form.

$$\frac{15}{2} = \frac{n}{14}$$ $$\frac{15}{2} = \frac{7 \times 15}{7 \times 2}$$

$\begin{pmatrix} \text{compare} \\ \text{terms} \end{pmatrix}$ $= \dfrac{105}{14}$

By comparing terms   Check whether your
$n = 105$ answer is reasonable.
Thus, Wanda can pick 105 apples in 14 min.

To solve some problems, you may first need to write a unit rate as shown in the next example.

Example 2   Tracey works in a fast food place and makes $32.80 for 8 h work. How much will she earn for 15 h?

Estimate first.
Then calculate.

Solution   In 8 h Tracey earns $32.80

In 1 h Tracey earns $\frac{\$32.80}{8}$ or $4.10

(The unit rate is $4.10/h)

In 15 h Tracey will earn 15 × $4.10 or $61.50

6.5 exercise

A

1 What is meant by each of the following rates?

(a) $\frac{120 \text{ km}}{10 \text{ min}}$

(b) $\frac{\$36}{12 \text{ records}}$

(c) $\frac{2.5 \text{ kg}}{2 \text{ persons}}$

(d) 30 m/s

(e) $\frac{21 \text{ m}^2}{2 \text{ L}}$

(f) $5/h

(g) 11 L/100 km

(h) 12%/a

2 Write a unit rate for each of the following.

(a) 250 g of fertilizer for 2 m²

(b) $40 earned in 10 h

(c) 120 km travelled in 6 h

(d) 18 rolls of wallpaper for 2 rooms

(e) 36 points scored in 18 games

(f) 48 min of penalties in 6 games

(g) 120 marshmallows for 6 girls

(h) 288 students in 6 buses

(i) 400 words typed in 8 min

(j) 48 hot dogs for 16 players

3 Calculate the unit cost (cost for one item) for each of the following.

(a) 8 hot dog buns for 90¢

(b) 3 tennis balls for $2.67

(c) 12 packages for $15.60

(d) 24 cans of soda for $9.60

4 Find the unit cost for each of the following consumer purchases. Round your answers to the nearest cent where appropriate.

(a) 1 dozen eggs cost $1.42

(b) 8 weiners for $1.75

(c) 25 m of tape cost 95¢

(d) 12 m² of carpeting for $227.40

(e)

284 mL
46¢

5 Find the speed (unit rate) for each of the following distances travelled.

   (a) The light aircraft flew 250 km in 2 h.

   (b) Jennifer jogged 270 m in 45 s.

   (c) The train travelled 560 km in 7 h.

   (d) Mohamed cycled 36 km in 4 h.

   (e) Kirsten swam 100 m in 80 s.

   (f) The space probe travelled 70 500 km in 3 h.

6 Write a unit rate for each of the following.

   (a) $\dfrac{200 \text{ km}}{10 \text{ h}}$ (b) $\dfrac{40 \text{ L}}{20 \text{ min}}$ (c) $\dfrac{16 \text{ cm}}{8 \text{ s}}$

   (d) $\dfrac{36 \text{ g}}{2 \text{ m}^2}$ (e) $\dfrac{\$18.00}{4 \text{ m}^2}$ (f) $\dfrac{200 \text{ mg}}{40 \text{ mL}}$

B

7 Find the missing value for each rate.

   (a) $\dfrac{60 \text{ km}}{2 \text{ h}} = \dfrac{\square \text{ km}}{4 \text{ h}}$ (b) $\dfrac{25 \text{ g}}{10 \text{ mL}} = \dfrac{40 \text{ g}}{\square \text{ mL}}$

   (c) $\dfrac{\$15}{3 \text{ h}} = \dfrac{\$\square}{4 \text{ h}}$ (d) $\dfrac{100 \text{ m}}{40 \text{ s}} = \dfrac{150 \text{ m}}{\square \text{ s}}$

   (e) $\dfrac{56 \text{ L}}{8 \text{ min}} = \dfrac{35 \text{ L}}{\square \text{ min}}$ (f) $\dfrac{75 \text{ g}}{250 \text{ mL}} = \dfrac{\square \text{ g}}{425 \text{ mL}}$

   (g) $\dfrac{10 \text{ m}^2}{\$120} = \dfrac{\square \text{ m}^2}{\$144}$ (h) $\dfrac{25 \text{ cm}}{10 \text{ d}} = \dfrac{\square \text{ cm}}{6 \text{ d}}$

8 (a) Asham can type 96 words in 2 min. How many words can he type in 5 min?

   (b) Three litres of milk cost $1.78. Find the cost of 9 L of milk.

9 Michael earns $29.75 in 7 h of work at Beck's Hamburgers. How much will he earn in 12 h?

10 Gertrude walked 9 blocks in 15 min. At the same rate, how long will it take her to walk 12 blocks?

11 In a survey, there were 60 *yes* responses to every 25 *no* responses. If there were 720 *yes* responses how many *no* responses were there?

12 Ingmar paid $36 for 4 m of fabric. How much would 7 m of the same fabric cost?

13 One evening 2.5 cm of snow fell in 2 h. If it continued to snow at the same rate, how much snow fell in 6 h?

14 Jackson used 10 kg of fertilizer for 100 m² of his backyard. How much will he use for a 12 m × 10 m rectangular lawn?

15 Shelagh read 45 pages of her novel in $1\frac{1}{2}$ h. At the same rate how long will it take her to read 70 pages?

16 The fastest recorded rate in canoeing was 19.6 km in 60 s. At that rate, find the distance travelled in 50 s.

Many years ago the canoe was a means of transportation. In modern times, canoeing has become a competitive sport, and is part of the events of the Olympic Games.

17 The most intense rainfall on record was 75 mm in 2 min at Barst Guadeloupe. At this rate how much rain would you expect to fall in 8 min?

18 The earliest steamship run was at the rate of 240 km in 32 h. How far would you expect the ship to travel in 13 h?

C

19 Ruta scored 8 points in 12 games.

   (a) How may points would you expect her to score in 18 games?

   (b) What assumption did you make to obtain your answer in (a)?

6.6 problem solving: making assumptions

To solve problems there are two important questions you need to answer before you begin your written work:

    I What information am I asked to find?
    II What information am I given?

Once you have the answer to these questions, you can use the Steps for Solving Problems to organize your work.

In solving problems about rate you often make assumptions, as shown in this example.

> **Steps for Solving Problems**
>
> A Ask yourself:
>   *I What information am I asked to find?*
>   *II What information am I given?*
> B Decide on a method.
>   *Which operation do I use?*
> C Do the work.
>   *Complete the calculation.*
> D Check your work.
>   *Use your rounding skills.*
> E Make a final statement.
>   *Answer the original problem.*

Example   At Harry's Car Wash it takes 4 min to wash a car.

    (a) If a car wash costs $2.25, how much money would Harry collect during an 8 h day?

    (b) What assumption did you make in finding your answer in (a)?

Solution   (a) **Step 1** Find the number of minutes in 8 h.
            8 h = 8 × 60 min
                = 480 min

        Step 2 Find the number of cars.
            In 4 min, Harry washes 1 car.
            In 480 min, Harry washes
            480 ÷ 4 cars or 120 cars.

        Step 3 Find the total money collected.
            1 car costs $2.25
            120 cars cost 120 × $2.25 or $270.

        Harry would collect $270.

    (b) To solve the problem, the assumption made was that a car was washed every 4 min. In other words, it was assumed that the car wash was working *every* minute for an 8 h day.

6.6 exercise

A

1 Express each rate in your own words.

(a) Harry walks at a rate of 2 m/s.

(b) Jean jogs at a rate of 4 m/s.

(c) The truck travelled at 75 km/h.

(d) The toothpaste cost $1.92/100 mL.

2 Calculate the cost of one item. (Remember: The cost of one item is often called the **unit cost** or **unit price**.) Express your answer to the nearest tenth of a cent.

(a) 4 tins of apple juice, $4.76.

(b) A package of 10 garbage bags, $1.89.

(c) 2-roll package of paper towels, $1.29

(d) 24 tins of soft drinks, $7.99

3 Pierre babysits and charges $1.50/h. How many hours did he babysit if he earned $150.00 last summer?

4 (a) How much would 8 glasses cost if 5 glasses cost $2.00?

(b) How much would 100 kg of birdseed cost if 25 kg cost $36.49?

B

For each of the following problems:
▶ Solve the problem.
▶ List any assumptions you made to obtain the answer.

5 Nathan types at a rate of 45 words per minute. How long would it take him to type 900 words?

6 (a) Steven scored 7 goals in 14 games. How many goals did he score per game?

(b) How many goals would you expect him to score in 36 games?

7 (a) Nyghi walked 10 blocks in 25 min. How many blocks did she walk per minute?

(b) How many blocks could she walk in 2 h?

8 Susan scored 28 points in 4 games of basketball.

(a) How many points did she score per game?

(b) How many points would you expect her to score in 20 games?

9 (a) One week Jon worked 18 h washing cars and was paid $58.50. What is his rate of pay per hour?

(b) If Jon worked 65 h in July, how much was he paid?

10 Use these ads to answer the following questions.

Store A	Store B
3 Badminton birds for $1.99	5 Badminton birds for $2.77

(a) Calculate the unit price at Store A.

(b) Calculate the unit price at Store B.

(c) Which store has the better rate?

11 (a) A solid milk-chocolate bunny costs $5.78. It is made of 500 g of creamy chocolate. Calculate the cost per gram.

(b) A common brand of chocolate bar has a mass of 35 g. The cost is 45¢. Calculate the cost per gram.

(c) Compare the unit prices in (a) and (b). Give reasons why the prices would differ.

C

12 (a) Find ads in newspaper that give prices for the same items: fruit juices, chocolate, sugar, etc.

(b) Collect the ads and calculate unit prices to compare the costs. Determine which store has the better buy.

6.7 applications: skills for travelling

Rates involving time and distance occur frequently in your everyday travels and in your reading.

A jet travels at 625 km/h.

Each speed in the examples is expressed as a unit rate. To find the distance travelled, you use the following relationship.

$$\boxed{\text{distance travelled} = \text{speed} \times \text{time taken}} \quad \left(d = v \times t \right.$$

Example 1 Tanya travelled at 60 km/h for 3 h. Find the distance she travelled.

Solution Use the relationship :
distance travelled = speed × time taken

$$d = v \times t$$
$$= 60 \times 3$$

in kilometres per hour ⟶   ⟵ (in hours

$$= 180 \longleftarrow \text{(in kilometres}$$

The distance she travelled is 180 km.

An olympic swimmer travels at the speed of 2 m/s.

In problems, "speed" refers to "average speed". To find the average speed or speed, you use the relationship :

$$\boxed{\text{speed} = \frac{\text{distance travelled}}{\text{time taken}}} \quad \left(v = \frac{d}{t} \right.$$

One of the fastest speeds for a track racing car is 257.1 km/h.

Example 2 Karl ran 200 m in 50 s. Calculate his speed in metres per second.

Solution
$$\text{speed} = \frac{\text{distance travelled}}{\text{time taken}}$$
$$v = \frac{d}{t}$$
$$= \frac{200}{50} \quad \left(\begin{array}{l} \text{Think :} \\ \text{What units did I use?} \end{array} \right.$$
$$= 4$$
Karl's speed was 4 m/s.

To find the time taken you use:

$$\boxed{\text{time taken} = \frac{\text{distance travelled}}{\text{speed}}}$$

$$\left(t = \frac{d}{v} \right.$$

6.7 exercise

A Express your answers to one decimal place when needed.

1 Find the distance travelled for each of the following.

	Speed	Time
(a)	15 km/h	2 h
(b)	25 km/h	3 h
(c)	2 m/s	15 s

2 Find the speed for each of the following.

	Distance travelled	Time taken
(a)	40 km	4 h
(b)	180 km	6 h
(c)	100 m	5 s

3 Find the time taken for each of the following.

	Distance travelled	Speed
(a)	200 km	50 km/h
(b)	60 km	20 km/h
(c)	100 m	2 m/s

B For each of the following problems, you need to decide whether the information you are asked to find is the *distance travelled*, the *time taken* or the *speed*.

4 A truck travelled 250 km in 5 h. At this speed, how long would it take to complete a trip of 650 km?

5 Mary Rose ran a distance of 3.5 km in 70 min. Calculate her average speed in kilometres per minute.

6 George's father drove the family car 150 km in 2.5 h. At this speed, how far would he travel in 10 h?

7 During the motoring trip Helen recorded the total distance as 325 km. The actual driving time was 4.2 h. Calculate her average speed in kilometres per hour.

8 Maggie's mother jogs at a speed of 2 m/s.

(a) How far would she jog in 1 min?

(b) How long would it take her to jog 100 m?

9 Steven rides his bicycle at a speed of 15 km/h. How long would Steven take to ride 225 km at this speed?

10 The fastest swimming bird is the Gentoo penguin clocked at 14.5 m/s. How far will the bird swim in 1.5 min?

11 The first supersonic flight was at the speed of 0.3 km/s. How far would the jet travel in 2.5 h?

12 One of Air Canada's planes, the jumbo jet, has a cruising speed of about 1000 km/h.

(a) How far would you expect the plane to fly in 3.5 h? 6.7 h? 8.25 h?

(b) How long would it take to fly 2000 km? 900 km? 1500 km? 2300 km?

(c) What assumption did you make in finding your answers in (a) and (b)?

C

13 (a) A lion travels at the speed of 25 m/s. How long would it take a lion to run 1 km?

(b) An elephant travels at the speed of 12 m/s. How long would it take to run 1 km?

(c) How much longer would it take an elephant to go 2.5 km than a lion?

6.8 skills for consumers: percent

Melissa is a disc jockey. 60% of the music she plays on her night-time show is Canadian. The symbol 60% means 60 out of 100.

You can write $60\% = \frac{60}{100}$ in fractional form.

(The % symbol means per hundred or out of one hundred.

Thus, if she plays 100 songs, 60 of them are Canadian. But what if she plays fewer than 100 songs? 60% can be thought of as a ratio.

$$60\% = \frac{60}{100} = \frac{6}{10} = \frac{3}{5}$$

$$60\% = \frac{60}{100} = 0.60$$

This shows that 6 out of every 10 songs, or 3 out of every 5 songs, are Canadian. Thus, to write a ratio as a percent, you need to find an equivalent ratio, for which the second term is 100.

Example 1   Write 23 out of 50 as a percent.

Solution   23 out of 50 is written $\frac{23}{50} = \frac{\square}{100}$

Think: Find the missing term.

$$\frac{23}{50} = \frac{23 \times 2}{50 \times 2} = \frac{46}{100}$$

$$\frac{23}{50} = \frac{46}{100} = 46\%$$

Thus, 23 out of 50 represents 46%.

To solve problems about percent, you need to develop other skills, as shown in the next example. Does your calculator have a $\boxed{\%}$ key?

Example 2   (a) Write 46.5% as a decimal.

(b) Write 75% in fraction form

(c) Write $\frac{7}{8}$ as a percent.

Solution

(a) $46.5\% = \frac{46.5}{100}$
$= 0.465$

(b) $75\% = \frac{75}{100}$
$= \frac{3}{4}$ *(Divide each term by 25.)*

(c) $\frac{7}{8} = 0.875$
$= \frac{87.5}{100} = 87.5\%$

6.8 exercise

A

1   Each diagram is made from 100 squares. Express the shaded part as a fraction and as a percent of the whole diagram.

(a)   (b)   (c)

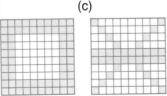

2   For each diagram:
  ▶ What percent is shaded?
  ▶ What percent is not shaded?

(a)   (b)   (c)

3 Express each of the following as a percent.

(a) $\frac{25}{100}$ (b) $\frac{27}{100}$ (c) $\frac{15}{100}$

(d) $\frac{10}{100}$ (e) $\frac{37.5}{100}$ (f) $\frac{16.7}{100}$

(g) $\frac{800}{100}$ (h) $\frac{85}{1000}$ (i) $\frac{865}{1000}$

4 Write each percent as a decimal.

(a) 48%   (b) 85%   (c) 25%   (d) 75%

(e) 6%   (f) 3%   (g) 10%   (h) 23%

(i) 70.5% (j) 17.5% (k) 80.5% (l) 0.6%

5 Write each percent as a decimal.

(a) 61%   (b) 45%   (c) 7%   (d) 8%

(e) 12.5% (f) 37.5% (g) 1.5%   (h) 0.5%

B

Estimate first.
Then calculate.

6 Write each fraction as a percent. You may first need to express the fraction in lowest terms.

(a) $\frac{17}{25}$ (b) $\frac{47}{50}$ (c) $\frac{3}{4}$

(d) $\frac{15}{20}$ (e) $\frac{39}{75}$ (f) $\frac{16}{80}$

7 Express each percent in fraction form. Write the fractions to lowest terms.

(a) 50%   (b) 75%   (c) 20%   (d) 60%

(e) 30%   (f) 4%   (g) 5%   (h) 88%

(i) 62.5% (j) 87.5% (k) 1.25% (l) 12.5%

8 Write each decimal as a percent.

(a) 0.73   (b) 0.48   (c) 0.09

(d) 0.3   (e) 0.125   (f) 0.625

(g) 0.58   (h) 0.25   (i) 0.005

9 Write each fraction as a percent. Round answers to one decimal place (as needed).

(a) $\frac{7}{10}$ (b) $\frac{11}{20}$ (c) $\frac{1}{10}$

(d) $\frac{37}{50}$ (e) $\frac{1}{50}$ (f) $\frac{2}{5}$

(g) $\frac{3}{8}$ (h) $\frac{7}{8}$ (i) $\frac{2}{3}$

(j) $\frac{1}{9}$ (k) $\frac{4}{11}$ (l) $\frac{9}{11}$

10 Find the missing values.

(a) $\frac{\blacksquare}{100} = 5\%$ (b) $\frac{1}{5} = \blacksquare\%$ (c) $\frac{3}{5} = \frac{\blacksquare}{100}$

(d) $\blacksquare\% = \frac{4}{5}$ (e) $\frac{\blacksquare}{100} = 0.96$ (f) $36\% = \frac{\blacksquare}{100}$

(g) $\frac{3}{4} = \blacksquare\%$ (h) $42\% = \frac{42}{\blacksquare}$ (i) $\blacksquare\% = \frac{2}{100}$

11 In each statement a ratio occurs. Express the ratio as a percent.

(a) In Allan's class 6 out of 10 students have blue eyes.

(b) 4 out of 5 students take a bus to school.

(c) Out of every 20 households, 15 have a dog.

12 Out of 500 students interviewed, 375 said they have too much homework.

(a) Write a percent for the information.

(b) Create a similar problem and write a percent.

C

13 Write these in order from least to greatest.

$\frac{3}{12}$ 0.28   0.20 $\frac{2}{9}$ $\frac{2}{7}$

$\frac{4}{15}$ 0.24   0.21 $\frac{6}{26}$ $\frac{14}{54}$

problem-solving: puzzler

What property do these words have in common?
CODE   HEX   HIKE   DOE
What is another word that has the same property?

(Clue: turn to page 176. Do you see the clue?)

6.9 using percent: comparisons

Your understanding of percents can help you make comparisons. For example, the results of a survey are shown.

Survey Question.

| Would you like to take |
| a space shuttle |
| ride to the moon? |

Survey results

	yes	no	total
Bow City	70	55	125
Cranbrook	22	18	40

Space Shuttle Challenger prepares to touch down after completing its mission carrying the first five-member crew including the first woman astronaut, Sally Ride.

The results are hard to compare because the totals are different. To compare the results, you can use a percent.

	Bow City	Cranbrook
number of yes answers) $\rightarrow$	$\frac{70}{125} = 0.56$	$\frac{22}{40} = 0.55$
total number of answers) $\rightarrow$	$= 56\%$	$= 55\%$

You could also use your skills with proportion to find the percent.

$\frac{22}{40} = \frac{\square}{100}$ or $\frac{11}{20} = \frac{\square}{100}$

$\frac{55}{100} = \frac{\square}{100}$ Thus $\frac{22}{40} = 55\%$.

When the results are expressed as percents, you can easily compare them.

6.9 exercise

A

1 Copy and complete the chart.

	Percent form	Fraction form	Decimal form	Ratio form
(a)	50%	?	?	?
(b)	?	$\frac{3}{5}$	?	?
(c)	?	?	0.08	?
(d)	?	?	?	1:10
(e)	?	$\frac{1}{4}$	?	?

2 Write each as a percent.

(a) 17 out of 25   (b) 39 out of 50

(c) 2 out of 16   (d) 6 out of 11

(e) 2 out of 6   (f) 6 out of 9

3 Find each percent. Round off your answer to the first decimal place (when necessary).

(a) What percent of 24 is 6?   (Use a calculator.

(b) What percent of 60 is 7.5?

(c) What percent of 55 is 12?

4 What percent is

(a) 20 cm out of 125 cm?

(b) 25 cm out of 2.5 m?

(c) $60 out of $250?

(d) 25 mm of 5 cm?

(e) 30 s out of 4 min?

(f) 2 m of 8 m?

B Percents can help you make comparisons.

5 Solve.

(a) Of 45 people in the room, 27 were women. What percentage were women?

(b) A macaroni and cheese dish had 250 g of macaroni and 45 g of cheese. What percentage of the dish was cheese?

(c) Terry picked 8 baskets of tomatoes. His sister threw away 1 of the baskets due to bruising. What percentage were good?

6 What percent of the keys on the keyboard are

(a) black?   (b) white?

(c) Which percent is greater?

Estimate first.
Then calculate.

Check whether your
answer is reasonable.

7 Who saves the greater percent of her earnings? Estimate first, then calculate.
▶ Sara earns $20 a week part-time and saves $12.
▶ Mirium earns $23 a week part-time and saves $14.

8 Who received the better mark?

(a)
Student	Mark
Bruce	38 out of 50
Joelle	17 out of 20

(b)
Glen	48 out of 60
Wendy	25 out of 30

9 The chart shows the results for the question asked in a survey,

"Do you enjoy winter sports more than summer sports?"

Day	Number of persons	Yes
Sat.	112	86
Sun.	89	64

On which day did the greater percentage say yes?

10 Vaughan earned $32 last week and spent $18. Ruth earned $27 and spent $21. Who spent the greater percentage?

11 In the voting for school president, the number of votes cast is shown. Everyone in the school voted.

Election Results	
Ruttan	125
Beavin	150
Truman	133

(a) Calculate the percentage of votes each candidate received. (Round your answer to 1 decimal place.)

(b) What do you notice about the total of the percentages? Why is this so?

C

12 The Garfields spend $450 a month on housing.

(a) If the income is $2250 each month, what percentage of money is spent on housing?

(b) What percentage is not spent on housing?

(c) Find your answer in (b), using a different method.

problem-solving: strategy

To solve this problem you've really got to ask some important questions. (How can numbers and letters be related?)

The value of SUMMER HOLIDAYS is 182. What value would you expect for WINTER VACATION?

applications: performance in sports

If you are the coach of a team, you need to make important decisions. For example, if you know which player performs the best in certain situations, you will use that player to help you help your team. The data in the chart show the performance of two goalies. For example, a goalie's job in hockey is to keep the puck out of the net during the game. But nobody's perfect all the time, so some shots taken on goal get past the goalie and a goal is scored. To compare the performance of goalies, data are collected.

Performance at home

Player	Number of shots on goal	Number of goals
Tremblant	865	44
Hickey	796	51

Performance on the road

Player	Number of shots on goal	Number of goals
Tremblant	696	43
Hickey	583	32

13 Use the data in the chart for performance at home. What percent of the shots on goal became goals for

  (a) Tremblant?   (b) Hickey?

  (c) Based on the data, which player would you probably use in goal during the playoffs for a home game?

14 Use the data in the chart for performance on the road. What percent of the shots on goal became goals for

  (a) Tremblant?   (b) Hickey?

  (c) Based on the data, which player would you probably use in goal during the playoffs at an away game?

15 The Atlantic Conference passing records are shown for each quarterback.

Player	Number of completed passes	Number of passes thrown
French	50	76
Kay	18	43
Dawson	16	23
DeCarlo	24	40
Thompson	36	90
McWhirter	30	71
Szasz	48	118

  (a) For each quarterback, calculate as a percent.

$$\left(\begin{array}{c}\text{number of passes}\\ \text{completed}\end{array}\right) \div \left(\begin{array}{c}\text{number of passes}\\ \text{thrown}\end{array}\right)$$

  (b) Which two quarterbacks would you like to have on a team you coach?

  (c) Which two quarterbacks would you wish were on the opposing team in a playoff game?

16 For each pitcher in baseball, the records are compiled so that comparisons of performance can be made.

Player	Innings Played	Innings Won
Jeff MacNabb	185	126
Mark Louden	128	76
Jay Liptay	136	93
Steve Habron	176	141
Mike Beresford	249	103
Jeff Boyd	216	189

  (a) Calculate for each pitcher, a percentage for

  (innings won) ÷ (innings played)

  (b) Which 4 pitchers would you use in the World Series?

  (c) If Mike Beresford were to win 23 of the next 30 innings played, by how much would his percentage change?

6.10 finding the percent of a number

Did you know that about 90% of the mass of an orange is really water?

An orange has a mass of 120 g. How much water is in the orange?

To answer the question, you can do the following calculation. Write a decimal for the percent.

90% of 120 = 0.90 × 120
= 108

The orange has 108 g of water.

The skills for finding the percent of a number can be used to calculate how much money you save, as shown in the example.

To make the frozen orange concentrate you buy at a store, the water is removed from oranges. Then the pulp and concentrated juice are placed in cans and frozen. To make orange juice, you just add the water again.

Example   The original price on a bicycle is reduced by 10%, if you pay cash. If the original price is $150, find the selling price.

Solution   **Step 1:** Calculate the reduction.
                    10% of 150
                    = 0.10 × 150
                    = 15

Step 2: Calculate the selling price.

original price	$150
amount reduced	$ 15
selling price	$135

The selling price of the bicycle is $135, (if you pay cash).

(Use your calculator to try other numbers.

6.10 exercise

A   Remember: to find the percent of a number, write a decimal for each percent.

1 Calculate 10% of each of the following.

(a) 120 g   (b) 600 m   (c) 45 km

(d) 130¢   (e) 160 people (f)   480 beads

2 Calculate 1% of each of the following.

(a) 100 m   (b) 1000 km   (c) 3000 cars

(d) 30 cm   (e) 150 g   (f)   35 kg

3 For each of the following:
   ▶ Estimate the value.   ▶ Calculate the value.

(a) 60% of 35 people   (b) 20% of $30

(c) 35% of 80 g   (d) 75% of 28 L

(e) 64% of 50 m   (f)   18% of 500 cm

(g) 12.5% of 64 steps

(h) 30% of 150 doughnuts

B   For each of the following, round your answers to one decimal place or to the nearest cent.

4 Find the following. Check whether your answer is reasonable.

(a) 45% of 16 people   (b) 78% of 24 stamps

(c) 39% of 18 tires

(d) 11% of 32 computers

(e) 17% of $77   (f)   2.5% of 34¢

(g) 12.5% of 19 words (h) 15% of 23 songs

5 Calculate.

(a) 15% of 27 lines   (b) 27% of $19

(c) 45% of 35 min   (d) 37% of 87 laps

(e) 63% of 49 cm   (f) 1.5% of 18 L

(g) 7.5% of $1.75   (h) 46.5% of 525 g

(i) $8\frac{1}{2}$% of 120 L   (j) $9\frac{1}{4}$% of $620

6 Each article has a 15% discount. (The price is reduced by 15%.) Copy and complete the chart.

	Original Price	Discount	Selling Price
(a)	$120	?	?
(b)	$342	?	?
(c)	$96	?	?

7 Find the selling price of each item. **15% off**

(a)
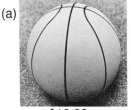
$18.99

(b) $386.88

8 (a) Estimate which is more money.
   A 18% of $300   B 28% of $150

(b) Calculate A and B. How close were you?

9 Wendy has 240 computer programs. If 75% of them are games, how many games does she have?

10 Lori was at bat 120 times during the baseball season. If she hit the ball 15% of the time, how many times did she have a hit?

11 Neil has completed 60% of his practice time for the track meet. If he is expected to practise for 18 h, how long has he already practised?

12 In a computer program 255 characters can be stored in a string. If 20% of the string is filled, how many characters are there?

13 When water freezes, it increases in volume by about 12%. Calculate the volume of each amount of water after it freezes.

(a) 100 L   (b) 150 L   (c) 300 L

(d) 12 L   (e) 18 L   (f) 250 L

Do you know why an iceberg floats? When water freezes it increases in volume. For this reason ice is less dense than water and floats.

14 The total length of the Trans-Canada Highway is 7870 km. About 6% of the highway is in Alberta. How many kilometres are in Alberta?

15 Of the persons surveyed, 70% chose the compact car. If 270 persons were surveyed, how many chose the compact car?

16 43% of the mass of the average person is muscle.

(a) How much muscle does Ali have if he has a mass of 123 kg?

(b) How much of your body mass is muscle?

17 About 30% of the movies shown are Canadian. If 4820 movies were shown, how many were Canadian?

computer tip

Do you want to know the percent you received on a test? Use this program.

```
10  PRINT "PERCENT ON TEST"
20  INPUT "TEST OUT OF"; T
30  INPUT "MY MARK IS"; M
40  LET P = 100 * M/T
50  PRINT "MY PERCENT ON TEST IS"; P
60  END
```

applications: sales tax for travelling

When you purchase something, in most provinces you need to pay sales tax. Each provincial government uses this method to raise money.

For example, if you buy a $10.00 item and pay 8% sales tax, the total amount you pay is $10.80.

Cost of item $10.00
Sales tax   0.80   (8% of $10.00)
Total price $10.80

If you were to take a trip across Canada, the chart shows the sales tax you would expect to pay on purchases in the various provinces. Use the chart to calculate sales tax when necessary, in the exercises that follow.

Rate of sales tax	Province
11%	Newfoundland
9%	Prince Edward Island
8%	New Brunswick Quebec Nova Scotia
7%	British Columbia Ontario
5%	Manitoba Saskatchewan
No Tax	Alberta

18 (a) The price of a pair of jeans is $21.90. If the rate of sales tax is 7%, calculate the total price you must pay for them.
  (b) Calculate the sales tax at 8% on a watch selling at $13.50.
  (c) How much sales tax would you pay if a hockey net costs $39.50? The rate of sales tax is 5%.

19 Calculate the sales tax on each purchase at the rate shown.

	Purchase price	Rate of sales tax
(a)	$30.00	7%
(b)	$16.50	8%
(c)	$18.95	9%

20 During a shopping trip 5 items were bought. Their prices are listed below. If the sales tax is 8%, calculate the sales tax paid on your purchases. $16.96, $11.50, $12.50, $1.96, $4.89

21 (a) Estimate the amount of sales tax you will pay in New Brunswick for each item.
        L.P. record $8.96
        All-weather sweater $32.00
        Stereo set $495.00
  (b) Calculate the sales tax.

22 For each purchase, estimate which amount, A or B, is the correct amount of sales tax you would pay in Quebec.

			A	B
(a)	fishing pole	$26.90	$0.22	$2.15
(b)	skis	$196.00	$15.68	$1.57
(c)	video tape	$14.99	12¢	$1.20
(d)	bicycle	$169.89	$13.59	$1.36

23 On a trip, to a neighbouring province, Sharon bought these souvenirs.
    Provincial emblem $11.90
    Photo of national flower $ 8.60
She paid $22.35 in all. Which province did Sharon visit ?

calculator tip

To calculate the total price of a purchase you can use your calculator.

> Set of Record Albums
> $43.65

Item costs $43.65   Calculator Display
6% Sales Tax   0.06 × 43.65 = 2.619
Total Cost   + 43.65 = 46.269
Round off.
The record albums cost $46.27.

6.11 using percent: finding the number

An advertisement shows that 10% of the regular price of a tennis racket is $6.25. What is the regular price of the tennis racket?

To find the regular price, you want to find 100% of the price. You know that

> The method of finding 1% of the number to find the number is called **the 1% method**.

$$10\% \text{ of the price is } \$6.25$$

$$1\% \text{ of the price is } \frac{\$6.25}{10}$$

$$100\% \text{ of the price is } 100 \times \frac{\$6.25}{10} \text{ or } \$62.50.$$

Thus, the regular price is $62.50.

To check whether the answer is correct,
find 10% of $62.50 = 0.10 \times \$62.50$
$= \$6.25$ ✔ checks

In solving a problem in mathematics you can often find the answer in a different way. For example, you can use a proportion to do the following example.

Example   If 20% of a number is 12, find the number.

Solution   Use n to represent the number.

Step 1: Write a proportion.

$$\frac{20}{100} = \frac{12}{n}$$

Step 2: Solve the proportion.

$$\frac{20}{100} = \frac{1}{5}$$

$$\frac{1}{5} = \frac{12}{60}$$

$$\frac{12}{60} = \frac{12}{n}$$

(Since the numerators are equal, then the denominators are equal.)

The number is 60.   Thus $n = 60$

Check:
20% of 60 = 0.20×60
$= 12$ ✔ checks

6.11 exercise

A

1 Find ? for each of the following.

(a) 1% of a number is 15.
6% of a number is ?

(b) 1% of a number is $\frac{16}{5}$.
15% of a number is ?

(c) 1% of a number is $\frac{24}{5}$.
12% of a number is ?

2 Find the missing values in the solution of each proportion.

(a) $\frac{3}{10} = \frac{15}{n}$

$$\frac{3}{10} = \frac{15}{?}$$

$$\frac{15}{?} = \frac{15}{n}$$

$$n = ?$$

(b) $\frac{28}{n} = \frac{80}{100}$

$$\frac{80}{100} = \frac{4}{?}$$

$$\frac{4}{?} = \frac{28}{?}$$

$$\frac{28}{n} = \frac{28}{?}$$

$$n = ?$$

3 Find 100% of each number.

   (a) 1% of a number is 8.
      100% of the number is ▢.

   (b) 1% of a number is 6.2.
      100% of the number is ▢.

   (c) 1% of a number is 15.6.
      100% of the number is ▢.

4 Of the bolts, 1% are defective. There are 62 defective bolts. How many bolts in all are there?

5 Of the people surveyed, 1% did not reply. There were 42 persons who did not reply. How many persons in all were surveyed?

6 Find each number.

   (a) 1% of a number is 16.

   (b) 10% of a number is 6.3

   (c) 50% of a number is 140.

7 Find n in the following.

   (a) 10% of n is 3.   (b) 40% of n is 10.

   (c) 50% of n is 16.   (d) 6% of n is 24.

8 Find the number if

   (a) 8% of the number is 32.

   (b) 25% of the number is 5.

   (c) 13% of the number is 65.

   (d) 8% of the number is 64.

   (e) 8% of the number is 12.

   (f) 15% of the number is 18.

B For each of the following, express your answers to one decimal place or the nearest cent.

9 (a) Sarah needs 5 cards to complete her collection. If this is 10% of the total collection, how many cards are in the set?

   (b) About 15% of the tree seedlings planted grew. If 375 seedlings grew, how many were planted?

   (c) Sasha hit 20% of the pitches thrown to her. If she had 8 hits, how many pitches were thrown?

10 The mass of a table tennis ball is 2.5 g. Its mass is 10% of the mass of a golf ball. Find the mass of a golf ball.

11 (a) Did you know that TIP means To Improve Performance? At the restaurant Betty left a 10% tip. If the amount of the tip was $1.50, how much was the restaurant bill?

   (b) A customer left a 12% tip since the service was good. How much was the bill if the amount left as a tip was $2.40?

12 Justin paid $1.75 sales tax on the desk set he bought. If sales tax is at the rate of 8%, calculate the total amount of the bill.

13 At the Olympic Games, 85% of the stadium was full. There were 35 700 people.

   (a) What is the seating capacity of the stadium?

   (b) What assumption did you make in finding your answer in (a)?

14 Of the garbage collected each day, 9.8% is metal. If 28.3 kg of metal were collected, how much garbage was there in all?

C

15 If 15% of 10% of a number is 9, find the number.

---

problem-solving: puzzler

Gregory grew 10% of his height and then grew 20% of his original height. If he grew 3.3 cm altogether, find his original height.

6.12 saving and borrowing money: interest

When you deposit money in a bank account you are paid interest while the bank uses your money. The amount of money in your bank account is called the **principal amount**. Suppose you have $100 and the bank pays you a rate of interest of 7% per year (7% per annum or 7%/a). To calculate the balance of your account at the end of the year you need to use your skills with percent.

CANADA BANK
Earn daily interest
7% per annum

Principal (or balance at beginning of year)	$100	7% of $100
Amount of interest	$ 7 ◄	= 0.07 × $100
Balance of account (at end of year)	$107	= $7.00

Accounts add the interest to your account monthly, quarterly, (every 3 mon), semi-annually, or some even daily.

Example   A bank pays interest at the rate of 8%/a (8% per annum). If you have $650 saved, how much will you earn in a quarter (3 mon)?   Estimate first. Then calculate.

Solution   Principal = $650   Rate of interest 8%/a

For 12 mon, amount of interest   = 8% of $650
                                 = $52.00

For a quarter, amount of interest = $\frac{\$52.00}{4}$ or $13.00

Thus, interest earned for a quarter is $13.00.

If you borrow money from the bank you need to pay interest for the use of the bank's money. The *same* skills used to calculate interest on deposited money are used to calculate interest on borrowed money.

Suppose you borrowed $150 for a year at a rate of interest of 12%/a (12% per annum). You would need to pay the following amount back to the bank, at the end of your loan.

Principal amount	$150	12% of $150
Interest charged	$ 18 ◄	= 0.12 × $150
Total payable	$168.	= $18

Look for
Computer Tips.

A Note: Different places pay different rates of interest for deposits.

1 Calculate the interest paid for each deposit for a year.

	Principal	Rate of interest
(a)	$150	6%/a
(b)	$250	8%/a
(c)	$325	7.5%/a
(d)	$420	6.5%/a

2 Calculate the interest charged for each loan.

(Note: Different places charge different rates of interest for loans.

	Loan amount	Rate of interest
(a)	$220	10%/a
(b)	$315	12%/a
(c)	$400	9.5%/a
(d)	$275	$10\frac{1}{2}$%/a

3 Find the interest received for each deposit.

	Principal	Rate	Time
(a)	$450	8%/a	6 mon
(b)	$2100	7%/a	6 mon
(c)	$575	6.5%/a	3 mon

4 Find the interest paid for each loan.

	Principal	Rate	Time
(a)	$350	12%/a	6 mon
(b)	$580	13%/a	6 mon
(c)	$960	$11\frac{1}{2}$%/a	3 mon

B In each of the following problems, you need to calculate the amount of interest received for a deposit or the interest paid for a loan.

5 Calculate the interest payable on each of these loans. Round off each answer to the nearest cent.   Estimate first. Then calculate.

(a) $45 at 10%/a for 1 a.

(b) $125 at 12%/a for 6 mon.

(c) $120 at $12\frac{1}{2}$%/a for 6 mon.

(d) $450 at 14%/a for 1 mon.

(e) $275 at $14\frac{1}{4}$%/a for 6 mon.

(f) $450 at $12\frac{1}{2}$%/a for 1 mon.

6 (a) A bank pays 8% per annum (per year) as the rate of interest. You deposited $125.30 for 1 a. Calculate the interest earned (to the nearest cent).

(b) The rate of interest paid is $6\frac{1}{2}$%/a. Find the interest paid after 1 a if you deposited $150.00.

7 (a) Calculate the interest charged on a loan of $250 for 9 mon, if the rate of interest is 14%/a.

(b) What assumption did you make in finding your answer in (a)?

8 (a) Calculate the interest on a loan of $350.50. The rate of interest is $11\frac{1}{2}$%/a. The money was borrowed for 6 mon.

(b) How much will be repaid at the end of the loan period?

9 When you purchase a Canada Savings Bond it pays interest as if you had deposited the money in a bank. How much interest would a $100-bond pay for one year at 12%/a (calculated yearly)?

Each year The Bank of Canada sells Canada Savings Bonds. The amount you pay for the bond is also called the principal. The bond pays a certain rate of interest each year to the owner of the bond.

10 The rate of interest on a Canada Savings Bond is $9\frac{1}{4}$%/a.

(a) How much would your $100-bond earn for you in one year (interest is calculated yearly)?

(b) How much would your bond earn in 1 a 7 mon?

11 (a) Leah's dad borrowed $1250 at a rate of 12%/a interest. Calculate the amount he paid back to the bank at the end of the year.

Consolidate your debts into one loan. Borrow today, and pay a fixed interest rate for 12 mon. **12%**

(b) Calculate the monthly interest on a loan of $500.00 if the rate of interest is $16\frac{1}{2}$%/a.

12 Samuel borrowed $350.00 for 1 a at a rate of interest of $15\frac{1}{2}$%/a.

(a) Calculate the interest he would need to pay on his loan in 1 mon, 6 mon, 1 a.

(b) Calculate the total he would need to pay back at the end of a year.

13 Last month Jeff did not pay the telephone bill of $28.45. On overdue bills, the telephone company charges interest at the rate of 1.75%/mon.

(a) Calculate the interest charged.

(b) How much will Jeff need to pay in all this month to discharge last month's telephone bill?

14 The rate of interest at a bank is 11%/a. The bank also states that interest is calculated or *compounded* monthly.

(a) Calculate the interest earned on a deposit of $200 after one month.

(b) What is the total amount in your bank account at the end of the month in (a)?

(c) Now calculate the total interest earned in the second month.

(d) Why is the amount of interest earned more at the end of the second month than at the end of the first month?

Interest calculated monthly is often stated as "interest compounded monthly".

15 Use a newspaper and collect the ads.

(a) Find what the current rates are for borrowing money.

(b) What interest would you pay to borrow $100 for a year?

C

16 Find the missing values of ▢ in this table. The interest is calculated each month.

	Amount deposited	Rate of interest	Length of time	Balance in account
(a)	$100	8%/a	1 mon	▢
(b)	$250	6%/a	2 mon	▢
(c)	$340	8%/a	3 mon	▢
(d)	$250.60	6.5%/a	2 mon	▢

6.13 percents for the consumer

To solve consumer problems, you need to understand the vocabulary. For example, suppose you want to buy a stereo made by a manufacturer.

▶ The manufacturer suggests a **list price**, $200, at which the store would sell to you, the consumer.
▶ The store decides to sell the stereo less than the list price, and gives a **discount** of $50.
▶ The **selling** or **net price** of the stereo is $200 − $50 or $150.

To make comparisons, you need to calculate the percent rate of discount. The rate of discount is given by the calculation shown.

$$\left(\begin{array}{ll} \text{List price} & \$200 \\ \text{Discount} & \$\ 50 \\ \text{Selling or} & \$150 \\ \text{Net price} \end{array}\right.$$

$$\frac{\text{Amount of discount)} \rule{0pt}{0pt} 50}{\text{List price)} \rule{0pt}{0pt} 200} = 0.25$$

$$= 25\%$$

rate of discount

In some stores, the sales clerk may be paid a **commission** on each sale made. A commission is a fee paid by the store to its sales people for making sales.

$\left(\begin{array}{l}\text{A commission is often paid as a}\\ \text{bonus to persons working on a}\\ \text{regular salary.}\end{array}\right.$

Example   Joelle sold a stereo for $219.75 to a customer. The rate of commission is 4% of the amount of sales. Calculate the amount of commission.

Solution   Amount of the sale $219.75   Rate of commission 4%
Amount of commission = 4% of $219.75
= 0.04 × $219.75
= $8.79
Joelle earned $8.79 as a commission on the sale.

6.13 exercise

A

1   For each sale estimate the amount of discount, then calculate the amount of discount.

	Item	List price	Rate of discount
(a)	Ski jacket	$ 89.75	20%
(b)	Skates	$129.80	15%
(c)	Video Game	$219.80	6%
(d)	Home Computer	$489.65	12%

2   Often a store may offer an additional discount. Find the sale price of each purchase.

(a) **New stock — Hand Held Printer** (display)
Selling price
$58.95

(b) **Microscope lab —** includes 3 lenses, prepared slides, for the young student.
$47.99

Check whether your answer is reasonable.

3 Jackie sells magazines at a rate of commission of 12%. She sold $245 of magazines last week. Calculate the amount she earned as a commission.

4 Copy and complete this table.

	List price	Rate of discount	Selling price
(a)	$25.00	☐	$20.00
(b)	$40.00	☐	$36.00
(c)	$80.00	☐	$48.00
(d)	☐	20%	$45.00
(e)	☐	25%	$ 7.50

B Refer to The Steps for Solving Problems to organize your solutions.

5 For selling magazines Jennifer receives a rate of commission of 10%. This means she receives 10% of her total sales. If her total sales amounted to $50.00, how much commission did she earn?

6 (a) Swim suits sell regularly for $15.95. At a sale an additional discount of 25% was given. Calculate the sale price.

(b) The list price for a game is $6.89. Calculate the selling price if a discount of 40% is given.

7 (a) The total sales made by a salesperson for copperware last year were $360. Calculate the amount of commission paid if the rate was 6%.

(b) The rate of commission is 4.5%. Calculate the amount made on sales totalling $46.50.

(c) The total sales were $200. The commission paid was $30. Find the rate of commission.

8 The list price of a snorkel set is $120.00. The rate of discount is 15%.

(a) Calculate the amount of the discount.

(b) How much is the selling price?

(c) The sales tax is 8%. How much will the customer pay in all?

9 Bruce bought a pair of pro-style skates at a 50% off sale.

(a) If the list price was $58.00, calculate the sale price.

(b) The sales tax is 7%. Calculate the total cost.

10 (a) George's father makes $350.00 per week plus a commission of $2\frac{1}{2}$% on all sales over $5000.00 per week. Calculate his salary for the month of August.
Week 1 $8000   Week 3 $ 9650
Week 2 $4500   Week 4 $11 600

(b) Calculate the salary for George's father if during December his sales were as shown.
Week 1 $11 900   Week 3 $12 600
Week 2 $13 800   Week 4 $ 8500

11 Sheila earned $345 in commission last month and $375 in commission this month. If her rate of commission is 6%, find her increase in sales over the month.

12 A computer had a regular price of $239. The sales tag was discounted 15% and then another 10%. Doug calculated a discount of 25% on the regular price. By how much do the two sale price tags differ?

13 The suggested list price of a track suit was $65.00. A discount of 15% was given by the store. A defect was noticed by Nita and the track suit was sold at $50. What rate of discount of the selling price was given for the defect?

Look for Math Tips.

C

14 Samantha expected sales to average $4800. If she asked for $260 in basic salary, then what rate of commission would she need in order to earn a total salary of $500?

More than 100%

Often you will see newspaper clippings or guarantees showing 100% or more. The skills you have learned with percent extend to skills with more than 100%.

Each year the population grows. The population of a city is 150% of what it was 10 a ago. What does this mean?

10% of a population of 10 000 is
$$10\% \text{ of } 10\ 000 = 0.10 \times 10\ 000$$
$$= 1000$$

150% of a population of 10 000 is
$$150\% \text{ of } 10\ 000 = 1.50 \times 10\ 000$$
$$= 15\ 000$$

15 Calculate.

(a) 150% of 200 cm

(b) 175% of 100 mg

(c) 300% of 200 L

(d) 160% of 125 kg

(e) 325% of $1000

(f) 175% of 125 mL

16 Calculate each of the following. Round off your answer (when necessary) to the first decimal place.

(a) 120% of 200

(b) 125% of 175

(c) 150% of 350

(d) 200% of 300

(e) 225% of 80

(f) 250% of 450

17 The population last year was 6875. The population this year is 108% of last year's figure.

(a) Calculate this year's population.

(b) By how much did the population increase?

(c) By what per cent did the population increase?

18 When a certain gas was heated it expanded to 125% of its original volume. If the original volume was 22 L, calculate the new volume.

19 15 L of gas are heated. The resulting volume is 150% of the original volume.

(a) Calculate the resulting volume.

(b) By how much did the volume increase?

(c) By what per cent did the volume increase?

20 John was 165 cm tall last year. His height this year is 103% of last year's height.

(a) Calculate his height this year. Express your answer to the nearest centimetre.

(b) By how much did he grow?

(c) By what per cent did he grow in height?

21 The traffic in downtown Calgary increases by 120% during the summer vacation. If 25 000 cars are downtown normally, how many cars are there during the summer vacation?

22 (a) A coin gained in value by 165%. If the original value was $125, what is the coin worth today?

(b) A stamp gained in value by 128%. The original value of the stamp was $96. What is the stamp worth today?

6.14 problem solving: which skill to use?

To solve a problem about per cent, you need to decide which type of problem you are solving. To do so, you need to read the problem carefully and look for the clues.

1 Find what per cent one number is of another.
What percent is 40 of 50?
$\frac{40}{50} = \frac{\square}{100}$ $\square = 80$
40 is 80% of 50.

2 Find the per cent of a number.
Find 30% of 120.
30% of 120 = 0.30 × 120
= 36
30% of 120 is 36.

3 Find the whole amount when a percentage is given.
20% of what number is 10?
20% of a number is 10
1% of a number is $\frac{10}{20}$
100% of a number is
100 × $\frac{10}{20}$ or 50
The number is 50.

Once you have decided on which skills to use, then organize your solution — use the *Steps for Solving Problems*.

6.14 exercise

A Questions 1 to 5 review your percent skills needed to solve problems. Round off your answers to 1 decimal place (where necessary).

1 Find the values of $\square$.

(a) 40% of a number is 60.
1% of the number is $\square$.
100% of the number is $\square$.

(b) 20% of a number is 80.
1% of the number is $\square$.
100% of the number is $\square$.

(c) 8.25% of a number is 80.
1% of the number is $\square$.
100% of the number is $\square$.

2 Calculate.

(a) 5% of 600 students
(b) 72% of 625 girls
(c) 5% of 250 g
(d) 40% of 40 games
(e) 35% of 120 viewers
(f) 43% of 275 points
(g) 23.5% of 45 km
(h) $12\frac{1}{2}$% of 36 km
(i) 2% of 14.5 L
(j) 8% of 465 L

3 Find the missing term in each proportion.

(a) $\frac{25}{100} = \frac{50}{\square}$
(b) $\frac{40}{100} = \frac{20}{\square}$
(c) $\frac{70}{100} = \frac{35}{\square}$
(d) $\frac{15}{\square} = \frac{60}{100}$
(e) $\frac{25}{100} = \frac{250}{\square}$
(f) $\frac{15}{100} = \frac{75}{\square}$

4 Calculate each answer.

(a) What per cent is 45 of 165?
(b) Express 94 as a per cent of 126.
(c) What per cent is 162 of 340?
(d) Express 128 as a per cent of 296.
(e) What per cent is 25.8 of 465?
(f) Express 12.3 as a per cent of 49.8.
(g) What per cent is 16.9 of 1789?

5 The three types of per cent problems occur among the following. Show how you found the answer in each case.

(a) What is 50% of 700?

(b) 50% of what number is 37?

(c) 30 is what per cent of 120?

(d) What is 12.5% of 32?

(e) 60% of 80 is what number?

(f) 40 is what per cent of 75?

(g) 80% of what number is 48?

(h) 75 is what per cent of 200?

(i) What per cent of 600 is 150?

(j) What is 30% of 150?

B Solve each of the following. Be sure to check whether your answer is reasonable.

6 Linda correctly answered 80% of the 20 questions in a quiz.

(a) How many did she answer correctly?

(b) How many did she miss?

7 (a) Some milk has 2% fat. Calculate the amount of fat in 25.6 L of milk.

(b) Air is 78% nitrogen. Calculate the amount of nitrogen in a balloon that has a volume of 6.8 m³.

8 (a) Mary Rose earns $3.50/h. If she receives a 10% increase, how much will she make per hour now?

(b) A gym suit sells regularly for $8.96. Calculate the price if there is a 20% discount.

9 Three students at Oakwood School did an environment survey. One question they asked was

Would you be willing to buy milk and other drinks in only returnable containers?

They found that 83% were willing to do so. If 249 persons said yes,

(a) how many persons were interviewed?

(b) how many said no?

10 Read this article.

What Part of the Human Body is Water?

A recent study was made to determine the amount of water in the human body. Experiments show, that the average person, by mass, is 65% water. During the study, the results also showed that this figure varied from person to person. A lean person may have as much as . . .

(a) George worked out how much water was in his body. His calculations showed he has 47 kg of water. What is George's mass?

(b) Susan found she has 30 kg of water in her body. What is her mass?

11 (a) In Susan's class 25% of the students walk to school. There are 32 students in the class. How many do not walk to school?

(b) Out of a total of 125 points, Cheryl scored 35 points. What per cent did she score?

(c) A badminton set regularly sells for $6.96. Calculate the sale price if there is a 10% discount.

12 (a) At training camp, there were 16 pitchers. They made up 8% of the players trying out. How many players were trying out?

(b) Last week 450 students attended the badminton semi-finals. This week 625 students attended the finals. By what per cent did the attendance increase?

(c) Recently, 75% of the kettles were returned because they were defective. If 120 kettles were returned, how many kettles were there altogether?

C

13 A bicycle depreciates (reduces) in value each year at the rate of 8%.

(a) A bicycle initially costs $129.80. Calculate its value at the end of a year.

(b) What would be the value of this bicycle at the end of 2 a?

practice and problems: a chapter review

(6.1) 1 Write a ratio to compare the number of

(a) circles to triangles.

(b) triangles to squares.

(6.2) 2 The largest book ever published measured 305 cm by 270 cm. Write a ratio in lowest terms to compare the length to the width.

(6.3) 3 The CN Tower was drawn to the scale of 1:2000. If the drawing was 27.5 cm tall, then how tall is the tower?

(6.4) 4 Refer to the stamp. The scale of the toy train is 1:20. Calculate its height, its length.

(6.5) 5 Write a unit rate for 245 words typed in 4.5 min.

(6.6) 6 The fastest typing ever was at the rate of 1911 words in 13 min. How long would it take to type a 5000 word essay?

(6.7) 7 (a) In a class of 32 students, 4 are left-handed. What percentage is this?

(6.8) (b) If 18% of the school is away on a field trip, how many of the 420 students are on the trip?

(6.9) (c) Terri used 30% of a tape to tape a 5 h show. Find the total time on the tape.

(6.10) (d) Jennifer deposited $980.00 for 3 mon. Find the interest paid at 11.5%/a.

(6.11) 8 Dean sells subscriptions and earns $52 commission. If the total sales are $650, find the rate of commission.

test for practice

1 Write each ratio in lowest terms.

(a) 12:36　　(b) 10:6:4　　(c) 15:10

2 The standings for the ping pong playoff tournament are shown below.

TOURNAMENT STANDINGS			
	Games played	Games won	Games lost	Games tied
Windwards	16	12	3	1
Triaps	15	10	1	4
Spinoffs	16	11	4	1

For each team write a ratio (in lowest terms) for

(a) games won:games lost

(b) games won:games lost:games played

3 Find the missing term in each of the following.

(a) $50:k = 5:3$　　　(b) $12:6:k = m:2:1$

4 Find the unit price 85 g of chips for 45¢

5 (a) An elephant's fastest speed is 40 km/h. Calculate how long the elephant would take to run 96 km.

(b) A tower drawn in a diagram is 12 cm high. Calculate the actual height of the tower if the scale is 1:200.

(c) When 5 L of gas were heated, the volume increased 20%. Calculate the volume of the gas after it was heated.

6 Write

(a) $\frac{3}{5}$ as a percent.　　(b) 0.38 as a percent.

(c) 125% as a common fraction.

(d) 97.5% as a decimal.　　(e) 0.5% as a fraction.

7 (a) By selling a house Michael's mother made 3% commission. If the house sold for $58 000 calculate the amount of commission.

math is plus: probability — using skills with data

You often hear predictions on the news, such as the following.

▶ The Sabres have 3 out of 4 chances of winning.
▶ Keast will probably win the election.
▶ The price of beef will probably rise during the summer vacation.
▶ If you draw a card from a deck there is a 25% chance of its being a heart.
▶ You have an even chance of flipping a head when you toss a coin.

Probability is that branch of mathematics that you can use to help predict the outcomes of various events. This Math Is Plus will explore some concepts about probability.

A box contains 5 black marbles and 5 red marbles.
Your chance of picking a black marble is

$$\left(\begin{array}{l}5 \text{ black} \\ \text{marbles}\end{array}\right) \overset{5 \text{ out of } 10.}{\longrightarrow} \left(\begin{array}{l}10 \text{ possible marbles} \\ \text{to choose from}\end{array}\right)$$

$$\text{Probability}\left(\begin{array}{l}\text{black} \\ \text{marble}\end{array}\right) = \frac{5}{10} \left(\begin{array}{l}\text{number of favourable} \\ \text{choices or outcomes}\end{array}\right.$$
$$\left(\begin{array}{l}\text{total number of possible} \\ \text{choices or outcomes}\end{array}\right.$$

(The result of choosing a red marble
or black marble is called an **outcome**
or **possibility**.

(The chance of an outcome or event
occurring is called the **probability**
of the event.

If you reach into the box your chances of pulling a marble, either red or black, are 10 chances out of 10, or 1. What are your chances of pulling a green marble?

(There are no green marbles

$$\text{Probability (green)} = \frac{0}{10}$$

(Total possible number of marbles

This number line shows what your chances are of pulling marbles. You can also record the probability as a percent, as shown.

0	$\frac{1}{2}$	1

Impossible to happen (pulling a green marble).
$$P = \frac{0}{10} = 0$$
$$= 0\%$$

Equally as likely to happen (pulling a red marble, or pulling a black marble).
$$P = \frac{5}{10} = \frac{1}{2}$$
$$= 50\%$$

Definitely will happen (pulling a marble that is red or black).
$$P = \frac{10}{10} = 1$$
$$= 100\%$$

The exercise that follows develops the vocabulary of probability as well as some useful skills for working with probability. Essentially there are two basic ways of determining the measure of probability.

A: Finding probability by experiment.

When you toss a fair coin, you expect either possibility, a head or a tail, to be an equally likely outcome. Toss a coin 70 times. Collect data from the experiment.

Number of heads	28
Number of tosses	70

Use the data.

Probability (head) = $\dfrac{\text{number of heads occurring}}{\text{total number of tosses}}$

$= \dfrac{28}{70}$ or $\dfrac{14}{35}$ or 0.4

$\left(\begin{array}{l}\text{This value is called}\\ \text{the } \textbf{experimental probability.}\end{array}\right.$

B: Finding expected probability or theoretical probability.

When you toss a coin, you expect one of two outcomes or events.

▶ a head will occur or   ▶ a tail will occur

Thus, you can find the **expected** or **theoretical** probability.

Probability (head) = $\dfrac{\text{number of favourable outcomes}}{\text{total number of possible outcomes}}$

$= \dfrac{1}{2}$ or 0.5

$\left(\begin{array}{l}\text{This value is the } \textbf{expected} \text{ or}\\ \textbf{theoretical} \text{ probability.}\end{array}\right.$

In the activities and questions that follow you will explore both experimental and expected probabilities.

Throughout these activities and exercises, you need to decide whether you are working with probability obtained by experiment or by theory.

1 Assign an approximate value, 0 to 1, to show the probability of each of the following events occurring.

(a) What are the chances of your swimming outdoors on January 1 this coming year?

(b) A light bulb is dropped. What are the chances it will break?

(c) What are the chances of rain tomorrow?

(d) List different events of your own. Assign a value of 0 to 1 to describe the probability of each event happening?

2 Express each probability as a percent.

(a) The probability is $\frac{4}{5}$ that the team will score a touchdown from that position.

(b) There is a 2 in 3 chance that it will rain.

(c) For 30 people, the probability is 0.7 that two people have the same birthday.

3 (a) A coin can land either heads or tails. What is the probability of
▶ flipping a head?
▶ flipping a tail?

(b) For 100 tosses of a coin, how many times would you expect a head to come up? a tail?

(c) Use a coin. Record the number of heads and tails for 100 tosses of the coin.

(d) Compare your answers in (b) and (c). What do you notice?

4 A nickel and dime are tossed. List the different outcomes that can occur.

(a) What is the probability of tossing 2 heads?

(b) What is the probability of tossing 2 tails?

(c) What is the probability that a head and a tail are tossed?

5 (a) Use two coins. Toss them 100 times and record your results. Use a chart.

Two heads	
One head and one tail	
Two tails	

continued →

(b) Compare your results above with your answers in the previous question.

6 A deck of cards has 52 cards in all, consisting of 13 diamonds, 13 clubs, 13 hearts, 13 spades. What is the probability of taking from a well-shuffled deck

(a) an ace?   (b) a king?

(c) a 5 of clubs?   (d) a 6 of hearts?

(e) a black ace?   (f) a red king?

(g) a face card?   (h) an even-numbered card?

7 (a) A box contains 10 pennies, 5 dimes, and 5 nickels. What is your chance of picking a nickel? picking a dime? picking a penny?

(b) Use pennies, nickels and dimes and do an experiment to test your predictions.

(c) Would you expect your predictions to be exactly the same as your experimental results? Why or why not?

8 (a) In flipping a nickel, dime, and penny, what are the different possible outcomes?

(b) Study this diagram. How does this diagram help you find the different possible outcomes in (a), when the coins are tossed? H means a head is tossed, T means a tail is tossed.

Nickel Dime Penny   Nickel Dime Penny

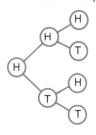 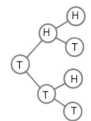

(c) What is the probability of tossing 3 heads? What other toss is as equally likely?

(d) What is the probability of tossing 2 heads and a tail?

(e) What other probabilities can you write for tossing the 3 coins?

9 At an exhibition, 4 gates are used. A bar graph shows the number of people using a gate during a one-hour peak period.

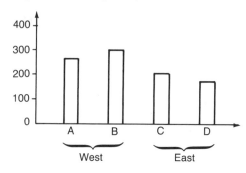

(a) What is the probability that a person will use Gate A? Gate D?

(b) What is the probability that a person will use a West Gate?

10 To make a prediction, a sample of data is often used. For example, in a poll of 100 persons, 66 answered *yes* to this question.

Would you buy all your milk in returnable containers?

Use the data to answer these questions.

(a) Which is more likely to happen?

▶ The next person will say *yes*.
▶ The next person will say *no*.

(b) If another 100 persons were asked the same question which would be the most likely to happen?
▶ About 3 out of 4 will say *yes*.
▶ 66 will say *yes*.
▶ More than half will say *yes*.

11 A sample of 1000 persons was taken. Out of 1000 persons, 896 answered *yes* to this question.

Would you like to have more parks in your neighbourhood?

Use these data to answer the question: Which is more likely to happen?
▶ The next person will say *yes*.
▶ The next person will say *no*.

7 solving problems: data and diagrams

Gathering data, organizing data, stem and leaf plots, pictographs and bar graphs, broken line graphs, circle graphs, distorting information, mean, median, mode, and range, Venn diagrams, problem solving skills, solving problems and applications

Each day you are bombarded with data. Data occur in the newspaper, magazines, on television, on radio.

Data from resource books:
the Olympic Games

1912	Kenneth McArthur, South Africa	2 h 36 min 54.8 s
1920	Hannes Kolehmainen, Finland	2 h 32 min 35.8 s
1924	Albin Stenroos, Finland	2 h 41 min 22.6 s
1928	A.B. El Ouafl, France	2 h 32 min 57 s
1932	Juan Zabala, Argentina	2 h 31 min 36 s
1936	Kitei Son, Japan	2 h 29 min 19.2 s
1948	Delfo Cabrera, Argentina	2 h 34 min 51.6 s
1952	Emil Zatopek, Czechoslovakia	2 h 23 min 03.2 s
1956	Alain Mimoun, France	2 h 25 min
1960	Abebe Bikila, Ethiopia	2 h 15 min 16.2 s

As shown, facts and figures, or data, are used in different ways to give information: lists, charts, tables, graphs, and so on.

Statistics is an important branch of mathematics that uses data to solve problems. A fact is sometimes called a **statistic**. Each number above is a statistic. Considering that many of the earlier skills in this book were studied for thousands of years, the study of statistics is a relatively new subject. As people's daily living became more complex, and more data-oriented, statistics problems grew into a separate and important study. There are three important steps in solving problems about data, the study of statistics.

▶ Collecting the data.

▶ Organizing the data: charts, tables, graphs, and so on.

▶ Interpreting the data to solve problems, predict results, obtain conclusions, make decisions, and so on.

You will study each of these steps in this chapter. To solve problems that use data, you will need to use your skills for computation, as well as other skills in geometry (circle graphs), percent, ratio, and so on.

Data in a pictorial form: a graph
The Canadian interconnect industry

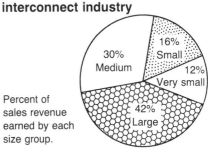

Percent of sales revenue earned by each size group.

Source: The Telemanagement Report

Data for standings in sports.

National League CAMPBELL CONFERENCE Norris Division							
	G	W	L	T	F	A	P
Minnesota	27	14	10	3	129	126	31
Toronto	26	11	12	3	112	124	25
Chicago	27	11	14	2	97	109	24
Detroit	25	10	13	2	89	101	22
St. Louis	26	9	14	3	99	118	21
Smythe Division							
Edmonton	28	20	5	3	166	112	43
Calgary	26	11	11	4	97	105	26
Vancouver	27	11	13	3	114	117	25
Winnipeg	26	9	14	3	110	130	21
Los Angeles	28	7	16	5	114	136	19

7.1 gathering data: using samples

Many important decisions are based on gathered data.
▶ How many compact cars should a large automobile manufacturer build this year?
▶ Where is the best location for a new grain storage facility?
▶ At which intersections should stoplights be placed?

To answer questions such as those above, there are three important steps to follow.

Step A   Gather the data.
Step B   Organize the data.
Step C   Interpret the data. Make decisions and answer questions.

In this section, you will explore skills for gathering data (Step A).

Suppose you wanted to know the answer to the question:
What is the favourite sport in Canada?

To answer the question, you would need to gather information or data.

▶ You could ask every person in the **population**. The things or people about which you are trying to gather information are referred to as the population.

▶ To ask every person in Canada what their favourite sport is, would be an enormous time-consuming task. If you ask only some of the population, you are taking a **sample**. The sample should be representative of the complete population. Each member of the population should have an equal chance of being chosen. For example, people at a tennis tournament would not be a representative sample. This sample would be **biased**.

Data can be obtained from a variety of sources.
▶ encyclopedias   ▶ results of experiments   ▶ measurements
▶ surveys   ▶ observations   ▶ newspapers

The choice of the source depends on the type of information required to answer the question.

Surveys of people's opinions can be conducted in different ways.
▶ personal interviews   ▶ mailed questionnaires   ▶ telephone interviews

Once the data are gathered (Step A), they are organized into charts and graphs (Step B). Then they are analysed to provide information or answer questions (Step C). Steps B and C will be done in the later sections.

7.1 exercise

A

1 The Rockford City Council wants input from the community on a new shopping mall. The council decides to telephone all of the 15 000 people in the community.

(a) List the advantages and disadvantages of this method of gathering data.

(b) Suggest another method which would be better. Give reasons for your answer.

2 A researcher at Trident Super Market sends out 25 000 questionnaires. 8000 are returned. The researcher is happy with the return. Do you agree or disagree? Give reasons for your answer.

3 An architect is designing a new office building.

(a) Why would a telephone survey of opinions not be wise?

(b) What method would you suggest? Give reasons for your answer.

4 The chart shows three methods of gathering information from people.

	Method	Advantages	Disadvantages
(a)	Telephone survey		
(b)	Questionnaire		
(c)	Personal interview		

Copy and complete the chart using phrases such as the following. (Include some of your own as well.)

▶ personal contact   ▶ time consuming
▶ inexpensive   ▶ fast results
▶ questions may be misunderstood
▶ questions can be rephrased to help understanding

5 To solve each of the following problems, decide whether you would use
    ▶ the entire population
    ▶ or a representative sample.
Give reasons for each choice.

(a) You have purchased 200 bags of apples. How would you check the condition of the apples?

(b) You manufacture jet engines. How would you check whether the engines work?

(c) You manufacture computer diskettes. How would you check the quality of the diskettes?

(d) You sell cylinders of oxygen for Scuba divers. How would you check the cylinders?

(e) You grow cauliflower. How would you check whether you are ready to harvest the crop?

6 The stamps show different events in the Olympic Games.

(a) Which activity do you like the best?

(b) Predict which activity you think most people would like the best.

(c) How would you check your answer in (b)?

An event in men's gymnastics is the rings. You need much balance and strength to obtain 19.275 points.

The women's 800-m event requires great speed. Can you run 800 m in 1 min 58.6 s?

Fencing is an event for men and women. The different Olympic events are Foil Individual and Foil Team.

7 Three shapes are shown.

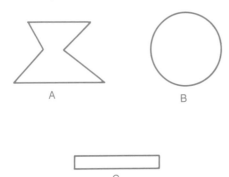

A   B   C

(a) Which shape do you like the best, A, B, or C?

(b) Predict which shape most of your class will choose.

(c) How can you check your answer in (b)?

B

8 A sample of 500 persons was asked, "Which of the following fast foods do you like the best?"

A Hamburger   B Hot Dog   C Pizza

The following data were obtained.

Fast food	Replies
A Hamburgers	183
B Hot Dogs	48
C Pizza	123
No Opinion	146

(a) What percent of the people had no opinion?

(b) Of the persons who replied, what percent chose
A Hamburgers?   B Hot Dogs?
C Pizza?

(c) Based on the survey, which fast food is liked the best?

(d) Suggest a method to find the answer for the members of your class. How do your results compare to those in (b)?

9 Data were gathered using the methods described below. The following conclusions were made. Is each conclusion justified? Give reasons for your answers.

(a) *Survey* The people living near the railroad tracks were asked if they wanted the tracks moved.
Conclusion Most people want the tracks moved.

(b) *Survey* A telephone survey of teenagers was made in July.
Conclusion Most teenagers don't have summer jobs.

(c) *Survey* People in the line-up for "Return of the Jedi" were asked their favourite type of movie.
Conclusion Most people like science fiction movies best.

(d) *Survey* Sales of jeans over a one year period were examined.
Conclusion Most people prefer to wear styled jeans.

10 A manufacturer is choosing a name for its new hand soap. The three suggested names are
Dewfresh   Tingle   Bubbles

(a) Describe how the manufacturer would find out which of the three names most people prefer.

(b) Which name do you prefer?

(c) Collect data to find which of the names most people in your class prefer.

11 Advertisers write catchy phrases to advertise products. They test the phrases before they use them.

(a) Write a catchy phrase to advertise one of the following products:
sweat shirts, computers, a new ice-cream flavour.

(b) Decide on a method to gather data. List the advantages of your method.

(c) How would you test whether people like your phrase?

12 Choose four current television commercials.

  (a) Which one do you like best?

  (b) Predict which of the four commericals most people would choose.

  (c) How could you check your answer in (b)?

Questions 13 to 16 are based on the following information.

A market research firm is hired to find out which one of five new cereals most people prefer. The real names of the cereals are not used. Instead, the cereals are labelled A, B, C, D, and E. Three researchers, Michael, Jeff, and Lesley, take samples of the cereals to people's homes to test their preferences.

13 Michael returned with the following results:

  A 38   B 41   C 17   D 25   E 32

  (a) Which cereal is most popular based on Michael's data?

  (b) From how many people did Michael obtain an opinion?

14 Jeff collected these preferences:

  A 4   B 37   C 19   D 21   E 27

  (a) Which cereal is most popular based on Jeff's data?

  (b) How many people did Jeff survey?

15 Lesley's results were as follows:

  A 29   B 45   C 13   D 34   E 28

  (a) Which cereal is most popular based on Lesley's test?

  (b) From how many people did Lesley collect a preference?

16 Use the data in the previous questions.

  (a) Predict which cereal most people preferred.

  (b) Construct a chart to organize the data collected by the three researchers.

  (c) Which cereal was most popular overall?

17 What method would you use to obtain a representative sample to answer each of the following questions?

  (a) How many of the students in your school have a computer in their home?

  (b) What are the populations of the ten largest cities in Canada?

  (c) What are the current NHL team standings?

  (d) How long does a bean take to sprout?

  (e) Which movie rental company has the cheapest rates?

  (f) Of the current top ten singles, which one do the students in your school like best?

math tip

When you choose a sample, what you should try to do is choose representatives of the population that truly represent the population. Thus if the representatives are evenly distributed throughout the population, then what you learn would be representative of the population. This sampling is said to be **unbiased**.

choose every 4th person

In the sample below, the representatives are clustered and occur in one part of the population. The sample is said to be **biased**.

problem-solving: history

Goldbach, a mathematician many years ago noticed that every even number except the number 2, can be shown as a sum of prime numbers. For example,

$$8 = 5 + 3 \qquad 18 = 7 + 11$$
$$22 = 11 + 11 \qquad 50 = 47 + 3$$

But even though Goldbach could not prove the result for every even number, history has honoured him. This observation is called **Goldbach's Conjecture**.

7.2 organizing data

It is often helpful to organize data into a chart.

A cable T.V. station asks its viewers to choose which one of three movies they would prefer to watch. The viewers call the station to vote for their choice. The votes are recorded in a **tally chart**, as shown on the right.

The tally chart also shows the frequencies. For this reason, the chart is often called a **frequency table**.

From the chart you can draw conclusions.
► Most viewers chose Movie 2.
► More viewers chose Movie 3 than Movie 1.
► The total number of votes recorded were 66.   (17 + 28 + 21)

Choice	Tally	Frequency
Movie 1	₦₦ ₦₦ ₦₦ ‖	17
Movie 2	₦₦ ₦₦ ₦₦ ₦₦ ₦₦ ‖‖	28
Movie 3	₦₦ ₦₦ ₦₦ ₦₦ ‖	21

Each tally mark represents one vote. The tally marks are grouped in fives to make them easier to total.

The frequency shows the number of times a vote was made for each choice.

You can use your earlier skills to answer questions such as,
"What percent of the viewers chose Movie 1?"
Number of viewers that chose Movie 1 = 17
Total number of viewers called   = 66

Percent of viewers $\frac{17}{66} \times 100\%$ = 25.8% (to 1 decimal place)

Example   The types of vehicles passing by a school were recorded for a period of one hour.

(a) Construct a frequency table for the data.

(b) How many vehicles passed the school during the hour?

(c) What percent of the vehicles were buses? Express your answer to one decimal place.

(d) Based on the data, how many vehicles would you expect to be buses out of 750 vehicles passing the school?

C	C	B	T	C	C	M
T	C	C	B	C	T	C
C	C	B	M	C	C	C
C	T	C	C	C	T	C
M	C	C	B	T	C	C
C	C	B	T	C	C	C

Car (C)   Bus (B)   Truck (T)
Motorcycle (M)

Solution   (a)

Type of vehicle	Tally	Frequency
Car	₦₦ ₦₦ ₦₦ ₦₦ ₦₦ ‖	27
Bus	₦₦	5
Truck	₦₦ ‖	7
Motorcycle	‖‖	3

A tally chart that also shows the frequency is called a **frequency table**.

(b) Total number of vehicles = 27 + 5 + 7 + 3
$$= 42$$
During the hour, 42 vehicles passed the school.

(c) Number of buses 5
Total number of vehicles 42
Percent of buses is given by $\frac{5}{42} \times 100\%$ or   11.9%

(d) Percent of buses passing the school is 11.9%
Number of buses expected is given by 11.9% of 750
$$= 89.25$$
About 89 buses would pass the school out of 750 vehicles.

Before you begin to construct graphs in the following sections, you need to practise collecting and organizing information.

Use your calculator. Check your calculations.

7.2 exercise

A

1 A survey was done to determine the types of bicycles students ride. Find the frequency for each type of bicycle.

Types of Bicycles Students Ride

	Type	Tally	Frequency
(a)	10-speed	##H ##H ##H II	?
(b)	5-speed	##H	?
(c)	3-speed	##H IIII	?
(d)	regular	##H ##H III	?

2 The information in the chart shows the number of each type of book borrowed. Copy and complete the chart.

Type of Book Borrowed

	Type	Tally	Frequency
(a)	Science fiction	##H ##H IIII	?
(b)	Mystery	?	22
(c)	Romance	?	7
(d)	Biography	IIII	?
(e)	Other	?	13

Questions 3 to 6 refer to the following frequency table. People were asked to name their favourite type of music.

Favourite Type of Music

Music	Tally	Frequency
Country	##H I	6
Rock	##H ##H ##H I	16
Jazz	IIII	4
Classical	##H III	8
Other	##H I	6

3 How many people preferred the following types of music?
(a) Jazz   (b) Classical   (c) Rock

4 How many people were surveyed?

5 Which type of music was the most popular?

6 Where would you place a tally for a person whose favourite music is big band?

B

7 People were asked which jam they like. The results were recorded in a frequency table.

Favourite Jam

Jam	Tally	Frequency
Grape	卌 卌 ‖	?
Strawberry	卌 卌 卌 卌 ‖‖	?
Marmalade	卌 卌 卌 ‖‖	?

(a) Complete the table.

(b) What percent of the people like grape jam?

(c) Vernon, B.C. has a population of about 14 000. Use the information in the table to predict how many people would like strawberry jam.

8 The following pizzas were sold in 1 h.

Small	卌 卌 卌 卌 卌 ‖
Medium	卌 卌 卌 卌 ‖
Large	卌 卌 卌 卌 卌
Extra Large	卌 卌 ‖

(a) What percent of the pizzas sold were medium?

(b) The average price of a medium pizza is $4.50. How much money was spent on medium pizzas?

(c) The total number of pizzas sold in one working day is 750. How many large pizzas would you expect to sell?

(d) What assumption did you make to obtain your answer in (c)?

———

Questions 9 to 11 are based on the following information. The makes of jeans worn by students were recorded.

Levis (L)　Wrangler (W)　Designer (D)　Other (O)

W	L	L	O	D	O	L	W	L	D	O	L	O	W	O
L	O	L	W	L	D	O	L	L	W	L	O	O	L	O

9 (a) Construct a frequency table to show the information.

(b) Which make of jeans had the greatest frequency? The least frequency?

10 (a) How many students wearing jeans were surveyed?

(b) What percent of the students wore designer jeans?

11 (a) Which make of jeans was worn by most of the students?

(b) Based on the data in the table, how many teenagers out of 200 wearing jeans would probably wear Wrangler jeans?

12 A music store sold the following types of recorded music one day.

Long Playing Albums (L)　Singles (S)　Cassette Tapes (C)

S	L	L	C	L	C	S	L	L	C	S	C	L	L	L
S	C	L	L	S	S	L	C	L	L	S	C	L	C	L
L	C	S	L	L	S	L	S	C	L					

(a) Construct a frequency table to show the information in a more compact way.

(b) If the cassette tapes sell for $9.85 each, how much did the store take in for sales of cassette tapes that day?

(c) The store is ordering 500 items for the next week. Based on the data above, how many of the items ordered should be singles?

grouping data

Often the data can be very varied and as a result they can be grouped.
For example, the marks on a test out of 100 are shown

```
70 46 73 51 61 52 41 84 67 53 75 39 62 86 64 56
93 59 17 55 31 71 66 57 49 62 60 64 88 69 68 44
42 71 65 82 66 53 47 69 55 35 44 58 80 56 67 58
78 52 70 45 51 64 76 54 23 52 79 68 90 28 44 77
95 86 54 55 82 37 63 71 60 72 66 47 49 56 34 78
47 59 75 41 62 69 80 76 36 65 73 55 52 75 52 48
35 84 22 66 33 56 42 51 61 66 30 75 65 43 51 63
55 57 64 52 74 60 78 19
```

The data can be grouped as suggested by the table. The large array of numbers are compressed into "classes" called **class intervals**.

For the data, the convenient number of classes is 10. The smallest and greatest number in each class are called the **class limits**. The number of marks in each class is called the **frequency** of that class as shown in the table. Class intervals should be chosen to have the same length.

The data above are shown in a graph. Note that there are no spaces between the bars. Graphs of this type are often called **histograms**.

Marks Awarded	Tally	Frequency
1 – 10		0
11 – 20	ll	2
21 – 30	llll	4
31 – 40	JHT lll	8
41 – 50	JHT JHT JHT l	16
51 – 60	JHT JHT JHT JHT JHT JHT ll	32
61 – 70	JHT JHT JHT JHT JHT lll	28
71 – 80	JHT JHT JHT JHT	20
81 – 90	JHT lll	8
91 – 100	ll	2

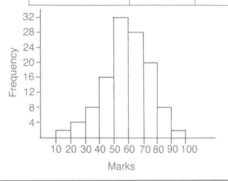

---

13 The distances (kilometres) that various people jog each week are shown in the table.

```
11 18 10 25  6  15 21  6  16 19  8  20 20 25 15
21  9  17 13 20 11 20 11 22 12 14 17 19 17 22
14 23  4  25  8  16 32 18 15 33 23 14  9  23 30
30 16 18  5  12 27  5  30  7  18 19 24 28  8  22
 8  17 10 26 24 11 35 17 22 10 11 15
```

(a) Construct a frequency table for the data. Choose a suitable class interval.

(b) Draw a graph of the data in (a).

(c) What percent of the people interviewed are represented in each class?

(d) In which 2 classes do most of the joggers occur?

(e) Create a problem about the data. Write a solution to the problem.

14 The time taken (seconds) to run 100 m was recorded for the students.

```
16.2 17.6 15.0 15.6 15.3 13.1 17.1 16.2 15.6 14.5 18.9
14.1 18.0 13.1 17.3 18.0 16.8 15.1 13.3 16.8 18.1 14.5
15.2 15.5 16.6 12.7 15.5 14.7 17.9 16.0 18.1 15.3 13.9
15.7 17.4 14.1 16.4 15.3 16.6 13.0 17.3 14.7 15.5
16.6 13.7 16.0 15.4 14.7 14.3 15.5 16.8 14.5 16.4
14.7 16.4 15.4 16.4 15.2 15.7 15.9 13.6 15.4 13.9
```

(a) How many students participated in the test?

(b) Construct a frequency table for the data.

(c) Draw a graph of the data in (b).

(d) Estimate the average length of time taken to run 100 m. In which class does your estimate fall?

(e) Calculate the average length of time taken to run 100 m. In which class does your calculated average fall? How close were you?

7.3 data: stem and leaf plots

A telephone company is revising its long-distance charges. As part of the research, the company analyzes data on the length, in minutes, of calls between two cities. The results of a sample of 30 calls are shown.

22	17	5	11	31	13	6	10
12	12	30	19	14	10	8	26
23	14	9	5	18	37	15	
40	27	21	9	6	51	48	

With the data presented in this form, it is hard to draw any conclusions about the length of the phone calls. However, if you record the data as a stem and leaf plot, then you can make some observations about the information. Squared paper is used to record the data.

Stem and leaf plot for the first row of the data.

The ones digits are called the leaves.

This square shows the number 13.

Label as many tens digits as needed.

The tens digits are called the stems.

This branch represents the numbers 17, 11, 13, and 10.

Stem and leaf plot for all the data.

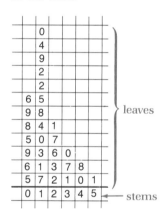

leaves

stems

You may record the same information in a different way. For example, the following diagram records the same data on a stem and leave plot that is horizontal.

▶ How are they alike?   ▶ How are they different?

Tens	Ones			
0	5	6		
1	7	1	3	0
2	2			
3	1			
4				
5				

Remember: This digit refers to 31.

Tens	Ones											
0	5	6	9	5	8	9	6					
1	7	1	3	0	4	8	5	2	2	9	4	0
2	2	3	6	7	1							
3	1	7	0									
4	0	8										
5	1											

Look for Calculator Tips.

Example Use the data for the telephone research to answer each question.

(a) How many telephone calls lasted 10 min?

(b) How many calls lasted 30 min or longer?

(c) How many calls lasted less than 10 min?

(d) What percent of the calls were less than 20 min? Express your answer to 1 decimal place. Estimate first. Then calculate.

Solution (a) 2 telephone calls lasted 10 min.

(b) 6 calls lasted 30 min or longer.

(c) 7 calls lasted less than 10 min.

(d) Number of calls less than 20 min = 19
   Total number of calls = 30
   Percent of calls is given by
   $\frac{19}{30} \times 100\%$ or 63.3% (to 1 decimal place).

(Use the data shown in the stem and leaf plot

7.3 exercise

A

Questions 1 and 2 are based on the following stem and leaf plot. The data show the daily high temperature, in degrees Celsius, during the month of April.

Tens	Ones
0	8 7 9 5 2 6 9 8 6 9
1	0 5 7 2 4 5 5 8 1 2 3 4 6 5 9
2	2 1 0 3 1

1 On how many days was the high temperature

(a) 15°C?   (b) 9°C?   (c) 25°C?

2 (a) How many days had a high temperature of 20°C or greater?

(b) How many days had a high temperature that was below 10°C?

Questions 3-5 are based on the stem and leaf plot shown. The pulse rates, in beats per minute, of the students (at rest) in one class were recorded.

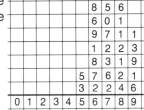

3 How many students had a pulse rate of

(a) 67 beats/min?

(b) 81 beats/min?

4 (a) How many students had a pulse rate greater than or equal to 90 beats/min?

(b) How many students had a pulse rate lower than 70 beats/min?

5 How many students were in the class?

B

Questions 6-10 are based on the following information.

A farm research station is developing a new variety of corn. The stem and leaf plot shows the height, in centimetres, of 50 test plants after growing one month.

Tens	Ones
1	9
2	3 7 5 2
3	8 6 9 0 7 2
4	7 2 6 8 9 1 5
5	8 4 7 6 5 2 9 6 0 5
6	3 8 1 0 6 7 5 2 2 8
7	4 7 2 9 5 1 4 8
8	9 5 3 2

6 (a) What was the height of the tallest plant?

(b) What height was the shortest plant?

7 (a) How many of the plants had a height of less than 30 cm?

(b) How many plants had a height of 60 cm or greater?

8 What percentage of the plants had reached a height of more than 70 cm? Check whether your answer is reasonable.

9 On Hybird Farm there are 650 test plants.

(a) Based on your results, predict how many plants are 50 cm in height or more.

(b) Check whether your answer is reasonable.

10 On another test farm, 5000 plants are used to obtain experimental data.

(a) How many plants would you expect to have a height of 40 cm to 49 cm?

(b) How many plants would you expect to have a height of 70 cm or more?

(c) What assumptions did you make to obtain your answers in (a) and (b)?

Questions 11 to 16 are based on the following data.
The number of people using a skating rink each evening during December was recorded.

52	85	97	108	47	115	37	64	92	78
83	14	20	75	66	39	42	21	103	31
49	36	63	71	94	101	58	69	25	

11 Use the data in the form given.

(a) How many evenings did more than 100 people use the rink?

(b) What percent of the evenings were there fewer than 50 people?

12 (a) Construct a stem and leaf plot for the data.

(b) Answer the questions in the previous question using the stem and leaf plot.

(c) List advantages of recording data as a stem and leaf plot.

13 (a) On how many evenings were there fewer than 30 people using the rink?

(b) On how many evenings did more than 100 people use the rink?

14 (a) What was the greatest number of people using the rink during one evening?

(b) If the rink charges $1.50 admission, how much was taken in on the busiest evening?

15 How many evenings was the rink open during the month? Why do you think it was closed on the other evenings?

16 The rink owner is happy if there are 70 or more people at the rink. What percent of the days was the rink owner happy?

calculator tip

Does your calculator have a square $\sqrt{x}$ root key? Read your manual. How does it work?

7.4 displaying data: pictographs and bar graphs

You have used a frequency table and a stem and leaf plot to organize data. Once you have organized the data, you can then display them by drawing graphs.

For example, the frequency chart shows the number of records owned by each of four students. The data can be displayed in a pictograph or a bar graph.

Student	Tally	Frequency
Jason	ЖЖ ЖЖ ЖЖ	15
Ivan	ЖЖ ЖЖ ЖЖ ЖЖ ЖЖ ||	27
Hannah	ЖЖ ЖЖ	10
Leanne	ЖЖ ЖЖ ЖЖ	15

Both graphs below
▶ provide information visually   ▶ allow quick comparisons
▶ provide data for answers   ▶ require a title

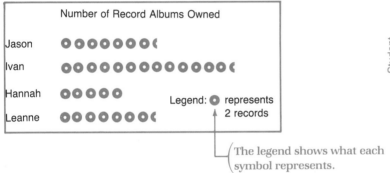

The legend shows what each symbol represents.

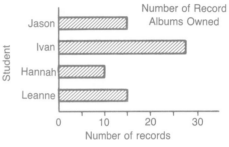

A bar graph has equal spaces between bars

A pictograph uses a **legend** to represent the data. A bar graph uses a **scale** to show the data.

A pictograph often shows approximate numbers. Because one symbol is sometimes used to represent more than one item, numbers may have to be rounded. A bar graph can show data more accurately than a pictograph.

Different forms of bar graphs can be used to show information.

▶ **Horizontal bar** graphs might show data about lengths of rivers, snakes, horizontal distances, walking distances, and so on.

▶ **Vertical bar** graphs might show data about heights of people, mountains, vertical distances, altitudes, and so on.

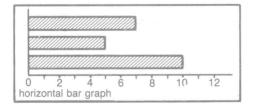

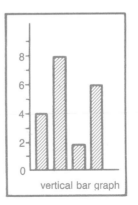

vertical bar graph

Once you have constructed a graph to show the information in a visual manner you can solve many problems, as shown in the following example.

Example   Use the previous bar graph to answer the following questions.

(a) Which student has the greatest number of records?

(b) What is the total number of records owned by the four students?

(c) What is the ratio of the number of records owned by Ivan compared to the number owned by Leanne?

(d) What percentage of the records owned by the four students belongs to Leanne?

Solution   (a) Ivan has the greatest number of records.

(b) $15 + 27 + 10 + 15 = 67$.
There are 67 records owned by the four students.

(c) The ratio of Ivan's records compared to Leanne's records is 27:15 or 9:5.

(d) The percentage owned by Leanne is $\frac{15}{67} \times 100\% = 22.4\%$ (rounded to 1 decimal place).   Check whether your answer is reasonable.

7.4 exercise

A

Questions 1 to 3 are based on the pictograph.

Number of Volumes in Different Encyclopedias

World Book ▭▭ ▭▭ ▭▭ ▭▭▭▭

Canadiana ▭▭▭▭

Britannica ▭▭ ▭▭ ▭▭ ▭▭ ▭▭ ▭▭ ▭▭ ▭▭ ▭▭▭▭

Legend: ▭▭ represents 4 volumes

1   (a) Which encyclopedia has the greatest number of volumes?

(b) How many volumes does it have?

2 (a) What does the symbol ▭▭ represent?

(b) Draw the symbols that you would use to represent an encylopedia with 9 volumes.

3 Does this pictograph show exact numbers or approximate numbers? Give reasons for your answer.

Use the vertical bar graph for Questions 4 to 8.

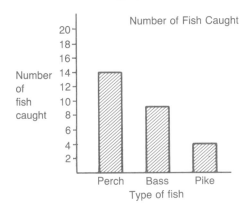

Number of Fish Caught

4 (a) What label would you put on the horizontal axis?

(b) Suggest a title for the bar graph.

5 (a) Which type of fish was caught the most? the least?

(b) How many fish were caught altogether?

6 Write as a ratio the number of

(a) perch to pike   (b) pike to bass

(c) bass to perch   (d) bass to all fish

7 What percentage of the fish caught were

(a) perch?   (b) bass?   (c) pike?

(d) What do you notice about the sum of your answers?

8 List some people that would be interested in the results of this survey. Give reasons for your answer.

9 Refer to the bar graph and pictograph in the previous questions.

(a) How are bar graphs and pictographs alike?

(b) How are they different?

(c) List some situations when you might use a pictograph rather than a bar graph to represent information.

Questions 10 to 13 are based on the following information.
The numbers of the different types of campsites at a Provincial Park are as follows.

Type of site	Number of sites
Tent	136
Trailer	29
Mobile home	11

10 You are going to show the information in the chart in a camper's guide. Which type of graph would be more suitable, a pictograph or a bar graph? Give reasons for your answer.

11 If the symbol ∧ represents 10 sites, how many symbols would you use to represent the number of sites for

(a) tents?   (b) trailers?   (c) mobile homes?

12 (a) Construct a pictograph to display the data.

(b) Does your pictograph show exact numbers or approximate numbers?

13 (a) Construct a bar graph for the data.

(b) How are the bar graphs and pictographs alike? How are they different?

B

Questions 14 to 17 refer to the following pictograph which shows calculator sales in Canada for 1 mon. Each calculator symbol represents 1000 calculators.

Calculator Sales in Canada

British Columbia ▭ ▭ ▭ ▭

Alberta ▭ ▭ ▭

Saskatchewan ▭ ▭

Manitoba ▭ ▭

Ontario ▭ ▭ ▭ ▭ ▭ ▭ ▭ ▭ ▭

Quebec ▭ ▭ ▭ ▭ ▭ ▭

Atlantic Provinces ▭ ▭ ▭

Legend: ▭ represents 1000 calculators

14 (a) Compare the number of calculators sold in Alberta with the number sold in Ontario.

(b) Discuss some reasons for this difference.

15 (a) *Estimate* what percentage of the calculators sold in Canada were sold in Quebec.

(b) *Calculate* the percentage of calculators sold in Quebec.

(c) How do your answers compare in (a) and (b)?

16 (a) Estimate the percentage of calculators sold in Saskatchewan. Then calculate.

(b) Compare the percentage of calculators sold in Manitoba with the percentage sold in British Columbia.

17 Make up two other questions about the data in the graph. Answer your questions.

Questions 18 to 20 are based on the following horizontal bar graph.

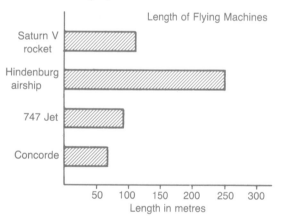

18 (a) What features of a horizontal bar graph are the same as those of a vertical bar graph?

(b) What features are different?

19 Concorde is what fraction of the length of the Saturn V rocket?

20 (a) Which of the flying machines would fit in a hangar that is 100 m long?

(b) How many Hindenburg airships could fit nose to tail on a 1 km long runway?

21 The vertical bar graph shows the heights of the four highest mountains in North America.

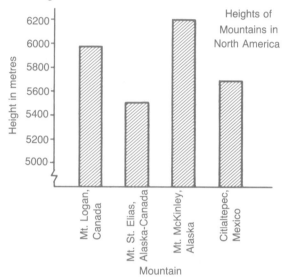

(a) How does this bar graph differ from the one in the previous questions? How is it similar?

(b) Why is this form of bar graph suitable for displaying these data?

(c) How many times as high as Mt. St. Elias is Mt. McKinley?

22 The data show the number of games won by each person in a badminton tournament.

Player	Games won
Sharon	16
Jaysen	27
Christie	18
Kenneth	14

(a) What type of graph would you use to show the information: pictograph or bar graph?

(b) Construct a graph to show the information.

(c) Create one problem based on the information in the graph. Solve the problem.

23 National soccer teams compete every four years, for the World Cup. The winners of the cup are listed.

1930	Uruguay	1962	Brazil
1934	Italy	1966	England
1938	Italy	1970	Brazil
1950	Uruguay	1974	West Germany
1958	Brazil	1978	Argentina
		1982	Italy

(a) Draw a pictograph to compare the number of times that each country has won the world cup.

(b) Make up two questions about your pictograph.

(c) Answer the questions in (b).

24 Gravity affects how high you can jump. The table shows the heights that you would jump if you used the same effort as in jumping to a height of 1 m on Earth.

Height jumped

Earth	100 cm
Jupiter	43 cm
Venus	113 cm
Mars	262 cm
Moon	623 cm

(a) Which would be more appropriate to display these data, a horizontal bar graph or a vertical bar graph?

(b) Construct the bar graph.

(c) Where is gravity stronger than on Earth? Where is gravity less?

25 In each of the following:
► Decide on a graph to show the data.
► Make up 3 questions based on your graph.
► Answer the questions.

(a) The maximum number of players per team allowed on the playing area in some sports is shown in the chart.

Football	12
Basketball	5
Baseball	9
Waterpolo	7

(b) The maximum depth of each of the Great Lakes is shown in the chart.

Superior	390 m
Michigan	275 m
Huron	225 m
Erie	63 m
Ontario	230 m

(c) The average annual snowfall for selected Canadian cities is shown in the chart.

Edmonton	131 cm
Vancouver	52 cm
St. John's	364 cm
Montreal	240 cm
Ottawa	216 cm

C
26 (a) Choose 5 current popular songs. Conduct a survey of students to find out which of the songs most students prefer. Organize the data in a frequency chart.

(b) Construct a graph to display the data.

(c) Make up one question about your graph. Answer the question.

problem-solving: research

Compile a list of how computers are used. Compile another list of how computers are misused.
You may need to do some research on these uses and misuses of computers.

Remember: computer programs are dealt with on pages 36, 74, 192.

7.5 interpreting broken-line graphs

Would you believe that the water lost from a dripping tap costs you thousands of dollars over a lifetime?

The water from a dripping tap was collected as shown in the table. To organize and display these data, a bar graph was drawn.

A dripping tap wastes energy. It only costs a few dollars to stop a dripping tap, yet it saves a lot of money.
When the water is used in another part of the house, the tap drips slower.

Recorded Data

Time elapsed	Volume of water
1 h	185 mL
2 h	370 mL
3 h	490 mL
4 h	600 mL
5 h	710 mL
6 h	900 mL

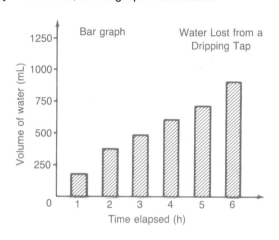

The amount of water lost is increasing with time. The bar graph shows a change over a period of time. To show a trend or change in data, usually related to time, a **broken-line graph** can also be used.

Join the midpoints of the top of the bars with line segments to show a broken-line graph.

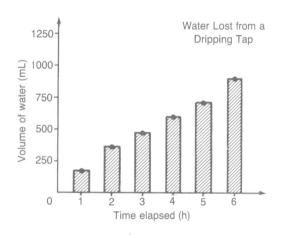

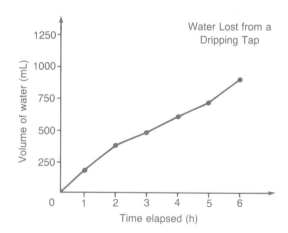

The broken-line graph shows the amount dripped with respect to the time elapsed.

► Interpolation

From the broken-line graph, information can be obtained about points between the marked points. Finding information in this way is called **interpolation**. For example, the amount of water lost in 2.5 h is about 440 mL.

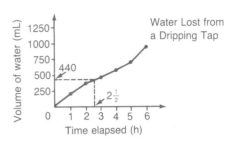

► Extrapolation

The graph could also be extended and approximate data could be predicted from the graph. Finding information in this way is called **extrapolation**. For example, the amount of water lost in 10 h would be about 1850 mL.

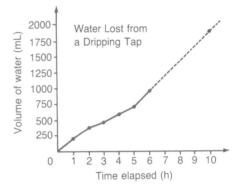

You can use a graph to answer two basic types of questions. Refer to the previous graphs.

A   Questions based on the graph that require a simple, factual answer. For example:

► What was the volume of water lost after 3 h?   (490 mL)

B   Questions based on the graph that require you to interpret the data or use other skills. For example:

► Estimate the amount of water lost in a day.

$\left(\begin{array}{l}\text{In 6 h 900 mL are lost}\\\text{In 24 h about 3600 mL are lost.}\end{array}\right.$

$\left(\begin{array}{l}\text{Broken-line graphs are used to show}\\\text{data that are changing, usually with}\\\text{time. To draw a broken-line graph,}\\\text{you can plot the points and then join}\\\text{them using line segments.}\end{array}\right.$

7.5 exercise

A   Questions 1 to 3 are based on the following information. The growth of a tropical plant is shown on the broken-line graph.

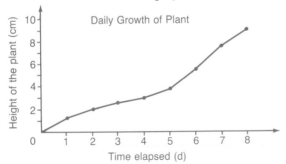

1 (a) How are each of the axes of the graph labelled? What are the units?

   (b) Suggest a title for the graph.

2 What was the height of the plant after each amount of time?

   (a) 3 d   (b) 5 d   (c) 7 d

3 About how long did it take the plant to reach each height?

   (a) 2 cm   (b) 4 cm   (c) 6 cm

4 What was the height after each amount of time?

   (a) $1\frac{1}{2}$ d   (b) $4\frac{1}{2}$ d   (c) $6\frac{1}{2}$ d

5 About how long did it take the plant to reach each height?

   (a) 3.5 cm   (b) 5.5 cm   (c) 7.5 cm

For Questions 6 to 9, use the following broken-line graph.

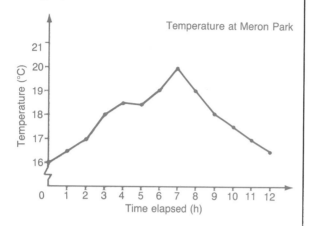

Temperature at Meron Park

6 (a) How are each of the axes of the graph labelled? What are the units?

(b) Look at the vertical axis. What information has not been shown? Why do you think this has been done?

7 What was the temperature at Meron Park after
(a) 6 h?   (b) 9 h?   (c) 12 h?

8 (a) What was the greatest temperature during this 12 h period?

(b) After how many hours was the greatest temperature reached?

9 (a) What was the temperature after $8\frac{1}{2}$ h?

(b) Predict what the temperature might be after 13 h.

B

10 A school is holding a month long campaign to raise money for a swimming pool. The broken-line graph shows the total amount collected by the end of each day, for the first 10 d.

(a) The goal for the end of the first week of the campaign was $5000. Did the school reach its goal? How much over or under the goal was it?

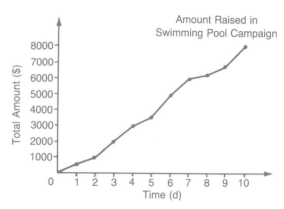

Amount Raised in Swimming Pool Campaign

(b) On which day was the greatest amount of money raised? About how much was collected during that day?

(c) The goal for the end of the month is $25 000. Based on the amount raised so far, do you think the school will reach its goal in month?

11 The growth pattern for a spruce tree is shown as a broken-line graph.

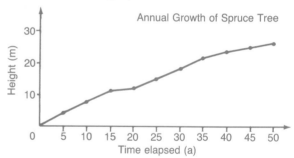

Annual Growth of Spruce Tree

(a) How long did it take the tree to grow to 20 m?

(b) How much did the tree grow in 10 a?

(c) How long did it take the tree to reach half of its final height?

(d) A spruce tree is worth about $1.75/m, after its tenth year. What is the value of the tree after 20 a?   after 40 a?

(Think: Is your
  answer reasonable?)

(e) When was the growth of the tree the slowest? Suggest a reason for this.

Questions 12 to 15 are based on the following information.
The data shows the depth of water in a reservoir at the beginning of each month.

Month	1	2	3	4	5	6	7	8
Depth of water (m)	20	19	17	15	15	16	17	16

12 Use the following steps to draw a broken-line graph for the data.

   (a) Draw and label the axes. Show the months on the horizontal axis and the depth of the water on the vertical axis.

   (b) Plot the points.

   (c) Join the points in order using line segments.

   (d) Give your graph a title.

13 Use your graph to estimate the depth of water after the following time periods.

   (a) $2\frac{1}{2}$ mon   (b) $4\frac{1}{2}$ mon   (c) $7\frac{1}{2}$ mon

14 Can you use your graph to predict the depth of water after 10 mon? Why or why not?

15 The value of the water is $25 000 for each metre of depth.

   (a) Estimate the value of the water in month four.

   (b) Calculate the value of the water in month four. How do your answers compare?

Questions 16 to 20 are based on the following data, which are the amounts of interest earned on a deposit of $100 at 12%/a.

Time (years)	1	2	3	4	5	6	7
Interest (dollars)	12	24	36	48	60	72	84

16 Draw a broken-line graph to display the data.

17 Use your graph to estimate, to the nearest dollar, the amount of interest earned on $100 at 12%/a in the following times.

   (a) $2\frac{1}{2}$ a   (b) $4\frac{1}{2}$ a   (c) 6 mon

   How can you check your answers?

18 (a) Use the graph to help you estimate the amount of interest earned on $100 at 12%/a in 8 a.

   (b) Check your answer to part (a).

19 Use the data in the graph.

   (a) Last summer you earned $600. Estimate the interest you will receive if you deposit the money for 3 a.

   (b) Calculate your answer in (a). How do your answers compare?

20 (a) You have invested $1200. How much interest will you have after 5 a?

   (b) Check whether your answer is reasonable.

   (c) Use the graph to make up two other questions. Solve your problems.

C
21 The table shows the perimeter of squares with the given side measures.

Length of side (cm)	1	2	3	4	5
Perimeter (cm)	4	8	12	16	20

   (a) Display the data in a broken-line graph.

   (b) What is the perimeter of a square whose sides measure 3 cm? 4.5 cm?

   (c) Use the graph to help you predict the perimeter of a square whose sides measure 8 cm. How can you check your answer?

   (d) Use the graph to find out how much the perimeter increases when the side increases by 1 cm.

   (e) Use the graph to make up two other questions. Solve your problems.

7.6 applications: circle graphs

In working with data, you have used the steps shown in the chart. You can often show the same data in different ways. For example, you can show the following data as a bar graph.

In a survey, 50 people were asked to name their favourite fruit.

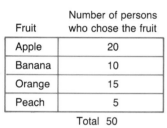

Fruit	Number of persons who chose the fruit
Apple	20
Banana	10
Orange	15
Peach	5
Total	50

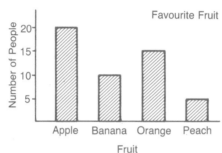

Working with Data

Step A Gather the data or information.

Step B Organize the data. You can use graphs.

Step C Interpret and analyze the data.

You can use the bar graph to make comparisons and answer questions.

However, a **circle** or **pie graph** can also be used to show this information. For example, a circle or pie graph is often used to display data that can be expressed as percents of the whole data.

For a circle graph,
100% represents 360°
1% represents $\frac{360°}{100}$ or 3.6°

In a circle graph, each piece of data is expressed as a percent of the total. The percents are then used to calculate the size of each central angle for the sectors of the circle graph, as shown.

Fruit	Number who chose it	Percent	Size of central angle
Apple	20	40%	144°
Banana	10	20%	72°
Orange	15	30%	108°
Peach	5	10%	36°
Totals	50	100%	360°

40% of 360° = 144°

These two totals can be used to check your calculations.

In your study of mathematics you often need to use the same skills. For example, to construct a circle graph, you need to use your skills with percent and angles.

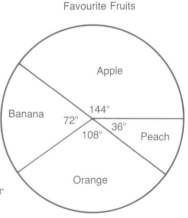

7.6 exercise

A To construct circle graphs, you need to use skills with percent and angles. Questions 1 to 6 review these skills. Express your answers to 1 decimal place unless indicated otherwise.

1 Express each as a percent.

   (a) 12 out of 40   (b) 8 out of 25

   (c) $\frac{60}{80}$ (d) $\frac{3}{20}$ (e) $\frac{17}{20}$

2 Calculate the following angles to the nearest degree.

   (a) 25% of 360°   (b) 15% of 360°

   (c) 8% of 360°   (d) 70% of 360°

3 For a circle graph, this relationship 1% represents 3.6° is useful to remember. Find what angle is represented by each of the following.

   (a) 10%   (b) 100%   (c) 25%

   (d) 5%   (e) 76%   (f) 83%

4 For each of the following:
   ▶ Estimate the measure of the central angle.
   ▶ Measure the central angle.
   ▶ Calculate the percent of the circle shaded.

   (a)   (b)

   (c)   (d)

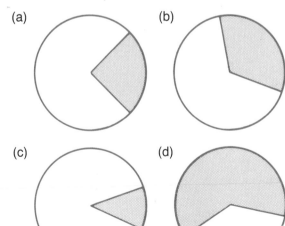

5 Construct a circle with radius 4 cm. Draw the following sector angles in the circle. The points A, B, C, and D are marked on the circumference of the circle.

   (a) ∠AOB = 90°   (b) ∠BOC = 120°

   (c) ∠COD = 80°

   (d) What is the measure of ∠DOA?

   (e) Suggest two different ways to obtain your answer for (d).

6 You are given the following data to draw a circle graph.

   (a) How can you do a quick check to see if the data are correct?

   (b) Check the data. Make any necessary corrections.

Percents	Angle measures
12.5	45°
50.0	180°
37.5	235°

Questions 7 to 9 are based on the following survey.

A survey was conducted to obtain an answer to the following question: "Should the seating capacity of the stadium be increased?" The answers are shown.

Yes	43%
No	35%
Undecided	12%
No opinion	10%

7 What central angle (to the nearest degree) would represent each answer?

   (a) yes   (b) no   (c) undecided

8 (a) Construct a circle graph to show the information.

   (b) Suggest a title for the graph.

9 For the information in the table, the "No Opinion" persons said "No" in the next survey.

(a) Construct a circle graph for the new survey.

(b) Find the measure of each central angle in the circle graph. What should the sum of all angles be?

B

10 The circle graph shows the food content in cheddar cheese.

Food Content of Cheddar Cheese

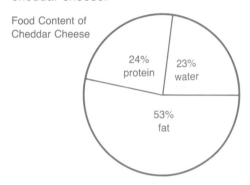

In a 500 g piece of cheese, calculate the amount of

(a) protein (b) water (c) fat

11 A large egg has a mass of 60 g. Its food content is found to be as follows.

water	44 g	protein	8 g
fat	7 g	carbohydrate	1 g

(a) Calculate the percentage of each type of food in the whole egg.

(b) Construct a circle graph to display these data.

12 The circle graph shows the basic blood types and the distribution.

Distribution of Blood Types

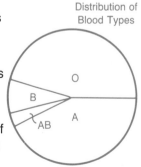

(a) Which blood type is most common? least common?

(b) What percentage of the total population has type O blood?

(c) The population of Dartmouth, N.S. is 64 770 (latest census). Estimate how many people would have type A blood? Calculate your answer.

(d) The population of Red Deer, Alta. is 27 674 (latest census). How many people in Red Deer have type AB blood?

(Check whether your answer is reasonable.

(e) What assumption did you make in obtaining your answer in (d)?

13 Vanier Public School collected $440 in a fundraising campaign. The distribution of the money is shown on the circle graph.

(a) Measure the central angle for club activities. What percent is represented?

(b) How much money was spent on club activities?

(c) What percent of the money was spent on athletic uniforms? How much money is this?

(d) How much money was given to special events?

(e) Find the sum of the monies in (b), (c), and (d). Is the sum exactly $440? Why or why not?

14 The data show Canada's employment structure in 1979.

Agriculture and Forestry	6%
Mining	3%
Manufacturing	19%
Construction	5%
Trade and Transportation	25%
Insurance and Real Estate	5%
Services	29%
Public Service	8%

(a) Construct a circle graph to display this information.

(b) In 1979 there were approximately 10 000 000 people with employment. How many people were employed in mining?

(c) Make up two questions of your own based on the information.

(d) Exchange your questions with others in your class. Solve each problem.

15 Refer to the information in the previous circle graph. The population of Fredericton based on the last census is 24 254.

(a) How many people would you expect to be employed in manufacturing?

(b) What assumption did you make in (a) to obtain your answer?

16 For the following data:
  ▶ Construct a circle graph.
  ▶ Create one problem based on the circle graph.
  ▶ Solve your problem.

(a) The Hockey Association collected money from the following sources.

Sponsors	$ 6000
Registrations	$25 000
Dances	$ 3500
Ticket Sales	$ 2750

(b) The human body consists of the following

Muscle	49.8%	Fat	18.6%
Bone	17.8%	Other	13.8%

(c) Over the last few years, the record of the Winnipeg Jets was as follows.

Number of games won	48
Number of games lost	26
Number of games tied	8

17 The two circle graphs show the relationships of various exports that Canada had in 1964 and 1974.

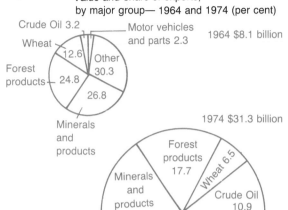

Value and share of exports, by major group— 1964 and 1974 (per cent)

Crude Oil 3.2
Motor vehicles and parts 2.3
1964 $8.1 billion
Wheat
12.6
Other 30.3
Forest products 24.8
26.8
Minerals and products

1974 $31.3 billion
Forest products 17.7
Wheat 6.5
Minerals and products 19.5
Crude Oil 10.9
Motor vehicles and parts 17.7
Other 27.7

Source: Statistics Canada

(a) From the two circle graphs, *estimate* how many times the exports in 1974 increased from 1964?

(b) Calculate to one decimal place

$$\frac{\text{area of large circle}}{\text{area of small circle}}$$

This value helps you decide how many times the exports in 1974 increased from 1964. Why?

(c) Calculate to one decimal place $\frac{31.3}{8.1}$

This value gives you (to one decimal place) the number of times the exports in 1974 increased from 1964. Why?

(d) How do your answers in (b) and (c) compare?

(e) Measure the angle of the sector showing crude oil in each graph. Use your answer to find how many times the export of crude oil in 1974 has increased.

(f) Make similar comparisons (decrease or increase) for other exports shown in the two circle graphs.

7.7 which is a suitable graph?

As you have seen, there are many different types of graphs that can be used to display data. The type of graph that is chosen often depends on the nature of the data and how the graph is to be used.

> - pictograph
> - stem-leaf plot
> - bar graph
> - broken-line graph
> - circle graph
> - other graphs

Before you construct a graph, you need to make some decisions.

▶ Which type of graph is most suitable to display the information?
▶ How visual do I want the graph? Do I want to use a pictograph?
▶ Do I want to use a horizontal or vertical bar graph?
▶ What should the title be?
▶ How should the axes be labelled?
▶ What scale is to be chosen for the horizontal axes? for the vertical axes?
▶ What calculations are needed to construct the graph?

In the exercise that follows, you will need to make decisions about which type of graph you might use to display the data given.

Use your calculator. Check your calculations.

7.7 exercise

A

1 Sonya is organizing a party. The graphs show how she plans to spend the money she has budgeted for the party.

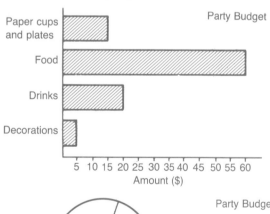

(a) Which graph would you use to find how much Sonya budgeted to spend on the party altogether?

(b) Which graph would be more appropriate for finding what fraction of the budget Sonya spends on drinks?

(c) Which graph would you use to tell how many times as much Sonya spends on food than on drinks?

2 The number of players on a team for various sports is given.

Curling	4	Field Hockey	11
Lacrosse	12	Softball	9
		Waterpolo	7

(a) Why would a circle graph not be suitable for displaying these data?

(b) Why should you not use a broken-line graph to display the data?

(c) Construct a bar graph to display the data.

3 The data show the food content of a 300 g container of fruit yogurt.

Water   228 g   Fat   6 g
Protein   12 g   Carbohydrate   54 g

(a) Display the data in a bar graph.

(b) Display the data in a circle graph.

(c) Which graph, (a) or (b), is more suitable to display the data? Why?

4 In a bikeathon the number of kilometres cycled by each participant was recorded.

28 15 32 61 54 47 19 27 44 31 45
17 10 29 16 36 35 42 56 20 33 25
 8 13 53 65 12 36 53 27 19 30

(a) What difficulties occur if you use each of the following types of graphs to show the data? ▶ pictograph ▶ bar graph
▶ broken line graph

(b) Record the data on a stem and leaf plot. Why is this form a more suitable graph?

(c) Use your graph to create three questions about the data.

(d) Use the graph to answer the questions in (c).

B

5 The average normal human pulse rate changes with age.

(a) Which type of graph could you use to display the information?
▶ pictograph
▶ stem-leaf plot
▶ broken-line graph
▶ circle graph
▶ bar graph

Age	Pulse rate (beats/min)
newborn	135
10 a	87
20 a	71
30 a	72
40 a	72
50 a	72
60 a	73
70 a	75

(b) Draw the graph that you think is most suitable for displaying the data. Give reasons for your choice.

6 The table shows the temperature inside an oven after it is turned on.

Time elapsed (min)	0	5	10	15	20	25
Temperature (0°C)	25	50	125	160	180	180

(a) Construct a graph of your choice to show the data. Give reasons for your choice.

(b) During which 5 min interval was there the greatest temperature increase?

(c) What temperature do you think the oven was set at?

(d) Estimate the temperature inside the oven after 7 min.

7 In a survey, people were asked the number of pets in their home. Their responses are recorded below.

5 0 1 2 1 3 2 0 1 6 8 2 0
1 2 5 1 0 2 1 0 3 2 4 0 1
1 3 2 0 1 4 1 0 3 2 1 2 3
1 1 1 2 5 1 0 3 6 1 4

(a) Use a tally chart to organize the data.

(b) Construct a graph of your choice to display the data. Give reasons for your choice.

(c) Use your graph to create two questions about the data.

(d) Use the graph to answer the questions in (c).

8 The sound levels of different noises are measured in decibels.

Average talking	60 dB
Loud shout	100 dB
Heavy traffic	90 dB
Discotheque (at full volume)	117 dB

(a) Construct the graph that you think is most appropriate to display this information.

(b) Explain why you chose this type of graph and not one of the others.

9 The monthly total precipitation (in millimetres) is shown for two places in Canada.

	J	F	M	A	M	J	J	A	S	O	N	D
Greenwood Nova Scotia	117	97	77	79	75	74	63	91	74	87	111	115
Estevan Point B.C.	385	318	292	233	120	97	88	90	171	376	421	436

(a) Construct a graph of your choice to display the data. Give reasons for your choice.

(b) Create two problems based on your graph.

(c) Use the graph to answer the questions in (b).

10 For each set of data:
▶ Draw a suitable graph to display the data. Give reasons for your choice.
▶ Use your graph to create two questions about the data.
▶ Answer your questions.

(a) Did you know that data are collected on how much sunshine there is in various places in Canada? The table shows the average monthly sunshine (in hours) during February.

Prince Albert	115 h
London	90 h
St. John's	76 h
Inuvik	68 h
Sept Iles	135 h
Prince Rupert	59 h

(b) The data show the vitamins and minerals found in a cereal.

VITAMINS AND MINERALS PER SERVING	
Vitamin B₁, Thiamine	0.6 mg
Vitamin B₂, Riboflavin	1.0 mg
Vitamin, Niacinamide	6.0 mg
Iron	4.0 mg

Check whether your answer is reasonable.

11 For each question:
▶ Collect data to answer the question.
▶ Draw a suitable graph to display the data.
▶ Use your graph to answer the original question.
▶ Create two other questions that can be answered using your graph. Answer the questions.

(a) How does your pulse rate change when you perform different activities such as walking, running, sleeping, or riding a bicycle?

(b) What are the four favourite rock groups of the students in your class?

(c) Does the temperature in your house vary during the night?

(d) Which of the names of these 6 great Canadian sailboats of the past is most appealing to you?

Nonsuch Bluenose Atlanta
Driftwood Innisfree Patricia

If you look on the reverse side of most Canadian dimes, you see a picture of the Bluenose. The Bluenose was one of our most famous racing schooners ever built.

(e) Which sign of the zodiac is most common for the birthdates of students in your school?

(f) How much of the day is cloudy for a month?

(g) What percent of the cartoons are about animals? people? other?

applications: multiple types of graphs

In the previous sections you saw a variety of graphs being used to display data. In the following exercises, a few other types are dealt with.

12 A **double bar graph** can be used to compare related data as shown in the following graph.

Canada's Foreign Trade

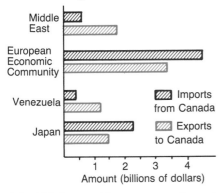

(a) Which countries or areas import more from Canada than they export to Canada?

(b) Which countries or areas export more to Canada than they import from Canada?

13 This multiple graph shows the average temperature and the amount of precipitation for each month.

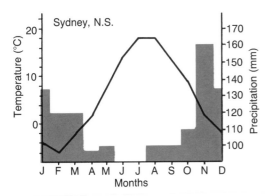

(a) Which two months have the least amount of precipitation?

(b) Which two months have the greatest temperature?

(c) How do your answers in (a) and (b) compare? Do you think there is a connection between the amount of precipitation and the temperature?

14 Use this graph to answer the following questions.

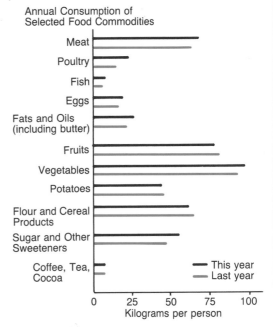

(a) Which foods have decreased in consumption?

(b) Which foods have increased in consumption?

(c) Which food has increased the most in consumption?

(d) Use the data to calculate the total mass of food consumed in one year for a person.

(e) Make up two other questions about the graph. Exchange your questions with other students and solve them.

7.8 distorting information

Graphs are very useful for presenting data in a clear, visual way. However, they can also be used to distort information and create false impressions. For example, the information in the chart can be distorted by drawing this bar graph.

Data

Points Scored on a Videogame

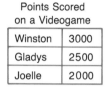

Winston	3000
Gladys	2500
Joelle	2000

Bar Graph

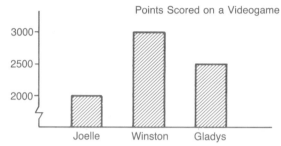

Look at the bars on the graph. It appears that Winston's score is three times greater than Joelle's score. However, in reality this is not the case, since the bars of the graph do not show the amount between 0 and 2000.

Example   Use the circle graphs.

(a) Based on the graph, can you determine who spends more money on clothes, Mark or Nancy? Why or why not?

(b) What false impressions might be assumed from the two graphs?

(c) How can you correct the false impressions?

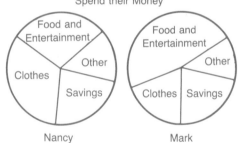

Solution   (a) No, you cannot determine from the graph who spends more money on clothes. To determine how much each spends on clothes, you need to know how much money each student has to begin with.

(b) Nancy's food and entertainment sector is smaller than Mark's. However, this does not mean Nancy spends less money. How much each spends depends on what money they began with.

(c) To correct the false impressions, record the amount of money each person has. Then the actual amount spent on each item by each student can be found.

A

1 A company asked two artists to draw a graph of the company's profits for a six-month period.

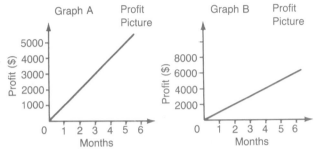

(a) How are the graphs alike? How are they different?

(b) If you were the president of the company, which graph would you choose to publish? Explain why.

(c) Predict the company's profit for the seventh month. What assumption do you make to obtain your answer?

2 For a T.V. documentary on inflation, the following visual was prepared.

(a) From the graph find the ratio:

$$\frac{\text{Area of 1970 dollar}}{\text{Area of 1980 dollar}}$$

(b) Find the ratio:

$$\frac{\text{Buying power 1970 dollar}}{\text{Buying power 1980 dollar}}$$

(c) How would you expect the ratios in (a) and (b) to be related? Why?

(d) How are the ratios in (a) and (b) related?

3 The value of exports made by a company in two consecutive years is shown by the diagram.

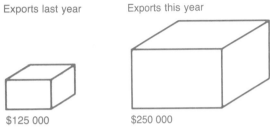

(a) Which statement appears to be the best description of the information in the diagram?
   A Exports increased twice as much from last year.
   B Exports increased three times as much from last year.
   C Exports increased four times as much from last year.

(b) Compare the volumes of the boxes. Each dimension of the small box has doubled. By how many times has the volume increased?

(c) Use the dollar figures. By how much has the dollar value of the exports increased?

(d) What false impression does the diagram give?

B

4 Two graphs show the same information.

(a) Which graph creates a false impression?

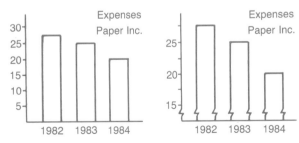

(b) What false impression is created? Give examples or reasons for your answer.

5 The graph shows the components that make up the selling price of gasoline.

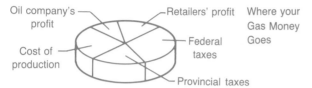

Where your Gas Money Goes

(a) What false impression does this graph give?

(b) How would you correct the false impression?

(c) Who do you think produced the graph, the oil company or the government? Explain your answer.

6 A pictograph shows the number of hotels at three resort areas.

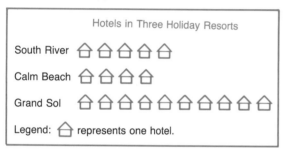

(a) From the pictograph, which holiday resort appears to be the biggest?

(b) Explain why this impression may be false.

7 Study each of the following carefully.
▶ Describe any false impressions that might be obtained from each.
▶ Suggest changes that should be made to remove the false impression.

(a) A record company shows its increase in sales as follows.

(b) The distance recorded by three students in the long-jump event is shown.

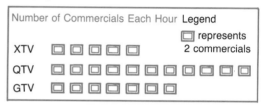

(c) The pictograph shows the number of commercials per hour for three T.V. stations.

8 Use the data:
▶ Draw a graph to make the data appear distorted.
▶ Create one problem based on the graph. Solve the problem you have created.

(a) The amount of milk exported to foreign countries in January and February is shown as a percent of the total milk exported.

| January | 28% |
| February | 14% |

(b) The expenses for two consecutive years is shown for a manufacturing company.

Amount of expenses	
This year	$1.6 million
Last year	$2.1 million

(c) The greatest purses for the Canadian rodeos are shown.

Manitoba Stampede, Morris, Manitoba	$26 000
Canadian Western Super Rodeo, Edmonton, Alberta	$27 000
Calgary Exhibition and Stampede, Calgary, Alberta	$211 650
Cloverdale Rodeo, Cloverdale, B.C.	$18 750
North American Chuck Wagon Races, High River, Alberta	$20 000

7.9 characteristics of data: mean, median, mode

Although a graph may be used to provide information about data, you may want to know other characteristics about the data. For example, averages are often used to show a characteristic (property) of the data. For any set of data, the three terms **average** (or **mean**), **median**, and **mode** are used to describe or provide useful information. The following example shows how these three measures are found.

AVERAGE TRIPS

During a recent study, the figures compiled show that Canadians on vacation travel about 560 km. This study was based on data collected from vacationers who voluntarily completed a questionnaire provided by tourist offices located on main thoroughfares.

Example   The number of people at the Audio Visual Club each week for ten weeks is shown.

    18   15   23   12   20   26   14   17   22   20

(a) Calculate the mean of the data.

(b) Calculate the median of the data.

(c) Calculate the mode of the data.

Solution   (a) mean = $\dfrac{\text{total number of people}}{\text{number of weeks}}$

The **average** or **mean** of a set of data is equal to

$\dfrac{\text{the sum of all the data}}{\text{the number of pieces of data}}$

$= \dfrac{18 + 15 + 23 + 12 + 20 + 26 + 14 + 17 + 22 + 20}{10}$

$= \frac{187}{10}$ The mean of the data is 18.7.

(b) Arrange the data in order from least to greatest.

    12   14   15   17   18   20   20   22   23   26

$\left(\begin{array}{l}\text{Since there are an even number of} \\ \text{data, the median is the average} \\ \text{of the middle values, namely 19.}\end{array}\right.$

The median of the data is 19.

For an odd number of data, the **median** is the middle number of the data arranged in order from least to greatest.

For an even number of data, the **median** is the average of the middle two numbers.

(c) The number 20 occurs most frequently (twice). The mode of the data is 20.

The **mode** of a set of data is the number that occurs most frequently.

Another characteristic of data which provides additional information is the **range**. For example, for the previous data:

The **range** is the difference between the greatest and smallest pieces of data.

greatest value   26
smallest value   12   range = 26 − 12 or 14

The characteristics of data you have learned:
  ▶ mean ▶ mode ▶ median ▶ range
provide useful information about your data, whether you know all the data or not. For example, a company may know the mean, mode, median and range of its sales. Without knowing information about each sale, the company can use the characteristics to make useful predictions.

The method you are going to use is important in solving problems.

I Collect information or obtain the characteristics of data: median, mode, mean, range.

II Use the information or characteristics to predict what the actual data might appear as.

Scientists work using similar methods. G. Bohr *never* saw an atom, but he was able to describe it fairly accurately because of this method:

I Collect information about some item or problem.

II Use the information to predict the appearance of the item or the solution to the problem.

7.9 exercise

A Where necessary, express your answer to 1 decimal place.

1 Calculate the mean for each of the following.

(a) 8, 7, 9, 11, 10, 5, 7, 8, 6, 9

(b) 36, 38, 42, 40, 40, 43, 39

(c) 4.6, 3.9, 4.8, 7.6, 3.2, 4.9, 8.9, 6.8, 7.6

(d) 14.3, 20.3, 19.8, 14.6, 17.6, 16.8, 19.5, 13.5, 14.6, 12.8

2 Find the mode for each of the following.

(a) 2, 3, 2, 2, 4

(b) 12, 15, 13, 14, 15, 13, 11

(c) 8.5, 3.8, 5.2, 6.9, 7.5, 6.7, 6.9, 7.2

(d) 5, 6, 4, 5, 7, 4, 5, 6, 5, 4, 7, 5, 6

3 Find the median for each of the following.

(a) 7, 6, 10, 5, 8, 11, 9

(b) 2, 2, 4, 3, 2, 1, 3

(c) 9, 12, 8, 11, 10, 11, 11, 12

(d) 15, 17, 14, 16, 18, 18, 16, 15

4 Find the mean, median, mode, and range for each of the following.

(a) 61, 56, 49, 73, 86, 72, 56, 75

(b) 36, 38, 40, 40, 42, 43, 39

(c) 4.6, 3.9, 4.8, 7.6, 3.2, 4.9, 8.9, 6.8, 7.6

(d) 16, 16, 15, 14, 17, 16, 16, 17, 18, 19, 20

(e) 14.3, 20.3, 19.8, 14.6, 17.6, 16.8, 19.5, 13.5, 14.6, 12.8

5 (a) Find the mean, median, and mode for the following data.
       2, 9, 9, 3, 4, 6, 3, 5, 2, 1, 3

   (b) Which characteristic, the median, mode, or mean, is the easiest to find? Why?

6 (a) If the mean of a set of data is 23, must 23 be one of the data values? Use an example to illustrate your answer.

   (b) Construct a set of data whose mean is one of the data values.

   (c) Construct a set of data whose mean is not one of the data values.

7 (a) If the median of a set of data is 23, must 23 be one of the data values? Use an example to illustrate your answer.

(b) Construct a set of data whose median is one of the data values.

(c) Construct a set of data whose median is not one of the data values.

8 If the mode of a set of data is 23, must 23 be one of the data values? Use an example to illustrate your answer.

B

9 The average salary paid to each person in various companies is shown. Calculate the total payroll for each company.

	Company	Average salary	Number of employees
(a)	Comstock	$9650	65
(b)	Perron	$11 696	48
(c)	Lorimar	$10 965	96

10 The highest temperature each day at Honey Harbour for the week is shown.

31°C 28°C 23°C 23°C 28°C 27°C 25°C

(a) A newscaster indicated on the news that the mode of the temperatures at Honey Harbour last week was 23°C. Why is this statement misleading?

(b) Give other examples of how the mode might mislead you about the data.

(c) Calculate the average of the temperature.

(d) Does the average give a better representation of the data? Why or why not?

11 The number of persons attending a local golf tournament each day is shown.

Day	1	2	3	4	5	6	7	8	9
Attendance	965	836	753	921	862	903	1048	2012	6012

(a) Calculate the average attendance per day. Round your answer to the nearest whole number.

(b) A tournament official was overheard saying that "The average attendance each day was about 2000 persons". Explain why the statement could be justified based on your knowledge of mathematics.

(c) Why is the statement in (b) misleading? Give reasons for your answer.

C

12 The longest paved road in the world is the Trans-Canada Highway with a length of 7871 km. The part of the road in each province is shown in kilometres.

Newfoundland	892	Manitoba	497
Prince Edward Is.	114	Saskatchewan	653
Nova Scotia	512	Alberta	454
New Brunswick	628	British Columbia	914
Quebec	644	Ontario	2338
		Amount of road in National Parks	225

(a) Calculate the average amount of road in each province. Calculate the range.

(b) Which province has the amount of road nearest the average?

skills quiz

How well do you remember the meaning of words? Each of the words that follow occurs in this chapter. For each word give an example to illustrate its meaning. If you forget the meaning of a word, use your index or the glossary to find its meaning.

sample	tally	pie graph
bar graph	legend	mode
scale	interpolation	
central angle	circle graph	
mean	frequency	
biased	pictograph	
extrapolation	distorted	
average	range	
survey	stem and leaf	
sector	median	
frequency table	horizontal bar graph	
vertical bar graph	broken line graph	

7.10 problem-solving: making decisions

In the previous sections you learned a number of skills which you can use to solve problems about data.
▶ Skills for gathering information.
▶ Skills for displaying data: pictographs, bar graphs, stem and leaf plots, broken-line graphs, and so on.
▶ Skills for working with data: mean, median, mode, range.

In planning to solve problems, you have often asked the same questions over and over again. However, to solve a problem about data, you may need to ask the same questions from a slightly different point of view, since the skills you are applying are different. For example:

> **Steps for Solving Problems**
>
> A Ask yourself:
>   *I What information am I asked to find?*
>   *II What information am I given?*
> B Decide on a method.
>   *Which operation do I use?*
> C Do the work.
>   *Complete the calculation.*
> D Check your work.
>   *Use your rounding skills.*
> E Make a final statement.
>   *Answer the original problem.*

A Ask yourself:
  I What are you asked to find?
  II What information is given?

> In some problems you will need to obtain data. Use charts to organize your work. Record your data accurately.

B Decide on a method.

> After you have collected your data, decide whether the problem can be better solved by drawing a graph, making appropriate calculations, finding medians, and so on.

C Do the work.

> Once you have planned which skills to use, you do the calculations. Where necessary, record any assumptions you make in finding an answer. Estimate the answer. Then check by calculating.

D Check your work.

> Check to see whether your answer is reasonable. Does your answer make sense?

E Make a final statement.

> You were asked to solve a problem about data. Thus, you need to make a final statement. Then check whether you answered the question properly.

In your earlier work in this chapter you have already practised solving problems with each skill. Now you need to decide which skill to use to solve the problem.

Use your calculator. Check your answers for the problems.

7.10 exercise

B

Questions 1 to 5 are based on the information shown.

January 8, Ski Shop Sales

January 8, Ski Shop Sales	
Skis	$1600
Boots	$900
Poles	$400
Suits	$500
Accessories	$200

Jan 8, Ski Shop Sales

Skis	XXX XXXXX
Boots	XX XX /
Poles	XX
Suits	XX /
Accessories	X

Legend: each X represents $200.

1. Do the sales figures appear to be exact? To what accuracy do you think the data are recorded?

2. (a) What is the legend for the pictograph?

    (b) Using the same symbol, how would sales of $478 be shown?

3. (a) What percentage of the total sales comes from the sale of boots?

    (b) Which graph displays this information better?

    (c) From the circle graph, how can you tell that the value of the skis sold was less than 50% of the total sales?

4. Draw a bar graph to display the data. What are the advantages and disadvantages of using the bar graph?

5. (a) Which graph best displays the percentage of sales for each item?

    (b) Which graph displays the ratio of skis to poles best?

(c) Which graph do you think requires the most time to construct: pictograph, bar graph, circle graph? Is the time worth it? Give reasons for your answer.

6. Benton bowls three games each night, five nights a week.

	Game 1	Game 2	Game 3
Monday	236	201	190
Tuesday	262	211	186
Wednesday	251	135	209
Thursday	183	213	253
Friday	149	218	243

   (a) Calculate his average score for each night. Round your answer to 1 decimal place.

   (b) Find the average of the "averages" in (a).

   (c) Calculate the averages of all 15 games.

   (d) Would you expect your answers in (b) and (c) to be the same? Why or why not?

7. The number of emergency cases that occurred for 9 consecutive weekends was recorded as

   38, 40, 28, 26, 39, 41, 28, 42, 36

   (a) Find the mean of these data.

   (b) Find the mode of these data.

   (c) You are the doctor in charge of assigning staff to the emergency ward on weekends. On which result would you base your decision: the mean (a) or the mode (b)?

8. On a class test marked out of 20, the following results were obtained.

2 students scored 9	6 students scored 15
8 students scored 10	2 students scored 19
3 students scored 12	2 students scored 20
6 students scored 18	

   (a) What information does the median, mode, and average tell us about the data?

   (b) Which characteristic in (a) is the most useful?

9 The number of delivery trucks passing through an intersection each hour was recorded for a 24 h period, starting at noon.

38, 35, 12, 6, 36, 38, 4, 2, 2, 1, 0, 1, 0, 0, 0, 0, 1, 1, 3, 12, 26, 3, 2, 4

(a) Calculate the mean, median, and mode of the data.

(b) Which characteristic of these data is most meaningful: the mode, the average, or the median?

(c) Which of the following are misleading characteristics of these data: the mode, the mean, or the median?

10 A department store records the weekly sales of summer sports shoes during July. The results are shown.

Brand name	Pairs of shoes sold
Pro II	54
Sonic	51
Leisure	55
Pacer II	30
Marathon	66
North Star	27
Court	53

(a) Calculate the mean, median, mode, and range.

(b) You have been asked to place an order for the August shipment of shoes. You can order up to 150 dozen pairs of shoes to be sold in August. Use the above data to decide on how to organize your order for shoes. Justify your answer.

(c) List any assumptions you make in obtaining your answer for (b).

11 The characteristics, the mean, median, mode, and range are given for data. For each of the following, construct a set of data that have the following characteristics.

	(a)	(b)	(c)	(d)
Average	12	12	18	16
Median	10	12	15	16
Mode	8	12	15	12
Range	18	19	36	21

12 Do you like tomatoes? Predict what you think is the most popular vegetable?

(a) Copy and complete the following chart to investigate the favourite vegetable in your class.

Vegetable	Number of persons that like the vegetable
Tomato	
Onion	

(Make up a list of other vegetables to include in your chart.

(b) Which three vegetables are the runner-ups for "the most liked vegetable"?

13 Tastes in music vary.

(a) How would you find out which instruments are the best liked in your class?

(b) Use a graph to display your results.

(c) Which characteristic can you determine for the data you collect; median, mean, mode, or range?

C

14 Did you know that the average Canadian eats approximately 4.8 m of hot dogs a year?

(a) Decide on a topic of your own which you would like to investigate. (For example, investigate the "length" of hot dogs eaten in your class in a year.)

(b) Draw a graph to show your results.

(c) What information can you obtain from your graph in (b)?

(d) Decide on who you think would be interested in obtaining the data you have collected. List the reasons for their interest in the data.

practice and problems: a chapter review

1 A survey on the number of viewers watching a TV mini-series was run. Describe the different methods that could be used and the advantages and disadvantages of each method.

2 The following data show the students buying different flavours of sundaes.

Hot Fudge (F)   Strawberry (S)   Pineapple (P)
```
F S F P F S S F F P S P F S
F F S F F P F S S S F F S F F
```

(a) Construct a freqency table.

(b) What percent of the students bought strawberry sundaes?

3 The number of people shopping at a local corner store for the same 2 h period each day for a month was recorded.
```
28 43 18 34 32 29 47 36 52 42 36 42 41 35 28
30 42 12 32 30 25 34 30 27 34 29 35 46 46 31
```

(a) Construct a stem and leaf plot

(b) How many times did more than 40 people come into the store?

(c) Construct a pictograph for the data.

(d) Construct a bar graph for the data.

(e) How are the graphs in (a), (c), and (d) alike? How do they differ?

4 A hot dog bun has a mass of 50 g. Its food content is

moisture 15.5 g   protein 2.5 g
carbohydrates 25 g   other 7.0 g

Construct a circle graph to display the data.

5 In a tournament Kalana bowled 5 games with scores: 194, 215, 187, 152, and 220.

(a) Construct a graph of your choice to display the data. Give reasons for your choice.

(b) Construct a graph that distorts the information.

6 Find the mean, median, and mode for
(a) 35, 30, 28, 33, 35, 32, 31.
(b) 2.6, 3.5, 4.2, 5.1, 3.6, 4.1, 3.5, 3.4.

test for practice

1 A survey on the number of viewers for the Grey Cup game was given. Why would a telephone survey be better than other methods? Explain.

2 Data were collected on food purchases at the school cafeteria. Sandwiches (S), Daily Special (D), Hot Soup (H), Milk (M).

```
M D M S D H S S H H M M S D
H D M D S H S S S M D S
H S D M H S H D M H S H D M
```

Construct a frequency table and a bar graph to show the information.

3 The heights of people in a classroom are recorded.
```
157 173 182 163 159 146 172 179 153 161
159 165 159 154 152 162 159 166 163 168
154 172 159 162 164 169 154 153 172 195
```

(a) Construct a stem and leaf plot for the data.

(b) Use the results in (a) to determine the median.

4 (a) Use the data on growth patterns to draw a line graph.

(b) What would be the height of a 6 year old? 20 year old?

Years Passed	Height
birth	50 cm
2	86 cm
4	101 cm
8	128 cm
12	148 cm
16	170 cm
18	173 cm

5 A hot dog with mass 50 g has the following food content.

Moisture   29 g   Protein   7 g
fat   10 g   carbohydrate 1 g
other   3 g

(a) Calculate the percentage of each type of food content and construct a circle graph.

(b) Use the data. Construct a graph that distorts the information.

6 Find the mean, median, mode, and range for
(a) 15, 18, 13, 15, 16, 13, 14, 15, 15
(b) 2.4, 2.5, 2.1, 3.1, 2.8, 2.7
(c) What is a best characteristic of the data?

math is plus: John Venn and his diagrams

The mathematician, John Venn, developed a method for showing relationships among sets in a special kind of diagram. The Venn diagram shows the relationship between set A = {1, 2, 3, 4, 5, 6} and set B = {2, 4, 6, 8, 10}. The members of each set are often referred to as **elements**.

The set of all the elements that are in either set A or set B is called the **union** of the two sets. The union is written as A ∪ B. Venn diagrams can be useful in solving problems.

The elements that are common to both sets are shown in the overlap. This is the **intersection** of set A and set B. The intersection is A ∩ B.

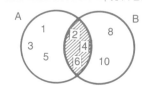

Example

31 people who play sports are interviewed. The results are

> 17 play baseball   13 play hockey
>   6 play neither hockey nor baseball

How many play baseball and hockey?

Solution

Draw a Venn diagram.
You are given

play baseball	17
play hockey	13
total	30
	25
	5

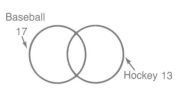

But the number of persons in the Venn diagram is

$$31 - 6 = 25$$

Thus 5 people play baseball and hockey.

31 interviewed   6 do not play either sport   play either baseball or hockey

---

1 Use the diagram to find the members of each of the following sets.

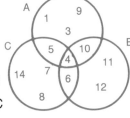

   (a) Set A   (b) Set B

   (c) A ∩ B   (d) A ∩ C

2 Use the diagram in the previous question.

   (a) Which numbers belong to A but not to B?

   (b) Which numbers belong to C but not to A?

   (c) Which numbers belong to B and C but not to A?

   (d) Which numbers belong to A and B and C?

   Make up one other question about the diagram.

3 (a) Draw a Venn diagram to show these data.
        65 persons were polled.
        47 liked calculators.
        15 liked calculators and computers.

   (b) Use your diagram in (a). How many liked computers? How many liked *only* calculators?

4 The total membership in the chess and badminton club is 57. Eleven students belong to the chess club and also the badminton club. Thirty-five students belong to the badminton club only. How many students belong to the chess club?

5 In a recent poll, of 91 students, it was found that 34 students liked chocolate K and chocolate C. Sixty-two students liked chocolate C. How many students liked only chocolate K?

6 Use the following statistics to answer the question:
        185 persons liked only T.V.
        463 persons liked T.V. and movies.
        832 persons liked movies.
   How many persons were interviewed?

8 fractions: operations and applications

Language with fractions, adding, subtracting, multiplying, and dividing fractions, catalogue shopping, skills with reciprocals, substitution skills, problems with missing information, problem solving skills, solving problems and applications

Fractions are a part of your everyday living.

Fractional numbers occur in shopping.

Fractional numbers occur in cooking.

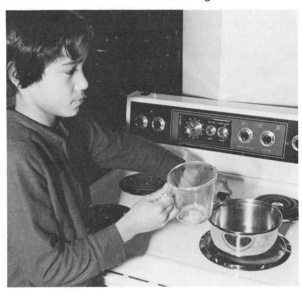

You need fractions to answer questions.

What fraction of the vehicles are commercial vehicles i.e. trucks, vans, and so on?

What fraction of the books are about business? Fictional? About geography?

8.1 skills with fractions

To learn skills with fractions, you must know the meanings of the words used.

▶ Fractions are used to describe part of a whole.

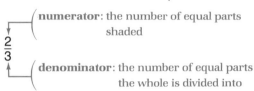

$\frac{2}{3}$

numerator: the number of equal parts shaded

denominator: the number of equal parts the whole is divided into

$\frac{2}{3}$ of the diagram is shaded

When the numerator is smaller than the denominator, the fraction is a **proper fraction**. The fraction $\frac{2}{3}$ is a proper fraction.

▶ Fractions can also be used to describe part of a group.
In the diagram, the 6 people are arranged into 3 equal groups. Each group is made up of 2 people.

For the people shown:

$\frac{2}{3}$ are girls $\frac{4}{6}$ are girls

$\left(\frac{2}{3}\text{ is equivalent to }\frac{4}{6}\right)$

▶ To find equivalent fractions, *multiply* by a suitable form of 1.

$\frac{2}{3} \times \frac{2}{2} = \frac{4}{6}$ $\left(\begin{array}{l}\text{Multiply by a}\\ \text{form of 1.}\end{array}\right)$

$\frac{2}{3} \times \frac{3}{3} = \frac{6}{9}$

$\frac{2}{3} \times \frac{5}{5} = \frac{10}{15}$ $\left(\begin{array}{l}\frac{4}{6}, \frac{6}{9}, \frac{10}{15} \text{ are}\\ \textbf{equivalent fractions.}\end{array}\right)$

▶ To write fractions in lowest terms, *divide* by a suitable form of 1.

$\frac{4 \div 2}{6 \div 2} = \frac{2}{3}$

$\frac{10 \div 5}{15 \div 5} = \frac{2}{3}$

$\frac{6 \div 3}{9 \div 3} = \frac{2}{3}$

$\left(\begin{array}{l}\text{When you multiply or divide}\\ \text{by a form of 1, you are multiplying}\\ \text{the numerator and denominator of}\\ \text{the fraction by the same number.}\end{array}\right)$

Example 1   Write each fraction in lowest terms.

(a) $\frac{10}{25}$ (b) $\frac{12}{18}$

$\left(\begin{array}{l}\text{A fraction is in lowest terms if the}\\ \text{numerator and denominator have}\\ \text{no common factors other than one.}\end{array}\right)$

Solution   (a) $\frac{10 \div 5}{25 \div 5} = \frac{2}{5}$ $\left(\begin{array}{l}\textbf{Step 1}\ \ \text{Find the greatest common factor}\\ \text{of the numerator and denominator.}\end{array}\right)$

(b) $\frac{12 \div 6}{18 \div 6} = \frac{2}{3}$ $\left(\begin{array}{l}\textbf{Step 2}\ \ \text{Divide both the numerator and}\\ \text{denominator by the same number.}\end{array}\right)$

Fractions in which the numerator is greater than the denominator are called **improper fractions**.

$\frac{3}{2}$ is improper $\left(\dfrac{\text{numerator}}{3}\right) > \left(\dfrac{\text{denominator}}{2}\right)$

The meaning of $\frac{3}{2}$ can be illustrated by a diagram.

$\left(\begin{array}{l}\text{A diagram is often useful in helping you} \\ \text{understand the meaning of words} \\ \text{used in mathematics.}\end{array}\right.$

$\frac{3}{2}$ ⟵(Think: 3 equal parts shaded
      ⟵(Think: 2 equal parts in a whole

To write an improper fraction as a mixed number, you can use a diagram to help you, as shown in the next example.

$\left(\begin{array}{l}\text{A mixed number is a number that} \\ \text{has a whole part and a fraction part.}\end{array}\right.$

Example 2   Write $\frac{13}{4}$ as a mixed number.

Think: 4 parts in a whole
        13 parts in all

Solution $\frac{13}{4} = \frac{12}{4} + \frac{1}{4}$

$= 3 + \frac{1}{4}$

$= 3\frac{1}{4}$

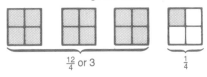

$\frac{12}{4}$ or 3 $\frac{1}{4}$

$\frac{13}{4}$ and $3\frac{1}{4}$ are different forms of the same number. They are **equivalent**. You can also think of $\frac{13}{4}$ as $13 \div 4$, as shown in the next example.

Example 3   Write $\frac{23}{4}$ as a mixed number.

Solution $\frac{23}{4}$ means $23 \div 4$

$\frac{23}{4} = 5 + \frac{3}{4} = 5\frac{3}{4}$

⟵3 parts remainder

⟶ 4 parts in a whole

Think:

$\begin{array}{r} 5 \\ 4\overline{)23} \\ 20 \\ \hline 3 \end{array}$ ⟵$\left(\begin{array}{l}\text{means 3 parts} \\ \text{are a remainder}\end{array}\right.$

To write a mixed number as an improper fraction, you reverse the steps.

$3\frac{2}{5} = 3 + \frac{2}{5}$

$= \frac{17}{5}$ ⟵ 17 parts in all
      ⟵ 5 parts in one whole

Think: 3 $\frac{2}{5}$

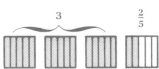

8.1 exercise

A

1 What type of fraction is each of the following?
   ▶ proper   ▶ improper   ▶ mixed

   (a) $\frac{3}{4}$ (b) $\frac{4}{3}$ (c) $1\frac{1}{3}$ (d) $1\frac{2}{3}$

   (e) $\frac{5}{3}$ (f) $\frac{3}{5}$ (g) $2\frac{1}{5}$ (h) $\frac{5}{11}$

2 What fraction of each figure is shaded?

   (a)   (b)

   (c)   (d)

3 What part of each group is shaded?

   (a)    (b)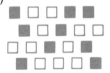

4 Match each number with a suitable diagram.

   (a) $1\frac{2}{3}$ A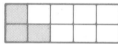

   (b) $\frac{3}{5}$ B

   (c) $\frac{8}{5}$ C

   (d) $1\frac{1}{5}$ D

5 For each diagram, what part is shaded?

   (a)

   (b)

   (c)

   (d)

6 Write 2 equivalent fractions to show what part
   of each diagram is shaded.

   (a)   (b)

   (c)   (d)

7 Draw one diagram for each pair of equivalent
   fractions.

   (a) $\frac{1}{2}, \frac{3}{6}$ (b) $\frac{2}{3}, \frac{4}{6}$ (c) $\frac{3}{4}, \frac{9}{12}$ (d) $\frac{2}{5}, \frac{4}{10}$

8 Use a diagram to help you find the missing
   terms.

   (a) $\frac{3}{4} = \frac{\blacksquare}{8}$ (b) $\frac{2}{3} = \frac{6}{\blacksquare}$ (c) $\frac{2}{10} = \frac{\blacksquare}{5}$

9 Find the values of ■.

   (a) $\frac{1}{3} = \frac{1 \times 2}{3 \times \blacksquare} = \frac{2}{6}$ (b) $\frac{3}{4} = \frac{3 \times \blacksquare}{4 \times 4} = \frac{12}{16}$

   (c) $\frac{1}{5} = \frac{\blacksquare \times 5}{5 \times 5} = \frac{5}{25}$ (d) $\frac{3}{5} = \frac{3 \times \blacksquare}{5 \times 5} = \frac{15}{25}$

   (e) $\frac{1}{7} = \frac{1 \times 2}{\blacksquare \times 2} = \frac{2}{14}$ (f) $\frac{7}{10} = \frac{\blacksquare \times 4}{10 \times 4} = \frac{28}{40}$

10 Simplify each of the following.

   (a) $\frac{6 \div 3}{9 \div 3}$ (b) $\frac{10 \div 5}{15 \div 5}$ (c) $\frac{24 \div 6}{30 \div 6}$

   (d) $\frac{28 \div 2}{30 \div 2}$ (e) $\frac{30 \div 5}{25 \div 5}$ (f) $\frac{125 \div 25}{75 \div 25}$

11 To write the fraction in lowest terms, each term
   of the fraction is divided by a number.
   ▶ Find the values of ■.
   ▶ Write each fraction in lowest terms.

   (a) $\frac{12 \div \blacksquare}{16 \div \blacksquare}$ (b) $\frac{24 \div \blacksquare}{32 \div \blacksquare}$ (c) $\frac{30 \div \blacksquare}{75 \div \blacksquare}$

   (d) $\frac{12 \div \blacksquare}{18 \div \blacksquare}$ (e) $\frac{20 \div \blacksquare}{25 \div \blacksquare}$ (f) $\frac{24 \div \blacksquare}{40 \div \blacksquare}$

B

12 Express each fraction in lowest terms.

(a) $\frac{12}{18}$ (b) $\frac{16}{24}$ (c) $\frac{18}{27}$ (d) $\frac{40}{50}$

(e) $\frac{27}{45}$ (f) $\frac{20}{45}$ (g) $\frac{32}{48}$ (h) $\frac{27}{36}$

(i) $\frac{45}{60}$ (j) $\frac{35}{56}$ (k) $\frac{5}{25}$ (l) $\frac{30}{32}$

13 Write each as an improper fraction.

(a) $1\frac{1}{4}$ (b) $1\frac{2}{5}$ (c) $1\frac{7}{8}$ (d) $2\frac{1}{5}$

(e) $2\frac{3}{10}$ (f) $3\frac{7}{10}$ (g) $1\frac{3}{8}$ (h) $1\frac{7}{10}$

14 Write each as a mixed number.

(a) $\frac{7}{4}$ (b) $\frac{17}{2}$ (c) $\frac{17}{4}$ (d) $\frac{17}{5}$

(e) $\frac{11}{3}$ (f) $\frac{11}{10}$ (g) $\frac{21}{10}$ (h) $\frac{37}{10}$

15 Express each of the following as a mixed number in lowest terms.

(a) $\frac{8}{6}$ (b) $\frac{10}{4}$ (c) $\frac{15}{10}$ (d) $\frac{12}{8}$

(e) $\frac{20}{16}$ (f) $\frac{24}{18}$ (g) $\frac{24}{20}$ (h) $\frac{15}{9}$

(i) $\frac{20}{8}$ (j) $\frac{16}{12}$ (k) $\frac{42}{12}$ (l) $\frac{22}{6}$

16 Which pairs are equivalent?

(a) $\frac{3}{4}, \frac{6}{8}$ (b) $\frac{5}{10}, \frac{3}{5}$ (c) $\frac{65}{100}, \frac{13}{20}$

(d) $3\frac{1}{4}, 3\frac{2}{8}$ (e) $4\frac{1}{8}, 3\frac{8}{8}$ (f) $4\frac{1}{2}, 3\frac{3}{2}$

(g) $\frac{18}{3}, 6$ (h) $4, \frac{12}{6}$ (i) $\frac{14}{2}, 5$

17 Which fractions in the diagram are equivalent?

A	B	C	D	E
$\frac{2}{5}$	$\frac{4}{6}$	$\frac{1}{3}$	$\frac{5}{10}$	$\frac{3}{4}$
F	G	H	I	J
$\frac{12}{16}$	$\frac{15}{20}$	$\frac{50}{100}$	$\frac{3}{10}$	$\frac{4}{20}$
K	L	M	N	O
$\frac{2}{6}$	$\frac{6}{12}$	$\frac{6}{8}$	$\frac{10}{15}$	$\frac{3}{9}$

18 Find the value of x in each of the following.

(a) $\frac{10}{15} = \frac{x}{5}$ (b) $\frac{x}{36} = \frac{1}{3}$ (c) $\frac{10}{x} = \frac{5}{6}$

(d) $\frac{x}{27} = \frac{1}{3}$ (e) $\frac{28}{x} = \frac{14}{15}$ (f) $\frac{16}{20} = \frac{4}{x}$

(g) $\frac{12}{20} = \frac{x}{5}$ (h) $\frac{27}{36} = \frac{x}{4}$ (i) $\frac{15}{x} = \frac{3}{5}$

19 Find two equivalent fractions for each fraction.

(a) $\frac{1}{4}$ (b) $\frac{2}{5}$ (c) $\frac{3}{4}$ (d) $\frac{2}{3}$

(e) $\frac{5}{6}$ (f) $\frac{4}{7}$ (g) $\frac{3}{5}$ (h) $\frac{3}{10}$

(i) $\frac{50}{100}$ (j) $\frac{4}{25}$ (k) $\frac{25}{100}$ (l) $\frac{300}{1000}$

20 Find two equivalent numbers for each of the following.

(a) $1\frac{2}{3}$ (b) $3\frac{2}{5}$ (c) $10\frac{1}{6}$ (d) $3\frac{1}{3}$

(e) $2\frac{3}{4}$ (f) $4\frac{4}{5}$ (g) $8\frac{5}{6}$ (h) $9\frac{7}{10}$

21 Everybody knows an hour has 60 min. What part of an hour is each time shown?

(a) 30 min (b) 15 min (c) 45 min

(d) 12 min (e) 10 min (f) 75 min

C

22 Express the fraction in each question in lowest terms.

(a) A bus has 48 seats. There were 36 persons on the bus. Write a fraction to show what part of this bus is full.

(b) Out of 100 persons interviewed, 80 liked the movie *Return of the Jedi*. What fraction liked the movie?

(c) Out of 72 piper cubs at the airport, 48 were refuelled. What fraction was not refuelled?

computer tip

Remember: computer programs are dealt with on pages 36, 74, 192.

8.2 comparing fractions: applications

Refer to the chart. Which team has the better record?
To compare the records, you need to find which of two fractions is
greater. One way of doing this is to use a number line.

	Games won	Games played
Canucks	2	5
Canadiens	1	2

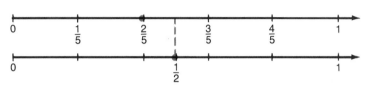

$\frac{2}{5}$ is to the left of $\frac{1}{2}$, thus $\frac{2}{5} < \frac{1}{2}$.

Therefore, Canadiens have the better record.

Drawing a number line each time you want to compare fractions is
very time-consuming. The following example shows a method of
comparing fractions that uses your earlier skills with equivalent
fractions.

Example 1 Replace ○ by $>$, $<$ or $=$ to make the statement
true. $\frac{4}{5}$ ○ $\frac{2}{3}$

Solution

$\frac{4}{5} = \frac{4 \times 3}{5 \times 3}$ $\frac{2}{3} = \frac{2 \times 5}{3 \times 5}$ $\left(\begin{array}{l} \text{Write equivalent} \\ \text{fractions for each.} \end{array} \right.$

$= \frac{12}{15}$ $= \frac{10}{15}$

Since $\frac{12}{15} > \frac{10}{15}$, then $\frac{4}{5} > \frac{2}{3}$. $\left(\begin{array}{l} \text{Since both fractions have the same} \\ \text{denominator, 15, compare the} \\ \text{numerators. } 12 > 10 \end{array} \right.$

Example 2 At a police checkpoint near Bridlegate Mall, $\frac{5}{8}$ of
the drivers stopped were wearing their seat belts.
At another checkpoint on Spruce Avenue, $\frac{7}{12}$ of
the drivers stopped had their seat belts on. At
which checkpoint did the greater fraction of the
drivers have their seat belts on?

$\left(\begin{array}{l} \text{Remember to think of} \\ \text{how to organize your solution.} \end{array} \right.$

Solution

Bridlegate $\frac{5}{8} = \frac{15}{24}$ Spruce $\frac{7}{12} = \frac{14}{24}$

Since $\frac{15}{24} > \frac{14}{24}$, then $\frac{5}{8} > \frac{7}{12}$.

Thus, the greater fraction of the drivers had their
seat belts on at the Bridlegate Mall checkpoint.

A

1 Two fractions are shown on each number line. Which is greater?

(a)

(b)

(c)

(d)

2 Use a number line. Decide which fraction in each pair is greater.

(a) $\frac{1}{4}, \frac{1}{2}$ (b) $\frac{5}{8}, \frac{1}{4}$ (c) $\frac{1}{2}, \frac{7}{8}$

(d) $\frac{7}{8}, \frac{3}{4}$ (e) $\frac{1}{4}, \frac{3}{8}$ (f) $\frac{1}{8}, \frac{3}{4}$

3 Which fraction is greater in each pair?

(a) $\frac{3}{4}, \frac{1}{4}$ (b) $\frac{7}{10}, \frac{9}{10}$ (c) $\frac{5}{8}, \frac{3}{8}$

(d) $\frac{1}{3}, \frac{2}{3}$ (e) $\frac{4}{5}, \frac{2}{5}$ (f) $\frac{3}{20}, \frac{7}{20}$

4 Write a fraction to show what part of each diagram is shaded. In each pair, which diagram is shaded more?

(a)

(b)

5 Find the lowest common denominator for each pair of fractions. Which fraction is greater?

(a) $\frac{1}{3}, \frac{5}{6}$ (b) $\frac{3}{4}, \frac{1}{2}$ (c) $\frac{2}{3}, \frac{1}{2}$

(d) $\frac{4}{5}, \frac{1}{4}$ (e) $\frac{7}{8}, \frac{7}{10}$ (f) $\frac{3}{4}, \frac{5}{6}$

6 Part of the work needed to compare two fractions is shown. Copy and complete the work. Find the missing values ■.

(a) Which is greater?

$\frac{2}{5}$ or $\frac{1}{4}$

$\frac{2}{5} = \frac{■}{20}$ $\frac{1}{4} = \frac{■}{20}$

So, $\frac{2}{5} \bigcirc \frac{1}{4}$

(b) Which is greater?

$\frac{5}{6}$ or $\frac{3}{4}$

$\frac{5}{6} = \frac{■}{12}$ $\frac{3}{4} = \frac{■}{12}$

So, $\frac{5}{6} \bigcirc \frac{3}{4}$

B

7 Replace $\bigcirc$ by $>$, $<$, or $=$ to make each statement true.

(a) $\frac{2}{3} \bigcirc \frac{5}{6}$ (b) $\frac{3}{8} \bigcirc \frac{2}{3}$ (c) $\frac{7}{5} \bigcirc \frac{4}{3}$

(d) $\frac{3}{4} \bigcirc \frac{18}{24}$ (e) $\frac{5}{12} \bigcirc \frac{3}{8}$ (f) $\frac{7}{9} \bigcirc \frac{7}{12}$

(g) $\frac{4}{5} \bigcirc \frac{5}{8}$ (h) $\frac{1}{3} \bigcirc \frac{5}{15}$ (i) $\frac{9}{20} \bigcirc \frac{8}{25}$

8 Which fraction is greater in each pair?

(a) $\frac{1}{4}, \frac{3}{8}$ (b) $\frac{4}{5}, \frac{7}{10}$ (c) $\frac{2}{3}, \frac{7}{12}$

(d) $\frac{3}{4}, \frac{11}{16}$ (e) $\frac{1}{3}, \frac{1}{4}$ (f) $\frac{2}{3}, \frac{3}{5}$

(g) $\frac{5}{9}, \frac{1}{6}$ (h) $\frac{3}{8}, \frac{5}{12}$ (i) $\frac{3}{2}, \frac{5}{3}$

9 Which of the following are true (T)?

(a) $\frac{2}{3} < \frac{5}{6}$ (b) $\frac{7}{10} < \frac{1}{2}$ (c) $\frac{3}{4} < \frac{2}{3}$

(d) $\frac{4}{5} > \frac{7}{8}$ (e) $\frac{3}{10} > \frac{1}{4}$ (f) $\frac{5}{8} > \frac{7}{12}$

10 Write the fractions in order from the least to the greatest.

(a) $\frac{1}{4}, \frac{3}{4}, \frac{1}{2}$ (b) $\frac{2}{5}, \frac{1}{2}, \frac{1}{4}$ (c) $\frac{5}{8}, \frac{3}{4}, \frac{1}{2}$

(d) $\frac{7}{12}, \frac{5}{8}, \frac{2}{3}$ (e) $\frac{4}{5}, \frac{9}{10}, \frac{3}{4}$ (f) $\frac{2}{3}, \frac{5}{9}, \frac{5}{6}$

11 Which soccer goalie had the better record during the season?

	Shots stopped	Shots on goal
Cora	105	120
Paula	126	140

12 Cassette tapes come in different sizes: 30 min, 60 min, 90 min, 120 min. What part of each tape has been used?

	Length of tape	Time used
(a)	30 min	20 min
(b)	90 min	60 min
(c)	60 min	30 min
(d)	120 min	90 min
(e)	60 min	20 min
(f)	90 min	30 min

Did you know that the first tape recorder was patented in 1898? It used magnetized piano wire instead of tape. In 1935, tape recorders began to use plastic tape as you know it today.

13 Refer to the chart. The number of stamps in each collection is shown.

	Canada	United States	Mexico
Wayne	20	25	5
Cathy	12	20	8

(a) What fraction of Wayne's stamps are Canadian?

(b) What fraction of Cathy's stamps are Canadian?

(c) Which fraction is greater, Wayne's or Cathy's?

(d) Write a problem about the information in the chart. Solve the problem.

14 Sandy knew $\frac{4}{5}$ of the people at the party. Jeff knew $\frac{2}{3}$ of the people. Who knew more of the people at the party, Sandy or Jeff?

15 Ken saves $\frac{1}{3}$ of his allowance. Sharon saves $\frac{1}{5}$ of hers. Which person saves the greater fraction of his or her allowance?

16 Generally by his thirteenth birthday, a boy is $\frac{7}{8}$ of his full grown height. By that age a girl is $\frac{19}{20}$ of her full grown height. By age thirteen who is closer to their full grown height?

17 The mass of an elephant's skin is $\frac{1}{8}$ of its total mass. The mass of a human's skin is $\frac{4}{25}$ of the total body mass. Which has the greater fraction of its total mass in its skin?

C
18 Canada, Australia, and India are three Commonwealth countries.

(a) What fraction of the letters in the name CANADA are vowels?

(b) In which of the countries' names is the fraction of the letters that are vowels the greatest?

---

calculator tip   Look for other
You can use a calculator to   Calculator Tips.
investigate many number patterns
that might otherwise be very time-
consuming.
▶ Find the decimal equivalents for
  $\frac{1}{99}$, $\frac{2}{99}$, $\frac{3}{99}$.
▶ Use the pattern to predict the
  decimal equivalent for $\frac{78}{99}$.
Use your calculator to check your prediction.

8.3 adding fractions

Misha ate $\frac{1}{8}$ of the melon. Brad ate $\frac{3}{8}$ of the melon.
What fraction of the melon was eaten?

$$\frac{1}{8} + \frac{3}{8} = \frac{4}{8}$$

$$= \frac{1}{2}$$

$\left(\begin{array}{l}\text{Since the denominators are} \\ \text{the same, add the numerators} \\ \text{to add the fractions.}\end{array}\right.$

Thus, $\frac{1}{2}$ of the melon was eaten.

To add fractions, thinking of a diagram is helpful.

$\frac{1}{8}$ $\frac{3}{8}$ $\frac{1}{8} + \frac{3}{8} = \frac{4}{8}$ or $\frac{1}{2}$

$\underbrace{\qquad}_{\frac{1}{2}}$

To add *unlike fractions*, the fractions must first be expressed as like fractions by using a common denominator. The skills you learned earlier with equivalent fractions are used to add unlike fractions, as shown in the next example.

$\left(\begin{array}{l}\text{Fractions that have the same or like} \\ \text{denominators are called \textbf{like}} \\ \textbf{fractions. Unlike fractions} \text{ have} \\ \text{different denominators.}\end{array}\right.$

Example 1   Add $\frac{1}{6} + \frac{2}{3}$.

Solution $\frac{1}{6} + \frac{2}{3} = \frac{1}{6} + \frac{4}{6}$

                 $= \frac{5}{6}$

$\left(\begin{array}{l}\text{Think:} \\ \text{Find the common denominator to} \\ \text{add the unlike fractions. 6 is the} \\ \text{lowest common denominator.} \\ \text{Use } \frac{2}{3} = \frac{2 \times 2}{3 \times 2} = \frac{4}{6}\end{array}\right.$

To add the above fractions, you can think of a diagram.

$\frac{1}{6} + \frac{2}{3}$ $\frac{1}{6} + \frac{4}{6}$ $\frac{1}{6} + \frac{4}{6} = \frac{5}{6}$

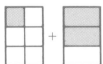

The answer you obtain in working with fractions should always be expressed in lowest terms, as shown in the next example.

Example 2   Add $\frac{5}{6} + \frac{3}{10}$.

Solution
$$\frac{5}{6} + \frac{3}{10} = \frac{25}{30} + \frac{9}{30}$$
$$= \frac{34}{30}$$
$$= \frac{17}{15} \text{ or } 1\frac{2}{15}$$

The skills with adding fractions extend to adding mixed numbers such as the following.

$$1\frac{1}{2} + 2\frac{3}{5} = 1\frac{5}{10} + 2\frac{6}{10}$$

▶ Find the sum of the whole number parts.
▶ Find the sum of the fraction parts.

$$= 3 + \frac{11}{10}$$
$$= 3 + 1\frac{1}{10}$$
$$= 4\frac{1}{10}$$

In the exercise you will practise the skills you learned with adding fractions and then apply these to solving problems.

Use your calculator. Check your calculations.

8.3 exercise

A

1 Find each sum. Use the diagram to help you.

(a) $\frac{3}{6} + \frac{2}{6}$

(b) $\frac{5}{10} + \frac{2}{10}$

(c) $\frac{1}{2} + \frac{1}{4}$

(d) $\frac{1}{3} + \frac{1}{6}$

(e) $\frac{3}{8} + \frac{1}{8}$

2 Find each sum. Think of a diagram to help you.

(a) $\frac{1}{5} + \frac{2}{5}$ (b) $\frac{2}{9} + \frac{5}{9}$ (c) $\frac{4}{15} + \frac{7}{15}$

(d) $\frac{3}{10} + \frac{4}{10}$ (e) $\frac{5}{8} + \frac{2}{8}$ (f) $\frac{3}{100} + \frac{4}{100}$

3 Find the lowest common denominator for each pair of fractions. Then find the sum.

(a) $\frac{1}{2}, \frac{1}{4}$ (b) $\frac{3}{10}, \frac{2}{5}$ (c) $\frac{1}{4}, \frac{1}{8}$

(d) $\frac{3}{8}, \frac{1}{4}$ (e) $\frac{1}{2}, \frac{7}{10}$ (f) $\frac{1}{3}, \frac{1}{6}$

(Once you have found the sum of fractions, check that your answer is expressed in lowest terms.

4 Express each fraction in lowest terms.

(a) $\frac{2}{6}$　　　(b) $\frac{4}{8}$　　　(c) $\frac{10}{15}$

(d) $\frac{6}{10}$　　　(e) $\frac{6}{9}$　　　(f) $\frac{12}{16}$

5 Add. Express you answers in lowest terms.

(a) $\frac{3}{6} + \frac{1}{6}$　　(b) $\frac{4}{8} + \frac{2}{8}$　　(c) $\frac{5}{10} + \frac{1}{10}$

(d) $\frac{3}{10} + \frac{1}{10}$　(e) $\frac{1}{8} + \frac{3}{8}$　(f) $\frac{2}{9} + \frac{4}{9}$

6 The steps needed to add fractions are shown. Copy and complete the missing steps. Find the missing values ■.

(a)　$\frac{1}{3} + \frac{1}{2}$

$= \frac{■}{6} + \frac{■}{6}$

$= \frac{■}{■}$

(b)　$\frac{5}{6} + \frac{1}{8}$

$= \frac{■}{24} + \frac{■}{24}$

$= \frac{■}{■}$

B Estimate first. Then calculate.

7 Find each sum. Express the sums in the lowest terms.

(a) $\frac{1}{4} + \frac{1}{4}$　(b) $\frac{1}{8} + \frac{5}{8}$　(c) $\frac{3}{10} + \frac{3}{10}$

(d) $\frac{1}{12} + \frac{5}{12}$　(e) $\frac{41}{100} + \frac{39}{100}$　(f) $\frac{5}{16} + \frac{7}{16}$

8 Add. Express each sum in lowest terms.

(a) $\frac{1}{3} + \frac{1}{6}$　(b) $\frac{1}{5} + \frac{3}{10}$　(c) $\frac{7}{20} + \frac{1}{4}$

(d) $\frac{1}{2} + \frac{1}{4}$　(e) $\frac{5}{12} + \frac{1}{3}$　(f) $\frac{4}{15} + \frac{2}{5}$

9 Find each sum.

(a) $\frac{1}{2} + \frac{1}{5}$　(b) $\frac{2}{5} + \frac{1}{4}$　(c) $\frac{3}{8} + \frac{2}{5}$

(d) $\frac{7}{10} + \frac{1}{4}$　(e) $\frac{5}{12} + \frac{5}{8}$　(f) $\frac{2}{15} + \frac{3}{10}$

10 Express each sum in lowest terms.

(a) $\frac{1}{4} + \frac{1}{5}$　(b) $\frac{3}{10} + \frac{2}{5}$　(c) $\frac{1}{6} + \frac{5}{8}$

(d) $\frac{3}{5} + \frac{3}{8}$　　(e) $\frac{5}{8} + \frac{1}{4}$　　(f) $\frac{7}{10} + \frac{13}{100}$

(g)　$\frac{7}{10}$
$+ \frac{1}{15}$

(h)　$\frac{3}{8}$
$+ \frac{5}{12}$

(i)　$\frac{2}{9}$
$+ \frac{5}{6}$

11 Copy and complete.

Add ⟶		
$\frac{3}{4}$	$\frac{7}{8}$	?
$\frac{1}{2}$	$\frac{2}{3}$	?
?	?	?

Add ↓

12 For some answers, you need to write improper fractions as mixed numbers. Write the following as mixed numbers in lowest terms.

(Note: You can use the answers you obtain in the next question.)

(a) $\frac{8}{5}$　　(b) $\frac{9}{8}$　　(c) $\frac{4}{3}$

(d) $\frac{3}{2}$　　(e) $\frac{5}{4}$　　(f) $\frac{19}{12}$

(g) $\frac{27}{20}$　　(h) $\frac{7}{6}$　　(i) $\frac{23}{15}$

13 Add each of the following.

(a) $\frac{4}{5} + \frac{4}{5}$　(b) $\frac{5}{8} + \frac{4}{8}$　(c) $\frac{2}{3} + \frac{2}{3}$

(d) $\frac{4}{5} + \frac{7}{10}$　(e) $\frac{3}{4} + \frac{1}{2}$　(f) $\frac{3}{4} + \frac{5}{6}$

(g) $\frac{3}{5} + \frac{3}{4}$　(h) $\frac{1}{2} + \frac{2}{3}$　(i) $\frac{7}{10} + \frac{5}{6}$

14 Find each sum.

(a) $1\frac{3}{5} + 2\frac{1}{5}$　(b) $3\frac{7}{10} + 1\frac{1}{10}$　(c) $2\frac{1}{8} + 3\frac{3}{8}$

(d) $5\frac{1}{2} + 3\frac{1}{4}$　(e) $\frac{5}{8} + 2\frac{1}{4}$　(f) $3\frac{3}{10} + 5\frac{2}{5}$

(g) $1\frac{2}{3} + 1\frac{1}{4}$　(h) $2 + 3\frac{2}{5}$　(i) $4\frac{5}{8} + 6\frac{1}{3}$

15 Copy and complete.

Add ⟶

$4\frac{2}{3}$	$2\frac{4}{5}$	?
$1\frac{3}{4}$	$3\frac{1}{10}$	?
?	?	?

Add ↓ (label on left)

16 To add three fractions, you need to find a common denominator for all three fractions. Add the fractions.

(a) $\frac{1}{5} + \frac{3}{10} + \frac{4}{5}$ (b) $\frac{1}{2} + \frac{3}{4} + \frac{1}{2}$

(c) $\frac{1}{2} + \frac{1}{3} + \frac{2}{3}$ (d) $\frac{1}{2} + \frac{1}{3} + \frac{1}{6}$

(e) $\frac{3}{4} + \frac{1}{2} + \frac{1}{6}$ (f) $\frac{2}{10} + \frac{3}{100} + \frac{3}{10}$

(g) $4\frac{3}{10} + 2\frac{1}{10} + 1\frac{1}{2}$ (h) $2\frac{1}{2} + 3\frac{1}{4} + 2\frac{1}{2}$

(i) $4\frac{3}{4} + 2\frac{1}{3} + 1\frac{1}{6}$ (j) $1\frac{1}{100} + 3\frac{1}{10} + 2\frac{7}{10}$

17 Sheila planted a tray of tomato plants.
▶ $\frac{1}{10}$ of them died after planting.
▶ $\frac{1}{8}$ of them grew no tomatoes
What fraction of the plants in all either died or did not produce tomatoes?

18 In Alan's record collection $\frac{1}{2}$ of the records are rock music and $\frac{1}{3}$ are new wave. What fraction of his collection is either rock or new wave?

19 Patty used $\frac{3}{4}$ of a can of paint for the trim in her bedroom. She used $2\frac{1}{3}$ cans for the walls. How much paint did she use altogether?

20 Jeremy spent his time working at the Pizza Palace, as follows:
▶ $2\frac{1}{2}$ h preparing dough mixture
▶ $3\frac{1}{4}$ h preparing toppings
How much did he work in all?

21 Cleo ran 15 min on Saturday and 20 min on Sunday. What part of an hour did she run on the weekend?

22 At the competition, $\frac{1}{3}$ of the athletes were from the Prairie Provinces. One quarter were from the Atlantic Provinces. What fraction of the athletes is this in all?

23 The earth's crust is composed of various chemical elements. Many of these are extracted for use in our industries. The chart shows, in order, the elements which occur in the greatest amounts.

Element	Fraction of the earth's crust
Oxygen	$\frac{2}{5}$
Silicon	$\frac{3}{10}$
Aluminum	$\frac{1}{25}$

What fraction of the earth's crust is made up of these three chemicals?

C

24 In Luke's class
▶ $\frac{3}{5}$ of the students have brown eyes
▶ $\frac{1}{3}$ have blue eyes
(a) What fraction of the class has either brown or blue eyes?
(b) What fraction of the class does not have either brown or blue eyes?

---

calculator tip

Can you use a calculator to add or subtract fractions? To add $\frac{2}{5} + \frac{7}{10}$ use the steps in the flow chart.

(Remember: The calculator converts to decimals to do calculations.)

C 2 ÷ 5 × 10 + 7 ÷ 10 =

(Can you explain why you need to do this step?)

Try some other questions in this chapter.

8.4 subtracting fractions

To help you learn mathematics, look for similarities. For example, look for similarities in the skills of adding and subtracting fractions.

At the beginning of the trip, Dino's gas tank was $\frac{3}{4}$ full. By the end of the trip it was $\frac{1}{4}$ full. What fraction of a tank was used on the trip?

$$\frac{3}{4} - \frac{1}{4} = \frac{2}{4} \text{ or } \frac{1}{2}$$

$\left(\begin{array}{l}\text{To subtract like fractions,}\\\text{subtract the numerators.}\end{array}\right.$

Thus, $\frac{1}{2}$ of a tank of gas was used.

You can again use a diagram to help you think about subtraction.

To subtract *unlike fractions*, the fractions must first be expressed as like fractions, as shown in the examples.

Example 1   Subtract $\frac{5}{9} - \frac{1}{6}$.

Solution $\frac{5}{9} - \frac{1}{6} = \frac{10}{18} - \frac{3}{18}$

$= \frac{7}{18}$

$\left(\begin{array}{l}\text{18 is the lowest common denominator.}\\[4pt]\quad\frac{5}{9} = \frac{10}{18} \text{ and } \frac{1}{6} = \frac{3}{18}\end{array}\right.$

Similar skills are again used to subtract mixed numbers.

Example 2   Subtract.

(a) $2\frac{7}{10} - 1\frac{1}{5}$ (b) $2\frac{1}{3} - 1\frac{3}{4}$

$\left(\begin{array}{l}\text{To subtract mixed numbers, subtract}\\\text{the fraction parts. Then subtract the}\\\text{whole numbers.}\end{array}\right.$

Solution   (a) $2\frac{7}{10} - 1\frac{1}{5}$ (b) $2\frac{1}{3} - 1\frac{3}{4}$

$= 2\frac{7}{10} - 1\frac{2}{10}$ $= 2\frac{4}{12} - 1\frac{9}{12}$

$= 1\frac{5}{10}$ $= 1\frac{16}{12} - 1\frac{9}{12}$

$= 1\frac{1}{2}$ $= \frac{7}{12}$

$\left(\begin{array}{l}\text{Regrouping is necessary}\\\text{to allow subtraction}\\\text{of the fraction parts.}\end{array}\right.$

8.4 exercise

A

1 Find each answer. Use the diagram to help you find the difference.

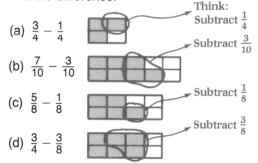

Think:
Subtract $\frac{1}{4}$

Subtract $\frac{3}{10}$

Subtract $\frac{1}{8}$

Subtract $\frac{3}{8}$

(a) $\frac{3}{4} - \frac{1}{4}$

(b) $\frac{7}{10} - \frac{3}{10}$

(c) $\frac{5}{8} - \frac{1}{8}$

(d) $\frac{3}{4} - \frac{3}{8}$

2 Subtract.

(a) $\frac{4}{5} - \frac{3}{5}$ (b) $\frac{2}{3} - \frac{1}{3}$ (c) $\frac{7}{11} - \frac{4}{11}$

(d) $\frac{13}{15} - \frac{11}{15}$ (e) $\frac{6}{7} - \frac{5}{7}$ (f) $\frac{13}{25} - \frac{9}{25}$

3 Once you subtract, check that your answer is expressed in lowest terms.

(a) $\frac{5}{8} - \frac{3}{8}$ (b) $\frac{3}{4} - \frac{1}{4}$ (c) $\frac{5}{6} - \frac{1}{6}$

(d) $\frac{9}{10} - \frac{3}{10}$ (e) $\frac{11}{20} - \frac{7}{20}$ (f) $\frac{11}{12} - \frac{5}{12}$

4 To subtract some fractions, you need to find the lowest common denominator. Find the lowest common denominator for each pair.

(a) $\frac{1}{4}, \frac{3}{8}$ (b) $\frac{3}{5}, \frac{7}{10}$ (c) $\frac{1}{3}, \frac{1}{6}$

(d) $\frac{3}{4}, \frac{2}{5}$ (e) $\frac{5}{8}, \frac{1}{6}$ (f) $\frac{3}{10}, \frac{2}{5}$

5 The steps needed to subtract fractions are shown. Copy and complete the steps. Find the missing values ■.

(a) $\frac{2}{3} - \frac{1}{2}$

$= \frac{■}{6} - \frac{■}{6}$

$= \frac{■}{■}$

(b) $\frac{3}{4} - \frac{7}{10}$

$= \frac{■}{20} - \frac{■}{20}$

$= \frac{■}{■}$

B

6 Find each difference. (Remember to express your answers in lowest terms.

(a) $\frac{5}{8} - \frac{1}{4}$ (b) $\frac{11}{12} - \frac{3}{4}$ (c) $\frac{2}{3} - \frac{1}{6}$

(d) $\frac{8}{15} - \frac{2}{5}$ (e) $\frac{7}{8} - \frac{1}{2}$ (f) $\frac{9}{10} - \frac{3}{5}$

(g) $\frac{4}{5} - \frac{3}{4}$ (h) $\frac{1}{2} - \frac{1}{3}$ (i) $\frac{7}{8} - \frac{2}{3}$

(j) $\frac{5}{6} - \frac{3}{10}$ (k) $\frac{3}{4} - \frac{7}{10}$ (l) $\frac{5}{12} - \frac{1}{8}$

7 Find each difference.

(a) $\frac{7}{15} - \frac{1}{5}$ (b) $\frac{9}{10} - \frac{5}{6}$ (c) $\frac{19}{20} - \frac{11}{20}$

(d) $\frac{3}{4} - \frac{2}{9}$ (e) $\frac{4}{5} - \frac{3}{10}$ (f) $\frac{7}{8} - \frac{5}{6}$

(g) $\begin{array}{r}\frac{7}{10}\\[-2pt] -\ \frac{6}{25}\\ \hline\end{array}$ (h) $\begin{array}{r}\frac{13}{20}\\[-2pt] -\ \frac{5}{8}\\ \hline\end{array}$ (i) $\begin{array}{r}\frac{1}{2}\\[-2pt] -\ \frac{7}{16}\\ \hline\end{array}$

8 Copy and complete.

Subtract   Subtract →

	$\frac{7}{8}$	$\frac{3}{4}$	?
Subtract ↓	$\frac{2}{3}$	$\frac{1}{2}$	?
	?	?	

9 (a) Subtract.

A $\frac{3}{4} - \frac{1}{2}$ B $\frac{5}{6} - \frac{1}{2}$ C $\frac{7}{10} - \frac{1}{2}$

(b) Which answer is the greatest, A, B, or C?

10 Subtract.

(a) $2\frac{7}{10} - 1\frac{3}{10}$ (b) $3\frac{5}{8} - 2\frac{3}{8}$ (c) $1\frac{5}{6} - \frac{1}{6}$

(d) $3\frac{7}{10} - 1\frac{1}{2}$ (e) $4\frac{3}{5} - 2$ (f) $1\frac{3}{8} - 1\frac{1}{8}$

(g) $2\frac{3}{4} - 1\frac{1}{3}$ (h) $4\frac{2}{3} - 2\frac{1}{2}$ (i) $1\frac{3}{4} - \frac{7}{10}$

11 To subtract in some questions, you need to write mixed numbers in another form. Complete each to make true statements.

$\left(\begin{array}{l}\text{Use your answers to help you}\\\text{in the next question.}\end{array}\right)$

(a) $3\frac{1}{4} = 2\frac{?}{4}$

(b) $4\frac{3}{8} = 3\frac{?}{8}$

(c) $3\frac{1}{3} = 2\frac{?}{3}$

(d) $2\frac{3}{8} = 1\frac{?}{8}$

12 Subtract.

(a) $3\frac{1}{4} - 1\frac{3}{4}$

(b) $4\frac{3}{8} - 2\frac{5}{8}$

(c) $3\frac{1}{3} - 2\frac{2}{3}$

(d) $2\frac{3}{8} - 1\frac{5}{8}$

(e) $1 - \frac{3}{5}$

(f) $6 - 3\frac{1}{10}$

13 Find each difference.

(a) $4\frac{3}{10} - 1\frac{7}{10}$

(b) $5\frac{1}{4} - 2\frac{3}{4}$

(c) $3 - 1\frac{5}{8}$

(d) $2\frac{3}{5} - 1\frac{4}{5}$

(e) $4\frac{7}{12} - 1\frac{1}{3}$

(f) $5\frac{3}{4} - 3$

(g) $2 - \frac{3}{5}$

(h) $3\frac{2}{5} - 1\frac{7}{10}$

(i) $\begin{array}{r} 2\frac{2}{3} \\ - 1\frac{1}{4} \\ \hline \end{array}$

(j) $\begin{array}{r} 4 \\ - \frac{4}{9} \\ \hline \end{array}$

(k) $\begin{array}{r} 2\frac{1}{3} \\ - \frac{3}{8} \\ \hline \end{array}$

14 (a) Subtract.

A $4\frac{1}{3} - 2\frac{1}{2}$ B $2\frac{7}{10} - 1\frac{2}{5}$ C $2\frac{3}{5} - 1$

(b) Which answer is the greatest, A, B, or C?

15 Copy and complete the chart.

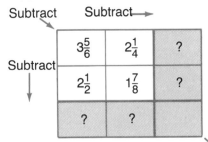

16 Cassandra took $\frac{3}{4}$ h to walk to school. Gustave rides to school on his bicycle in $\frac{1}{3}$ h.

(a) Who takes longer to go to school?

(b) How much longer?

17 On Saturday it snowed for $4\frac{1}{2}$ h. On Sunday it snowed for $1\frac{3}{4}$ h. How many more hours did it snow on Saturday than on Sunday?

18 It took Paula $8\frac{1}{2}$ min to get up the ski slope. It took $1\frac{3}{4}$ min to ski down. How much longer did it take her to go up the slope?

19 At the movies, Gary ate $\frac{1}{3}$ of the container of popcorn, Ralph ate $\frac{1}{4}$ and Collette ate the rest.

(a) What fraction more of the container did Gary eat than Ralph?

(b) What fraction of the popcorn did Collette eat?

C

20 Is the following statement reasonable? Give reasons for your answer.

After the basketball practice the coach ordered a pizza for the team.
▶ Jennifer ate $\frac{1}{8}$ of the pizza and Audry ate $\frac{1}{4}$.
▶ Also, Arlene ate $\frac{1}{4}$, Claudia ate $\frac{1}{8}$, and Monica ate $\frac{1}{4}$ of the pizza.

calculator tip

Does your calculator round off or truncate (chop off)? To decide whether your calculator rounds off or truncates, do these steps.

	Calculator rounds off	Calculator truncates
C	0	0
1	1	1
÷	1	1
18	18	18
×	0.0555555	0.0555555
18	18	18
=	1	0.9999999

8.5 multiplying fractions

To learn skills for multiplying fractions, you will follow these steps.
These same steps occur many times in your study of mathematics.

Step A	**Step B**	**Step C**	**Step D**
Use a diagram to understand the skill.	Look for a pattern that simplifies the work.	Practise the skill.	Apply the skill to solve problems.

Step A

Diagrams can be used to help you understand the skill.

The diagram shows why $4 \times \frac{2}{3} = \frac{8}{3}$.

The diagrams show why $\frac{1}{2} \times \frac{3}{5} = \frac{3}{10}$.

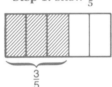

Step 1. Show $\frac{3}{5}$

Step 2. Show $\frac{1}{2}$ of $\frac{3}{5}$

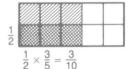

$\frac{1}{2} \times \frac{3}{5} = \frac{3}{10}$

Step B

Drawing diagrams to find answers is time-consuming. However, the diagrams are helpful to see a pattern for multiplying fractions.

$\frac{1}{2} \times \frac{3}{4} = ?$ $\left(\text{Think:} \frac{1}{2} \text{ of } \frac{3}{4} \right)$ $\frac{2}{3} \times \frac{1}{5} = ?$ $\left(\text{Think:} \frac{2}{3} \text{ of } \frac{1}{5} \right)$

Step 1. Show $\frac{3}{4}$ **Step 2.** Show $\frac{1}{2}$ of $\frac{3}{4}$ **Step 1.** Show $\frac{1}{5}$ **Step 2.** Show $\frac{2}{3}$ of $\frac{1}{5}$

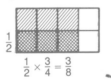 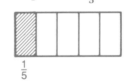 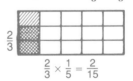

$\frac{1}{2} \times \frac{3}{4} = \frac{3}{8}$

$\frac{2}{3} \times \frac{1}{5} = \frac{2}{15}$

From the previous diagrams, you obtained these answers to multiplying fractions:

$\frac{1}{2} \times \frac{3}{5} = \frac{3}{10}$ $\frac{1}{2} \times \frac{3}{4} = \frac{3}{8}$ $\frac{2}{3} \times \frac{1}{5} = \frac{2}{15}$ (Do you see a pattern?

From the above results, and other examples, you find this pattern:

> To multiply fractions, multiply the numerators and multiply the denominators.

Example 1   Find each product.

(a) $\frac{1}{5} \times \frac{3}{4}$ (b) $\frac{3}{4} \times \frac{2}{9}$

Solution   (a) $\frac{1}{5} \times \frac{3}{4} = \frac{1 \times 3}{5 \times 4}$ (b) $\frac{3}{4} \times \frac{2}{9} = \frac{3 \times 2}{4 \times 9}$

$= \frac{3}{20}$ $= \frac{6}{36}$ or $\frac{1}{6}$ $\left(\begin{array}{l}\text{Express you answer} \\ \text{in lowest terms.}\end{array}\right.$

The skills you learn to multiply fractions extend to multiplying mixed numbers, as shown in the next example. However, you first need to write each mixed number as an improper fraction.

Example 2   Find the product $1\frac{3}{4} \times 2\frac{1}{2}$.

Solution $1\frac{3}{4} \times 2\frac{1}{2} = \frac{7}{4} \times \frac{5}{2}$ $\left(\begin{array}{l}\text{Write each mixed} \\ \text{number as an improper} \\ \text{fraction.}\end{array}\right.$

$= \frac{7 \times 5}{4 \times 2}$

$= \frac{35}{8}$ or $4\frac{3}{8}$ $\left(\begin{array}{l}\text{Write the answer} \\ \text{as a mixed number.}\end{array}\right.$

You have now completed Step A and Step B for multiplying fractions. In the exercise you will do Step C and Step D.

Use your calculator. Check your answers for the problems.

8.5 exercise

A

1 Use the diagram to help you find the product, $\frac{1}{2} \times \frac{1}{2}$.

Step 1

Step 2

2 Use the diagram to help you find the product $\frac{1}{3} \times \frac{2}{3}$.

Step 1

Step 2

3 Find each product. Use the diagram to help you.

(a) $\frac{1}{2} \times \frac{1}{4}$ Think:

(b) $\frac{2}{3} \times \frac{1}{2}$ Think:

(c) $\frac{1}{2} \times \frac{4}{5}$ Think:

(d) $\frac{3}{4} \times \frac{2}{3}$ Think:

4 Find each product. Think of a diagram.

(a) $\frac{1}{2} \times \frac{1}{3}$ (b) $\frac{1}{4} \times \frac{3}{5}$ (c) $\frac{1}{2} \times \frac{1}{4}$

(d) $\frac{1}{2} \times \frac{3}{4}$ (e) $\frac{1}{3} \times \frac{2}{5}$ (f) $\frac{2}{5} \times \frac{2}{3}$

5 After you multiply fractions, check that your answer is expressed in lowest terms. Find each product.

(a) $\frac{1}{2} \times \frac{2}{5}$ (b) $\frac{2}{5} \times \frac{1}{4}$ (c) $\frac{1}{3} \times \frac{3}{4}$

(d) $\frac{2}{3} \times \frac{3}{5}$ (e) $\frac{4}{5} \times \frac{1}{2}$ (f) $\frac{3}{4} \times \frac{2}{5}$

6 A product is shown on a number line.

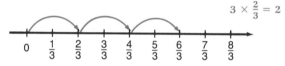

$$3 \times \frac{2}{3} = 2$$

(a) $2 \times \frac{4}{3} = ?$

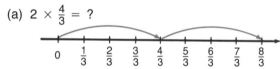

(b) $4 \times \frac{2}{5} = ?$

(c) $3 \times \frac{3}{4} = ?$

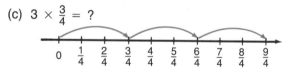

7 Use a number line to find each product.

(a) $4 \times \frac{2}{5}$ (b) $3 \times \frac{1}{8}$ (c) $3 \times \frac{3}{4}$

8 To calculate $\frac{2}{3}$ of 60, you write $\frac{2}{3} \times 60$. Calculate each of the following.

(a) $\frac{1}{2}$ of 60 (b) $\frac{2}{3}$ of 90 (c) $\frac{1}{4}$ of 50

(d) $\frac{3}{4}$ of 100 (e) $\frac{1}{10}$ of 70 (f) $\frac{3}{10}$ of 20

(g) $\frac{1}{3}$ of 36 (h) $\frac{2}{5}$ of 45 (i) $\frac{7}{10}$ of 90

math tip

In some questions, you can simplify your work before you multiply.

$$\frac{3}{4} \times \frac{1}{6} = \frac{\cancel{3}^{1}}{4} \times \frac{1}{\cancel{6}_{2}}$$
$$= \frac{1 \times 1}{4 \times 2}$$
$$= \frac{1}{8}$$

B

9 Multiply.

(a) $\frac{2}{5} \times \frac{3}{5}$ (b) $\frac{4}{7} \times \frac{3}{5}$ (c) $\frac{3}{4} \times \frac{5}{7}$

(d) $\frac{3}{4} \times \frac{5}{8}$ (e) $\frac{1}{2} \times \frac{5}{8}$ (f) $\frac{7}{8} \times \frac{3}{5}$

10 Find each product.

(a) $\frac{1}{2} \times \frac{2}{3}$ (b) $\frac{3}{5} \times \frac{2}{3}$ (c) $\frac{2}{5} \times \frac{5}{8}$

(d) $\frac{8}{25} \times \frac{15}{16}$ (e) $\frac{4}{21} \times \frac{7}{8}$ (f) $\frac{5}{8} \times \frac{16}{35}$

(g) $\frac{3}{16} \times \frac{4}{5}$ (h) $\frac{5}{8} \times \frac{12}{25}$ (i) $\frac{5}{27} \times \frac{9}{10}$

11 Copy and complete.

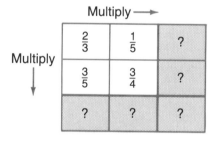

Multiply →

	$\frac{2}{3}$	$\frac{1}{5}$	?
Multiply ↓			
	$\frac{3}{5}$	$\frac{3}{4}$	?
	?	?	?

12 The steps needed to multiply these mixed numbers are shown. Copy and complete the steps. Find the missing values ■.

(a) $1\frac{3}{4} \times 1\frac{4}{5}$

$= \frac{■}{■} \times \frac{■}{■}$

$= \frac{■}{■}$ or $3\frac{■}{■}$

(b) $2\frac{1}{2} \times 2\frac{1}{3}$

$= \frac{■}{■} \times \frac{■}{■}$

$= \frac{■}{■}$ or $5\frac{■}{■}$

13 To multiply mixed numbers, you need to write improper fractions. Write each mixed number as an improper fraction.

$\left(\begin{array}{l}\text{Use your answers to help you}\\\text{in the next question.}\end{array}\right.$

(a) $1\frac{2}{3}$ (b) $1\frac{1}{2}$ (c) $1\frac{3}{4}$ (d) $2\frac{3}{5}$

(e) $2\frac{3}{4}$ (f) $2\frac{1}{2}$ (g) $3\frac{1}{4}$ (h) $2\frac{1}{3}$

14 Find each product.

(a) $1\frac{2}{3} \times 2\frac{1}{2} = ?$ (b) $1\frac{3}{4} \times 2\frac{3}{5} = ?$

(c) $2\frac{3}{4} \times 1\frac{1}{2} = ?$ (d) $3\frac{1}{4} \times 2\frac{1}{3} = ?$

15 Find each product.

(a) $2\frac{1}{4} \times \frac{1}{2}$ (b) $1\frac{2}{5} \times 3\frac{1}{3}$ (c) $3\frac{1}{3} \times 2\frac{1}{5}$

(d) $2\frac{1}{5} \times 4\frac{3}{8}$ (e) $1\frac{3}{5} \times 6\frac{2}{3}$ (f) $60 \times 6\frac{1}{5}$

(g) $4\frac{1}{2} \times 3\frac{3}{5}$ (h) $2\frac{3}{5} \times 10$ (i) $4\frac{1}{6} \times 7\frac{3}{4}$

(j) $24 \times \frac{5}{6}$ (k) $1\frac{2}{5} \times 3\frac{3}{4}$ (l) $4\frac{1}{4} \times 3\frac{1}{3}$

16 Copy and complete.

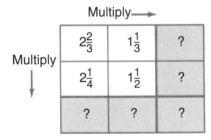

17 To multiply three fractions, you follow the same steps as for multiplying two fractions. Find the products.

(a) $\frac{1}{2} \times \frac{3}{4} \times \frac{1}{5}$ (b) $\frac{2}{3} \times \frac{5}{6} \times \frac{3}{8}$

(c) $\frac{1}{6} \times \frac{4}{5} \times \frac{5}{8}$ (d) $\frac{3}{5} \times \frac{7}{8} \times \frac{1}{3}$

(e) $\frac{1}{4} \times \frac{7}{8} \times \frac{3}{10}$ (f) $\frac{9}{10} \times \frac{1}{3} \times \frac{2}{5}$

18 Calculate.

(a) $\frac{1}{2} \times 2\frac{3}{5} \times \frac{3}{4}$ (b) $2\frac{1}{3} \times 1\frac{1}{2} \times \frac{1}{4}$

(c) $1\frac{1}{2} \times 3\frac{1}{3} \times \frac{2}{3}$ (d) $\frac{1}{4} \times 2\frac{1}{3} \times 1\frac{1}{4}$

(e) $4\frac{1}{2} \times 3\frac{1}{3} \times 1\frac{1}{4}$ (f) $2\frac{1}{3} \times 1\frac{2}{3} \times 2\frac{1}{4}$

19 What do you notice about the following products?

(a) $\frac{2}{3} \times 1\frac{1}{8}$ (b) $\frac{4}{5} \times \frac{15}{16}$ (c) $\frac{1}{2} \times 1\frac{1}{2}$

(d) $\frac{3}{5} \times 1\frac{1}{4}$ (e) $\frac{1}{3} \times 2\frac{1}{4}$ (f) $\frac{2}{5} \times 1\frac{7}{8}$

20 The same answer is obtained for each multiplication expression.

▶ $\frac{4}{5} \times \frac{5}{6} = \frac{2}{3}$ ▶ $1\frac{1}{3} \times \frac{1}{2} = \frac{2}{3}$

Write a multiplication expression of two fractions to obtain each answer.

(a) $\frac{1}{2}$ (b) $\frac{1}{4}$ (c) $\frac{3}{5}$ (d) $\frac{7}{10}$ (e) $1\frac{1}{2}$

21 Roxane took $\frac{2}{5}$ of her savings with her on her holiday trip. She used $\frac{1}{4}$ of the money to buy gifts. What fraction of her savings did she spend on the gifts?

22 Cindy takes $2\frac{1}{2}$ times as long to eat her supper as her brother Darryl. Darryl eats his supper in 5 min. How long does Cindy take?

23 Tinker is a fully grown cat. He eats $\frac{2}{3}$ of a can of cat food a day. How many cans does Tinker eat in a week?

24 Crystal swam $5\frac{1}{3}$ lengths of the pool. Brenda swam $1\frac{1}{2}$ times as far as Crystal. How many lengths did Brenda swim?

25 Paddy uses $1\frac{1}{4}$ packages of chocolate chips in his cookie recipe. He made $2\frac{1}{2}$ times the recipe. How many packages of chocolate chips did he use?

applications: fractions and catalogue sales

A catalogue often provides you with a better price. Fractions are used to show how much you save. The catalogue description tells you the features of the item that you are buying.

Regular Price $279.60
$\frac{1}{4}$ off $69.90
Sale Price $209.70

$\frac{1}{4}$ of $279.60
$= \frac{1}{4} \times \$279.60$
$= \$69.90$

1 Automatic 12 Portable Electric Typewriter. Has automatic carriage return, 84-character keyboard, 9-position pre-set tab, power space key, power back space, page gage, touch selector, half spacer, variable line spacing.
A69-34B $279.60

---

26 Read each ad carefully. Find the sale price for each item.

1 New Cabinet Dartboard Set. Dartboard, 6 darts, scoreboards inside double doors of the wooden cabinet. Fancy front design.
K29-39G $36.40

clearance $\frac{1}{2}$ off

2 Tourist Camp Stove. 2 stainless steel burners, naphtha gas.
K22-68F $32.99

$\frac{1}{3}$ Off

3 35mm Zoom Skyline Binoculars. Excellent quality for wide angle or closeup viewing. Switch to double power with lever-action ease. Centred lenses stay aligned throughout focusing.
K39-93-B. $79.80

$\frac{1}{4}$ off

27 Each item is advertised as $\frac{1}{4}$ off. Calculate the price you will pay in all. Include sales tax at 8%.

4 Big Shot Lantern. Sealed beam search light/ automatic amber flasher— 2 separate switches.
M28-32S $15.49

5 Professional Circular Saw. Burnout protected motor. 5200 rpm. Tilting shoe with scale. Extra-wide wraparound guard and ball bearings for long life.
B96-88X $89.50

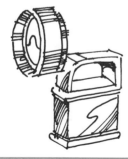

28 An ad shows that each item is from $\frac{1}{4}$ to $\frac{1}{2}$ off. For each item.
▶ what is the most you would pay?
▶ what is the least you would pay?
Include sales tax at 7%.

2 Smoke Sensor. Features a piezolectric 'modulated' alarm for less battery drain. Loud, pulsed horn. Dual ionization chamber for earliest warning. Test button. ULC approved. Battery included.
C36-29E $26.89

3 Safety House Dry Chemical Fire Extinguishers. Rechargeable. Non-corrosive valves. ULC and DOT approved. **Class A** for paper, wood, fabrics, etc. **Class B** for flammable liquids. **Class C** for electrical equipment (fridges, ranges, etc.).
E43-59A $26.25

29 Often a problem may not have all the information you need to solve it.

(a) You are travelling in Nova Scotia and you buy the camera bag. What will be your total cost? (You need to know what the sales tax rate is in Nova Scotia. See Chapter 6.)

A Large, Deluxe Camera Bag. Removable tray for camera and lens mount. Divided bottom. Adjustable shoulder strap. Camera and lens not incl.
P37-77Q $48.79

(b) What will be the total price in Manitoba for the pocket camera?

4 Tele-Lens Pocket Camera. Extended range gives better pictures under all lighting. Built-in 2X telephoto lens. Built-in electronic flash. Zoom viewfinder.
F23-31K $33.33

$\frac{1}{2}$ price

8.6 exploring skills: reciprocals

Each of these products has a special answer. Each product is equal to 1.

$$\frac{3}{4} \times \frac{4}{3} = 1 \qquad \frac{4}{5} \times \frac{5}{4} = 1 \qquad \frac{1}{3} \times 3 = 1$$

Since the product of $\frac{3}{4}$ and $\frac{4}{3}$ is 1, you say that

▶ $\frac{3}{4}$ is the reciprocal of $\frac{4}{3}$.

▶ $\frac{4}{3}$ is the reciprocal of $\frac{3}{4}$.

Thus, $\frac{3}{4}$ and $\frac{4}{3}$ are called **reciprocal fractions**.

The skills you will explore in the following exercise are needed to develop your skills with division by fractions.

Does your calculator have an inverse key? Read your manual. How does it work?

8.6 exercise

1 What is the reciprocal of each fraction?

(a) $\frac{2}{5}$　　(b) $\frac{3}{4}$　　(c) $\frac{1}{2}$　　(d) $\frac{5}{6}$

(e) $\frac{3}{10}$　　(f) $\frac{2}{3}$　　(g) $\frac{5}{8}$　　(h) $\frac{4}{5}$

2 Write the reciprocal of each mixed number.

(a) $1\frac{2}{3}$　　(b) $1\frac{3}{10}$　　(c) $2\frac{1}{4}$　　(d) $2\frac{3}{4}$

(e) $3\frac{5}{6}$　　(f) $1\frac{9}{10}$　　(g) $2\frac{1}{3}$　　(h) $2\frac{5}{8}$

3 Show that each pair of numbers are reciprocals.

(a) $\frac{2}{7}, \frac{7}{2}$　　(b) $\frac{3}{7}, \frac{7}{3}$　　(c) $\frac{3}{8}, \frac{8}{3}$

(d) $4, \frac{1}{4}$　　(e) $\frac{1}{8}, 8$　　(f) $\frac{2}{9}, 4\frac{1}{2}$

4 Multiply each number by its reciprocal.

(a) $\frac{3}{4}$　　(b) $\frac{8}{3}$　　(c) $\frac{1}{7}$　　(d) 3

(e) $\frac{1}{3}$　　(f) $1\frac{1}{3}$　　(g) $2\frac{3}{7}$　　(h) $1\frac{5}{8}$

5 Which of the following pairs are reciprocals?

(a) $\frac{1}{3} \times 3$　　(b) $\frac{7}{8} \times \frac{1}{8}$　　(c) $\frac{1}{4} \times 4$

(d) $1\frac{4}{5} \times \frac{5}{9}$　　(e) $\frac{4}{5} \times 1\frac{1}{5}$　　(f) $2\frac{2}{3} \times \frac{3}{8}$

6 Find the values of ■.

(a) $\frac{2}{3} \times ■ = 1$　　　　(b) $\frac{7}{2} \times \frac{2}{7} = ■$

(c) $\frac{1}{5} \times ■ = 1$　　　　(d) $7 \times \frac{1}{7} = ■$

(e) $2 \times ■ = 1$　　　　(f) $\frac{1}{2} \times ■ = 1$

(g) $\frac{1}{3} \times ■ = 1$　　　　(h) $\frac{5}{8} \times \frac{8}{5} = ■$

7 Find the products. Which pairs are reciprocals?

(a) $\frac{2}{3} \times \frac{3}{5}$　　(b) $\frac{4}{5} \times \frac{4}{5}$　　(c) $10 \times \frac{3}{10}$

(d) $\frac{2}{3} \times \frac{3}{2}$　　(e) $1\frac{4}{5} \times \frac{5}{4}$　　(f) $8 \times 1\frac{1}{2}$

(g) $\frac{3}{4} \times 1\frac{1}{3}$　　(h) $\frac{4}{5} \times \frac{3}{2}$　　(i) $\frac{3}{4} \times \frac{3}{4}$

(j) $1\frac{1}{4} \times \frac{4}{5}$　　(k) $2\frac{3}{4} \times 2\frac{4}{3}$　　(l) $\frac{3}{8} \times 2\frac{2}{3}$

8.7 dividing fractions

Often in mathematics, diagrams help you to understand how a skill works. Anita bought a block of fudge. She is deciding how to divide it up.

Have you ever made fudge? At this fudge factory they use a lot of ingredients to make large quantities of fudge.

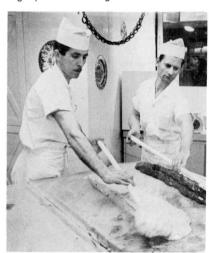

If she divides the block into halves, how many pieces are there?

$$1 \div \frac{1}{2} = 2$$

There are 2 pieces.

If she divides the block into fourths, how many pieces are there?

$\frac{1}{4}$	$\frac{1}{4}$
$\frac{1}{4}$	$\frac{1}{4}$

$$1 \div \frac{1}{4} = 4$$

There are 4 pieces.

If she divides the block into eighths, how many pieces are there?

$\frac{1}{8}$	$\frac{1}{8}$	$\frac{1}{8}$	$\frac{1}{8}$
$\frac{1}{8}$	$\frac{1}{8}$	$\frac{1}{8}$	$\frac{1}{8}$

$$1 \div \frac{1}{8} = 8$$

There are 8 pieces.

Look at the pattern in the above example. Division by a fraction seems to be related to multiplication.

Division $\qquad 1 \div \frac{1}{2} = 2 \qquad$ Multiplication $\qquad 1 \times \frac{2}{1} = 2$

$$1 \div \frac{1}{4} = 4 \qquad\qquad\qquad 1 \times \frac{4}{1} = 4$$

$$1 \div \frac{1}{8} = 8 \qquad\qquad\qquad 1 \times \frac{8}{1} = 8$$

(These are reciprocal fractions.)

It appears that to divide by a fraction, you multiply by the reciprocal of the fraction.

Example 1   Divide $2\frac{1}{4} \div \frac{3}{4}$

Solution

$$2\frac{1}{4} \div \frac{3}{4}$$

$$= 2\frac{1}{4} \times \frac{4}{3}$$

$\left(\text{To divide by } \frac{3}{4}, \text{ multiply by its reciprocal, } \frac{4}{3}.\right)$

$$= \frac{9}{4} \times \frac{4}{3}$$

$\left(\begin{array}{l}\text{To multiply, express} \\ \text{the mixed number as} \\ \text{an improper fraction.}\end{array}\right)$

$$= \frac{36}{12}$$

$$= 3$$

Think:

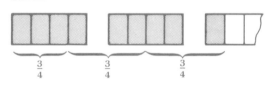

$$\frac{3}{4} \qquad \frac{3}{4} \qquad \frac{3}{4}$$

The diagram shows that there are 3 three-quarters in $2\frac{1}{4}$.

Using a diagram has helped you see a pattern for dividing by fractions. For the previous example, you can use your earlier work with equivalent fractions to show why dividing fractions is related to multiplication. Every skill in mathematics has a logical reason.

$$2\frac{1}{4} \div \frac{3}{4} = \frac{2\frac{1}{4}}{\frac{3}{4}}$$ $\left(\begin{array}{l}\text{You can write the division}\\ \text{question in another form.}\end{array}\right.$

$$= \frac{2\frac{1}{4} \times \frac{4}{3}}{\frac{3}{4} \times \frac{4}{3}}$$ $\left(\begin{array}{l}\text{Multiply the numerator \textit{and}}\\ \text{denominator by the same number.}\\ \text{The value remains the same.}\end{array}\right.$

$$= \frac{2\frac{1}{4} \times \frac{4}{3}}{1}$$

$$= 2\frac{1}{4} \times \frac{4}{3}$$

> To divide by a fraction, multiply by its reciprocal.

To divide mixed numbers, you need to write them as improper fractions, as shown in the next example.

Example 2   Calculate $5\frac{1}{3} \div 1\frac{3}{5}$

Solution $5\frac{1}{3} \div 1\frac{3}{5} = \frac{16}{3} \div \frac{8}{5}$ $\left(\begin{array}{l}\text{Express both mixed numbers}\\ \text{as improper fractions.}\end{array}\right.$

$$= \frac{16}{3} \times \frac{5}{8}$$ $\left(\begin{array}{l}\text{Remember: To divide by a}\\ \text{fraction, you multiply}\\ \text{by its reciprocal.}\end{array}\right.$

$$= \frac{80}{24}$$

$$= \frac{10}{3} \text{ or } 3\frac{1}{3}$$ Look for Math Tips.

8.7 exercise

A

1 What is the reciprocal of each fraction?

(a) $\frac{1}{2}$ (b) $\frac{1}{3}$ (c) $\frac{3}{2}$ (d) 4

(e) $\frac{2}{3}$ (f) $\frac{5}{4}$ (g) $\frac{9}{2}$ (h) $\frac{1}{10}$

2 Write the reciprocal of each mixed number.

(a) $2\frac{1}{2}$ (b) $1\frac{2}{3}$ (c) $4\frac{1}{2}$ (d) $2\frac{3}{5}$

(e) $4\frac{1}{5}$ (f) $3\frac{1}{10}$ (g) $3\frac{3}{4}$ (h) $4\frac{7}{10}$

3 Copy and complete the chart. Find the missing answers.

	Division	Multiplication
(a)	$\frac{4}{5} \div \frac{1}{5} = ?$	$\frac{4}{5} \times \frac{5}{1} = ?$
(b)	$\frac{3}{5} \div \frac{1}{5} = ?$	$\frac{3}{5} \times \frac{5}{1} = ?$
(c)	$\frac{2}{5} \div \frac{1}{5} = ?$	$\frac{2}{5} \times \frac{5}{1} = ?$
(d)	$\frac{1}{5} \div \frac{1}{5} = ?$	$\frac{1}{5} \times \frac{5}{1} = ?$

4 Match the division with its corresponding multiplication, then find each answer.

(a) $4 \div \frac{1}{2}$ A $\frac{1}{2} \times \frac{4}{3}$

(b) $\frac{4}{5} \div 2$ B $\frac{5}{6} \times \frac{3}{2}$

(c) $\frac{1}{2} \div \frac{3}{4}$ C $\frac{4}{1} \times \frac{2}{1}$

(d) $\frac{5}{6} \div \frac{2}{3}$ D $\frac{4}{5} \times \frac{1}{2}$

5 Jean used the pattern shown to divide fractions. Find each quotient.

$$\frac{3}{4} \div \frac{4}{5} = \frac{3}{4} \times \frac{5}{4}$$
$$= \frac{3 \times 5}{4 \times 4}$$
$$= \frac{15}{16}$$

(a) $\frac{1}{3} \div \frac{3}{8}$ (b) $\frac{2}{3} \div \frac{4}{5}$

(c) $\frac{9}{10} \div \frac{2}{3}$ (d) $\frac{3}{4} \div \frac{2}{3}$

---

math tip

In some questions you can simplify your work before you complete the calculations.

$$\frac{3}{4} \div \frac{5}{8} = \frac{3}{4} \times \frac{8}{5}$$
$$= \frac{3}{\underset{1}{4}} \times \frac{\overset{2}{8}}{5}$$
$$= \frac{3 \times 2}{1 \times 5}$$
$$= \frac{6}{5} \text{ or } 1\frac{1}{5}$$

Look for other Math Tips.

---

6 Complete. Do you see a pattern?

(a) $\frac{3}{4} \div \frac{1}{4} = \blacksquare$, $\frac{3}{4} \div \frac{2}{4} = \blacksquare$, $\frac{3}{4} \div \frac{3}{4} = \blacksquare$

(b) $\frac{4}{5} \div \frac{1}{5} = \blacksquare$, $\frac{4}{5} \div \frac{2}{5} = \blacksquare$, $\frac{4}{5} \div \frac{3}{5} = \blacksquare$

7 Copy and complete. Do you see a pattern?

(a) $2 \div \frac{1}{2} = 4$ (b) $8 \div \frac{1}{2} = \blacksquare$

     $3 \div \frac{1}{3} = \blacksquare$ $8 \div \frac{1}{4} = \blacksquare$

     $4 \div \frac{1}{4} = \blacksquare$ $8 \div \frac{1}{8} = \blacksquare$

(c) $10 \div \frac{1}{2} = \blacksquare$ (d) $20 \div \frac{1}{4} = \blacksquare$

     $10 \div \frac{1}{3} = \blacksquare$ $20 \div \frac{1}{5} = \blacksquare$

     $10 \div \frac{1}{4} = \blacksquare$ $20 \div \frac{1}{6} = \blacksquare$

B   Check whether your answer is reasonable.

8 Find each quotient.

(a) $3 \div \frac{3}{4}$ (b) $6 \div \frac{3}{7}$ (c) $15 \div \frac{5}{7}$

(d) $\frac{2}{3} \div 2$ (e) $\frac{6}{7} \div 3$ (f) $\frac{3}{5} \div 6$

9 Divide.

(a) $5 \div \frac{1}{2}$ (b) $6 \div \frac{3}{5}$ (c) $\frac{3}{5} \div 5$

(d) $\frac{2}{5} \div \frac{3}{10}$ (e) $4 \div \frac{8}{9}$ (f) $\frac{2}{5} \div \frac{2}{15}$

10 Calculate.

(a) $\frac{1}{5} \div \frac{2}{3}$ (b) $\frac{3}{5} \div \frac{4}{7}$ (c) $\frac{5}{6} \div \frac{3}{5}$

(d) $\frac{3}{10} \div \frac{4}{5}$ (e) $\frac{4}{7} \div \frac{8}{21}$ (f) $2 \div \frac{4}{5}$

(g) $\frac{1}{2} \div 4$ (h) $\frac{1}{3} \div \frac{5}{3}$ (i) $\frac{5}{6} \div \frac{2}{3}$

(j) $\frac{6}{7} \div \frac{9}{10}$ (k) $\frac{3}{8} \div 6$ (l) $10 \div \frac{2}{5}$

11 Divide the fraction at the centre by each of the other fractions.

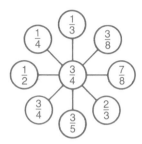

12 Copy and complete the table.

÷	$\frac{2}{3}$	$\frac{5}{8}$	$\frac{3}{4}$	$\frac{9}{10}$
$\frac{1}{4}$				$\frac{5}{18}$
$\frac{1}{3}$				
$\frac{3}{8}$				
$\frac{2}{5}$				

$\frac{1}{4} \div \frac{9}{10}$

$= \frac{1}{4} \times \frac{10}{9}$

$= \frac{10}{36}$

$= \frac{5}{18}$

13 Divide. Write the answers in increasing value.

(a) $2 \div \frac{3}{5}$ (b) $\frac{1}{3} \div 4$ (c) $\frac{1}{6} \div \frac{1}{12}$

(d) $\frac{2}{3} \div 4$ (e) $\frac{3}{4} \div \frac{3}{8}$ (f) $\frac{5}{8} \div \frac{3}{16}$

14 To divide mixed numbers, you need to write improper fractions. Write an improper fraction for each mixed number.

$\left(\begin{array}{l}\text{Hint: Use your answers} \\ \text{in the next question.}\end{array}\right.$

(a) $2\frac{1}{2}$ (b) $1\frac{3}{4}$ (c) $3\frac{1}{3}$ (d) $1\frac{3}{10}$

(e) $1\frac{1}{4}$ (f) $1\frac{2}{3}$ (g) $5\frac{2}{5}$ (h) $2\frac{2}{3}$

15 Divide.

(a) $2\frac{1}{2} \div 1\frac{3}{4}$ (b) $3\frac{1}{3} \div 1\frac{3}{10}$

(c) $1\frac{1}{4} \div 1\frac{2}{3}$ (d) $5\frac{2}{5} \div 2\frac{2}{3}$

16 Find each quotient.

(a) $1\frac{1}{3} \div \frac{3}{5}$ (b) $3\frac{1}{2} \div \frac{3}{5}$ (c) $2\frac{1}{4} \div \frac{5}{7}$

(d) $1\frac{3}{5} \div \frac{2}{3}$ (e) $2\frac{2}{5} \div \frac{4}{15}$ (f) $1\frac{4}{5} \div \frac{3}{4}$

17 Divide.

(a) $1\frac{1}{4} \div 1\frac{2}{5}$ (b) $2\frac{2}{5} \div \frac{5}{6}$

(c) $2\frac{1}{3} \div \frac{1}{6}$ (d) $1\frac{1}{3} \div 1\frac{5}{9}$

(e) $2\frac{1}{6} \div 1\frac{3}{4}$ (f) $3\frac{3}{4} \div \frac{5}{8}$

(g) $6 \div 1\frac{3}{8}$ (h) $3\frac{1}{3} \div 1\frac{3}{10}$

(i) $4\frac{3}{4} \div 1\frac{9}{10}$ (j) $5\frac{1}{5} \div 2\frac{1}{3}$

18 Divide. Which answer is the greatest?

(a) $2\frac{1}{2} \div 3\frac{1}{3}$ (b) $3\frac{3}{4} \div 1\frac{1}{2}$

(c) $5\frac{1}{3} \div 4\frac{4}{5}$ (d) $6\frac{2}{3} \div 3\frac{1}{3}$

19 Charlene knitted for $\frac{3}{4}$ h. If each row took her $\frac{1}{20}$ h, how many rows did she knit?

20 The gas tank in a bus is $\frac{7}{8}$ full. Each trip around its route uses $\frac{1}{12}$ of a tank of gas. How many trips can the bus make before its gas tank is empty?

21 Brian takes $2\frac{1}{2}$ min to read a page of his novel. How many pages can he read in 20 min?

22 Glen works in a shirt factory. It takes him $\frac{3}{4}$ h to make one shirt. How many shirts can he make in one $7\frac{1}{2}$ h shift?

23 Shirley ran $2\frac{1}{4}$ laps of the track in $8\frac{3}{4}$ min. How long did it take her to run 1 lap?

24 A record revolves $33\frac{1}{3}$ times each minute ($33\frac{1}{3}$ r/min). How many seconds does it take for the record to make one revolution?

8.8 substitution skills with fractions

An important nature of mathematics is that a skill you learn in one part of mathematics, extends to other parts. The rules for the order of operations you have learned extend to your work with fractions.

Compare the following. How are they alike? How are they different?

Skills with Whole Numbers

$$(2 + 6) \div 4 = 8 \div 4$$
$$= 2$$

Skills with Fractions

$$\left(\frac{1}{5} + \frac{3}{5}\right) \div \frac{4}{15} = \frac{4}{5} \div \frac{4}{15}$$
$$= \frac{4}{5} \times \frac{15}{4}$$
$$= \frac{\overset{1}{\cancel{4}}}{\cancel{5}_1} \times \frac{\overset{3}{\cancel{15}}}{\cancel{4}_1}$$
$$= 3$$

> **Rules for the Order of Operations**
>
> ▶ Perform the operations in brackets ( ) first.
>
> ▶ Then calculate the powers. Namely, find the value of expressions involving exponents.
>
> ▶ Then do multiplication or division in the order they appear.
>
> ▶ Then do addition or subtraction in the order they appear.

In your work with whole numbers and decimal fractions, you evaluated expressions with variables. Your earlier substitution skills extend to your work with fractions, as shown in the next example.

Example Find the value of the expression.
$$t^2 + 2t - \frac{5}{8} \qquad \text{Use } t = \frac{3}{4}.$$

Solution
$$t^2 + 2t - \frac{5}{8} = \left(\frac{3}{4}\right)^2 + 2 \times \frac{3}{4} - \frac{5}{8}$$
$$= \frac{9}{16} + 2 \times \frac{3}{4} - \frac{5}{8}$$
$$= \frac{9}{16} + \frac{3}{2} - \frac{5}{8}$$
$$= \frac{9}{16} + \frac{24}{16} - \frac{10}{16}$$
$$= \frac{23}{16} \text{ or } 1\frac{7}{16}$$

$$\begin{pmatrix} \text{Think:} \\ 2 \times \frac{3}{4} = \overset{1}{\cancel{2}} \times \frac{3}{\cancel{4}_2} \\ = \frac{3}{2} \end{pmatrix}$$

Use your calculator to try other numbers.

8.8 exercise

A

1 Calculate. Why are the answers different?

(a) $\left(\frac{1}{5} + \frac{3}{5}\right) \times \frac{5}{8}$ (b) $\frac{1}{5} + \frac{3}{5} \times \frac{5}{8}$

2 Calculate. Why are the answers the same?

(a) $\left(\frac{2}{5} + \frac{7}{10}\right) - \frac{1}{2}$ (b) $\frac{2}{5} + \frac{7}{10} - \frac{1}{2}$

3 Calculate. What do you notice about your answers?

(a) $\left(\frac{1}{6} + \frac{1}{4}\right) \times \frac{2}{5}$ (b) $\frac{1}{6} \times \frac{2}{5} + \frac{1}{4} \times \frac{2}{5}$

4 Calculate. What do you notice about your answers?

(a) $\frac{3}{8} \times \left(\frac{1}{15} + \frac{1}{5}\right)$ (b) $\frac{3}{8} \times \frac{1}{15} + \frac{3}{8} \times \frac{1}{5}$

5 Find the value of $2m + 3$ for each value.

(a) $m = \frac{1}{2}$ (b) $m = \frac{1}{4}$ (c) $m = \frac{1}{8}$

6 Find the value of the expression $2 - k$ for each of the following.

(a) $k = \frac{1}{2}$ (b) $k = \frac{2}{3}$ (c) $k = 1\frac{3}{4}$

7 Find the value of $a + \frac{2}{5}$ if

(a) $a = \frac{2}{5}$ (b) $a = \frac{3}{10}$ (c) $a = \frac{2}{3}$

B

8 Calculate. Watch your order of operations.

(a) $\frac{2}{3} + \frac{1}{4} - \frac{1}{6}$ (b) $\frac{2}{3} - \frac{1}{2} + \frac{5}{6}$

(c) $\frac{3}{8} \times \frac{4}{5} \div \frac{9}{25}$ (d) $\frac{2}{3} \div \frac{4}{9} \times \frac{1}{2}$

(e) $\frac{4}{5} + \frac{3}{10} \div \frac{3}{5}$ (f) $\frac{4}{5} \div \frac{3}{10} + \frac{3}{5}$

(g) $\frac{2}{3} \times \frac{9}{10} + \frac{3}{4}$ (h) $\frac{1}{2} - \frac{3}{5} \times \frac{1}{6}$

9 Use $>$, $<$, or $=$ in place of ⚪ to make the following sentences true.

(a) $\frac{1}{2} - \left(\frac{1}{3} - \frac{1}{6}\right)$ ⚪ $\frac{3}{4} + \frac{2}{3} \div \frac{1}{4}$

(b) $1\frac{3}{4} \times \frac{1}{4} + \frac{1}{2}$ ⚪ $\left(1\frac{1}{4} + \frac{1}{3}\right) - \frac{1}{3}$

(c) $\left(\frac{5}{8} + \frac{1}{4}\right) \div \frac{1}{2}$ ⚪ $1\frac{1}{2} \div \frac{9}{10} - \frac{1}{3}$

(d) $\left(\frac{1}{2} \div \frac{1}{3}\right) \div \frac{1}{4}$ ⚪ $1\frac{2}{5} \times \frac{3}{4} \div \frac{1}{2}$

(e) $\left(\frac{3}{4} + \frac{2}{3}\right) \times 1\frac{1}{4}$ ⚪ $\left(\frac{3}{4} - \frac{1}{2}\right) \div \frac{1}{8}$

10 To win a trip to the Rockies, you must answer the following skill testing question.

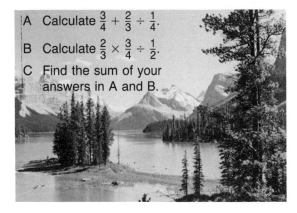

A Calculate $\frac{3}{4} + \frac{2}{3} \div \frac{1}{4}$.

B Calculate $\frac{2}{3} \times \frac{3}{4} \div \frac{1}{2}$.

C Find the sum of your answers in A and B.

11 If $n = \frac{2}{5}$ find the value of

(a) $n + 1$ (b) $n - \frac{4}{15}$ (c) $5n - \frac{1}{5}$

(d) $n^2 + 1$ (e) $n + 15$ (f) $2n - n^2$

12 If $p = \frac{3}{4}$ and $q = \frac{2}{9}$ find the value of

(a) $p - q$ (b) pq (c) $p \div \frac{27}{32}$

13 If $g = 1\frac{2}{3}$ and $h = 1\frac{1}{2}$, evaluate

(a) $g + h$ (b) $4h - 3g$ (c) $g - h$

(d) $g \div h$ (e) $g^2 + h$ (f) $(6g - h)\frac{5}{6}$

14 What do you notice about the answers for each of the following?

(a) $\left(\frac{2}{3} + \frac{1}{4}\right) \div 1\frac{1}{10}$ (b) $\left(\frac{3}{4} - \frac{1}{3}\right) \div \frac{1}{2}$

C

15 Use your observation in the previous question. You are to work backwards from the answer. Construct one expression for each of the following answers.

(a) $\frac{3}{4}$ (b) $1\frac{1}{3}$ (c) $2\frac{1}{2}$

(d) $\frac{3}{10}$ (e) $2\frac{7}{8}$ (f) 4

Be sure to check your work. Calculate the expressions you have constructed!

applications: fractions in music

The piece of music uses a number of different symbols. Each symbol has a special meaning to play the music.

The name given to this space is called a bar.

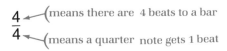 whole note   ♩ $\frac{1}{2}$ note   ♪ $\frac{1}{4}$ note   ♪ $\frac{1}{8}$ note   ♪ $\frac{1}{16}$ note

Each symbol in the piece of music is given a special name. The fraction below is not expressed in lowest terms. It has a special meaning.

$\frac{4}{4}$ ← (means there are 4 beats to a bar
   ← (means a quarter note gets 1 beat

$\frac{3}{4}$ ← (means there are 3 beats to a bar
   ← (means a quarter note gets 1 beat

The value of a note can be written in different forms as shown.

𝅝 1 whole note   is the same as

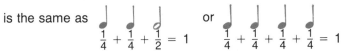

$\frac{1}{4} + \frac{1}{4} + \frac{1}{2} = 1$ or $\frac{1}{4} + \frac{1}{4} + \frac{1}{4} + \frac{1}{4} = 1$

16 To find the value of notes, you can use addition. What is the equivalent value of the notes shown?

(a)    (b)

(c)    (d)

17 A whole note is given the value of 1. These notes both show the same value of 1. What equivalent value does each of the following have?

(a)   (b)

(c)

18 Use your division skills to show how many $\frac{1}{4}$ notes are equivalent to each of the following.

(a)    (b)   (c)

19 (a) A line of music has 3 whole notes. How many $\frac{1}{8}$ notes have the equivalent value?

(b) A line of music has 5 whole notes. How many $\frac{1}{16}$ notes have the equivalent value?

20 Show an equivalent note that has the same value as each of the following.

(a)   (b)   (c)

(d)   (e)    (f)

21 A note is missing from each bar. Which note would make equal bars?

(a)    (b)   (c)

22 Each piece of music is written in $\frac{3}{4}$ time. What type of note is missing from each bar?

(a)

(b)

8.9 problem solving: problems with missing information

In some problems not all the information may be given to solve the problem. Throughout this book you have seen that research often has to be done to obtain the information needed. To solve the following problems, you need to use one of the following pieces of information. (You do not need to use them all.)

A   There are 12 monthly payments.
B   The gymnastic team has 20 students.
C   The gas tank holds 55 L of gas.
D   Weekly payments are $5.69.
E   The food cost $37.50.
F   There were 65 km of sightseeing on the trip.
G   The odometer read 46 939.2 at the end of the trip.
H   The shipment held 288 cans.
I   She worked 35 h last week.
J   The speed is 70 km/h.
K   It took 25 min to make the journey.

1   The odometer read 46 504.7 km when Jackson began the motor trip. How far did the family travel during the trip?

2   Michael's car can travel 10.7 km on 1 L of gas. How far can it travel on a tank of gas?

3   After the basketball game, the coach took the players to lunch and left a $4.50 tip. What was the total bill paid?

4   If you drive from Ottawa to Montreal, how long will it take you? The distance is 200 km.

5   A stereo is advertised for $295. If Janet pays one third in cash and the rest in monthly payments, how much is each monthly payment?

6   The average pizza is 30 cm in diameter. It will serve 4 people. How many pizzas are needed to feed the gymnastic team?

7   Ronnie drove 20 km to his music lesson. What was his average speed for the trip?

practice and problems: a chapter review

(8.1)   1   Express each fraction in lowest terms.

(a) $\frac{21}{30}$ (b) $\frac{20}{36}$ (c) $\frac{12}{48}$ (d) $\frac{36}{54}$

(e)   Find an equivalent fraction for each above.

(8.2)   2   Replace ⊙ by $<$, $>$ or $=$ to make each statement true.

(a) $\frac{3}{4}$ ⊙ $\frac{7}{8}$ (b) $\frac{7}{12}$ ⊙ $\frac{5}{8}$ (c) $\frac{1}{4}$ ⊙ $\frac{9}{36}$

(8.3)   3   Find each sum. Express the sum in lowest terms.

(a) $\frac{1}{3} + \frac{5}{9}$ (b) $\frac{1}{2} + \frac{7}{8}$ (c) $3\frac{3}{5} + 2\frac{3}{10}$

(8.3)   4   In a certain book, $\frac{2}{3}$ of the pages have pictures and $\frac{1}{2}$ the pages have words. What fraction of the book is both words and pictures?

(8.4)   5   Find each difference in lowest terms.

(a) $\frac{7}{8} - \frac{1}{4}$ (b) $3\frac{8}{9} - 1\frac{5}{6}$ (c) $1\frac{7}{10} - \frac{1}{6}$

(8.5)   6   Find each product.

(a) $\frac{8}{15} \times \frac{3}{4}$ (b) $1\frac{2}{5} \times 1\frac{1}{3}$ (c) $1\frac{3}{4} \times 8$

7   Hank scored $\frac{1}{8}$ of his total points in the first month of play, but scored $\frac{1}{3}$ times as many points in the second month. What fraction of his total points were scored in the second month?

(8.6)   8   Find each quotient.

(a) $6 \div \frac{3}{5}$ (b) $\frac{2}{3} \div \frac{8}{15}$ (c) $4\frac{4}{5} \div 2\frac{2}{5}$

(8.7)   9   Calculate.

(a) $\frac{3}{4} - \frac{3}{8} \div \frac{3}{4}$ (b) $\frac{3}{8} \times \frac{4}{9} + \frac{1}{3}$

(8.8)   10   Use $h = \frac{3}{5}$ and $g = \frac{2}{3}$. Find the value of

(a) $g \times h$ (b) $g + h$

(c) $5h + 6g$ (d) g^2

test for practice

1 Express $\frac{15}{45}, \frac{24}{30}, \frac{30}{42}$ in lowest terms.

2 (a) What fraction is shown by each figure?

(i)    (ii)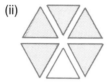

(b) Write the reciprocal of each fraction in (a).

(c) Write two other equivalent fractions for each figure in (a).

3 Arrange in order from greatest to least.

(a) $\frac{2}{7}, \frac{4}{7}, \frac{1}{14}$ (b) $\frac{3}{5}, \frac{3}{10}, \frac{2}{3}$ (c) $\frac{5}{8}, \frac{13}{32}, \frac{7}{16}$

4 Calculate.

(a) $\frac{2}{9} + \frac{5}{9}$ (b) $\frac{3}{8} + \frac{1}{4}$ (c) $\frac{7}{8} - \frac{5}{8}$ (d) $\frac{7}{8} \div \frac{1}{4}$

(e) $15 \times \frac{2}{5}$ (f) $\frac{3}{5} \times \frac{3}{10}$ (g) $6 \div \frac{1}{3}$ (h) $\frac{2}{3} - \frac{3}{5}$

5 Simplify each of the following.

(a) $\frac{7}{8} + \frac{5}{6}$ (b) $\frac{7}{8} - \frac{3}{10}$ (c) $\frac{5}{8} \times \frac{24}{25}$

(d) $1\frac{3}{4} + 2\frac{5}{6}$ (e) $3 - 1\frac{7}{10}$

(f) $1\frac{2}{3} \times 1\frac{4}{5}$ (g) $5\frac{1}{3} \div 3\frac{5}{9}$

6 After one day the Phillips had completed $\frac{1}{5}$ of the trip. On day two they completed $\frac{2}{3}$ of the trip. How much have they completed so far?

7 On day one the Fredericks completed $\frac{1}{5}$ of the trip. On the second day they completed $\frac{2}{3}$ of the trip. What fraction of the trip in all did they complete on day two.

8 Angie saved $\frac{1}{8}$ of her salary. To buy some presents she needs to save 4 times as much. How much of her salary is she now saving?

9 Shawn golfed $1\frac{1}{4}$ rounds of golf in $2\frac{1}{2}$ h. How long did it take to play one round?

looking back: a cumulative review

1 Evaluate.

(a) 4^3 (b) $3\frac{3}{4} + 1\frac{2}{5}$ (c) $12^2 - 9^2$

(d) $\frac{3^2 + 4^2}{5^2}$ (e) $10^3 \div 10^2$ (f) $10^3 \times 4.51$

(g) $\frac{6^2 - (6 \times 6)}{14 - (3 \times 4)}$ (h) 111^2 (i) $\frac{2070}{45}$

(j) $4.65 \div 100$ Look for
Computer Tips.

2 The amount, A, earned, in dollars, is given by
$$A = 4.63t + 1.12n$$
where t is the total number of hours worked. n is the number of bonus hours worked.
Calculate A for each of the following.

(a) $t = 12, n = 6$ (b) $t = 10.5, n = 3$

(c) $t = 14.5, n = 4.5$ (d) $t = 12.75, n = 6.5$

3 The measures of the height and radius of a storage tank are 18.6 m and 36.4 m respectively. How much does the tank hold?

4 The world's largest office building is the Pentagon in Arlington, Virginia.

(a) The perimeter of the outside wall of the Pentagon is 1404 m. What is the length of each side?

(b) What assumption did you make to find your answer in (a)?

5 (a) Which is the favourite of these drinks in your class?

▶ cola   ▶ orange   ▶ ginger ale

(b) Make a list of the different soft drinks by brand. Find out which drink is the favourite of your class.

(c) Draw a graph of your results in (b).

integers: addition and subtraction

Language with integers, comparing integers, adding and subtracting integers, wind chill factor, graphing solution sets, inequations, signed numbers and rationals, creating problems, problem solving skills, solving problems and applications

People use mathematics to help express ideas about numbers in a simple form.

▶ Because people needed to answer the question, "*how many*?", the **natural** or **counting numbers** were developed.

$$N = \{1, 2, 3, \ldots\}$$

▶ Later, people needed a symbol to describe the idea of nothing so a new symbol, **zero**, was invented. Zero and the natural numbers together make up the **whole numbers**.

$$W = \{0, 1, 2, 3, \ldots\}$$

▶ Ideas involving opposites led mathematicians to invent other numbers. Numerals written with the symbols $+$ and $-$ represent **signed numbers**. Numbers such as $+3$ and -3 are called **integers**.

Look at how integers are used in the examples shown.

Below Sea Level!

Since the 13th century the Netherlands have been increasing the area of their land by using dikes. Dikes are constructed along the coastland and the captured sea water is then pumped out using the windmills and electric pumps. Today almost half of the Netherlands lie below sea level. The elevation of Amsterdam airport reads about -4 m.

Hockey statistics

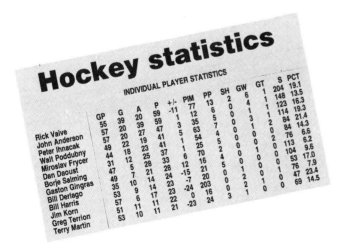

INDIVIDUAL PLAYER STATISTICS

	GP	G	A	P	+/-	PIM	PP	SH	GW	GT	S	PCT
Rick Vaive	55	39	20	59	-11	77	13	2	6	1	204	19.1
John Anderson	57	20	39	59	1	12	6	0	4	1	148	13.5
Peter Ihnacak	57	20	27	47	3	35	5	0	1	1	123	16.3
Walt Poddubny	49	22	19	41	5	63	4	0	0	3	114	19.3
Miroslav Frycer	44	18	23	41	1	25	5	0	0	2	84	21.4
Dan Daoust	31	12	25	37	6	70	4	5	0	0	84	14.3
Borje Salming	47	7	28	33	12	16	2	0	0	0	76	6.6
Gaston Gingras	49	10	21	24	-15	21	1	0	1	0	113	6.2
Bill Derlago	35	9	14	23	-7	20	5	0	2	0	104	9.6
Bill Harris	53	6	17	23	-24	203	0	0	1	0	53	17.0
Jim Korn	57	11	11	22	0	16	2	3	0	0	76	7.9
Greg Terrion	51	11	11	21	-23	24				0	47	23.4
Terry Martin	53	10									69	14.5

9.1 using integers

The following show opposite ideas.

Susan walked 4 paces right.	⟷	Michael walked 4 paces left.
The school choir gained 3 members.	⟷	The photography club lost 3 members.
Tom Watson was 2 over par.	⟷	Sandra Post was 2 under par.

+25°C    −25°C

Symbols are used to show opposite number ideas.

▶ To show ideas about up, gain, above, or increase, the symbol + is used. The symbol + means **positive**. +3 is read as *positive 3*.

▶ To show ideas about down, loss, below, or decrease, the symbol − is used. The symbol − means **negative**. −3 is read as *negative 3*.

+5 kg $\left(\begin{array}{l}\text{Think of a}\\\text{gain of 5 kg.}\end{array}\right.$

−5 kg $\left(\begin{array}{l}\text{Think of a}\\\text{loss of 5 kg.}\end{array}\right.$

−2 dollars $\left(\begin{array}{l}\text{Think of a loss}\\\text{of 2 dollars.}\end{array}\right.$

+2 dollars $\left(\begin{array}{l}\text{Think of a gain}\\\text{of 2 dollars.}\end{array}\right.$

These signed numerals are called **integers**.

..., −3, −2, −1, 0, +1, +2, ...

To draw the graph of integers, an integer number line is used.

Zero is neither negative nor positive.

These are negative integers.
▶ They are less than zero.
▶ They are to the left of zero on the number line.

These are positive integers.
▶ They are greater than zero.
▶ They are to the right of zero on the number line.

$$-6 \quad -5 \quad -4 \quad -3 \quad -2 \quad -1 \quad 0 \quad +1 \quad +2 \quad +3 \quad +4 \quad +5 \quad +6$$

$\left(\begin{array}{c}\text{These are}\\\text{opposite integers.}\end{array}\right)$

Example

The weather report gave the following temperatures.

Victoria +6°C   Winnipeg −3°C
Calgary 0°C   Fredericton −4°C

Draw the graph of these integers.

Solution

Step 1 Draw an integer number line.

Step 2 Use dots to show the integers on the number line.

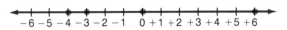

The symbol used to represent the set of integers is *I*.

$$I = \{\ldots, -3, -2, -1, 0, +1, +2, +3, \ldots\}$$

Working with integers is very basic to understanding your work in mathematics involving opposites. The exercise that follows develops some important ideas about integers.

9.1 exercise

A

1 For each of the following, what is the opposite?

(a) up   (b) left   (c) rise

(d) below   (e) gain   (f) drop

(g) behind   (h) withdraw   (i) increase

2 If +3°C means a rise of 3°C, what is the meaning of each of the following?

(a) +2°C   (b) +4°C   (c) −8°C

(d) 0°C   (e) −3°C   (f) +6°C

(g) −5°C   (h) +5°C   (i) −6°C

3 If −2°C means 2°C below zero, what is the meaning of each of the following?

(a) +3°C   (b) −4°C   (c) −1°C

(d) +2°C   (e) 0°C   (f) −3°C

(g) +4°C   (h) +1°C   (i) −10°C

4 If −5 m means 5 m below sea level, what do each of the following mean?

(a) +4 m   (b) −3 m   (c) +2 m

(d) +60 m   (e) −900 m   (f) 0 m

(g) −1800 m   (h) −15 m   (i) +17 000 m

5 What integer is represented by each letter, A, B, C, ... ?

(a)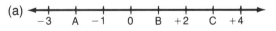

(b)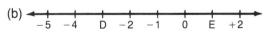

(c)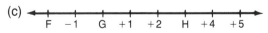

(d)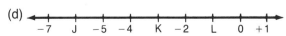

B

6 Use a suitable integer to show each of the following.

(a) a profit of 8 dollars (b) a loss of 6 points

(c) 4 steps backwards (d) 5 steps up

(e) 9 steps left (f) a gain of 10 kg

(g) a decrease of 4 m² (h) a decrease of 12 mL

7 Write the integers that are graphed on each number line.

(a)

(b)

(c)

(d)

8 Graph the following integers on number lines.

(a) −2, +4, −3, +1 (b) +4, −1, +2, 0

(c) −5, +5, +3, −3 (d) −4, 0, +3, −2, −1

9 Write the opposite for each integer.

(a) −6 (b) +3 (c) −5 (d) −9

(e) +18 (f) −100 (g) +40 (h) −65

(i) −4 (j) +5 (k) −1 (l) −23

10 For each letter on the number line, write the opposite integer.

(a)

(b)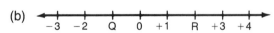

(c)

(d)

11 Graph each of the following sets of integers on a number line.

(a) integers between +3 and +6

(b) integers between 0 and +4

(c) integers between −2 and +1

(d) integers between −5 and −3

12 For each integer listed below, write a sentence to show its meaning.
The first one is done for you.

(a) +5 kg (Carlo increased the mass he could lift by 5 kg.)

(b) −2 dollars (c) +10°C

(d) +150 m (e) −3 steps

(f) −4 floors (g) +7 cm

C

13 Some common temperature ranges are shown.

+35°C to +40°C	very hot
+30°C to +35°C	hot
+25°C to +30°C	very warm
+20°C to +25°C	warm
+10°C to +20°C	cool
0°C to +10°C	cold
0°C	(freezing)
−10°C to 0°C	cold
−20°C to −10°C	very cold

Write an appropriate temperature range for each of the following activities.

(a) walking in a summer shower

(b) taking down the Christmas lights in a snow blizzard

(c) yelling at a football final

(d) shovelling the snow

(e) raking leaves

(f) being sick in bed

(g) skating at the rink

(h) planting seeds in the garden

applications: sea level and tides

Integers are often used to describe the distances above or below sea level of places on the earth's surface. Positive integers are used for distances above sea level, while negative integers indicate distances below sea level.

14 For each sentence, write a suitable integer.

(a) Little Bear, a mountain peak in Colorado, is 4278 m above sea level.

(b) The Caspian Sea in the USSR is 28 m below sea level.

(c) Lake Eyre in Australia is 12 m below sea level.

(d) Pike's Peak in Colorado is 4300 m above sea level.

(e) The elevation of the Teide Mountain on the Canary Islands is 3718 m above sea level.

(f) In October 1982, a Canadian reached the highest point on the earth's surface, the summit of Mount Everest, 8848 m above sea level.

(g) In 1960 two men descended in a bathysphere to the deepest point on the earth's surface. They went to the bottom of the Marianas Trench, 11 033 m below sea level.

(h) The highest altitude at which a plant has been found is 8199 m above sea level.

(i) Whales have been observed at a depth of 900 m below sea level.

(j) The highest inhabited human dwelling is located at 6000 m above sea level.

(k) The lowest point on the land surface of earth occurs where the Jordan River enters the Dead Sea. This point is 393 m below sea level.

Tides are affected both by the sun and the moon. The moon has the greater effect since it is closer to the earth. The moon "pulls" the water on the side of the earth nearest to it upwards, forming a tidal bulge.

Write a suitable integer for the following.

15 (a) In the Bay of Fundy tides rise as high as 16 m.

(b) In Lake Superior the tide is hardly noticed and rises about 5 cm.

(c) Sometimes a wall of water, called a tidal bore, rushing into the Petitcodiac River may rise higher than 1 m.

(d) In the Mediterranean Sea the tide dropped about 8 cm.

16 The tide is 4 m above sea level now. In 6 h 12 min it will be the exact opposite. Write the height as an integer for both times.

17 Marks are placed on a dock to show the tide level at different times. Which letters show each of the following?

(a) 2 m in high tide

(b) 3 m in low tide

(c) 1 m in low tide

(d) 1 m in high tide

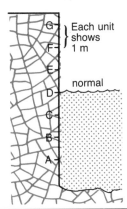

9.2 comparing integers

The overnight low in Vancouver was +3°C. In Chilliwack the overnight low was +5°C. Which city recorded the lower temperature that night? The number line can be used to compare integers.

```
←――+――+――+――+――+――+――+――+――+――+――→
  -5  -4  -3  -2  -1   0  +1  +2  +3  +4  +5
```

(+3 is to the left of +5

+3 is less than +5

$$+3 < +5$$

Vancouver had the lower temperature, +3°C.

The noon temperature at Regina was −1°C. At Saskatoon, the noon temperature was −5°C. Which city recorded the greater noon temperature that day?

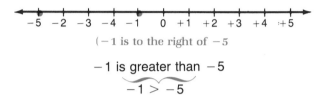

(−1 is to the right of −5

−1 is greater than −5

$$-1 > -5$$

Regina had the greater temperature, −1°C.

You can use the number line to arrange integers in order.

Example   Three golfers had scores as follows.
Mark +1   Tracy −2   Hilda −1

(a) Arrange the scores in order from least to greatest.

(b) Who had the best score?

(In golf the lowest score is the best score.

Solution   (a) Graph the integers on the number line.
−2, −1, +1

(b) The winner is Tracy since she had the best score. She had the lowest score.

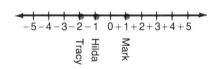

9.2 exercise

A

1 Write three integers that are
   ► greater than the number shown.
   ► less than the number shown.

(a)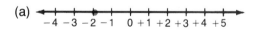

(b)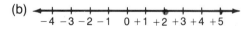

(c)
```
←――+――+――+――+――+――+――+――+――+――+――→
 -4 -3 -2 -1  0 +1 +2 +3 +4 +5
```

2 Which is the greater of each pair of integers shown?

(a)
```
←――+――+――+――+――+――+――+――+――+――+――→
 -4 -3 -2 -1  0 +1 +2 +3 +4
```

(b)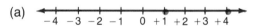

(c)
```
←――+――+――+――+――+――+――+――+――+――+――→
 -4 -3 -2 -1  0 +1 +2 +3 +4
```

3 Which is the lesser integer in each pair?

(a) $+4, -3$ (b) $-1, -3$ (c) $+1, +5$

(d) $-6, -2$ (e) $-2, -3$ (f) $+1, -4$

(g) $-5, +5$ (h) $0, -4$ (i) $0, +4$

4 Replace ◉ with the words "is greater than" or "is less than" to make a true statement.

(a) -2 ◉ $+4$ (b) $+2$ ◉ -4 (c) -2 ◉ -4

(d) $+2$ ◉ $+4$ (e) -3 ◉ -4 (f) $+2$ ◉ $+5$

(g) -4 ◉ $+4$ (h) $+3$ ◉ -3 (i) -1 ◉ -2

5 Write three integers greater than the given number.

(a) -4 (b) $+4$ (c) -1

(d) -6 (e) $+1$ (f) -3

(g) $+2$ (h) -5 (i) -2

6 Write three integers that are less than each number given in the previous question.

B

7 Replace ◉ with $<$ or $>$ to make each statement true.

(a) $+4$ ◉ $+8$ (b) -3 ◉ -2 (c) $+1$ ◉ -1

(d) 0 ◉ -4 (e) -100 ◉ 0 (f) -79 ◉ -19

(g) $+6$ ◉ -8 (h) -80 ◉ $+20$ (i) 0 ◉ $+1$

8 Pairs of integers are given. Use $<$ or $>$ to compare the integers.

(a) $+3, +8$ (b) $-2, -3$ (c) $+1, -1$

(d) $0, -3$ (e) $-90, 0$ (f) $+9, +6$

(g) $-8, +6$ (h) $+25, -75$ (i) $-14, +14$

9 (a) Write the set of integers between $+6$ and -3.

(b) Write the set of integers between -8 and -14.

(c) Write the set of integers greater than -3, but less than $+3$.

10 Write these integers in order from greatest to least.

(a) $-2, +1, -3$ (b) $+1, -1, +3$

(c) $-2, -3, -1$ (d) $+1, +3, +2$

(e) $+4, -2, -1$ (f) $-3, -4, 0$

11 Write these integers in order from least to greatest.

(a) $-2, +3, -4, +2, -8, +1$

(b) $-1, +2, -3, +4, -5, +6, -7$

(c) $+9, +8, +7, -6, -5, -4$

(d) $+1, -1, +5, -5$

(e) $+4, 0, -3, +8, +15, -20$

12 The record low temperatures for some Canadian cities are shown. Write the cities in order from the one with the lowest recorded temperature to the one with the highest.

Vancouver	$-18°C$	Winnipeg	$-48°C$
Victoria	$-16°C$	Ottawa	$-44°C$
Yellowknife	$-51°C$	Charlottetown	$-31°C$

13 Distances above or below sea level are shown. Write the integers in order from "highest" to "lowest".

▸ elevation of Quito, Ecuador   2811 m
▸ depth of breath-held dive -86 m
▸ elevation of Calgary   1079 m
▸ record depth drilled into ground -3840 m
▸ highest capital city, Lhasa, Tibet   3684 m
▸ depth of record scuba dive -133 m

C

14 Which integer is common to all of the following?

A It is less than 3.

B It is an odd number.

C It is a member of the set $\{-5, +1, -1, +5, -3, +3, 0\}$.

D It is greater than -3.

E It is between -6 and $+1$.

applications: wind chill factor

Extended exposure to cold air can cause frostbite to the exposed parts of the body. Combining cold temperatures with strong winds can create the same chilling result as a much lower temperature with no wind blowing. A chart summarizes data about the **wind chill factor.** For example, from the chart, when the temperature is $-15°C$, a wind speed of 24 km/h makes the air temperature feel like $-33°C$.

Wind Chill Factor Chart

Speed (km/h)	Actual thermometer reading (°C)												
	10	5	0	-5	-10	-15	-20	-25	-30	-35	-40	-45	-50
8	9	3	-3	-8	-13	-18	-23	-28	-33	-38	-44	-50	-57
16	4	-2	-9	-15	-21	-26	-33	-38	-44	-50	-57	-64	-72
24	2	-6	-13	-20	-26	-33	-40	-45	-51	-58	-65	-73	-81
32	0	-8	-16	-22	-30	-37	-44	-49	-55	-63	-71	-79	-88
40	-1	-9	-18	-25	-32	-40	-47	-53	-59	-67	-76	-83	-93
48	-2	-11	-19	-27	-34	-41	-50	-55	-62	-70	-78	-87	-97
56	-3	-12	-20	-28	-36	-42	-52	-57	-64	-72	-81	-89	-99

15 What are the wind chill temperatures for each of the following?

	Temperature	Wind speed
(a)	$-25°C$	8 km/h
(b)	$-10°C$	32 km/h
(c)	$-5°C$	48 km/h

16 Find the missing values. Use the wind chill factor chart.

	Wind speed	Actual temperature	Wind chill temperature
(a)	32 km/h	?	$-16°C$
(b)	24 km/h	$-40°C$	?
(c)	?	$-5°C$	$-25°C$

17 Estimate the wind chill temperature for each of the following.

	Wind speed	Temperature
(a)	20 km/h	$-20°C$
(b)	36 km/h	$-10°C$
(c)	12 km/h	$-12°C$

18 (a) Find the wind chill temperature at a wind speed of 24 km/h at $-5°C$.

(b) Find the wind chill temperature at a wind speed of 56 km/h at $0°C$.

(c) What do you notice about your answers in (a) and (b)?

19 Refer to the previous question. Find two combinations of actual temperature and wind speed to obtain each wind chill temperature.

(a) $-18°C$ (b) $-40°C$ (c) $-33°C$

20 Which has the lower temperature, A or B?

A Travelling on a snowmobile at 16 km/h when the temperature is $-5°C$.

B Cross-country skiing at 8 km/h when the temperature is $-15°C$.

21 While tobogganning, Malika found the wind chill temperature to be $-15°C$. The actual temperature was $-5°C$. How fast was the toboggan going?

9.3 graphing solution sets: inequations

The temperature at the base of a cumulus cloud is between $-5°C$ and $+15°C$. The integers that could be used to show the temperatures in this range are: -4, -3, -2, -1, 0, $+1$, $+2$, $+3$, $+4$, $+5$, $+6$, $+7$, $+8$, $+9$, $+10$, $+11$, $+12$, $+13$, $+14$

These integers can be graphed on a number line using a dot to show each integer.

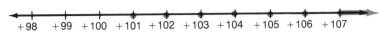

Some sets of integers have an unlimited number of members or elements. For example, water is a gas at temperatures above $+100°C$. The integers that can be used to show these temperatures are: $+101$, $+102$, $+103$, . . .

To graph these integers a *few* of them are shown using dots. Then, a large arrow is used to show the remaining integers.

$$+98 \quad +99 \quad +100 \quad +101 \quad +102 \quad +103 \quad +104 \quad +105 \quad +106 \quad +107$$

(The arrow shows that the integers 108, 109, . . . are on the graph.)

This set of integers can also be described using an inequation.

$$n > +100, n \in I$$

(I is the replacement set from which the values of n are to be taken.)

Example 1   Find and graph the solution for each inequation.

(a) $n < +3, n \in I$ (b) $n \leq +3, n \in I$

(The solution set is the set of numbers that make the inequation true.)

Solution

(a)
$$
\begin{aligned}
n &< +3 \\
+2 &< +3 \quad T \\
+1 &< +3 \quad T \\
0 &< +3 \quad T \\
-1 &< +3 \quad T
\end{aligned}
$$
.
.
.

(b)
$$
\begin{aligned}
n &\leq +3 \\
+3 &\leq +3 \quad T \\
+2 &\leq +3 \quad T \\
+1 &\leq +3 \quad T
\end{aligned}
$$
.
.
.

(Note that the solution set for the inequation $n \leq +3$ includes the value $+3$, but that for the inequation $n < 3$ does not.)

Thus, the solution set is
$\{+2, +1, 0, -1, -2, . . .\}$

The graph is

$$-3 \, -2 \, -1 \quad 0 \, +1 \, +2 \, +3 \, +4$$

Thus, the solution set is
$\{+3, +2, +1, 0, -1, . . .\}$

The graph is

$$-3 \, -2 \, -1 \quad 0 \, +1 \, +2 \, +3 \, +4$$

In mathematics, information is often written in a compact way. The two inequations $+2 < m$ and $m < +7$, $m \in I$ can be written compactly as

$$\underbrace{+2 < m}_{\substack{m \text{ is greater} \\ \text{than } +2}} \underbrace{< +7}_{\substack{m \text{ is less} \\ \text{than } +7}}, \quad m \in I$$

Together, the inequations mean that the value of m is between $+2$ and $+7$.

Example 2   Find and graph the solution set of

$$+4 \geq t \geq -1, t \in I$$

Solution

$$\underbrace{+4 \geq t}_{\substack{\text{Think: } t \text{ is less} \\ \text{than or equal} \\ \text{to } +4.}} \underbrace{\geq -1}_{\substack{\text{Think: } t \text{ is greater} \\ \text{than or equal} \\ \text{to } -1.}}$$

The solution set is $\{+4, +3, +2, +1, 0, -1\}$.

The graph is

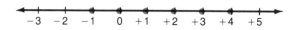

Check whether your answer is reasonable.

9.3 exercise

A

1 Express each inequation in words.

  (a) $b < +3$ (b) $y > -2$

  (c) $m \geq +2$ (d) $p \leq 0$

  (e) $w > +5$ (f) $k \leq +1$

  (g) $t < -3$ (h) $d \geq -5$

2 Match each inequation, with the correct solution set, A, B, C, ... The replacement set is I.

  (a) $a < +3$ A $\{-2, -1, 0, +1, +2, \ldots\}$

  (b) $c > -2$ B $\{+2, +1, 0, -1, -2, \ldots\}$

  (c) $k \leq +3$ C $\{-2, -3, -4, -5, \ldots\}$

  (d) $n < -2$ D $\{+3, +2, +1, 0, -1, \ldots\}$

  (e) $g \geq -2$ E $\{-3, -4, -5, -6, \ldots\}$

  (f) $m \leq -2$ F $\{-1, 0, +1, +2, +3, \ldots\}$

3 Match each inequation with the correct graph, A, B, C, . . . All variables represent integers.

  (a) $x \leq +2$ A

  (b) $q > -2$ B

  (c) $t < +2$ C

  (d) $r \geq -2$ D

4 Write the following using symbols.

  (a) d is greater than $+4$

  (b) n is less than or equal to -3

  (c) m is less than 0

(d) *t* is greater than or equal to -2

(e) *y* is less than or equal to $+1$

(f) *h* is greater than -6

5 (a) Find the solution set for $n < -3$, $n \in I$.

(b) Draw a graph of your solution set.

6 (a) Find the solution set for $n > -2$, $n \in I$.

(b) Draw a graph of the solution set in (a).

7 (a) Find the solution set for $n \geq -2$, $n \in I$.

(b) Draw a graph of the solution set in (a).

(c) How does your solution set in this question differ from the one in the previous question? How is it the same?

B

8 (a) Find the solution set for

$$n < -3, \quad n \in \{-4, -3, -2, -1\}.$$

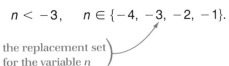

the replacement set for the variable *n*

(b) Draw a graph of your solution set.

9 Solve each inequation. The replacement set for each variable is shown.

　　Inequation　Replacement Set

(a) $m < +2$　　$m \in \{0, +1, +2, +3\}$

(b) $y \leq -3$　　$y \in \{-2, -3, -4, \ldots\}$

(c) $k > -2$　　$k \in \{-3, -2, -1, 0, +1\}$

(d) $0 \geq r$　　$r \in \{-1, 0, +1\}$

10 For each inequation the variable (placeholder) represents an integer.
   ► Find the solution set.
   ► Draw a graph of your solution set.

(a) $y < +2$　(b) $+3 < n$　(c) $-2 > x$

(d) $m \leq +2$　(e) $-3 \leq k$　(f) $s < -2$

(g) $m > 0$　(h) $m \leq 0$　(i) $0 \geq m$

11 Write two inequations shown by each of the following. The first one has been done for you.

   ► Find the solution set.
   ► Draw a graph of the solution set.

(a) $-3 < m < +2$　$\begin{pmatrix} \text{The inequations are:} \\ -3 < m \text{ and } m < +2 \end{pmatrix}$

(b) $+3 \geq y \geq -1$　　(c) $-6 < t \leq -1$

(d) $+2 < k < +9$　　(e) $+3 \geq d > -3$

(f) $0 \leq n \leq +5$　　(g) $-1 > p > -4$

12 The solution set for an inequation is shown. Write the inequation. The first one is done for you.

(a) $\{+1, +2, +3,\}$　$\begin{pmatrix} +1 \leq n < +4, n \in I \\ \textit{or you could write} \\ 0 < n < +4, n \in I \end{pmatrix}$

(b) $\{-3, -4, -5\}$　　(c) $\{-1, 0, +1\}$

(d) $\{-2, -1, 0\}$　　(e) $\{-9, -8, -7\}$

(f) $\{-1, -2, -3\}$　　(g) $\{+1, 0, -1, -2\}$

13 For cross-country skis, blue ski wax should be used when the temperature is between 0°C and -10°C. Write the integers that represent the temperatures when blue wax should be used.

14 Engine oil manufacturers recommend that 10W20 oil be used when the temperature is between -10°C and -30°C. Write the integers that represent this temperature range.

15 To store meat for an extended period of time in a freezer, the temperature should be kept in the range -5°C to -10°C. Write the integers that show these temperatures.

C

16 The base level temperature ranges of different types of cloud formations are given. Use a compact inequation with the solution set of integers described for each type of cloud.

(a) Cirrus　　　　　-20°C to -60°C

(b) Altocumulus　　$+10$°C to -30°C

(c) Nimbostratus　　$+10$°C to -15°C

9.4 adding integers

To solve certain problems, you need to know how to add positive and negative numbers.

At Brandon the evening temperature was $+2°C$. By dawn the temperature had fallen 6°C. What was the temperature by dawn? A vertical number line can help in finding the answer.

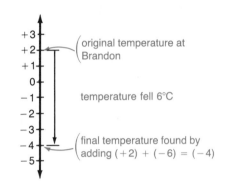

The temperature at dawn is given by the expression:

$(+2) + (-6)$

⎛ Brackets are used to separate the signed
⎝ numbers from the sign of the operation.

The temperature by dawn was $-4°C$.

To add integers, you use a number line or think of a related example which shows the facts given. "Picture the problem."

Or use a number line.

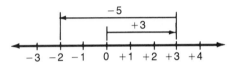

$(+3) + (-5)$

$= -2$

⎛ Think: A gain of 3 added
⎜   to a loss of 5
⎝   is a loss of 2.

Example   Find each sum.
(a) $(+3) + (+2)$ (b) $(+3) + (-2)$ (c) $(-6) + (+4)$

Use a number line.   Or think of a related example.

Solution   (a) $(+3) + (+2)$

$= +5$

A gain of 3 added
to a gain of 2
is a gain of 5.

(b) $(+3) + (-2)$

$= +1$

A gain of 3 added
to a loss of 2
is a gain of 1.

(c) $(-6) + (+4)$

$= -2$

6 steps to the left added
to 4 steps to the right
is 2 steps to the left.

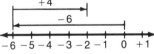

To learn the skill of adding integers or any other skill, you often follow these steps:

Step A	**Step B**	**Step C**	**Step D**
Understand the operation. Use an example to help your understanding.	Look for a pattern or a related example to help you find the answer.	Develop speed and accuracy with the skill	Apply the skill to solve problems.

9.4 exercise

A

1 For each of the following,
- ▶ match the expression with the related example,
- ▶ then find the sum.

(a) $(-3) + (+4)$ A $\begin{pmatrix} \text{a gain of 3 added} \\ \text{to a loss of 4} \\ \text{is a loss of } \blacksquare \end{pmatrix}$

(b) $(+3) + (+4)$ B $\begin{pmatrix} \text{a loss of 3 added} \\ \text{to a gain of 4} \\ \text{is a gain of } \blacksquare \end{pmatrix}$

(c) $(-3) + (-4)$ C $\begin{pmatrix} \text{a gain of 3 added} \\ \text{to a gain of 4} \\ \text{is a gain of } \blacksquare \end{pmatrix}$

(d) $(+3) + (-4)$ D $\begin{pmatrix} \text{a loss of 3 added} \\ \text{to a loss of 4} \\ \text{is a loss of } \blacksquare \end{pmatrix}$

2 A gain of 3 is followed by a loss of 6.

(a) Write an addition expression using integers.

(b) Find the answer.

3 A loss of 3 is followed by a loss of 6.

(a) Write an addition expression using integers.

(b) Find the answer.

4 A number line is used to find each sum.
- ▶ Match each expression with the correct diagram.
- ▶ Find the answer.

(a) $(-2) + (-1)$ A

(b) $(+2) + (-1)$ B

(c) $(-2) + (+1)$ C

(d) $(+2) + (+1)$ D

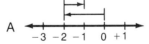

5 ▶ What addition expression of integers is shown by each diagram?
- ▶ Find the answer.

(a)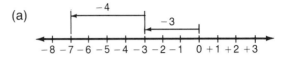

(b)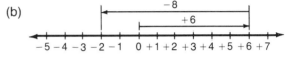

(c)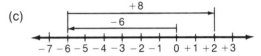

B

6 Use an example to help you find each sum.

(a) $(+2) + (-3)$ (b) $(+4) + (-2)$

(c) $(-4) + (+2)$ (d) $(-4) + (-2)$

(e) $(+3) + (-5)$ (f) $(+3) + (+5)$

(g) $(-3) + (-5)$ (h) $(-3) + (+5)$

(i) $(-6) + (+3)$ (j) $(+6) + (-3)$

7 Use a number line to help you find each of the following sums.

(a) $(+5) + (+2)$ (b) $(+3) + (-2)$

(c) $(-5) + (-3)$ (d) $(+2) + (+3)$

(e) $(-7) + (+2)$ (f) $(-2) + (-4)$

(g) $(+5) + (-8)$ (h) $(+2) + (-2)$

(i) $(-4) + (+4)$ (j) $(+5) + (-1)$

8 Find the sum of each pair of integers.

(a) $+3, -2$ (b) $-3, +2$ (c) $-3, -2$

(d) $-1, +5$ (e) $+1, -5$ (f) $-1, -5$

(g) $-4, -3$ (h) $-4, +3$ (i) $+4, -3$

(j) $-2, +2$ (k) $-2, -2$ (l) $+2, +2$

9 Which of the following sums are equal to -2?

(a) $(-1) + (-1)$ (b) $(-1) + (+3)$

(c) $(+3) + (-5)$ (d) $(+1) + (+1)$

(e) $(-4) + (-2)$ (f) $(-4) + (+2)$

(g) $(-2) + (0)$ (h) $(+4) + (-6)$

10 Find each sum.

(a) $(+3) + (-3)$ (b) $(-4) + (+4)$

(c) $(-1) + (+1)$ (d) $(+5) + (-5)$

What do you notice about your answers?

11 Copy and complete each chart.

(a)

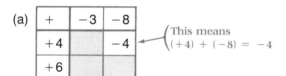

This means
$(+4) + (-8) = -4$

+	+5	−4
−3		
+2		

(b)

+	−9	+6
+7		
−5		

(c)

12 Find these sums.

(a) $(+2) + (+3) + (+2)$

(b) $(+2) + (-3) + (+2)$

(c) $(+2) + (-3) + (-2)$

(d) $(-2) + (+3) + (-2)$

(e) $(+4) + (+2) + (-3) + (-2) + (+6)$

(f) $(-4) + (+2) + (+3) + (-2) + (-6)$

(g) $(+4) + (-2) + (-3) + (+2) + (-6)$

(h) $(-4) + (-2) + (-3) + (+2) + (-6)$

13 Use addition of integers to find the answer for each.

(a) a deposit of 10 dollars and a withdrawal of 6 dollars.

(b) climbing up 3 steps and then down 5 steps.

(c) a rise in temperature of 2°C and a drop of 6°C.

(d) a round of golf 2 under par and another round of 1 over par.

(e) a loss of 7 m and a gain of 3 m.

14 The tallest mountain in the world is Mauno Koa in Hawaii. The base of this mountain is at -5486 m and the peak is at $+4201$ m. What is the full height of Mauno Koa?

C

15 The deepest lake in the world is Lake Bakal in the Soviet Union. The surface of this lake is at $+446$ m, while the bottom is at -1485 m. How deep is Lake Bakal?

Try the other problem solvers.

---

problem-solving: research

A container is constructed in the shape of a cone. The radius of the cone is 2.5 m and the slant height is 4.6 m. Find the surface area of the cone.

To solve this problem, you need to research the formula used to find the surface area of a cone.

---

computer tip

To prepare a table of values, you can use a computer. This program evaluates the expression $3x + 5$ for values of x from 0 to 10. It also prints the corresponding values.

```
10   PRINT "TABLE OF VALUES"
20   FOR X = 0 TO 10
30   LET F = 3 * X + 5
40   PRINT "VALUES ARE"; F, X
50   NEXT X
60   END
```

Write a BASIC program to prepare a table of values for $5m + 6$.

9.5 subtracting integers

Integers are useful in your everyday living. You often use concepts about integers without realizing it.

Gina lives on the second floor of an apartment building. How many floors does she have to travel to visit her friend Toby on the ninth floor?

This problem can be written as:

$(+9) - (+2) = \blacksquare$ To subtract think: What is
added to $+2$ to give $+9$?
$\qquad (+2) + \blacksquare = +9$
$\qquad\quad = +7$ Thus $\blacksquare = +7$

Gina must travel 7 floors up or $+7$ floors to visit Toby.

Gina's family parks its car on the third level below ground. How many floors does Gina have to travel to get to the car?

This problem can be written as:

$(-3) - (+2) = \blacksquare$ Think: What is added
to $+2$ to give -3?
$\qquad (+2) + \blacksquare = -3$
$\qquad\quad = -5$ Thus $\blacksquare = -5$

Gina must travel 5 floors down.

Often in mathematics, skills you have learned earlier help you to develop new skills. The examples above show how subtraction can be written in terms of addition.

To subtract $(-3) - (+2) = -5$ you have used a related addition shown as $(+2) + (-5) = -3$. You can use related addition to help you learn to subtract integers.

Compare the following.

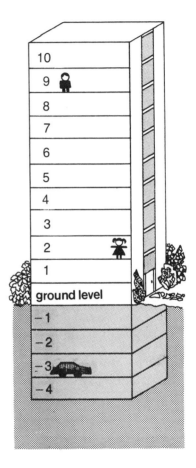

The answers are the same for each subtraction and related addition.

Subtraction		Related addition
$(+5) - (+2) = +3$	and	$(+5) + (-2) = +3$
$(+4) - (+6) = -2$	and	$(+4) + (-6) = -2$
$(+6) - (+2) = +4$	and	$(+6) + (-2) = +4$
$(-4) - (+1) = -5$	and	$(-4) + (-1) = -5$
$(-3) - (-1) = -2$	and	$(-3) + (+1) = -2$
$(-2) - (-5) = +3$	and	$(-2) + (+5) = +3$

By comparing subtraction and the related addition, you see that:

> To subtract an integer, you add the opposite integer.

Think:
opposite
operation
$(+5) - (-2) = (+5) + (+2)$
opposites

Example Find each difference.

(a) $(-6) - (+2)$ (b) $(-6) - (-2)$

Solution

(a) $(-6) - (+2)$ ⎛ Think: to subtract $+2$,
     $= (-6) + (-2)$ ⎜ add its opposite,
     $= -8$ ⎝ namely -2.

(b) $(-6) - (-2)$ ⎛ Think: to subtract -2,
     $= (-6) + (+2)$ ⎜ add its opposite,
     $= -4$ ⎝ namely $+2$.

9.5 exercise

A

1 To subtract $(+6) - (+8) = $ ■
   think of addition   ■ $+ (+8) = (+6)$
   Find the value of ■.

2 For each subtraction question,
   ▶ write a related addition question.
   ▶ find the value of ■.

   (a) $(+6) - (+8) = $ ■

   (b) $(+9) - (+8) = $ ■

   (c) $(+9) - (+9) = $ ■

   (d) $(-4) - (-3) = $ ■

   (e) $(+6) - (-8) = $ ■

   (f) $(+3) - (-2) = $ ■

   (g) $(-4) - (-6) = $ ■

   (h) $(-8) - (-3) = $ ■

3 Complete these patterns.

   (a)   Subtraction   Related addition
       $(+6) - (+3) = +3$ $(+6) + (-3) = +3$
       $(+6) - (+2) = +4$ $(+6) + (-2) = $ ■
       $(+6) - (+1) = +5$ $(+6) + (-1) = $ ■
       $(+6) - 0 = $ ■ $(+6) + 0 = $ ■
       $(+6) - (-1) = $ ■ $(+6) + (+1) = $ ■
       $(+6) - (-2) = $ ■ $(+6) + (+2) = $ ■

   (b)   Subtraction   Related addition
       $(+3) - (+1) = +2$ $(+3) + (-1) = +2$
       $(+2) - (+1) = +1$ $(+2) + (-1) = $ ■
       $(+1) - (+1) = 0$ $(+1) + (-1) = $ ■
       $ 0 - (+1) = $ ■ $ 0 + (-1) = $ ■
       $(-1) - (+1) = $ ■ $(-1) + (-1) = $ ■
       $(-2) - (+1) = $ ■ $(-2) + (-1) = $ ■

   (c)   Subtraction   Related addition
       $(+7) - (+4) = +3$ $(+7) + (-4) = $ ■
       $(+7) - (+2) = +5$ $(+7) + (-2) = $ ■
       $(+7) - 0 = $ ■ $(+7) + 0 = $ ■
       $(+7) - (-2) = $ ■ $(+7) + (+2) = $ ■
       $(+7) - (-4) = $ ■ $(+7) + (+4) = $ ■

4 What is the opposite of each integer?

   (a) $+3$ (b) -1 (c) $+4$

   (d) $+1$ (e) -2 (f) -5

5 Express each difference as a related addition.

   (a) $(+5) - (-3)$ (b) $(+5) - (+4)$

   (c) $(-8) - (+4)$ (d) $(-9) - (-5)$

   (e) $(+9) - (-4)$ (f) $(-5) - (+3)$

   (g) $(-2) - (-6)$ (h) $(+7) - (-5)$

   (i) $(-4) - (+3)$ (j) $(+2) - (+8)$

   ▶ Find the answer for each of the above.

B

6 ▶ Rewrite each subtraction as a related addition.
 ▶ Then find the value of each ■.

(a) $(+6) - (-4) = $ ■

(b) $(-4) - (-3) = $ ■

(c) $(-8) - (-2) = $ ■

(d) $(+11) - (-8) = $ ■

(e) $(-12) - (+4) = $ ■

(f) $(-12) - (-7) = $ ■

(g) $(+16) - (+11) = $ ■

(h) $0 - (-3) = $ ■

(i) $(+8) - 0 = $ ■

(j) $(+3) - (-3) = $ ■

(k) $(-3) - (-3) = $ ■

(l) $(-3) - (+3) = $ ■

7 Calculate each of the following.

(a) $(+2) - (+1)$ (b) $(+1) - (+3)$

(c) $(-1) - (+3)$ (d) $(-1) - (-3)$

(e) $(+1) - (-3)$ (f) $(+2) - (+5)$

(g) $(+2) - (-5)$ (h) $(-2) - (+5)$

(i) $(-2) - (-5)$ (j) $(+3) - (-3)$

(k) $(+3) - (+3)$ (l) $(-3) - (-3)$

(m) $(-3) - (+3)$ (n) $(-2) - (-1)$

8 Subtract. Arrange your answers in order from least to greatest.

(a) $(+4) - (-3)$ (b) $(+8) - (-8)$

(c) $(-3) - (+6)$ (d) $(-12) - (+8)$

(e) $(-7) - (-9)$ (f) $(-6) - (+4)$

9 Do these calculations. Watch the operation signs.

(a) $(+4) + (-7)$ (b) $(+11) - (+14)$

(c) $(-15) - (+12)$ (d) $(+10) + (-5)$

(e) $(-7) + (-2)$ (f) $(+35) - (-19)$

(g) $(+80) + (-17)$ (h) $(-12) - (-5)$

(i) $(+3) - (-1)$ (j) $(+35) + (-18)$

(k) $(-25) - (-18)$ (l) $(+14) + (+10)$

(m) $(-25) + (-3)$ (n) $(-25) - (-3)$

(o) $(+16) - (-14)$ (p) $(-18) + (-12)$

(q) $(-36) - (+12)$ (r) $(-24) + (+16)$

10 Copy and complete the chart.

Place	High temp. °C	Low temp. °C	Difference °C (High − low)
(a) Kamloops	+4	+1	?
(b) Red Deer	+2	−3	?
(c) Estevan	+1	?	+5
(d) Selkirk	−2	−5	?
(e) Iron Bridge	?	−4	+1
(f) Hull	+3	?	+2
(g) Gagetown	−4	−6	?
(h) Pictou	−8	−14	?
(i) Buchans	+2	?	+7

11 The following expressions involve more than two integers.

Calculate.

(a) $(-3) + (-4) - (+2)$

⎛ To calculate $(-3) + (-4) - (+2)$,
⎝ find the answer to $(-3) + (-4)$ first.

(b) $(+4) - (-3) + (-2)$

(c) $(-6) - (-8) - (+9)$

(d) $(-12) - (-4) + (-3)$

(e) $(-7) + (-3) + (-2)$

(f) $(-6) - (-3) - (-2)$

(g) $(-2) + (-6) - (-2) - (-2) - (-3)$

(h) $(-1) - (-1) + (-2) + (-8) - (-3)$

12 Copy and complete each magic square.

(a)

+1		+3
	0	
		−1

(b)

+6			+3
	+1	0	
−1	−3	−4	+2
	+4		

13 The melting point of silver is +960°C. The melting point of gold is +1063°C. Which melting point is greater? By how much?

14 The melting point of krypton is −157°C. The melting point of platinum is +1773°C. How much greater is the melting point of platinum?

15 The temperature of the meat was −15°C in the freezer. After thawing, the temperature was +12°C. By how much did the temperature change?

16 The chinook is a warm wind that blows from the Pacific Ocean across the Rockies. One February day in Calgary, the temperature rose from −10°C to 24°C due to the chinook. By how many degrees did the temperature rise that day?

17 When Jamie walked, the temperature he felt on his face was −20°C. He travelled on his snow‑mobile and the temperature now felt like −33°C. By how much did the temperature appear to change?

18 Without a wind the temperature is −15°C. With a wind of 16 km/h, the temperature feels like −26°C. By how much does the temperature appear to change?

C

19 The warmest temperature on record in Canada is +45°C. This temperature was recorded at the towns of Midale and Yellow Grass in Saskatchewan on July 5, 1937. The coldest temperature on record occurred at Snag, in the Northwest Territories on February 5, 1947. The temperature was −63°C. What is the difference between these two temperature records?

skills quiz

All these calculations deal with adding and subtracting integers. How long did it take you?

(a) $(+2) + (-1)$
(b) $(+24) + (-37)$
(c) $(-15) + (-8)$
(d) $(-5) - (-7)$
(e) $(+26) - (-9)$
(f) $(-21) + (+8)$
(g) $(-3) + (-6)$
(h) $(-65) - (+64)$
(i) $(-9) + (-6)$
(j) $(-21) + (+14)$
(k) $(-21) - (-3)$
(l) $(-64) + (-23)$
(m) $(-64) + (+32)$
(n) $(-26) + (-33)$
(o) $(+9) + (-2)$
(p) $(-3) - (-2)$
(q) $(-3) - (-2) - (-2)$
(r) $(+6) + (-4) + (-6)$
(s) $(-9) + (-3) - (-2)$
(t) $(+4) - (-2) + (-6)$
(u) $(-3) + (-2) + (-3) + (-2) + (-6)$
(v) $(-2) + (-3) + (+4) + (-6) + (-3)$
(w) $(+4) + (-6) - (-2) - (-3) + (-4)$
(x) $(-6) + (-8) - (-2) + (-3) - (-6)$
(y) $(+4) + (-7) - (-3) - (-3) + (-6)$
(z) $(-4) + (-6) - (+4) + (-4) + (-8)$

9.6 writing integers

On the weather forecast map, the temperature in Vancouver is written as 7°C. The temperature in Goose Bay is shown as −10°C.

Often in everyday practice, the symbol + is not written for positive numbers.

$$7°C \text{ means } +7°C$$

However, the negative sign must always be written for negative integers.

Example   Find each answer.

(a) $5 + (-2)$ (b) $-3 - 4$ $\left(\begin{array}{l}\text{To subtract an integer,}\\ \text{add its opposite.}\end{array}\right)$

Solution   (a) $\begin{array}{l}5 + (-2)\\ = 3\end{array}$ $\left(\begin{array}{l}\text{Think:}\\ 5 + (-2)\text{ means}\\ (+5) + (-2)\end{array}\right)$ (b) $\begin{array}{l}-3 - 4\\ = -3 + (-4)\\ = -7\end{array}$ $\left(\begin{array}{l}\text{Think:}\\ -3 - 4\text{ means}\\ (-3) - (+4)\end{array}\right)$

9.6 exercise

A

1 Match each sum in the first column, with the equivalent expression, A, B, C, ...

(a) $-4 + 2$ A $(-4) + (-2)$

(b) $4 + (-2)$ B $(+4) + (+2)$

(c) $-4 + (-2)$ C $(-4) + (+2)$

(d) $4 + 2$ D $(+4) + (-2)$

2 Match each difference in the first column, with the equivalent expression, A, B, C, ...

(a) $3 - 5$ A $(+3) - (-5)$

(b) $-3 - 5$ B $(-3) - (-5)$

(c) $3 - (-5)$ C $(-3) - (+5)$

(d) $-3 - (-5)$ D $(+3) - (+5)$

3 Replace ■ with an integer in each of the following to make the statement true.

(a) $3 - 2 = 3 + ■$

(b) $-5 - (-1) = -5 + ■$

(c) $2 - (-2) = 2 + ■$

(d) $-1 - (-3) = -1 + ■$

4 Find each sum.

(a) $2 + (-1)$ (b) $-3 + 4$

(c) $6 + 3$ (d) $-5 + (-2)$

(e) $-4 + (-2)$ (f) $0 + (-4)$

5 Add.

(a) $\begin{array}{r}4\\ -2\end{array}$ (b) $\begin{array}{r}-3\\ 1\end{array}$ (c) $\begin{array}{r}-2\\ -2\end{array}$ (d) $\begin{array}{r}5\\ -3\end{array}$

(e) $\begin{array}{r}-6\\ -1\end{array}$ (f) $\begin{array}{r}4\\ -4\end{array}$ (g) $\begin{array}{r}-5\\ -4\end{array}$ (h) $\begin{array}{r}-3\\ 2\end{array}$

6 Find each difference.

(a) $4 - 2$ (b) $-3 - 1$ (c) $-3 - (-8)$

(d) $-4 - 2$ (e) $5 - 8$ (f) $-3 - (-6)$

B

7 For each expression
  ▸ write it without brackets.
  ▸ find the answer.

  (a) $(+1) + (-3) - (+2)$

  (b) $(+2) + (-1) - (-2)$

  (c) $(-1) + (-2) - (-4)$

  (d) $(-5) - (-2) + (-4) - (+5)$

  (e) $(+3) + (-3) + (-2) + (-4)$

8 Find each sum. Which has the greatest answer?

  (a) $2 + 3 - 4 + 1$

  (b) $-2 - 1 + 4 - 2$

  (c) $-4 + 2 - 3 - 1$

  (d) $4 - 2 + 1 + 2$

  (e) $-3 - 3 - 2 + 4$

  (f) $6 - 2 - 4 - 3$

  (g) $-2 + 4 - 6 + 2$

  (h) $1 - 2 + 4 - 5 + 3$

9 Copy and complete each pattern below.

  (a) $-2 + 2 = \blacksquare$
      $-2 + 2 - 2 = \blacksquare$
      $-2 + 2 - 2 + 2 = \blacksquare$
      $-2 + 2 - 2 + 2 - 2 = \blacksquare$

  (b) $3 - 3 = \blacksquare$
      $3 - 3 + 3 = \blacksquare$
      $3 - 3 + 3 - 3 = \blacksquare$
      $3 - 3 + 3 - 3 + 3 = \blacksquare$

10 Copy and complete each chart.

  (a)

+	3	−2	5	−4	4
−4					

  (b)

+	−1	0	4	−5	−7
6					

11 Find each answer.

  (a) $-4 + 2$ (b) $5 - (-1)$

  (c) $-2 - 3$ (d) $6 + (-3)$

  (e) $4 - (-2)$ (f) $-1 + (-2)$

12 Calculate each of the following.

  (a) $-2 + 3 + (-1)$

  (b) $6 + (-4) - 3$

  (c) $2 - (-3) + 1$

  (d) $-5 - 2 + 3 - (-2)$

13 In a round of golf, Tanya finished with a score of -2. Her friend Debbie had a score of 8. What was the difference between their two scores?

14 A Coast Guard patrol plane was at a height of 50 m when its computer detected a submarine at -30 m. What vertical distance separated the two vehicles?

15 In a golf tournament, Russell had a score of 3 on his first six holes, a score of -1 on the next six holes, and a score of 4 on the last six holes. What was his final score?

C

16 The chart shows the estimated average surface temperature on some of the planets.

Planet	Surface temperature
Earth	14°C
Jupiter	−151°C
Venus	477°C
Saturn	−184°C

  (a) Which is warmer, Jupiter or Saturn? How much warmer?

  (b) How much warmer is the average temperature on Earth than on Jupiter?

  (c) How many degrees colder is Saturn than Venus?

applications: Canadian temperatures

Canadians experience a very great range of temperatures, as shown in the chart.

City	Average low temperature in January (°C)	Average high temperature in July (°C)
Toronto	−11	27
Vancouver	0	22
Winnipeg	−23	26
Quebec	−16	25
Halifax	−8	22
Victoria	2	21
Saskatoon	−24	26

In Winnipeg, the difference between the average low −23°C in January and the average high 26°C in July is 49°C. Thus the *average temperature range* in Winnipeg is 49°C

$$26 - (-23) = 26 + 23$$
$$= 49$$

Questions 17–21 refer to the chart above.

17 What is the average temperature range in these cities?
   (a) Toronto   (b) Quebec   (c) Halifax

18 (a) In which of the cities listed is the average temperature range the greatest?

   (b) In which of the cities is the temperature range the least?

19 How many degrees greater is the average low temperature in January for Victoria than that for Saskatoon?

20 Suppose you lived in Winnipeg in the winter and then moved to Halifax in the spring. What average range of temperatures would you experience that year?

21 Use the chart to make up two problems about the temperature readings. Solve your problems.

22 Look at the following newspaper clipping.

Friday's Temperatures

	Low	High
Dawson	−4°C	8°C
Vancouver	2°C	8°C
Victoria	2°C	6°C
Edmonton	0°C	11°C
Calgary	−2°C	14°C
Yellowknife	−14°C	−5°C
Saskatoon	0°C	12°C
Regina	−1°C	18°C
Churchill	−11°C	−10°C

(a) Which city had the lowest temperature?

(b) Which city recorded the highest temperature?

(c) Which city recorded the greatest increase in temperature?

(d) Which city recorded the least change in temperature?

Questions 23 to 25 are based on the following information. The average January, February, and annual temperatures are shown in the chart.

	January	February	Annual
Regina	−17°C	−14°C	2°C
Sydney	−4°C	−6°C	6°C
Wiarton	−6°C	−7°C	6°C
Dawson	−29°C	−23°C	−5°C
Coppermine	−29°C	−31°C	−12°C

23 (a) Which city has the highest average temperature in January?
   (b) Which city has the lowest average temperature in February?

24 In Fort Smith, the annual temperature is 6°C warmer than in Coppermine. What is Fort Smith's annual average temperature?

25 Which city has the greatest difference between the January and February average temperature?

9.7 solving problems: making decisions

Skills with adding and subtracting integers can be applied to solving problems. As in any other problem, you must first read the problem carefully and then answer the questions:

   I What information am I asked to find?
   II What information am I given?

Once you know the answers to questions I and II, you need to decide on which operations to use. Remember to look for clue words, such as the following.

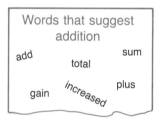

Words that suggest addition

add   sum
   total
gain increased plus

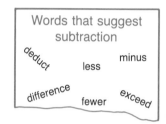

Words that suggest subtraction

deduct   minus
   less
difference   exceed
   fewer

Steps for Solving Problems

A Ask yourself:
    I What information am I asked to find?
    II What information am I given?
B Decide on a method.
    Which operation do I use?
C Do the work.
    Complete the calculation.
D Check your work.
    Use your rounding skills.
E Make a final statement.
    Answer the original problem.

Then you use the *Steps for Solving Problems* to organize your solution.

9.7 exercise

A

1 Match each problem with the calculation A, B, C or D, that you would use to solve the problem.

    A $-6 + (-2)$ B $-2 + 6$
    C $6 + (-2)$ D $2 - (-6)$

  (a) Barb parked her car 2 floors below ground. She took the elevator up 6 floors to her office. How many floors above ground is her office?

  (b) The temperature outside is $-6°C$. Inside the garage it is $2°C$. How much warmer is it in the garage?

  (c) Jake gained 6 m but then he fumbled and lost 2 m. What was his actual gain on the play?

  (d) Carrie lost 6 marks for spelling and 2 marks for incorrect grammar. How many marks did she lose altogether?

2 Read the problem. Which calculation would you use to solve the problem, A, B, or C?

    A $-10 + (-3)$
    B $-10 - (-3)$
    C $-3 - (-10)$

  The temperature in Churchill was $-10°C$. In Dauphin it was $-3°C$. How much warmer was it in Dauphin?

3 Which calculation would you use to solve the problem, A, B, or C?

    A $-2 - (-8)$
    B $-2 + 8$
    C $-2 + (-8)$

  When Sal left school the temperature was $-2°C$. By supper time the temperature had fallen by $8°C$. What was the temperature at supper time?

B For each question
  ▶ think carefully about the operation you will use.
  ▶ write a complete mathematical statement for each answer.

4 On Sunday morning the temperature read −4°C. The temperature rose 3°C before noon. What was the temperature at midday?

5 During the blizzard, the temperature was −6°C. The next day the temperature rose 8°C. What was the temperature reading the next day?

6 On Monday afternoon the temperature reading was 2°C. If the temperature had risen 6°C since morning, what was the temperature in the morning?

7 The temperature in Kapuskasing is 8°C. The temperature at Thunder Bay is −2°C. How much warmer is it at Kapuskasing?

Questions 8 to 10 are based on this experiment. In an experiment, a thermometer was placed outside the class window.

Readings were made every 10 min, as the temperature dropped.

After 10 min	18°C
After 20 min	16°C
After 30 min	14°C
After 40 min	12°C
After 50 min	▢°C

8 (a) What is the initial temperature?
  (b) Find the pattern. What would you expect the missing temperature to be?

9 (a) What would you expect the temperature to be after 1 h 20 min?
  (b) What assumption did you make to obtain the answer in (a)?

10 Is this statement true or false?
      "The information recorded can be used to predict the temperature in 5 h."
  Why or why not?

11 The average annual temperature for Victoria is 10°C. In Schefferville it is −5°C. Which temperature is cooler? By how much?

12 The boiling point of oxygen is −180°C. The boiling point of chlorine is −35°C. Which boiling point is greater? By how much?

13 In a round of golf, Judy finished with a score of +5. Her partner Molly finished with a score of −2. How much better was Molly's score than Judy's? Remember, in golf the lower score is better.

14 There are deep trenches on the floor of the Pacific Ocean. The Peru-Chile Trench is −8064 m, while the Japan Trench is −6412 m. How much deeper is the Peru-Chile Trench than the Japan Trench?

15 The deepest underwater descent ever made by a human is about −10 912 m. The Caspian Sea is −28 m deep. How much deeper is the human descent than the depth of the Caspian Sea?

C
16 Evaluate the following.
  (a) $c + d$ if $c = -2$, $d = 3$
  (b) $t - w$ if $t = -2$, $w = -3$
  (c) $q + r - t$ if $q = 3$, $r = -1$, $t = -5$
  (d) $k - s + x$ if $k = 4$, $s = +3$, $x = -4$

applications: integers in hockey

Integers are used in sports to make comparisons. A plus-minus system is used in hockey to rate a player.

▶ If a hockey player is on the ice when a teammate scores a goal, the player gets $+1$.

▶ If a hockey player is on the ice when the opposing team scores, then the player receives a -1.

The player in the photo has scored a goal. The player and his teammates each receive a $+1$.

After each game, a player's plus-minus standing is calculated. For example, a player's record after a game was the following.

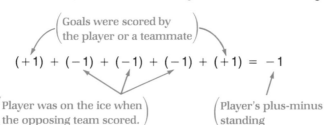

$$\left(\begin{array}{c}\text{Goals were scored by}\\\text{the player or a teammate}\end{array}\right)$$

$$(+1) + (-1) + (-1) + (-1) + (+1) = -1$$

$$\left(\begin{array}{c}\text{Player was on the ice when}\\\text{the opposing team scored.}\end{array}\right) \qquad \left(\begin{array}{c}\text{Player's plus-minus}\\\text{standing}\end{array}\right)$$

17 During the Canada Cup, players were given plus-minus standings. Calculate each plus-minus standing.

(a) Goulet $+1, -1, -1, +1, -1, -1$

(b) Simmer $-1, -1, +1, +1, -1, +1, -1$

(c) Gartner $-1, -1, -1, +1, +1, +1, -1$

18 Calculate the plus-minus standing for each player.

		Game 1	Game 2	Game 3
(a)	Reinhart	-2	$+1$	-3
(b)	Semenko	-2	-1	$+1$
(c)	Messier	$+2$	$+3$	-1

19 After the first 6 games of the season, the players had the following plus-minus standings.

Defence		Forwards			
Nackin	$+2$	Swartz	-1	Quirt	-2
Kirton	-1	Lawson	0	Martin	$+3$
Buton	$+1$	Devlon	-2	Dipisqua	-4
Thorton	-1	Lane	$+1$	Weber	$+5$
Pawson	-2	Johnson	$+1$	Eng	$+2$

(a) Calculate the total plus-minus standings for the defence.

(b) Calculate the total plus-minus standings for the forwards.

(c) Which has the better standings, defence or forwards?

20 For the next 3 games, the players in the previous question obtained these plus-minus results.

Defence		Forwards			
Nackin	-1	Swartz	$+1$	Quirt	-1
Kirton	$+1$	Lawson	-1	Martin	-2
Buton	$+1$	Devlon	-1	Dipisqua	$+2$
Thorton	-1	Lane	-1	Weber	$+2$
Pawson	$+1$	Johnson	$+1$	Eng	$+1$

(a) Update the table. Record the above results in the table in the previous question.

(b) Which has the better standings, A or B? How much better?
A: Swartz, Devlon, Eng
B: Johnson, Martin, Lawson

9.8 signed numbers: rationals

The integers $\{\ldots, -3, -2, -1, 0, +1, +2, +3, \ldots\}$

are a special set of positive and negative numbers. The numbers named by integers are part of a set of numbers, called **rational numbers**, which include numerals such as

$$-2\tfrac{1}{4}, \; -2.5, \; +4, \; -\tfrac{3}{4}, \; -3.63, \; +4.65, \; +\tfrac{1}{2}$$

These rational numbers can be shown on a number line.

Any number that can be expressed as the quotient of two integers, provided the divisor is not zero, is called a *rational number*.

Numbers such as $\sqrt{2}, \pi$ which *cannot* be expressed as a quotient of two integers are called **irrational numbers**.

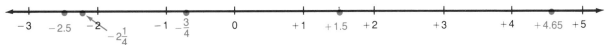

since $+4.65$ is to the right of -2.5, then $+4.65 > -2.5$

Since $-2\tfrac{1}{4}$ is to the left of $-\tfrac{3}{4}$, then $-2\tfrac{1}{4} < -\tfrac{3}{4}$

The rational number $-\tfrac{6}{8}$ would be graphed at the same point as $-\tfrac{3}{4}$, since $-\tfrac{6}{8}$ and $-\tfrac{3}{4}$ are equivalent fractions.

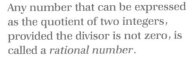
$$\left(-\tfrac{3}{4} \times \tfrac{2}{2} = -\tfrac{6}{8}\right)$$

9.8 exercise

A

1 Find the missing rational numbers.

(a) 0 $+\tfrac{1}{4}$ $+\tfrac{1}{2}$ ▢ $+1$ ▢   ▢ $+1\tfrac{3}{4}$

(b)   ▢ -0.5 0 ▢ $+1$ $+1.5$ ▢

(c) -3 ▢   ▢ -2 $-1\tfrac{2}{3}$ ▢ -1 ▢

(d) -0.4 ▢ 0 $+0.2$ $+0.4$ ▢   ▢ $+1$

2 Which is greater in each pair of rational numbers?

(a) $+\tfrac{1}{2}, -\tfrac{1}{2}$ (b) $-0.7, +0.7$

(c) $-\tfrac{1}{5}, -\tfrac{2}{5}$ (d) $+0.2, +0.3$

(e) $+\tfrac{1}{4}, -1\tfrac{1}{2}$ (f) $+1.2, -0.3$

3 Which is the lesser in each pair of rational numbers?

(a) $+\tfrac{1}{3}, -\tfrac{1}{3}$ (b) $-0.1, +0.2$

(c) $-\tfrac{1}{5}, -\tfrac{3}{8}$ (d) $+0.4, +0.2$

(e) $+1\tfrac{1}{5}, -1\tfrac{1}{10}$ (f) $-0.2, +0.1$

B

4 Graph the following set of numbers on a number line.
$$\{+0.5, -0.5, 0, +1\}$$

5 Graph the following set of numbers on a number line.
$$\left\{+\tfrac{1}{4}, +0.5, -\tfrac{1}{4}, -0.5, 0\right\}$$

6 Graph the following set of numbers on a number line.
$$\{-4, -2.5, -1, 0, +1\}$$

7 Use $<$ or $>$ in place of ● to write a true statement.

(a) $+1.6$ ● -1.6 (b) $+6.9$ ● $+9.6$

(c) -9.6 ● -6.9 (d) -3.2 ● $+4.6$

(e) $+\frac{1}{4}$ ● $-\frac{1}{3}$ (f) $-\frac{3}{4}$ ● $-\frac{5}{8}$

(g) $+6.9$ ● $-6\frac{4}{5}$ (h) $-3\frac{1}{2}$ ● $-3\frac{1}{3}$

8 In each set, which number has the greatest value?

(a) $\{+4, +3, -1\}$ (b) $\{+4, +4.5, -9\}$

(c) $\{+\frac{1}{4}, -3.2, +\frac{1}{8}\}$ (d) $\{-\frac{1}{3}, -\frac{1}{4}, -\frac{1}{5}\}$

9 In each set, which number has the least value?

(a) $\{+3, +2, -1\}$ (b) $\{+3, +3.5, -6\}$

(c) $\{+\frac{1}{3}, -3.2, +8\}$ (d) $\{-\frac{1}{3}, -\frac{1}{4}, -\frac{1}{5}\}$

---

working with rationals

In mathematics you often use skills learned previously to develop skills in a new area. The sum or difference of rational numbers can be found by extending the skills you learned when working with integers, decimals, and fractions.

Find the result of $(+8.2) - (-3.7)$.

$(+8.2) - (-3.7)$
$= (+8.2) + (+3.7)$ $\left(\begin{array}{l}\text{To subtract, add}\\\text{the opposite.}\end{array}\right)$
$= +11.9$

Calculate $\left(+2\frac{2}{3}\right) + \left(-1\frac{1}{2}\right)$.

$\left(+2\frac{2}{3}\right) + \left(-1\frac{1}{2}\right)$
$= \left(+2\frac{4}{6}\right) + \left(-1\frac{3}{6}\right)$
$= +1\frac{1}{6}$

10 Find the sums of these rational numbers.

(a) $\left(+\frac{1}{4}\right) + \left(+\frac{1}{4}\right)$ (b) $\left(-\frac{1}{3}\right) + \left(-\frac{1}{3}\right)$

(c) $\left(+\frac{1}{4}\right) + \left(-\frac{1}{3}\right)$ (d) $\left(-\frac{1}{4}\right) + \left(+\frac{1}{3}\right)$

(e) $(+2.5) + (+1.5)$ (f) $(-2.5) + (+1.5)$

(g) $(+2.5) + (-1.5)$ (h) $(-2.5) + (-1.5)$

11 Find the differences of these rational numbers.

(a) $\left(+\frac{5}{8}\right) - \left(+\frac{3}{8}\right)$ (b) $(-0.7) - (+0.4)$

(c) $(+1.75) - (-0.23)$ (d) $\left(-1\frac{3}{4}\right) - \left(+1\frac{1}{2}\right)$

(e) $\left(+2\frac{9}{10}\right) - \left(-3\frac{2}{5}\right)$ (f) $(-5.6) - (-2.4)$

(g) $(+6.5) - (+9.8)$ (h) $\left(+2\frac{3}{4}\right) - \left(+3\frac{7}{8}\right)$

12 Calculate each of the following for rational numbers.

(a) $\left(+\frac{3}{5}\right) + \left(+\frac{4}{5}\right)$ (b) $\left(+\frac{3}{6}\right) - \left(+\frac{4}{5}\right)$

(c) $(+1.6) - (+2.6)$ (d) $(-3.5) + (-2.6)$

(e) $\left(+1\frac{1}{2}\right) + \left(-1\frac{3}{4}\right)$ (f) $\left(-\frac{2}{3}\right) - \left(+\frac{5}{6}\right)$

(g) $\left(+\frac{5}{8}\right) - \left(-\frac{6}{8}\right)$ (j) $(-3.2) + (+4.8)$

13 The melting point of mercury is $-38.9°C$. The boiling point is $356.0°C$. How much greater is the boiling point than the melting point?

14 The temperature of the mixture was $-8.5°C$. The temperature rose $6.3°C$. What was the final temperature?

15 The temperature in London was $-9.6°C$. In Sackville, the temperature was $12°C$ warmer. What was the temperature in Sackville?

16 The temperature was $-16.8°C$. For a wind speed of 16km/h the wind chill temperature was $12.5°C$ lower. What was the temperature?

9.9 problem solving: creating problems

If you learn how to create problems, you will be better at solving problems. To create a problem, you need to know how to combine the answers to two important questions.

I What information am I asked to find?

II What information am I given?

From the same information, different people often create different problems.

For each of the following, two pieces of information, A and B, are given.

▶ Create two problems using the information.
▶ Solve each problem.

(a) A: The freight train pulled 100 box cars.
    B: It took 2.5 h to load each box car.

(b) A: The video game sells for $69.80.
    B: The computer outlet costs $349.50.

(c) A: There are 24 soup cans in a case.
    B: There are 6 cases piled on top of each other.

(d) A: The cost to phone 3 min is $1.69.
    B: The length of the call was 30 min.

(e) A: Tickets to the movie cost $4.25.
    B: Transportation costs $2.25.

(f) A: Jeff took 1.5 h to cut the lawn.
    B: He was paid $15.

(g) A: The distance from the lake to the city is 15.6 km.
    B: The mountain is half way.

(h) A: Michael sold 36 cakes to raise money for the trip.
    B: The trip costs $65.78.

practice and problems: a chapter review

(9.1) 1 Write the opposite of each integer.

   (a) $+2$ (b) -3 (c) $+4$ (d) -7

   (e) Graph each integer and its opposite on the number line.

(9.2) 2 Replace ● by $<$ or $>$.

   (a) $+6$ ● $+2$ (b) -2 ● $+3$

   (c) 0 ● -2 (d) -5 ● -7

(9.3) 3 ▶ Find each solution set.
       ▶ Draw a graph of each solution set.

   (a) $+2 > g$ (b) $-2 < r$

   (c) $-3 \geq c$ (d) $-4 \leq t$

   (e) $-3 < k \leq 5$ (f) $+3 > h \geq -5$

(9.4) 4 Find the answer for

   (a) a drop of 3°C followed by a rise of 2°C.

   (b) a loss of 2 kg followed by a gain of 3 kg.

(9.5) 5 Calculate the following.

   (a) $(+6) - (+2)$ (b) $(-6) - (+2)$

   (c) $(-6) - (-2)$ (d) $(+4) - (-3) - (+5)$

   6 Some people were standing on a tower. Cars were 25 m below the tower and flags were 4 m above the tower. What is the difference in distance between the cars and flags?

(9.6) 7 Simplify.

   (a) $3 - 2 - 4 + 6 - 2$

   (b) $-3 + 4 - 2 - 2 + 3 - 2$

(9.7) 8 The average winter temperature for Victoria is 4°C, while for Winnipeg it is $-17°C$. How much colder is the average temperature for Winnipeg?

test for practice

1 Use an integer to show each of the following.

   (a) 6 steps up   (b) a loss of $6

   (c) a profit of $200   (d) a drop of 4°C

2 Write $<$, $>$ or $=$ for ● to make a true statement.

   (a) $(+6) - (-3)$ ● -4

   (b) $+6$ ● $(-3) + (-3)$

   (c) -9 ● $(-3) + (-7)$

   (d) -16 ● $(+3) - (-14)$

3 Write the following sets of integers.

   (a) greater than -3 and less than $+4$

   (b) between -3 and -8

4 (a) Find the solution set for
        $n < -4, n \in \{-8, -6, -4, -2, 0\}$.

   (b) Draw a graph of the solution set on a number line.

5 Pairs of numbers are shown. Use the symbol $<$ or $>$ to write a true statement.

   (a) $-3, -3.2$ (b) $+4.6, +4$ (c) $-\frac{1}{3}, +\frac{1}{4}$

   (d) $+\frac{1}{3}, -\frac{1}{4}$ (e) $+4.8, +8.4$ (f) $-4.8, +8.4$

6 Write the opposite of each integer.

   (a) $+4$ (b) -6 (c) $+9$ (d) -16 (e) $+18$ (f) -23

7 Calculate each of the following.

   (a) $(+6) - (-6)$ (b) $(-6) + (-3)$

   (c) $(+12) + (-6)$ (d) $(-6) - (+12)$

8 On Saturday the temperature was $-3°C$. By Monday the temperature had risen 6°C. What was the temperature on Monday?

9 The temperature dropped 3°C overnight. If the temperature was initially $-4°C$, what was the final temperature?

maintaining skills: percent

An important skill is to do calculations with percent. Round off your answers to the first decimal place.

1 Calculate.
   (a) 16% of 105   (b) 11.5% of 900

   (c) $19\frac{1}{2}$% of 340   (d) $10\frac{1}{2}$% of 450

2 Solve.
   (a) What percent is 33 of 78?

   (b) 18 is what per cent of 116?

   (c) What is 45% of 13.8?

   (d) What percent is 116 of 238?

   (e) 50% of what number is 350?

3 Find the value of ■ in each question.
   (a) 20% of 96 = ■   (b) 80% of ■ = 72

   (c) ■% of 300 = 30   (d) 45% of ■ = 48

   (e) 34 is ■% of 170   (f) ■% of 32 is 8

4 Because Jim's dad paid cash he received a discount of 15% on the purchase of a bicycle priced at $89.80. Calculate the price he paid for it.

5 By selling a house Michael's mother made 3% commission. If the house sold for $28 000, calculate the amount of commission.

6 The fluid part of the blood is called plasma. Plasma is 90% water (by volume). Find the amount of water in 453 mL of plasma.

7 Milk received from the farmer is tested for butterfat. One supply of milk tested had 3.5% butterfat. How many litres of milk would be required to produce 7 L of butterfat?

8 The net price of a hockey mask was $8.95. Calculate the amount you would have to pay if the sales tax is 8%.

integers: skills with all operations

Patterns for multiplying integers, dividing integers, order of operations, language of mathematics, reading carefully, scientific notation, rationals and operations, co-ordinates and integers, problem solving skills, solving problems and applications

In the study of mathematics certain steps are used over and over again. For example, in developing skills, the following steps are often used.

Learn certain skills. → The skills you learned provide an important foundation for learning new skills.

You applied these steps in the previous chapter.

Learn to add integers. → The skills for learning to add integers are used to learn to subtract integers.

In this chapter, the same steps are used again.

Learn to multiply integers. → The skills for learning to multiply integers are used to learn to divide integers.

Other strategies that were used in your earlier work are again used in this chapter. Do you remember how often you have referred to each of the following?

Rules for the Order of Operations

► Perform the operations in brackets ( ) first.

► Then calculate the powers. Namely, find the value of expressions involving exponents.

► Then do multiplication or division in the order they appear.

► Then do addition or subtraction in the order they appear.

Steps for Solving Problems

A Ask yourself:
   I What information am I asked to find?
   II What information am I given?
B Decide on a method.
   Which operation do I use?
C Do the work.
   Complete the calculation.
D Check your work.
   Use your rounding skills.
E Make a final statement.
   Answer the original problem.

10.1 patterns for multiplication: integers

The skills and concepts you learned earlier with whole numbers, extend to your work with integers. For whole numbers, you can write the sum of several numbers that are the same in a simpler way by using multiplication.

as a sum

$$2 + 2 + 2 + 2 + 2 = 10$$

as a product

$$5 \times 2 = 10$$

For integers, you can also write:

$$(+2) + (+2) + (+2) + (+2) + (+2) = +10 \qquad (+5) \times (+2) = +10$$

Jennifer played a game five times, and lost 2 points each time. Each loss is shown by -2. You can write the loss

as a sum

$$(-2) + (-2) + (-2) + (-2) + (-2) = -10$$

as a product

$$(+5) \times (-2) = ?$$

Since the answers must be the same, then the example suggests:
$$(+5) \times (-2) = -10$$

A pattern can also be used to find the product of integers.

By using the pattern shown, you obtain the same result as in the example.

$$(+5) \times (-2) = -10$$

positive integer negative integer negative product

$$(+5) \times (+3) = +15$$
$$(+5) \times (+2) = +10$$
$$(+5) \times (+1) = + 5$$
$$(+5) \times 0 = 0$$
$$(+5) \times (-1) = - 5$$
$$(+5) \times (-2) = -10$$
$$(+5) \times (-3) = -15$$

The integers are decreasing by one.

The products are decreasing by five.

Thus, it appears that:

> The product of a positive integer and a negative integer is a negative integer.

$$\begin{pmatrix} \text{a positive} \\ \text{integer} \end{pmatrix} \times \begin{pmatrix} \text{a negative} \\ \text{integer} \end{pmatrix} = \begin{pmatrix} \text{a negative} \\ \text{integer} \end{pmatrix}$$

You can use other patterns to find the product of a negative and a positive integer. Thus, it appears that:

> The product of a negative integer and a positive integer is a negative integer.

$$\begin{pmatrix} \text{a negative} \\ \text{integer} \end{pmatrix} \times \begin{pmatrix} \text{a positive} \\ \text{integer} \end{pmatrix} = \begin{pmatrix} \text{a negative} \\ \text{integer} \end{pmatrix}$$

Throughout this section, you will often write the symbol + with positive numbers to help you understand finding products of integers.

Example Find each product. You can use a pattern to help you.

(a) $(+3) \times (-3) = \blacksquare$ (b) $(-2) \times (+3) = \blacksquare$

Solution

(a) Think of a pattern.

$(+3) \times (-3) = -9$

$(+3) \times (+1) = +3$
$(+3) \times \quad 0 = \quad 0$
$(+3) \times (-1) = -3$
$(+3) \times (-2) = -6$
$(+3) \times (-3) = -9$

(b) Think of a pattern.

$(-2) \times (+3) = -6$

$(+2) \times (+3) = +6$
$(+1) \times (+3) = +3$
$\quad 0 \times (+3) = \quad 0$
$(-1) \times (+3) = -3$
$(-2) \times (+3) = -6$

In developing skills, you often follow these steps.
▶ Do examples that help you understand how answers are obtained.
▶ Look for patterns to help you find answers.
In the following exercise you will do both steps.

Use your calculator to try other numbers.

10.1 exercise

A

1 Write each addition as multiplication.

Addition of negative integers
$(-3) + (-3) + (-3) + (-3)$
can be written as multiplication.
$(+4) \times (-3)$ or $4 \times (-3)$

(a) $(-2) + (-2) + (-2) + (-2)$

(b) $(-3) + (-3) + (-3)$

(c) $(+4) + (+4) + (+4) + (+4) + (+4)$

(d) $(-3) + (-3) + (-3) + (-3)$

(e) $(-4) + (-4) + (-4) + (-4) + (-4)$

(f) $(-1) + (-1) + (-1) + (-1) + (-1)$

2 (a) Find the sum.
$(-2) + (-2) + (-2) + (-2)$

(b) Use your answer in (a). Find the product.
$(+4) \times (-2)$.

3 (a) Find the sum.
$(-3) + (-3) + (-3) + (-3)$

(b) Write a multiplication expression for (a). What is the product?

4 Copy and complete the table. Use the sum to find the answer for each missing product.

Sum	Product
$(-1) + (-1) = \blacksquare$	$(+2) \times (-1) = \blacksquare$
$(-2) + (-2) + (-2) = \blacksquare$	
$(-4) + (-4) = \blacksquare$	
$(-3) + (-3) + (-3) = \blacksquare$	
$(-4) + (-4) + (-4) = \blacksquare$	
$(-5) + (-5) = \blacksquare$	

5 Use the results in the previous question to help you find the products of integers.

(a) Find an answer for $(+4)(-3)$.

(b) Find these products.   *Multiplication is understood here.*

$(+5)(-2)$ $(+3)(-6)$ $(+4)(-5)$

You can also use a pattern to help you understand finding products of integers. Questions 6 to 13 use patterns.

6 (a) Find the values of ■ for this pattern.

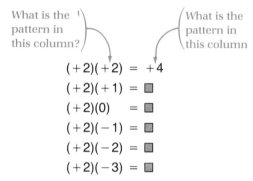

What is the pattern in this column?   What is the pattern in this column

$(+2)(+2) = +4$
$(+2)(+1) = $ ■
$(+2)(0) = $ ■
$(+2)(-1) = $ ■
$(+2)(-2) = $ ■
$(+2)(-3) = $ ■

Continue the pattern for two more rows.

(b) Use the pattern to find the products.
$(+2)(-2)$ $(+2)(-3)$

7 (a) Find the value of ■ in the pattern.

(b) Use the pattern to find the product.
$(+3)(-2) = $ ■

$(+3)(+2) = $ ■
$(+3)(+1) = $ ■
$(+3)(0) = $ ■
$(+3)(-1) = $ ■
$(+3)(-2) = $ ■
$(+3)(-3) = $ ■

8 (a) Find the value of ■ in the pattern

(b) Use the pattern to find the product.
$(-4)(+6) = $ ■

$(+3)(+6) = $ ■
$(+2)(+6) = $ ■
$(+1)(+6) = $ ■
$(0)(+6) = $ ■
$(-1)(+6) = $ ■
$(-2)(+6) = $ ■
$(-3)(+6) = $ ■

9 Use the pattern to find the missing values of ■. Write the next two lines of the pattern.

(a) $(+4)(+2) = $ ■   (b) $(+2)(+5) = $ ■
$(+4)(+1) = $ ■ $(+1)(+5) = $ ■
$(+4)(0) = $ ■ $(0)(+5) = $ ■
$(+4)(-1) = $ ■ $(-1)(+5) = $ ■
$(+4)(-2) = $ ■ $(-2)(+5) = $ ■
$(+4)(-3) = $ ■ $(-3)(+5) = $ ■
        ?   ?
        ?   ?

10 Use a pattern to help you find each product.

(a) $(+2)(-4)$ (b) $(+2)(-6)$

(c) $(+2)(-8)$ (d) $(+2)(-5)$

B

11 Study each pattern carefully. Find the missing values of ■.

(a) $(+2)(+4) = $ ■   (b) $(+3)(+2) = $ ■
$(+2)(+3) = $ ■ $(+2)(+2) = $ ■
$(+2)$ (■) $ = +4$ $(+1)$ (■) $ = +2$
$(+2)$ (■) $ = +2$ (0) (■) $ = $ 0
$(+2)(0) = $ ■ $(-1)(+2) = $ ■
$(+2)(-1) = $ ■   (■) $(+2) = -4$
$(+2)(-2) = -4$ (■) $(+2) = -6$
(■) (■) $ = $ ■   (■) (■) $ = $ ■

(c) $(+4)(+3) = $ ■   (d) $(+2)(+1) = $ ■
$(+3)$ (■) $ = +9$ $(+2)(0) = $ ■
$(+2)$ (■) $ = +6$ $(+2)$ (■) $ = -2$
$(+1)(+3) = $ ■ $(+2)$ (■) $ = -4$
$(0)(+3) = $ ■ $(+2)(-3) = $ ■
(■) $(+3) = -3$ $(+2)(-4) = $ ■
$(-2)(+3) = $ ■   (■) $(-5) = -10$
(■) $(+3) = -9$ (■) $(-6) = -12$
(■) (■) $ = $ ■   (■) (■) $ = $ ■

12 Find the following products. Use a pattern to help you.

(a) $(+3)(-2)$ (b) $(+4)(-2)$ (c) $(-3)(+2)$

(d) $(-4)(+1)$ (e) $(+6)(-2)$ (f) $(-2)(+4)$

13 Use the pattern to find the values of ■.

(a) $(+3)(+2) = +6$ (b) $(+2)(+3) = +6$
    $(+3)(+1) = +3$ $(+1)(+3) = +3$
    $(+3)(0)\ \ = ■$ $(0)(+3) = ■$
    $(+3)(-1) = ■$ $(-1)(+3) = ■$
    $(+3)(-2) = ■$ $(-2)(+3) = ■$

(c) From (a) and (b) what appears to be true about the following products?

$(+3)(-2)\quad (-2)(+3)$

14 The product of integers is commutative.

Namely, $(+3)(-2) = (-2)(+3)$

equal to -6 equal to -6

Find these products.

(a) $(+3)(+4)$ (b) $(+4)(+3)$ (c) $(+6)(-3)$

(d) $(-3)(+6)$ (e) $(-2)(+4)$ (f) $(+4)(-2)$

(g) $(+3)(-3)$ (h) $(+3)(-6)$ (i) $(-6)(+3)$

(j) $(-3)(+2)$ (k) $(+2)(-3)$ (l) $(+4)(-4)$

(m) $(-4)(+4)$ (n) $(-5)(+4)$ (o) $(+4)(-5)$

15 Calculate.

(a) $(-3)(+6)$ (b) $(-9)(+2)$ (c) $(+3)(-6)$

(d) $(+3)(-4)$ (e) $(+6)(-8)$ (f) $(-8)(+2)$

(g) $(-5)(+2)$ (h) $(+5)(-4)$ (i) $(+5)(-6)$

(j) $(+2)(-8)$ (k) $(-2)(+7)$ (l) $(-3)(+4)$

16 Jean found the following products.
$(-3)(+6) = -18$ $(-12)(+3) = -36$
$(+9)(-3) = -27$ $(+8)(-4) = -32$

(a) What do you notice about the above products? Are they positive or negative?

(b) What can you always tell about the product of a negative integer and a positive integer?

(c) What can you always tell about the product of a positive integer and a negative integer?

(d) Use the above examples. Decide on a method to help you find products quickly.

17 Find these products.

(a) $(+2)(+8)$ (b) $(-3)(+6)$ (c) $(+7)(-5)$

(d) $(-2)(+4)$ (e) $(-4)(+2)$ (f) $(+2)(-1)$

(g) $(+3)(-3)$ (h) $(+2)(-8)$ (i) $(-9)(+3)$

(j) $(+4)(+2)$ (k) $(-2)(+3)$ (l) $(+3)(-4)$

(m) $(+5)(-1)$ (n) $(+5)(-5)$ (o) $(+10)(+5)$

(p) $(-2)(+2)$ (q) $(+3)(-6)$ (r) $(-2)(+8)$

(s) $(+6)(+3)$ (t) $(+6)(-1)$ (u) $(-4)(+7)$

C

18 Copy and complete each sentence. What is the missing word?

(a) The product of a positive integer and a positive integer is a ▨ integer.

(b) The product of a positive integer and a negative integer is a ▨ integer.

(c) The product of a negative integer and a ▨ integer is a negative integer.

(d) The product of a ▨ integer and a negative integer is a negative integer.

(e) The product of a negative integer and a positive integer is a ▨ integer.

problem-solving: research

To solve some problems you need to do some research to obtain the needed information to answer the problem.

Look in any book and you will find an ISBN number.
International Standard Book Numbering

What is the significance of how this number is constructed?
ISBN 0-17-601728-3

using another strategy

In the study of mathematics, you can often use different strategies to learn and understand a skill. For example, in this section you used two methods to find products of integers.

$(+3)(-2) = -6$

Think:
$(-2) + (-2) + (-2) = -6$

$(+3)(-2) = -6$

Think:
$(+3)(+2) = +6$
$(+3)(+1) = +3$
$(+3)(0) = 0$
$(+3)(-1) = -3$
$(+3)(-2) = -6$

You can also use a number line to help you find products of integers.

Refer to the number line. The product of integers is shown on the number line.

$(+3)(-2) = -6$

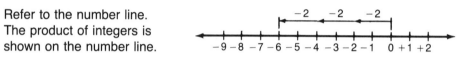

---

19 Write a suitable multiplication sentence for each number line. Find the product.

(a)

(b)
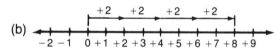

(c)
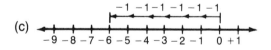

(d)
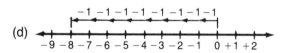

(e)
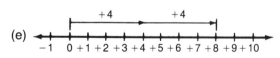

(f)
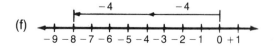

(g)
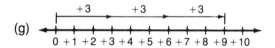

(h)
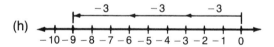

20 Use a number line. Show each product on the number line.

(a) $(+4)(+2)$ (b) $(+2)(-2)$ (c) $(+3)(-4)$

(d) $(+2)(+3)$ (e) $(+3)(-2)$ (f) $(+4)(-3)$

21 Find each product.

(a) $(+2)(+2)$ (b) $(+2)(-3)$ (c) $(+2)(-4)$

(d) $(-3)(+2)$ (e) $(+2)(-5)$ (f) $(+2)(-6)$

(g) $(-3)(+3)$ (h) $(+4)(+5)$ (i) $(-2)(+2)$

(j) $(+3)(-4)$ (k) $(-5)(+2)$ (l) $(+4)(-3)$

10.2 more multiplication patterns: integers

In the previous section you found the products of positive and negative integers and two positive integers.

$$(+3)(-2) = -6$$

positive   negative   negative
product

$$(-3)(+4) = -12$$

negative   positive   negative
product

$$(+3)(+4) = +12$$

positive   positive   positive
product

But what is the answer for the product of two negative integers? For example, what are the missing values of ■?

$$(-2) \times (-3) = ■ \qquad (-3) \times (-3) = ■$$

Once again you can use a pattern to help you find the answer. Look at the pattern to the right.

From the pattern,

$$(-2) \times (-3) = +6$$

and $(-3) \times (-3) = +9$

negative   negative   positive
integer   integer   product

$$(+3) \times (-3) = -9$$
$$(+2) \times (-3) = -6$$
$$(+1) \times (-3) = -3$$
$$0 \times (-3) = 0$$
$$(-1) \times (-3) = +3$$
$$(-2) \times (-3) = +6$$
$$(-3) \times (-3) = +9$$

The integers decrease by 1

The products increase by 3

Thus, it appears that:

> The product of a negative integer and a negative integer is a positive integer.

$$\left(\begin{array}{c}\text{a negative}\\\text{integer}\end{array}\right) \times \left(\begin{array}{c}\text{a negative}\\\text{integer}\end{array}\right) = \left(\begin{array}{c}\text{a positive}\\\text{integer}\end{array}\right)$$

10.2 exercise

A (Patterns are useful to help you find answers.

1 (a) Find the values of ■ for the pattern.

  (b) Use the pattern to find the product.

$$(-3)(-2) = ■$$

$$(+2)(-2) = -4$$
$$(+1)(-2) = ■$$
$$(0)(-2) = ■$$
$$(-1)(-2) = ■$$
$$(-2)(-2) = ■$$
$$(-3)(-2) = ■$$

2 (a) Find the values of ■ for the pattern.

  (b) Use the pattern to find the product.

$$(-3)(-3) = ■$$

$$(+3)(-3) = -9$$
$$(+2)(-3) = -6$$
$$(+1)(-3) = ■$$
$$(0)(-3) = ■$$
$$(-1)(-3) = ■$$
$$(-2)(-3) = ■$$
$$(-3)(-3) = ■$$

3 (a) Find the values of
      ■ for the pattern.

      (b) Use the pattern to
          find the product.

          $(-4)(-2) = $ ■

$(-4)(+4) = -16$
$(-4)(+3) = -12$
$(-4)(+2) = $ ■
$(-4)(+1) = $ ■
$(-4)(0)\ \ = $ ■
$(-4)(-1) = $ ■
$(-4)(-2) = $ ■

(b) What can you tell about the product of a
     negative integer and a negative integer?

8 Find these products.

   (a) $(-3)(-4)$ (b) $(-2)(-5)$ (c) $(-3)(-5)$

   (d) $(-6)(-3)$ (e) $(-5)(-4)$ (f) $(-7)(-2)$

   (g) $(-2)(-8)$ (h) $(-7)(-3)$ (i) $(-3)(-9)$

   (j) $(-4)(-8)$ (k) $(-5)(-5)$ (l) $(-3)(-8)$

   (m) $(-7)(-5)$ (n) $(-6)(-5)$ (o) $(-6)(-6)$

4 Use the pattern to find the missing values of ■.
   Complete the next two lines of the pattern.

   (a) $(+3)(-5) = $ ■   (b) $(-4)(+2) = $ ■
       $(+2)(-5) = $ ■ (-4) (■) $= -4$
       $(+1)$ (■) $= -5$ $(-4)(0)\ \ = $ ■
       (■) $(-5) = 0$ (■) $(-1) = +4$
       $(-1)(-5) = $ ■ $(-4)(-2) = $ ■

9 What is the missing word for each of the
   following? Use negative or positive.

   ▶ The product of a negative integer and a
     positive integer is always ▭ .

   ▶ The product of a negative integer and a
     negative integer is always ▭ .

5 Decide on a pattern to help you find each of the
   following products.

   (a) $(-3)(-2)$ (b) $(-4)(-3)$ (c) $(-2)(-3)$

   (d) $(-3)(-5)$ (e) $(-4)(-5)$ (f) $(-4)(-2)$

   (g) $(-7)(-2)$ (h) $(-1)(-8)$ (i) $(-6)(-2)$

10 For each question, use the pattern in the
    previous question to help you decide first
    whether your product is positive or negative.
    Then write the answer.

    (a) $(-3)(+5)$ (b) $(+6)(+2)$ (c) $(+3)(+8)$

    (d) $(-3)(+6)$ (e) $(-2)(-3)$ (f) $(-2)(+9)$

    (g) $(-6)(-7)$ (h) $(-1)(-1)$ (i) $(-3)(+8)$

    (j) $(+6)(-3)$ (k) $(+4)(+8)$ (l) $(+11)(+6)$

    (m) $(-3)(-4)$ (n) $(+3)(-4)$ (o) $(-5)(-2)$

B

6 Study each pattern carefully. Find the missing
   values of ■.

   (a) $(-3)(+1) = -3$ (b) $(-5)(+3) = -15$
       $(-3)(0)\ \ = $ ■ $(-5)(+2) = $ ■
       $(-3)(-1) = $ ■ $(-5)(+1) = $ ■
       $(-3)(-2) = $ ■ $(-5)(0)\ \ = $ ■
       $(-3)(-3) = $ ■ $(-5)(-1) = $ ■
       $(-3)(-4) = $ ■ $(-5)(-2) = $ ■
       $(-3)(-5) = $ ■ $(-5)(-3) = $ ■

C

11 Find the following products. Then arrange the
    products in order from least to greatest. By
    matching each answer to the letter of the
    question, you will find the answer to the
    question: What is one of the best-selling
    record albums to date?

7 By completing patterns, George found these
   products.

       $(-3)(-6) = +18$ $(-12)(-3) = +36$
       $(-9)(-3) = +27$ $(-8)(-4) = +32$

   (a) What do you notice about the above
        answers? Are they positive or negative?

A $(+6)(-3)$ N $(-2)(-1)$ T $(-4)(-3)$

F $(+4)(+4)$ E $(-3)(-6)$ U $(-5)(+3)$

G $(-2)(-4)$ S $(-2)(+10)$ H $(+2)(+5)$

T $(-4)(+4)$ R $(-5)(-5)$ V $(+10)(+2)$

D $(-4)(+2)$ Y $(+1)(0)$ E $(-4)(-6)$

R $(+3)(-4)$ A $(-3)(+1)$ I $(+3)(+2)$

10.3 practising skills: integers

To learn a skill, you must first understand how to find the answer.
Then you look for a pattern to help you.

$(+2)(+3) = +6$ $(+3)(+4) = +12$
$(-2)(+3) = -6$ $(-3)(+4) = -12$
$(+2)(-3) = -6$ $(+3)(-4) = -12$
$(-2)(-3) = +6$ $(-3)(-4) = +12$

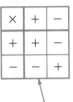

This means when you multiply a
positive integer by a negative integer,
you obtain a negative product.

After you have found the products of integers, you begin to see a
pattern. For example, from the products of the integers shown,
you can make up a table to show the sign of a product of two
integers.

Example 1   Use the table to help you find each product.

(a) $(+2)(+3)$ (b) $(+2)(-3)$

(c) $(-2)(+3)$ (d) $(-2)(-3)$

Think:

Solution   (a) $(+2)(+3) = +6$ $\begin{pmatrix} \text{positive} \\ \text{integer} \end{pmatrix} \times \begin{pmatrix} \text{positive} \\ \text{integer} \end{pmatrix} = \begin{pmatrix} \text{positive} \\ \text{integer} \end{pmatrix}$

(b) $(+2)(-3) = -6$ $\begin{pmatrix} \text{positive} \\ \text{integer} \end{pmatrix} \times \begin{pmatrix} \text{negative} \\ \text{integer} \end{pmatrix} = \begin{pmatrix} \text{negative} \\ \text{integer} \end{pmatrix}$

(c) $(-2)(+3) = -6$ $\begin{pmatrix} \text{negative} \\ \text{integer} \end{pmatrix} \times \begin{pmatrix} \text{positive} \\ \text{integer} \end{pmatrix} = \begin{pmatrix} \text{negative} \\ \text{integer} \end{pmatrix}$

(d) $(-2)(-3) = +6$ $\begin{pmatrix} \text{negative} \\ \text{integer} \end{pmatrix} \times \begin{pmatrix} \text{negative} \\ \text{integer} \end{pmatrix} = \begin{pmatrix} \text{positive} \\ \text{integer} \end{pmatrix}$

Skills with multiplying integers are used in many ways, such as
evaluating expressions.

Example 2   Find the value of each expression for $k = -2$.

(a) $3k - 2$ (b) $k^2 + 3$

Solution   (a) $3k - 2$ (b) $k^2 + 3$ Record the
       $= 3(-2) - 2$ $= (-2)^2 + 3$ original expression
       $= -6 - 2$ $= (-2)(-2) + 3$ as the first step
       $= -8$ $= 4 + 3$ of your solution.
                  $= 7$

10.3 exercise

A

1 For each of the following products, decide whether the answer is positive, negative, or zero.

(a) $(+2)(-1)$ (b) $(-2)(-3)$ (c) $(+3)(+3)$

(d) $(-3)(+6)$ (e) $(-2)(0)$ (f) $(-4)(+6)$

(g) $(0)(+4)$ (h) $(-2)(-5)$ (i) $(+3)(0)$

(j) $(+4)(-6)$ (k) $(-6)(+5)$ (l) $(-3)(-8)$

2 Find the following products. Compare the signs in column A and column B. What do you notice?

A	B
$(-1)(-4)$	$(-1)(+4)$
$(-2)(-6)$	$(-2)(+6)$
$(-3)(-8)$	$(-3)(+8)$
$(-4)(-10)$	$(-4)(+10)$

3 To find the product of integers, first decide on the sign of the product. Then find each product.

(a) $(-3)(+2)$ (b) $(+3)(0)$ (c) $(-6)(-1)$

(d) $(0)(+4)$ (e) $(-2)(-3)$ (f) $(+6)(-2)$

(g) $(+3)(-5)$ (h) $(-2)(-4)$ (i) $(-5)(0)$

4 Find each product. Which products are zero?

(a) $(-3)(+2)$ (b) $(+2)(+3)$ (c) $(-6)(-3)$

(d) $(0)(-8)$ (e) $(-4)(+3)$ (f) $(+8)(0)$

(g) $(+8)(-8)$ (h) $(0)(+3)$ (i) $(-7)(-2)$

(j) $(-6)(0)$ (k) $(-8)(-5)$ (l) $(0)(+6)$

5 Find the products.

(a) $(-1)(+3)$ (b) $(-3)(-2)$ (c) $(+3)(+6)$

(d) $(-4)(+3)$ (e) $(+4)(+3)$ (f) $(-2)(-6)$

(g) $(-4)(-3)$ (h) $(+4)(-1)$ (i) $(-3)(+4)$

(j) $(+3)(-6)$ (k) $(-2)(-2)$ (l) $(-3)(+22)$

(m) $(+6)(-1)$ (n) $(-16)(+4)$ (o) $(0)(+5)$

6 Remember, $(+4)(-3)$ can be written as $4(-3)$. Find each product.

(a) $3(-2)$ (b) $-6(-3)$ (c) $-3(-4)$

(d) $5(-2)$ (e) $-2(-3)$ (f) $9(-6)$

(g) $-8(-3)$ (h) $-6(0)$ (i) $9(-3)$

7 Copy and complete each table.

(a)

×	−2	4	0
3	?	?	?
−2	?	?	0
−4	?	?	?

To find this answer, find the product $(-2)(0) = 0$

(b)

×	4	−3	−5
−3	?	?	?
0	?	?	?
2	?	?	?

(c)

×	−3	0	4
−6	?	?	?
−3	?	?	?
0	?	?	?

8 Copy and complete each chart.

(a)

m	+2	−2	−4	−3	−2	+5	−3
n	+3	+3	−2	+6	+6	−4	−7
$m \times n$	?	?	?	?	?	?	?

(b)

a	−3	+4	0	−6	+6	−6	−3
b	−4	−3	−3	−2	−2	0	−4
ab	?	?	?	?	?	?	?

ab means $a \times b$

B

9 Find the products. Which answers are the same?

(a) $(+8)(+2)$ (b) $(-3)(-6)$ (c) $(-4)(-4)$

(d) $(-3)(+4)$ (e) $(-2)(-8)$ (f) $(-4)(+5)$

10 Find the products. Which answers are the same?

(a) $(-3)(-4)$ (b) $(-4)(+4)$ (c) $(-2)(+7)$

(d) $(+6)(-3)$ (e) $(-6)(-2)$ (f) $(+2)(-6)$

11 Find the products. Write your answers in order from least to greatest.

(a) $-3(-2)$ (b) $-4(+5)$ (c) $8(-3)$

(d) $4(-6)$ (e) $6(-2)$ (f) $-8(0)$

12 To find the products of more than two integers, first find the product of two of them.

$$(-3)(-2)(+2) \qquad (+3)(-2)(-2)$$
$$= \quad (+6)(+2) \qquad = \quad (-6)(-2)$$
$$= \quad +12 \qquad = \quad +12$$

Find the products.

(a) $(-6)(-2)(+2)$ (b) $(+3)(-2)(-6)$

(c) $(+4)(+3)(-2)$ (d) $(-6)(+6)(-3)$

(e) $(-3)(-2)(-19)$ (f) $(+5)(-2)(+18)$

(g) $(-7)(+6)(-2)$ (h) $(-18)(+12)(+9)$

(i) $(-40)(-3)(-11)$ (j) $(-4)(+6)(+19)$

(k) $(-8)(-6)(-13)$ (l) $(-16)(+3)(-21)$

(m) $(+9)(-46)(-23)$ (n) $(-6)(+4)(-7)$

(o) $(+6)(-3)(+2)$ (p) $(-9)(-3)(-1)$

13 (a) Find the value of $3m$ if $m = -2$.

Remember $3m$
means $3 \times m$

(b) Find the value of $2m$ if $m = -3$.

(c) Find the value of m^2 if $m = -3$.

14 (a) Find the value of $3t + 2$ if $t = -3$.

(b) Find the value of $4m + 6$ if $m = -2$.

(c) Find the value of $3k - 4$ if $k = -2$.

(d) Find the value of $6k - 2$ if $k = -1$.

15 (a) Find the value of $-2m + 3$ if $m = -4$.

(b) Find the value of $-4k - 3$ if $k = -2$.

(c) Find the value of $-6k + 6$ if $k = 0$.

16 Copy and complete the table below.

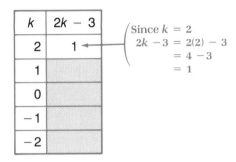

k	$2k - 3$
2	1
1	
0	
-1	
-2	

Since $k = 2$
$2k - 3 = 2(2) - 3$
$= 4 - 3$
$= 1$

17 Copy and complete the following tables.

(a)

p	$3p - 2$
$+2$	
$+1$	
0	
-1	

(b)

p	$-2p + 3$
$+2$	
$+1$	
0	
-1	

(c)

p	$-4p - 2$
$+1$	
0	
-1	
-2	

(d)

p	p^2
$+1$	
0	
-1	
-2	

18 Evaluate these number expressions. The value for each variable is given.

(a) $3m + 4$, $m = -1$ (b) $6y - 3$, $y = -4$

(c) $-3k + 5$, $k = -2$ (d) $p^2 + 3$, $p = -4$

(e) $k^2 - 4$, $k = -2$ (f) $-5x + 4$, $x = -3$

(g) $b + b$, $b = -1$ (h) $k + k + k$, $k = -3$

10.4 patterns for learning: dividing integers

To develop and apply skills in mathematics, you often follow these
steps.

Step A	Step B	Step C	Step D
Do examples to understand the skill.	Look for patterns to help you.	Practise the skill to gain accuracy and speed.	Apply the skill to solve problems.

▶ To develop your skills for multiplying integers, you followed the
above steps.

▶ To develop your skills for dividing integers, you follow the same
steps.

If you know how to find these products of integers,
you can apply these skills to learn to divide integers.

$$(+2)(+3) = +6 \qquad (+4)(-3) = -12 \qquad (-6)(+3) = -18 \qquad (-5)(-6) = +30$$

means   means   means   means

$$\frac{+6}{+3} = +2 \qquad \frac{-12}{-3} = +4 \qquad \frac{-18}{+3} = -6 \qquad \frac{+30}{-6} = -5$$

Thus, to find the answers for dividing integers, you only need to
think of a related multiplication question.

Example 1   Use your skills with multiplication to find each of
the following.

(a) $(-18) \div (+3)$ (b) $(-24) \div (-6)$

Solution   (a) $(-18) \div (+3) = \blacksquare$ means $(\blacksquare)(+3) = -18$

Thus, $(-18) \div (+3) = -6$ ← What number multiplied by
$(+3)$ gives -18?
$\blacksquare = -6$

(b) $(-24) \div (-6) = \blacksquare$ means $(\blacksquare)(-6) = -24$

Thus, $(-24) \div (-6) = +4$ ← What number multiplied by
(-6) gives -24?
$\blacksquare = +4$

By finding these answers, you can see a pattern to dividing integers.

Use your calculator to try other numbers.

$$\frac{+6}{+3} = +2 \qquad \frac{-6}{+3} = -2 \qquad \frac{+6}{-3} = -2 \qquad \frac{-6}{-3} = +2$$

$$\frac{+12}{+4} = +3 \qquad \frac{-12}{+4} = -3 \qquad \frac{+12}{-4} = -3 \qquad \frac{-12}{-4} = +3$$

The chart shows the pattern to find the sign when dividing by integers.

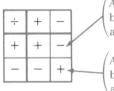

÷	+	−
+	+	−
−	−	+

A positive integer divided by a negative integer is a negative integer.

A negative integer divided by a negative integer is a positive integer.

Example 2   Find the value of $h \div (-3)$ for

(a) $h = +9$ (b) $h = -9$ (c) $h = 0$

Solution

(a) Use $h = +9$
$h \div (-3)$
$= (+9) \div (-3)$
$= -3$

$\Big($ A positive integer divided by a negative integer is negative $\Big)$

(b) Use $h = -9$
$h \div (-3)$
$= (-9) \div (-3)$
$= +3$

$\Big($ A negative integer divided by a negative integer is positive. $\Big)$

(c) Use $h = 0$
$h \div (-3)$
$= 0 \div (-3)$
$= 0$

$\Big($ Zero divided by any integer is zero. $\Big)$

10.4 exercise

A Remember, to learn to divide integers, you can use your skills with multiplying integers.

1 Copy and complete the chart. Find the missing values.

	Multiplication	Division
(a)	$(+6)(+3) = +18$ →	$(+18) \div (+3) = ?$
(b)	$(-6)(+3) = -18$ →	?
(c)	$(+6)(-3) = -18$ →	?
(d)	$(-6)(-3) = +18$ →	?

2 Copy and complete the chart. Find the missing values.

	Division	Related multiplication
(a)	$\frac{+18}{+3} = ?$	$(?)(+3) = +18$
(b)	$\frac{-25}{+5} = ?$	$(?)(+5) = -25$
(c)	$\frac{+36}{-6} = ?$	?
(d)	$\frac{-48}{-8} = ?$	?

3 What are the missing values?

Multiplication

(a) $(+4)(-3) = -12$ $\rightarrow$ $\frac{-12}{-3} = \blacksquare$

(b) $(-3)(+6) = -18$ $\rightarrow$ $\frac{-18}{+6} = \blacksquare$

(c) $(-2)(-3) = +6$ $\rightarrow$ $\frac{+6}{-3} = \blacksquare$

(d) $(+3)(+6) = +18$ $\rightarrow$ $\frac{+18}{+6} = \blacksquare$

Division

4 Henrietta wrote these answers to the following quotients.

$$\frac{+6}{+2} = +3 \qquad \frac{+12}{-3} = -4$$

$$\frac{-12}{+4} = -3 \qquad \frac{-12}{-4} = +3$$

(a) When are her answers negative?

(b) When are her answers positive?

(c) Decide on a rule to tell when the sign is positive or negative.

5 Find these quotients.

(a) $(+48) \div (-6)$ (b) $(-48) \div (-6)$

(c) $(-48) \div (+6)$ (d) $\frac{+54}{+9}$

(e) $\frac{-54}{-9}$ (f) $\frac{-54}{+9}$

6 For each of the following, decide first whether the answer is positive, negative, or zero. Then calculate.

(a) $(-20) \div (+4)$ (b) $(+15) \div (-3)$

(c) $\frac{+15}{-5}$ (d) $\frac{-45}{-5}$

(e) $\frac{-18}{+3}$ (f) $\frac{0}{+2}$

(g) $\frac{-30}{-6}$ (h) $(0) \div (-5)$

7 For each of the following:
▶ Decide first whether your answer is positive or negative.
▶ Then write your answer.

(a) $\frac{-25}{+5}$ (b) $\frac{-36}{+9}$ (c) $\frac{-49}{-7}$

(d) $\frac{+54}{-9}$ (e) $\frac{-66}{-6}$ (f) $\frac{+25}{-5}$

(g) $\frac{+36}{-6}$ (h) $\frac{+49}{+7}$ (i) $\frac{-54}{-9}$

(j) $\frac{+100}{-10}$ (k) $\frac{-75}{-15}$ (l) $\frac{-36}{+4}$

(m) $\frac{-24}{-6}$ (n) $\frac{+36}{-4}$ (o) $\frac{-100}{+10}$

(p) $\frac{+75}{-5}$ (q) $\frac{+66}{-11}$ (r) $\frac{-80}{+4}$

8 Copy and complete each sentence

(a) The quotient of a positive integer and a positive integer is a $\blacksquare$ integer.

(b) The quotient of a negative integer and a negative integer is a $\blacksquare$ integer.

(c) The quotient of a negative integer and a positive integer is a $\blacksquare$ integer.

(d) The quotient of a positive integer and a negative integer is a $\blacksquare$ integer.

Check whether your answer is reasonable.

B

9 Find the following quotients.

(a) $(+10) \div (-2)$ (b) $(-15) \div (+5)$

(c) $(-36) \div (-12)$ (d) $(+15) \div (-3)$

(e) $0 \div (+10)$ (f) $(-49) \div (+7)$

(g) $(+64) \div (-8)$ (h) $(+72) \div (-9)$

(i) $(-60) \div (+10)$ (j) $(+36) \div (-3)$

(k) $(+90) \div (-10)$ (l) $0 \div (-2)$

(m) $(+50) \div (-25)$ (n) $(-121) \div (-11)$

(o) $(-150) \div (-15)$ (p) $(+144) \div (-12)$

10 Find each answer.

(a) $\dfrac{+20}{-2}$ (b) $(+72) \div (+6)$

(c) $\dfrac{-45}{+9}$ (d) $\dfrac{+54}{-6}$

(e) $\dfrac{-45}{-9}$ (f) $(-20) \div (-4)$

(g) $\dfrac{-100}{+10}$ (h) $(-64) \div (-8)$

(i) $(+66) \div (-11)$ (j) $(-72) \div (-6)$

(k) $\dfrac{+28}{-4}$ (l) $\dfrac{-60}{+6}$

(m) $(-20) \div (-5)$ (n) $\dfrac{-28}{-7}$

11 Copy and complete each chart.

(a)

s	$+8$	-12	0	$+16$	-21	0	-36
t	-4	-6	-3	-4	-7	$+6$	$+12$
$\dfrac{s}{t}$	?	?	?	?	?	?	?

(b)

a	-12	-9	?	-60	?	-80	-49
b	-2	?	$+4$	?	-3	?	-7
$a \div b$	?	$+3$	-2	$+12$	-8	$+20$	?

12 Calculate. Which answers are the same?

(a) $\dfrac{-36}{+6}$ (b) $\dfrac{+49}{-7}$ (c) $\dfrac{-36}{-12}$ (d) $\dfrac{-12}{+2}$

(e) $\dfrac{+25}{-5}$ (f) $\dfrac{0}{-3}$ (g) $\dfrac{+18}{-3}$ (h) $\dfrac{+48}{-6}$

13 Calculate. Write your answers in order from greatest to least.

(a) $\dfrac{+49}{-7}$ (b) $\dfrac{-36}{+12}$ (c) $\dfrac{-9}{-3}$

(d) $\dfrac{+28}{+4}$ (e) $\dfrac{0}{-25}$ (f) $\dfrac{+35}{-7}$

14 Use $m = -3$. Find the value of each of the following.

(a) $m \div (-3)$ (b) $(+24) \div m$

(c) $\dfrac{m}{-1}$ (d) $\dfrac{-36}{m}$

15 (a) Find the value of $b \div (-3)$ if $b = -12$.

(b) Find the value of $y \div (-4)$ if $y = +24$.

(c) Find the value of $p \div (-2)$ if $p = -6$.

16 Find the value of ■ in each of the following.

(a) $(-25) \div ■ = +5$ (b) $(-36) \div ■ = +6$
(c) $■ \times (-4) = -20$ (d) $(-36) \div (-6) = ■$
(e) $(-8) \times ■ = +24$ (f) $(-36) \div (-12) = ■$
(g) $■ \times (-6) = +36$ (h) $(-9) \times ■ = +45$
(i) $(-54) \div (+9) = ■$ (j) $■ \div (-6) = +9$
(k) $(-8) \times (-4) = ■$ (l) $(-3) \times (+8) = ■$
(m) $(-36) \div ■ = -2$ (n) $■ \div (-4) = -12$
(o) $(-54) \div ■ = -2$ (p) $■ \times (-9) = +27$

C

17 Do you know the answer to the following question?
   Which mammal has the lowest blood temperature?
To find the answer, you need to find the missing values. Then arrange the answers from least to greatest. The variables give you the answer.

(a) $(+36) \div n = -4$ (b) $(-24) \div t = +6$
(c) $p \div (-2) = +8$ (d) $y \times (-3) = +24$
(e) $(+60) \div n = -12$ (f) $t \times (-6) = -36$
(g) $(-10) \div (-2) = a$ (h) $(-36) \div a = +6$
(i) $e \times (-3) = -27$ (j) $(+65) \div i = -5$
(k) $r \div (-3) = -12$ (l) $(+2) \times s = -36$
(m) $(-36) \div (-12) = e$

10.5 order of operations: integers

In your earlier work with numbers, you followed certain rules for the order of operations. Similarly, for working with integers, you follow the same rules for the order of operations.

Example 1   Calculate.

(a) $-3 \times [15 + (-3)]$

(b) $-3^2 \times 5 - [-15 + (-3)]$

Solution

(a) $-3 \times [15 + (-3)]$ (Brackets first.
$$= -3 \times 12$$ (Multiply.
$$= -36$$

(b) $-3^2 \times 5 - [-15 + (-3)]$
$$= -3^2 \times 5 - (-18)$$ (Brackets first. Calculate powers.
$$= -9 \times 5 - (-18)$$ (Multiply.
$$= -45 - (-18)$$ (Subtract.
$$= -45 + 18$$
$$= -27$$

The rules for the order of operations apply when you substitute integers and evaluate expressions.

Example 2   Calculate $2p^2 - 3p$. Use $p = -2$.

Solution

$2p^2 - 3p$ ⎛Record the original
$= 2(-2)^2 - 3(-2)$ ⎝expression; then substitute.
$= 2(+4) - 3(-2)$ (Calculate powers. Multiply.
$= 8 - (-6)$
$= 8 + 6$ Check whether your
$= 14$ answer is reasonable.

10.5 exercise

A

1 Evaluate these number expressions.

(a) $(-4) + 16 \div (-4)$ (b) $[(-4) + 16] \div (-4)$

(c) $(-8) \times (-9) + 5$ (d) $(-8) \times [(-9) + 5]$

(e) $(-8) \div (-4) + 2$ (f) $(-8) \div [(-4) + 2]$

(g) $(-8) - [(-4) \div 2]$ (h) $[(-8) - (-4)] \div 2$

2 Calculate. Why are your answers different?

(a) $(-36) \div [(-6) \div (-6)]$

(b) $[(-36) \div (-6)] \div (-6)$

3 Calculate. Why are your answers the same?

(a) $(-36) + [(-6) + (-6)]$

(b) $[(-36) + (-6)] + (-6)$

4 Calculate. Why are your answers different?

(a) $(-36) - (-25)$ (b) $(-25) - (-36)$

5 Copy and complete the following chart.

g	-36	-24	?	-100	-12	-42
h	$+6$	?	$+48$	?	?	?
$g + h$	?	-20	?	?	?	?
$g - h$	?	?	-144	?	?	?
$g \times h$	?	?	?	?	$+48$	?
$g \div h$	?	?	?	-10	?	-6

6 Copy and complete the following chart.

m	-36	$+18$	-25	-14	-64	$+72$
n	-6	-9	?	?	$+8$	?
$m \times n$	?	?	?	$+98$	?	?
$m \div n$	?	?	-5	?	?	-8

7 Find the square of each of the following.

(a) -3 (b) 6 (c) -4 (d) -10

(e) -12 (f) 91 (g) -36 (h) -1

8 (a) Find the value of $(-3)^2$

(b) Find the value of -3^2

(c) Why are the results in (a) and (b) different?

9 Calculate.

(a) $(-2)^2$ (b) $(-4)^2$ (c) $(+4)^2$

(d) $(-5)^2$ (e) $(-2)^3$ (f) $(-3)^3$

(g) $(-2)^2(-3)$ (h) $(-3)^2(-2)$ (i) $(-2)(-4)^2$

(j) $(-2)^2(-1)^2$ (k) $(-3)^2(-2)^2$ (l) $(-4)^2(-2)^2$

10 Calculate. (Remember: -3^2 means $-(3 \times 3)$ or -9.

(a) -2^2 (b) -1^2 (c) $(-3)(-4)$

(d) $(-3)^2$ (e) -3^2 (f) $(-1)^2$

11 Calculate.

(a) -2^2 (b) $(-2)^2$ (c) $(-6)^2$

(d) -6^2 (e) -4^2 (f) $(-4)^2$

(g) -5^2 (h) $(-5)^2$ (i) -2^3

(j) $(-2)^3$ (k) $(-3)^3$ (l) -4^3

B

12 Calculate. Remember the order of operations.

(a) $(-6) \times 3 - 2$

(b) $(-4) - 2 \times (-2)$

(c) $(-6) + (-12) \div (-2)$

(d) $(-6) \times (-3) \div 9$

(e) $[(-9) + 1] \div (-4)$

(f) $(-3)(-7) + 2$

(g) $(-15) \div [(-3) - 2]$

(h) $[(-8) - 3] + 5$

(i) $36 - (-3)[(-5) - 1]$

13 Follow the instructions in the flow chart.

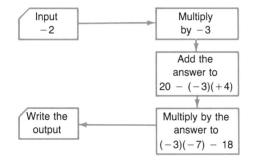

14 Calculate.

(a) $25 - 4^2$ (b) $25 - (-4)^2$

(c) $(-2)^2 - 6$ (d) $(-8)^2 + 9$

(e) $(-2)^2 - (-5)^2$ (f) $4^2 - (-3)^2$

(g) $8^2 - 7^2$ (h) $5^2 - 3^2 - 4^2$

(i) $(-5)^2 - 3^2 - (-4)^2$ (j) $0 - 6^2$

(k) $2(-4)^2 + 8$ (l) $3(-2)^2 - 2(-3)^2$

(What operation is understood here?)

15 Try these!

(a) $(-6) \times (-8) \div 2 + 36$

(b) $(-12) + 8 - 6 \div 3 + 2 \times (-3)$

(c) $(-8) \div (-4) + (-6) \div (-2)$

(d) $(-8) - [(-6) - 3] - [(-2) + 6]$

(e) $\dfrac{-8 - 36}{-11}$

(f) $\dfrac{-10 - 32}{-3}$

(g) $\dfrac{(-8) + (-4)}{(-8) - (-4)}$

(h) $\dfrac{-56 + 21}{(-5)(-7)}$

16 To win a trip to the Canada Cup finals, a contestant needed to answer a skill-testing question. What was the answer?

Step 1 Calculate. $\dfrac{-2 + (-32)(-4)}{(-3)(-2)(-7)}$

Step 2 Add the answer in Step 1 to the answer for $\dfrac{(-25) \div (-5) - (-10)}{(-3)(+5)}$

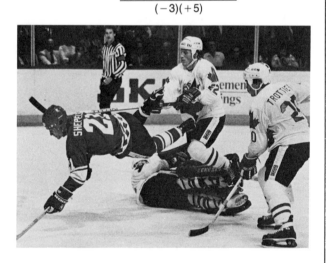

17 (a) The seventh Fibonacci number is given by the answer to the following calculation.

$$\dfrac{(+6)(-12) + (-2)(+16)}{(-4)(+2)}$$

(b) The famous Fibonacci numbers are given by the pattern 1, 1, 2, 3, 5, 8, . . .
You found the seventh number in (a). What is the eighth Fibonacci number?

18 (a) Find the values of $h \div (-6) + 6$ if $h \in \{-12, -24, -36\}$.

(b) Find the values of $(-24) \div y$ if $y \in \{-3, -4, -6, -8\}$.

(c) Find the values of $k \div (-2) - 3$ if $k \in \{-16, -8, 0, +8, +16\}$.

19 Evaluate the following number expressions.

(a) $b \div (-3), b = -9$

(b) $2y \div (-3), y = -9$

(c) $-3k - 4, k = -1$

(d) $m^2, m = -4$

(e) $m^2 \div 5, m = -5$

(f) $y^2 \div 3, y = -3$

(g) $(m + 2) \div (-2), m = -4$

(h) $(2m - 1) \div (-3), m = -4$

(i) $(3m + 2) \div 10, m = -4$

20 Calculate each expression if $y = -4$.

(a) $-3y^2$

(b) $(-3y)^2$

(c) $-(3y^2)$

(d) $-(3y)^2$

Which answers are the same? Why?
Which answers are different? Why?

21 Find the value of each number expression. The value of the variable is given.

(a) $5y^2, y = -2$

(b) $25 - x^2, x = -3$

(c) $a^2 - 6, a = -3$

(d) $b^2 - 12, b = -4$

(e) $-p^2, p = -2$

(f) $-y^2, y = -6$

(g) $-3y^2, y = -3$

(h) $-2k^2, k = -3$

C

22 Arrange the expressions in order of value from the least to the greatest, if
$$q = -3 \qquad t = -1 \qquad f = 2$$

(a) $q^2 - 5t$

(b) $t^2 - 3q$

(c) $t^2 - fq$

(d) $fq + 3t$

language of mathematics

To do mathematics, you often use charts to summarize patterns and skills.
The charts shown are helpful in finding the sign for the quotient or product of integers.

Multiplication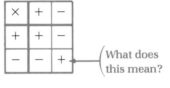

To do mathematics, you must not only know the language precisely, but you must also follow instructions exactly.
The questions that follow give you practice with important words in the language of mathematics.

Division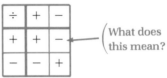

For the following questions first decide on the operations you will use, then find the answer.

23 (a) Add -4 to the sum of -7 and 8.

(b) Divide the product of -8 and -3 by 4.

(c) Subtract -8 from -10.

(d) Divide the sum of -11, 13, and -3 by -1.

(e) Multiply the sum of -7 and -8 by -3.

24 (a) Add 126 to the sum of -96 and 199.

(b) Subtract -23 from 96.

(c) Find the sum of -48, 96, -23, and -79.

(d) Subtract the sum of -29 and 36 from 45.

25 (a) Which number is divisible by -3?

-2986 4132 -1191 9145

(b) Which of the following numbers are not divisible by -8?

$-22\,924$ $-12\,140$ $84\,963$ $-19\,696$

26 (a) Subtract -396 from the sum of 648 and -971.

(b) Subtract the sum of -432 and 416 from -96.

27 (a) The sum of -8, -7, and ■ is 23. Find ■.

(b) The sum of -3, 6, and ■ is -12. Find ■.

(c) Subtract the sum of 12 and -19 from -23.

(d) Add the sum of -234 and -231 to the sum of 496 and -875.

28 (a) Subtract -936 from the sum of 1981 and -321.

(b) Add the square of -2 to the square of 5.

(c) Subtract the square of -3 from the square of -5.

29 (a) When $-36 + 18$ is divided by ■, the answer is $+2$. Find the value of ■.

(b) When $-16 + $ ■ is divided by $+2$, the answer is 1. Find the value of ■.

(c) When 14 is subtracted from the sum of -23 and ■, the answer is 8. Find the value of ■.

(d) When 12 is subtracted from the sum of -19 and ■, the answer is -6. Find the value of ■.

10.6 problem-solving: reading carefully

To solve any problem, you must read the information given in the problem carefully. To translate the information into mathematics, you need to understand the meaning of all the words. Often a clue word in the question will suggest how to do the calculation. You have seen this list before.

Addition is suggested by		Subtraction is suggested by		Multiplication is suggested by		Division is suggested by	
add	plus	difference	reduce	multiply	times	divide	left
total	total	less	deduct	product	doubled	quotient	each
together	gain	minus	fewer	square of	tripled	remainder	shared
increased by	and	decreased by	exceed			average	

Example   Increase the product of the numbers -2 and $+3$ by the sum of -3, $+4$, and $+8$.

Solution   Product is $(-2)(+3) = -6$.
Sum is $(-3) + (+4) + (+8) = +9$
Increase the product by the sum
   $(-6) + (+9) = +3$
The answer is $+3$.

Think:

Product suggests multiplication.
Increase suggests addition.
Sum suggests addition.

10.6 exercise

A

1 Match each written phrase with the suitable expression A, B, C, ...

   (a) -6 increased by -2 A $-2 - (-6)$

   (b) -6 decreased by -2 B $(-6)(-2)$

   (c) product of -6 and -2 C $-6 + (-2)$

   (d) -2 decreased by -6 D $-6 \div (-2)$

   (e) -6 divided by -2 E $-6 - (-2)$

2 Write an expression for each of the following. Then find the value.

   (a) Increase -4 by $+5$.

   (b) Find the sum of -2, -3, and -4.

   (c) Find the difference of -4, subtracted from $+6$.

   (d) Find the product of -4 and $+3$.

   (e) Subtract $+3$ from $+1$.

   (f) Divide -18 by $+3$.

   (g) Find the quotient of -21 divided by -7.

   (h) Add -4 to the sum of -2 and $+5$.

   (i) Subtract $+4$ from -3.

   (j) How much more is -3 than -8?

3 For each of the following:
▶ First write an expression using the symbols
  $+, -, \times, \div$.
▶ Then calculate.

(a) From the sum of -4 and $+3$, subtract $+7$.

(b) Subtract -4 from the sum of -3 and -6.

(c) Increase the product of -4 and -5 by -6.

(d) Divide the sum of -7 and $+15$ by -4.

(e) Increase the product of -2 and -5 by $+3$.

(f) Subtract the sum of -4 and -2 from $+5$.

B

4 Translate each of the following. The first one is done for you.

(a) $(-3)(-4) +2$ $\left(\begin{array}{l}\text{Add 2 to the product}\\ \text{of } -3 \text{ and } -4.\end{array}\right)$

(b) $(+6)(-3) -3$ (c) $(-6)(+8) \div 4$

(d) $16 \div (-2) + (-6)$ (e) $(-2)^2 + (-3)(-4)$

(f) $[(-6) + (-8)] \div 2$ (g) $(-3)^2 + (-2)^2 + 6$

(h) $8 - (-2)(-4)$ (i) $(-2)(-7) + 35$

5 To be accurate you must read instructions carefully. Do each of the following steps.
Step 1 Find the sum of -6 and -8.

Step 2 Square the answer in Step 1 and decrease it by -3.

Step 3 Add the answer in Step 2 to the quotient of -16 divided by -4.

Step 4 Decrease the answer in Step 3 by the product of -2 and 6.

Step 5 Multiply the answer in Step 4 by -6 and decrease it by the sum of $-3, -4$, and $+6$.
What is your final answer?

6 Find the sum of the answers for each of Step A to F.
A Subtract -15 from 6 then divide by -7.

B Find the product of -4 and $+3$ then divide by -12.

C By how much does the product of -4 and -3 exceed the product of -4 and $+3$?

D How much greater is -5 than the product of -2 and $+7$?

E By how much does the square of -3 exceed the quotient of -16 divided by 8?

F The sum of the differences $3 - 2$, $6 - 10$, and $9 - 6$ is divided by the product of $(-6)(-8)(-12)(-16)(-18)(-36)(-48)(-21)$

7 Each letter, A, B, C, . . . represents the answer for the calculation. When all calculations are done, find the answer F.

A Subtract 4 from the product of -3 and $+4$.

B To the product of 8 and -3, add -18.

C Decrease the square of -3 by the sum of -3 and $+4$.

D Divide the product of -12 and 3 by -6.

E Subtract -6 from 12 and divide the result by 3.

F To find the final answer F, read carefully. Add your answers in A and B to the product of your answers in C and D. From this result subtract the square of your answer in E. The final answer is F.
$\left(\begin{array}{l}\text{If your answer is correct}\\ \text{you win a free trip to}\\ \text{Erehwon, spelled backwards.}\end{array}\right)$

C

8 Try these tongue twisters. Read carefully!

(a) Add the quotient of $-25 \div (-5)$ to the product of the quotients $-6 \div (-3)$ and $8 \div (-4)$.

(b) Increase the square of -6 by the product of the products $(-3)(-2)$ and $(-4)(2)$.

(c) Decrease the square of -4 by the products of the squares of $(-3)^2$ and $(-1)^2$.

(d) Increase the square of the difference $6 - 8$ by the quotient of the sum $-8 + 6$ divided by the product $(-2)(+1)$.

10.7 applications with scientific notation

Did you know that our sun is really only an average-size star? It is called a yellow dwarf, the most common type of star observed by astronomers. Another group of stars you all know is the Big Dipper.

When working with facts about the solar system, often very large numbers are used. For example:

▶ The average or mean distance from the earth to the sun is about 150 000 000 km. To travel this distance you would need to go around the earth about 1900 times.

▶ The greatest distance from the planet Pluto to the sun is about 7 323 180 000 km. To travel this distance you would need to make about 25 round trips to the sun. (Or, how many trips around the earth would you need to take?)

Scientists also deal with facts about extremely small things. For example:

▶ The average diameter of a poliomyelitis virus is 0.000 025 mm.

▶ The average length of bacteria is 0.0015 mm.

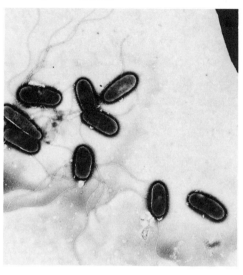

The virus in the photograph are enlarged 12 000 times. They are called escherichia colibacteria and are the normal inhabitants of your intestines.

To write very large numbers or very small numbers in a compact way, scientific notation is used. In scientific notation, the powers of 10 and integers are used in a special way. You need to learn the powers of 10 shown in the chart.

To write 150 000 000 in scientific notation, write:

$$150\ 000\ 000$$
$$= 1.5 \times 100\ 000\ 000$$
$$= 1.5 \times 10^8 \longleftarrow \left(\begin{array}{l} \text{Powers of} \\ \text{10 are used.} \end{array} \right.$$

$\left(\begin{array}{l} \text{This number is always} \\ \text{between 1 and 10.} \end{array} \right.$

To write 0.000 025 in scientific notation, write:

$$0.000\ 025$$
$$= 2.5 \times 0.000\ 01$$
$$= 2.5 \times 10^{-5} \longleftarrow \left(\begin{array}{l} \text{Read as ten to the} \\ \text{exponent negative five.} \end{array} \right.$$

$\left(\begin{array}{l} \text{Remember, this number is} \\ \text{between 1 and 10.} \end{array} \right.$

10^9	1 000 000 000	
10^8	100 000 000	
10^7	10 000 000	Compare the exponent with the number of zeros or the number of decimal places.
10^6	1 000 000	
10^5	100 000	
10^4	10 000	
10^3	1 000	
10^2	100	
10^1	10	
10^0	means	1
10^{-1}	means	0.1 or $\frac{1}{10}$
10^{-2}	means	0.01 or $\frac{1}{100}$
10^{-3}	means	0.001 or $\frac{1}{1000}$
10^{-4}	means	0.000 1 or $\frac{1}{10\ 000}$
10^{-5}	means	0.000 01 or $\frac{1}{100\ 000}$

Example   Write each number in scientific notation.

(a) 3 820 000   (b) 0.000 462

Solution

(a)   3 820 000
     = 3.82 × 1 000 000
     = 3.8 × 10^6

(b)   0.000 462
     = 4.62 × 0.0001
     = 4.62 × 10^{-4}

Powers of 10 also enable you to write decimal numerals in expanded form. The expanded form shows how decimals are constructed. For example:

42.98 ←————(standard form

= 4 × 10 + 2 × 1 + 9 × 0.1 + 8 × 0.01   } expanded
= 4 × 10^1 + 2 × 10^0 + 9 × 10^{-1} + 8 × 10^{-2} } forms

10.7 exercise

A

1 Write each as a power of 10.

(a) 100   (b) 1000   (c) 100 000

(d) 10   (e) 10 000   (f) 1 000 000

2 Write as a power of 10.

(a) 0.1   (b) 0.01   (c) 0.001

(d) 0.0001   (e) 0.000 01   (f) 0.000 001

3 To write a power, you can use integers.

$$\frac{1}{1000} = \frac{1}{10^3} = 10^{-3}$$

Express each of the following as a power of ten. Use negative integers as exponents.

(a) $\frac{1}{10^2}$ (b) $\frac{1}{10^3}$ (c) $\frac{1}{10^4}$

(d) $\frac{1}{10^5}$ (e) $\frac{1}{10^6}$ (f) $\frac{1}{10^7}$

(g) $\frac{1}{1000}$ (h) $\frac{1}{100}$ (i) $\frac{1}{10\,000}$

4 Study this pattern. Find the missing values.

(a)	$\frac{1}{10}$	0.1	10^{-1}
(b)	$\frac{1}{100}$	0.01	10^{-2}
(c)	$\frac{1}{1000}$	0.001	
(d)		0.0001	
(e)	$\frac{1}{100\,000}$		
(f)			10^{-6}
(g)			10^{-7}

5 Write each of the following using powers of 10.

(a) 0.1   (b) 10   (c) 0.01

(d) 1000   (e) 0.0001   (f) 100

(g) 0.000 01   (h) 0.001   (i) 10 000

(j) 10 000 000   (k) 0.000 000 01

6 Express each of the following as a number between 1 and 10 and a power of ten. The first one is done for you.

(a) 125 $\left(125 = 1.25 \times 100 = 1.25 \times 10^2\right.$

(b) 12.5   (c) 823   (d) 82.3

(e) 927   (f) 92.7   (g) 92.71

(h) 927.1   (i) 912.7   (j) 9271

7 Express each of the following as a number between 1 and 10 and a power of ten. The first one is done for you.

(a) 0.125 $\left(0.125 = 1.25 \times 0.1 = 1.25 \times 10^{-1}\right.$

(b) 0.73   (c) 0.073   (d) 0.0073

(e) 0.148   (f) 0.0148   (g) 0.001 48

(h) 0.1   (i) 0.001   (j) 0.01

8 (a) How many zeros are there when 10^4 is written in standard form?

(b) How many zeros are there when 10^5, 10^6, and 10^7 are written in standard form?

(c) How many zeros are there when 10^{100} and 10^{101} are written in standard form?

B

9 Write each number in scientific notation.

(a) 46 000   (b) 96 000 000

(c) 2 000 000   (d) 486 000

(e) 396 000 000   (f) 186 000 000 000

(g) 481 000 000 000 000 000 000

10 Each number is shown in scientific notation. Write each as a decimal in standard form.

(a) 3×10^4 (b) 3.2×10^4

(c) 4.6×10^8 (d) 3.9×10^5

(e) 6.15×10^5 (f) 6.93×10^3

(g) 4.25×10^6 (h) 9.69×10^8

11 Write each number in scientific notation.

(a) 0.003   (b) 0.0005   (c) 0.0045

(d) 0.000 61   (e) 0.000 02   (f) 0.000 083

12 Each number is shown in scientific notation. Write each as a decimal in standard form.

(a) 3.1×10^{-1} (b) 2.6×10^{-2}

(c) 3.81×10^{-1} (d) 4.69×10^{-2}

(e) 8.2×10^{-3} (f) 9.63×10^{-4}

13 Write the number in each sentence in scientific notation.

(a) The farthest distance the earth is from the sun is about 152 000 000 km.

(b) The closest distance the earth is from the sun is about 147 000 000 km.

(c) The event occurred in 0.0004 s.

(d) There are 604 800 s in a week.

(e) The metric prefix micro means to multiply by 0.000 001.

(f) The diameter of a virus is 0.000 003 cm.

(g) The van can hold about 1 610 000 beans.

14 The display on the calculator shows a number in scientific notation

● What do each of these displays mean on a calculator?

● How would you read each display in words?

(a) | 6.98   12 | (b) | 3.89   15 | (c) | 1.26   −03 |

(d) | 9.86   −08 | (e) | 7.32   07 | (f) | 8.08   23 |

problem-solving: puzzler

Michael has 2 containers, A and B. Container B holds twice as much as container A.

A is $\frac{1}{2}$ filled and B is $\frac{1}{3}$ filled with a syrup. The rest of each container he fills with water. He then pours the contents of both containers A and B into a third container. What fraction of the total contents is water?

10.8 signed numbers: rationals

You saw earlier that you could compare, add, or subtract rational numbers. To do so, you used your skills for working with fractions or decimal fractions as well as your skills for working with integers.

Example 1 Find each product.

(a) $-\frac{3}{4} \times 1\frac{5}{6}$ (b) $-1.5 \times (-2.7)$

Solution

(a) $-\frac{3}{4} \times 1\frac{5}{6}$

$= -\frac{3}{4} \times \frac{11}{6}$

$= \frac{-11}{8}$

$= -1\frac{3}{8}$

(b) $-1.5 \times (-2.7)$
$= + (1.5 \times 2.7)$
$= 4.05$

Skills with substitution can also be applied when the numbers to be substituted are rational numbers.

Example 2 Find the value of each expression.

(a) $2a + 3$, if $a = -\frac{3}{4}$ (b) $x - 2y$, if $x = 3.2$ and $y = -1.3$

Solution

(a) $2a + 3$

$= 2\left(-\frac{3}{4}\right) + 3$

$= \frac{2}{1}\left(-\frac{3}{4}\right) + 3$

$= \frac{-6}{4} + 3$

$= -1\frac{2}{4} + 3$

$= -1\frac{1}{2} + 3$

$= 1\frac{1}{2}$

(b) $x - 2y$
$= 3.2 - 2(-1.3)$
$= 3.2 + 2.6$
$= 5.8$

Check whether your answer is reasonable.

10.8 exercise

A

1 Calculate.

(a) $4.7 + (-1.3)$ (b) $-6.8 - 3.2$

(c) $-2.5 + 2.2$ (d) $-4.6 + (-2.1)$

(e) $-2\frac{9}{10} - 1\frac{3}{10}$ (f) $1\frac{1}{3} - \left(-2\frac{1}{4}\right)$

(g) $4 - \left(-1\frac{3}{4}\right)$ (h) $-8 + \left(-1\frac{3}{4}\right)$

2 For each of the following:
  ▶ Decide whether the product is positive or negative.
  ▶ Then do the calculation.

(a) $-\frac{1}{5} \times \frac{3}{4}$

(b) $\left(-\frac{3}{8}\right) \times \left(-\frac{4}{5}\right)$

(c) $\frac{5}{8} \times \left(-\frac{1}{2}\right)$

(d) $\left(-\frac{1}{3}\right) \times \left(-\frac{3}{5}\right)$

(e) 3×2.1

(f) $6.4 \times (-2)$

(g) $-6.3 \times (4.6)$

(h) $5.2 \times (-0.5)$

3 For each of the following:
  ▶ Decide whether the quotient is positive or negative.
  ▶ Then do the calculation.

(a) $3 \div \left(-\frac{1}{4}\right)$

(b) $\left(-\frac{1}{3}\right) \div \frac{2}{3}$

(c) $-\frac{3}{2} \div \left(-\frac{1}{2}\right)$

(d) $-4 \div \left(-\frac{4}{3}\right)$

(e) $-1.2 \div 0.2$

(f) $-5.2 \div (-1.3)$

(g) $\frac{4.5}{-1.5}$

(h) $\frac{7.2}{0.8}$

B

4 Find each product. Arrange the answers in order from least to greatest.

(a) $3\frac{3}{4} \times 1\frac{3}{5}$

(b) $-1\frac{7}{10} \times \left(-2\frac{2}{3}\right)$

(c) $\frac{-5}{12} \times \left(\frac{-3}{20}\right)$

(d) $\frac{-4}{5} \times 3$

5 Find each product. Arrange the answers in order from greatest to least.

(a) 0.03×2.4

(b) $(-4.6) \times (-0.22)$

(c) $-16.7 \times (-0.06)$

(d) -0.025×15

6 Find each quotient.

(a) $1\frac{1}{3} \div \frac{9}{10}$

(b) $4 \div \left(-\frac{2}{3}\right)$

(c) $-2\frac{1}{2} \div \left(-1\frac{7}{8}\right)$

(d) $\frac{3}{10} \div \left(-5\frac{1}{4}\right)$

(e) $-6\frac{1}{3} \div 2$

(f) $3\frac{3}{4} \div \left(-1\frac{3}{10}\right)$

7 Find each quotient.

(a) $3.6 \div (-0.3)$

(b) $\frac{-1.2}{4}$

(c) $-0.16 \div (-0.2)$

(d) $4.8 \div (0.08)$

(e) $\frac{51.5}{-0.5}$

(f) $-10.4 \div (-1.3)$

8 Calculate. Watch the signs!

(a) $\frac{1}{4} \div \left(-2\frac{2}{5}\right)$

(b) 0.8×1.5

(c) $-2\frac{1}{4} \times 1\frac{2}{3}$

(d) $-3\frac{1}{3} \div \left(\frac{-5}{8}\right)$

(e) $\frac{24}{-0.2}$

(f) $-1.8 \div 2.5$

9 Find the value of each of the following. Use $m = 4.5$ and $n = -3.2$.

(a) $m + n$

(b) $m - n$

(c) $3m - 3.2$

(d) $4n + 6.8$

(e) $2m - n$

(f) $m - 2n$

10 Evaluate each expression if $a = -\frac{1}{2}$ and $b = \frac{3}{4}$.

(a) $a + b$

(b) $a - b$

(c) $2a$

(d) ab

(e) a^2

(f) $2b - a$

11 Find the value of each expression if $t = \frac{1}{4}$ and $w = -1\frac{1}{2}$.

(a) $5t$

(b) tw

(c) $2t + w$

(d) $\frac{w}{t}$

(e) $w^2 - t$

(f) $t + \frac{1}{2}w$

C

12 The rate, r, of fuel consumption of a certain type of car is given by
$$r = -\frac{42}{5}h + \frac{33}{2}$$
where h is the fraction of driving done on the highway.

Find r for each value of h.

(a) $h = \frac{1}{4}$

(b) $h = \frac{2}{3}$

(c) $h = \frac{1}{2}$

10.9 co-ordinates and integers

You saw earlier how the position of a point on the number plane (grid) can be shown by an ordered pair of numbers.

By using a horizontal number line and a vertical number line intersecting at 0, you can extend your work to find points shown by ordered pairs of positive or negative numbers.

A diagram of the number plane is shown. The point where the two number lines intersect is called the origin (0). Each ordered pair names a point on the number plane. The ordered pair (4,5) names the point A.

The co-ordinates of A are (4,5).

The co-ordinates of point B are

The co-ordinates of A are (4,5).

Example　(a) What are the co-ordinates of C?

　　　　　　(b) What are the co-ordinates of D?

Solution　(a) The co-ordinates of C are $(-4, -5)$.

　　　　　　(b) The co-ordinates of D are $(4, -5)$.

Often the axes are given special names.

| horizontal axis | x-axis |
| vertical axis | y-axis |

When these names are used for the axes, the ordered pairs are written using these symbols.

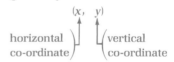

Special words are used to refer to parts of the plane. For example, the number plane is divided into four quadrants. The quadrants are named as shown.

The number plane is often referred to as the Cartesian plane, named in honour of the mathematician René Descartes. His use of the Cartesian plane opened up many new areas of study.

The exercise that follows develops your skill in using the Cartesian plane, with integers as co-ordinates.

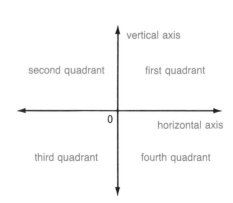

10.9 exercise

Throughout this exercise, use squared paper to draw the number planes.

A Questions 1 to 3 refer to the following diagram.

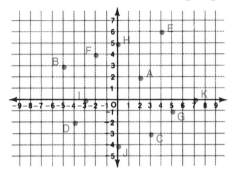

1 Each of the following ordered pairs names a point. Use a letter to name the point shown by each ordered pair.

(a) (2,2)   (b) (−2,4)   (c) (5,−1)

(d) (−4,−2)   (e) (4,6)   (f) (7,0)

(g) (0,−4)   (h) (−3,0)   (i) (0,5)

2 Which point has the following co-ordinate?
(a) vertical co-ordinate 4
(b) horizontal co-ordinate −4
(c) vertical co-ordinate 5
(d) horizontal co-ordinate −2

3 Each ordered pair has a co-ordinate missing. These ordered pairs name points on the number plane above. Find the missing value.

(a) (−5,■)   (b) (■,−3)   (c) (2,■)

(d) (■,5)   (e) (−4,■)   (f) (−3,■)

(g) (7,■)   (h) (0,■)   (i) (■,0)

4 (a) What are the co-ordinates of the origin?

(b) In which quadrant does the ordered pair (3,−2) name a point?

(c) In which quadrant does the ordered pair (−2,3) name a point?

(d) Why do your answers differ for (b) and (c)?

5 Refer to the following diagram. Answer the questions.

(a) Name a point which is 2 units above the horizontal axis. What are its co-ordinates?

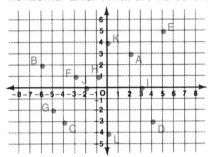

(b) Name a point which is 3 units to the right of the vertical axis. What are its co-ordinates?

(c) Name a point which is 2 units below the horizontal axis and 5 units to the left of the vertical axis. What are its co-ordinates?

(d) How would you describe the position of the labelled point at C?

(e) Use co-ordinates to describe the position of each of these points?
A   D   E   F   H   J   K   L

B

6 Draw a number plane. Locate each of the following ordered pairs on the number plane.

(a) (6,−4)   (b) (3,2)   (c) (−3,2)

(d) (3,−2)   (e) (−6,4)   (f) (6,4)

(g) (−6,−4)   (h) (−3,−2)   (i) (0,0)

7 Draw a number plane.

(a) Plot these points. ⎛Plot means to locate
                          ⎝and label.

A(4,−4)   B(−4,−4)   D(4,4)   C(−4,4)

(b) Draw the following line segments.
AB   BC   CD   DA

(c) What geometric figure have you drawn in (b)?

8 These ordered pairs represent some geometric figure.

$$A(-3,3) \quad B(6,3) \quad C(1,-2) \quad D(-8,-2)$$

(a) Join the points in order.

(b) What geometric figure have you drawn?

9 These ordered pairs represent a geometric figure.

$$A(-8,-2) \quad B(-5,4) \quad C(3,4) \quad D(5,-2)$$

(a) Join the points in order.

(b) What geometric figure have you drawn?

10 The co-ordinates of three of the vertices of the square KLMN are given.

$$K(-2,3) \qquad L(-7,3) \qquad M(-7,-2)$$

What are the co-ordinates of N?

11 The co-ordinates of three of the vertices of rectangle RSTU are given.

$$R(6,2) \qquad S(6,-4) \qquad T(-4,-4)$$

What are the co-ordinates of U?

12 Name the quadrant in which each ordered pair is located.

(a) (4,8)   (b) $(-3,-2\frac{1}{2})$ (c) $(2\frac{1}{2},-3)$

(d) $(-4.5,3)$ (e) (2.5,2.5)   (f) $(3\frac{1}{2},2\frac{1}{2})$

(g) $(-3.5,-3.5)$ (h) $(-2\frac{1}{4},2\frac{1}{2})$ (i) (14,12)

13 A letter is drawn by joining the points on a number plane.

Join $(-6,-2)$ to $(-6,4)$.
Join $(-3,4)$ to $(-3,-2)$.
Join $(-6,1)$ to $(-3,1)$.

What letter of the alphabet have you formed?

14 (a) Use the number plane you drew in the previous question. Follow these instructions. What word have you made?

Join $(-1,-2)$ to $(1,4)$.
Join $(1,4)$ to $(3,-2)$.
Join $(0,1)$ to $(2,1)$.
} (These line segments represent a letter.)

Join $(4,4)$ to $(8,4)$.
Join $(6,4)$ to $(6,-2)$.
} (These line segments represent a letter.)

(b) Use the method in (a). Create a word of your own. Provide the instructions needed to construct the word.

15 (a) Use the number plane. Follow these instructions. What figure have you drawn?

▶ Join $(-2,2)$ to $(2,2)$ to $(2,-2)$ to $(-2,-2)$ to $(-2,2)$

▶ Join $(-3,3)$ to $(3,3)$ to $(3,-3)$ to $(-3,-3)$ to $(-3,3)$.

(b) Use the method in (a). Create a diagram of your own. Provide the instructions needed to construct the diagram.

C

16 The following ordered pairs are used to make a message. To decode the message, draw a number plane. Find each letter of the message. Follow these instructions.

▶ Join $(-6,7)$ to $(-4,7)$ to $(-4,3)$.
Join $(-4,3)$ to $(-6,3)$ to $(-6,7)$.
▶ Join $(8,3)$ to $(9,-1)$ to $(9.5,1)$.
Join $(9.5,1)$ to $(10,-1)$ to $(11,3)$.
▶ Join $(6,0)$ to $(4,0)$ to $(4,4)$.
Join $(4,4)$ to $(6,4)$ to $(6,0)$.
▶ Join $(13,-2)$ to $(13,2)$ to $(15,-2)$.
Join $(15,-2)$ to $(15,2)$.
▶ Join $(0,5)$ to $(1,5)$ to $(2,4)$ to $(2,2)$.
Join $(2,2)$ to $(1,1)$ to $(0,1)$ to $(0,5)$.
▶ Join $(-8,8)$ to $(-10,8)$ to $(-10,4)$.
Join $(-10,4)$ to $(-8,4)$ to $(-8,6)$.
Join $(-8,6)$ to $(-9,6)$.

17 Use the method in the previous question to create a message of your own. Exchange your message with another student. Can your message be decoded?

10.10 problem-solving: using patterns

Often in mathematics, new strategies are discovered and used to solve problems in different ways. For example, you can easily find the following sum of integers. But, can you find it by looking for a pattern?

$$1 + (-2) + 3 + (-4) + 5 + (-6) + 7 + (-8) + 9 + (-10) + 11 + (-12)$$

To find a pattern, add fewer numbers at first.

$1 + (-2) = -1$
$1 + (-2) + 3 = +2$
$1 + (-2) + 3 + (-4) = -2$
$1 + (-2) + 3 + (-4) + 5 = +3$
$1 + (-2) + 3 + (-4) + 5 + (-6) = -3$ and so on.

Think!
Do you see a pattern
in the answers?

Using the above pattern, you can now find the sum.

$$1 + (-2) + 3 + (-4) + 5 + (-6) + 7 + (-8) + 9 + (-10) + 11 + (-12) = -6$$

10.10 exercise

1 Use the previous pattern to find each sum.

(a) $1 + (-2) + 3 + \ldots + (-12) + 13 + (-14)$

(b) $1 + (-2) + 3 + \ldots + (-22) + 23 + (-24)$

(c) $1 + (-2) + 3 + \ldots + 27 + (-28) + 29$

2 (a) Copy and complete the following pattern.

$(-1) + 2 = ?$
$(-1) + 2 + (-3) = ?$
$(-1) + 2 + (-3) + 4 = ?$
$(-1) + 2 + (-3) + 4 + (-5) = ?$
$(-1) + 2 + (-3) + 4 + (-5) + 6 = ?$

(b) Use the pattern in (a) to find the sum.
$(-1) + 2 + (-3) + \ldots + (-11) + 12$

3 Copy and complete the following patterns.

(a) $(-1)(-1) = ?$
$(-1)(-1)(-1) = ?$
$(-1)(-1)(-1)(-1) = ?$
$(-1)(-1)(-1)(-1)(-1) = ?$

(b) $(-2)(-2) = ?$
$(-2)(-2)(-2) = ?$
$(-2)(-2)(-2)(-2) = ?$
$(-2)(-2)(-2)(-2)(-2) = ?$

4 Use the patterns from the previous question. Which of the following will be negative or positive?

(a) $(-1)^{36}$ (b) $(-2)^7$ (c) $(-2)^4$

(d) $(-1)^{100}$ (e) $(-1)^{89}$ (f) $(-2)^8$

5 (a) Copy and complete the following pattern.

$(-3)^1 = ?$
$(-3)^2 = ?$
$(-3)^3 = ?$
$(-3)^4 = ?$
$(-3)^5 = ?$
$(-3)^6 = ?$

Think!
What pattern
do I see?

(b) Use the pattern in (a) to tell whether $(-3)^{25}$ will be negative or positive.

(c) Use the pattern in (a). Predict what the last digit in the answer to $(-3)^{20}$ will be?

practice and problems: a chapter review

(10.1) 1 Find each product.

    (a) $(+3)(+4)$ (b) $(-2)(+8)$ (c) $(+5)(-6)$

(10.2) 2 (a) What is the missing word? The product of a negative integer and a negative integer is a ▨▨▨ integer.

    (b) Find each product.
        (i) $(+5)(-2)$ (ii) $(+3)(-4)$ (iii) $(-7)(+1)$
        (iv) $(-9)(-9)$ (v) $(-3)(-2)$ (vi) $(-5)(+6)$

(10.3) 3 Find each value if $m = -3$ and $t = +4$.

    (a) $-3m + 4$ (b) $2t - m$ (c) $m^2 + t^2$

(10.4) 4 Calculate.

    (a) $(+6) \div (+3)$ (b) $(-6) \div (+6)$

    (c) $(+8) \div (-2)$ (d) $(-8) \div (-4)$

    (e) $(+16) \div (-8)$ (f) $(-16) \div (-2)$

5 Find the missing values of ▨.

    (a) $18 \div ▨ = -6$

    (b) $-12 \div (-2) = ▨$

    (c) $(▨) \div (-3) = -4$

    (d) $(-18) \div (▨) = +3$

(10.5) 6 Evaluate.

    (a) $(-5) + (-12) \div (+3)$

    (b) $[(+8) - (-7)] \div (-5)$

    (c) $(+8)(-3) \div (-6)$

    (d) $(-8) \div (+4)(-2)$

    (e) $(-2)^2 - (-3)$ (f) $(+5)^2 - (+4)^2$

(10.6) 7 (a) Subtract -3 from the sum of -5 and $+4$.

    (b) Add the square of -2 to the product of -5 and -4.

    (c) By how much does the product of -5 and -4 exceed the square of -3?

(10.7) 8 Express each number in scientific notation.

    (a) 63 000 (b) 391 000 000 (c) 0.000 036 41

    (d) The boiling point of gold is 2660°C.

    (e) Air contains 0.000 524% helium.

(10.8) 9 Calculate.

    (a) $\frac{-2}{3} + \frac{1}{3}$ (b) $\left(-1\frac{3}{5}\right) + \left(1\frac{1}{2}\right)$

    (c) $2.3 - (-3.5)$ (d) $\left(\frac{2}{-5}\right)\left(-1\frac{1}{4}\right)$

    (e) $-1\frac{7}{8} \div \frac{5}{16}$ (f) $(-2.3)(0.05)$

10 Plot the following on a number plane.

    (a) $(-3, 2)$ (b) $(5, 0)$ (c) $(2, -3)$

    (d) $(2, 3)$ (e) $(0, -2)$ (f) $(-5, -4)$

skills quiz

1 Calculate.

    (a) $(-3)(+2)$ (b) $(+3)(-3)$

    (c) $(-3)(-8)$ (d) $(-12) \div (+3)$

    (e) $(-16) \div (-4)$ (f) $(+18)(-6)$

    (g) $(-9)(-3)$ (h) $(-25) \div (+5)$

    (i) $(-96) \div (+12)$ (j) $(-26)(+2)$

    (k) $(+12)(-3)$ (l) $(+100) \div (-10)$

    (m) $(-225) \div (-25)$ (n) $(-9)(-9)$

    (o) $(-8)(+9)$ (p) $(+6)(-12)$

    (q) $(+144) \div (-6)$ (r) $(-60) \div (-10)$

2 Evaluate.

    (a) $(-3)(-4) \div (-2)$ (b) $(-8) \div (-4) + 2$

    (c) $\frac{-15 + 3}{-24}$ (d) $\frac{-10 - 38}{+12}$

    (e) $\frac{(-6) + (-3)(-8)}{(-12)(+5) \div (-4)}$ (f) $\frac{(-4)(+4) - (-4)(-4)}{(-3)(-2) + (-5)^2}$

test for practice

1 Calculate.

   (a) $(+2) + (-3)$ (b) $(-2) - (-1)$

   (c) $(-4) + (+6)$ (d) $(-5) - (-2)$

   (e) $(-2) + (+4) - (-3) + (-1)$

2 Complete the following sentences.

   (a) A positive integer divided by a ▓▓▓▓ integer is a negative integer.

   (b) The product of a ▓▓▓▓ integer and a positive integer is a negative integer.

3 Calculate.

   (a) $(-3)(+2)$ (b) $(+2)(-8)$

   (c) $(-4)(-5)$ (d) $(-18) \div (+6)$

   (e) $(-15) \div (-5)$ (f) $(+30) \div (-6)$

4 Calculate.

   (a) $(+5) + (-3) \div (-3)$

   (b) $(-6) - (-4)(+2)$ (c) $(-3)^2 + (-4)^2$

5 Write each number in scientific notation.

   (a) 37 000   (b) 1 380 000   (c) 0.000 0038

   (d) The longest golf course is 7300 m long.

   (e) The shortest earthworm is 0.0475 cm long.

6 Evaluate the following if $p = \frac{-3}{8}$ and $q = \frac{1}{2}$.

   (a) pq (b) $p \div q$ (c) $p^2q - q^2$

7 (a) Plot the points on a number plane.
     $A(-1, -1)$ $D(1, 4)$ $B(5, -1)$

   (b) What are the co-ordinates of C so that ABCD is a parallelogram?

8 (a) Copy and complete the pattern.
     $(+1) + (-3) = ?$
     $(+1) + (-3) + (+5) = ?$
     $(+1) + (-3) + (+5) + (-7) = ?$

   (b) What is the next row in the pattern?

maintaining skills: powers of 10

This exercise provides computation practice with 10's, 100's, and 1000's. *Try to do them mentally.*

   (a) 10×2.6 (b) $2 \div 100$

   (c) $\frac{1}{10} \times 4.9$ (d) 1000×4.98

   (e) 100×4.85 (f) $3.94 \div 10^2$

   (g) $1000 \div 100$ (h) 4.96×10

   (i) $10 \div 1000$ (j) $49.6 \div 10^2$

   (k) 2.96×100 (l) $10^3 \times 4.96$

   (m) $4.98 \div 10$ (n) $\frac{1}{100} \times 48.6$

   (o) $10^3 \times 4.33$ (p) 0.3×100

   (q) $\frac{1}{1000} \times 987.9$ (r) $4.86 \div 1000$

   (s) $14.2 \div 100$ (t) $149.6 \div 1000$

   (u) $0.3 \div 10^2$ (v) $28.6 \div 100$ (w) $0.1 \div 100$

   (x) $493 \div 10^3$ (y) 3.6×100 (z) 0.001×100

---

computer tip

You can use a computer to calculate values from a formula. What is the output of this program?

```
10   PRINT "TIME, DISTANCE, RATE"
20   INPUT R, T
30   LET D = R * T
40   PRINT "THE DISTANCE IS"; D
50   END
```

Write a BASIC program to calculate the time when the distance and speed are given.

---

math tip

List the mathematical symbols, words, and skills that you learned in this chapter. Give an example of each.

11 applications: geometries and their relations

Relations for geometric figures, triangles, parallel lines, numerical relations, graphs of relation, square roots from graphs, property of right triangles, transformations and co-ordinates, similar figures and size transformations, problem solving skills, solving problems and applications

No matter what field of study you decide to pursue, you will probably be asked to investigate relationships.

If you study transportation, you will be asked to investigate the traffic flow on major arteries, or at major intersections.

If you study animal medicine, you will be asked to investigate the similarities of the various types of illnesses and injuries of the animals you will need to serve.

In any investigation you do you will be asked to look for similarities and differences. In knowing similarities and differences, you can learn more easily large bodies of knowledge.

In this chapter, you will investigate various relations about geometric figures and apply them to solve problems. Remember, whether you solve problems about geometry, or number, you need to organize your steps for solving problems. Refer to the chart on the right.

Steps for Solving Problems

A Ask yourself:
  I *What information am I asked to find?*
  II *What information am I given?*
B Decide on a method.
  Which operation do I use?
C Do the work.
  Complete the calculation.
D Check your work.
  Use your rounding skills.
E Make a final statement.
  Answer the original problem.

11.1 problem-solving: using experiments about angle relations

To investigate the relations about numbers, you can use the skills you have learned about numbers, use calculators, use charts of values, use a computer, and so on.

To investigate relations about geometric figures, you can use your earlier contruction skills, as well as the skills you have learned about the figures. Some special relations exist among the angles of a figure.

In the exercise, you will investigate a number of relations about geometric figures. Make a summary of the relations you learn for later use.

Angle relations play an important role in construction.

GRENADA ½c

11.1 exercise

Investigation A: intersecting lines

1 In the following diagram, two lines intersect.

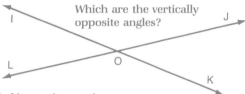

Which are the vertically opposite angles?

(a) Name the angles.

(b) Measure ∠IOJ and ∠LOK. How are ∠IOJ and ∠LOK related?

(c) Measure ∠IOL and ∠KOJ. How are these measures related?

2 (a) Draw any two intersecting lines and label the angles. Find the measures of vertically opposite angles as indicated in the previous question. How are the measures of the angles related?

(b) Repeat the steps in (a) for other pairs of intersecting lines.

3 Based on the results of the previous questions, what appears to be true about the measures of vertically opposite angles?

Investigation B: isosceles triangles

4 (a) Construct an isosceles △ABC so that AB = AC = 8.5 cm and ∠BAC = 40°.

(b) Measure the base angles ABC and ACB. What do you notice about your measures?

5 (a) Construct an isosceles triangle of your own choice.

(b) Measure the angles opposite the congruent sides. What do you notice about your measures?

6 Based on the results of the previous questions, what relation appears to be true about the measures of base angles of isosceles triangles?

Investigation C: equilateral triangles

7 (a) Construct an equilateral triangle of sides measuring 5 cm; measuring 8.5 cm.

(b) Measure the angles of each equilateral triangle. What do you notice?

8 (a) Construct an equilateral triangle of your own choice.

(b) Measure all the angles.

9 Based on the results of the previous questions, what relation appears to be true about the measure of the angles of an equilateral triangle?

Investigation D: sum of the angles of a triangle

10 (a) Draw any triangle.

(b) Measure the angles of your triangle. Record your answers in a chart.

(c) Find the sum of your measures.

(d) Round off your sum to the nearest 10°.

(e) Repeat steps (a) to (d) for other triangles.

11 Based on your results what relation appears to be true about the sum of the measures of the angles in any triangle?

Investigation E: angles of a quadrilateral

12 (a) Draw any quadrilateral.

(b) Measure the angles of your quadrilateral. Record your answers in a chart.

(c) Find the sum of your measures. Round your sum to the nearest 10°.

(d) Repeat steps (a) to (c) for other quadrilaterals. What do you notice about the sum of the angles each time? Test other quadrilaterals.

Investigation F: angles on the diameter

13 (a) In the circle, the diameter of the circle **subtends** an angle at the circumference. Measure ∠ABC in the diagram.

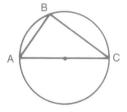

(b) Draw another circle with diameter AC = 8 cm. Choose any point B on the circumference. Measure ∠ABC.

(c) Repeat step (b) except choose B at different positions on the circumference. What do you notice about your answers each time?

Investigation G: quadrilaterals and circles

14 A quadrilateral is drawn in a circle so that each of its vertices is on the circumference of the circle.

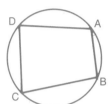

(a) Measure ∠DAB and ∠DCB. Find the sum of their measures. (Round off your answer to the nearest 10°.)

(b) Measure ∠ADC and ∠ABC. Find the sum of their measures. (Round off your answer to the nearest 10°.)

15 (a) Draw any circle with centre O.

(b) Draw any quadrilateral ABCD in the circle so that its vertices in order are on the circumference.

(c) Measure these pairs of angles:
▶ ∠DAB and ∠DCB   ▶ ∠ADC and ∠ABC

(d) Find the sum of each pair of angles in (c).

(e) Use your results. Write a conclusion about the angle sums of
▶ ∠A and ∠C   or   ▶ ∠B and ∠D
for any quadrilateral ABCD whose vertices in order are on the circumference of a circle.

16 (a) Make a summary of all the relations you have learned in the previous questions.

(b) Design an investigation to test the information given in the statement.
▶ In a rhombus, the diagonals are perpendicular.

problem-solving: "What if . . . ?" relations

Often a mathematician might ask "What if . . . ?" Often, in trying to answer the question other concepts and skills are discovered. In the questions that follow you are to answer the question "What if . . . ?" for relations about figures. You will need your construction tools.

17 "What if you draw all the bisectors of the angles of a triangle?"

   (a) Draw any acute triangle or obtuse triangle.

   (b) Bisect each angle of the triangle.

   (c) What do you notice when all the angle bisectors in (b) are extended?

18 (a) Draw any triangle of your own choice.

   (b) Bisect each angle.

   (c) What do you notice about the angle bisectors in (b) when they are extended?

19 Based on the results of the previous questions what relation appears to be true about the bisectors of the angles of a triangle?

20 "What if you draw all the perpendicular bisectors of the sides of a triangle?"

   (a) Draw any acute or obtuse triangle.

   (b) Construct the perpendicular bisector of each side.

   (c) What do you notice when you draw and extend the perpendicular bisectors?

21 (a) Draw any triangle.

   (b) Construct the perpendicular bisector of each side.

   (c) What do you notice when you draw and extend the perpendicular bisector?

22 Based on the results of the previous questions, what relation appears to be true about the perpendicular bisectors of the sides of a triangle?

23 "What if you draw all the altitudes of a triangle?"

   (a) Draw any acute triangle and right triangle.

   (b) Construct the three altitudes of the triangle.

   (c) What do you notice when you draw and extend the altitudes?

24 (a) Draw any triangle.

   (b) Construct all the altitudes.

   (c) What do you notice when you draw and extend all the altitudes of your triangle?

25 Based on your results what relation appears to be true about the altitudes of a triangle?

26 "What if you construct the perpendicular bisector of the base of an isosceles triangle?"

   (a) Construct an isosceles △ABC as shown in the sketch. BC is the base.

   (b) Bisect the side BC at right angles and extend the bisector. What do you notice?

27 (a) Construct an isosceles triangle of your choice.

   (b) Construct the perpendicular bisector of the base and extend it. What do you notice?

   (c) Use the results of your previous question. What seems to happen when the perpendicular bisector of the base of an isosceles triangle is extended?

28 (a) Make a list of other "what if" questions about geometric figures you have studied.

   (b) Investigate the results of your question, "What if . . . ?"

   (c) Write a statement about your findings in (b) about your geometric figure.

11.2 applying skills: geometric properties

By investigating the properties of figures, you learn about their properties. There are often different ways of learning about the properties of figures as shown in the diagram to the right.

You will obtain, by either method, a property about the sum of the angles of a triangle. There are properties about other figures that you can obtain.

▶ When two lines intersect, the vertically opposite angles are equal.

▶ In an equilateral triangle all angles are equal.

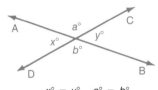

$x° = y°, \quad a° = b°$

$\angle A = \angle B = \angle C$

▶ The angles opposite the congruent sides of an isosceles triangle are equal.

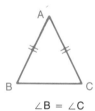

$\angle B = \angle C$

▶ In a circle, the angle subtended by the diameter is a right angle.

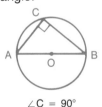

$\angle C = 90°$

▶ If a quadrilateral is drawn in a circle, the opposite angles are supplementary.

$\angle A + \angle C = 180°$
$\angle B + \angle D = 180°$

▶ The sum of the angles in a quadrilateral is 360°.

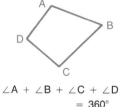

$\angle A + \angle B + \angle C + \angle D$
$= 360°$

The angle relations that you have investigated can be used to deduce (reason) the missing measures of angles in a figure, as shown in the following example.

Example   In △KPL, ∠LKP = 73° and ∠KLP = 61°. Find the measure of ∠KPL.

(Draw a sketch. Record the information on the sketch.)

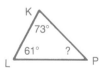

Solution

$$\angle LKP + \angle KLP + \angle KPL = 180°$$
$$73° + \quad 61° + \angle KPL = 180°$$
$$\angle KPL = 180° - 134°$$
$$= 46°$$

(Use the property: the sum of the angles in any triangle is 180°.)

A

1 KN and MP intersect at R. ∠MRN = 73°.

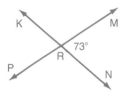

(a) How are ∠MRN and ∠PRK related?

(b) What is the measure of ∠PRK?

(c) How are ∠KRM and ∠PRN related?

(d) What is the measure of ∠PRN?

2 How are ∠A, ∠B, and ∠C related? Find the measure of ∠ABC.

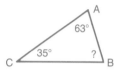

3 (a) How are ∠H and ∠J related?

(b) What is the measure of ∠J?

(c) How are ∠G and ∠I related?

(d) What is the measure of ∠I?

B

4 Calculate the missing angle measures in each of the following. *Do not use a protractor.*

(a)   (b)   (c)

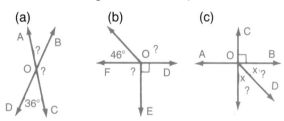

5 Find the missing measures in each of the following triangles. *Do not use a protractor.*

(a)   (b)   (c)

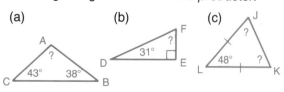

6 (a) Two angles of a triangle measure 36° and 42°. Find the measure of the remaining angle.

(b) A triangle has two angles that each measure 43°. Find the measure of the remaining angle.

(c) One angle of a triangle measures 49°, the other 90°. Find the measure of the remaining angle.

7 In each figure the measures of some angles are shown. Find the measures of the missing angles.

(a)   (b)   (c)

(d)   (e)   (f)

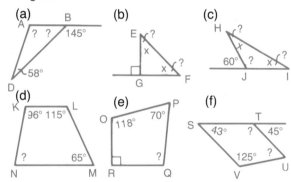

8 Find the missing measures of the angles in each of the following figures.

(a)   (b)   (c)

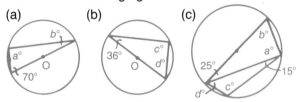

C

9 Find the missing measures.

(a)   (b)   (c)

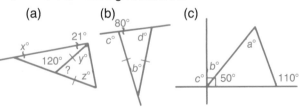

11.3 angle relations for parallel lines

If you draw two lines, AB and CD, perpendicular to EF, so that they will never meet then you have drawn **parallel lines** AB and CD.

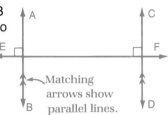

Matching arrows show parallel lines.

In the diagram, two parallel lines EF and GH are drawn. A line AB that crosses these parallel lines is called a **transversal**. This diagram contains pairs of angles with special names.

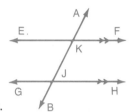

∠EKJ and ∠KJH are called **alternate angles**. Alternate angles occur in these positions.

∠EKA and ∠GJK are called **corresponding angles**. Corresponding angles occur in these positions.

∠FKJ and ∠HJK are called **interior angles on the same side of the transversal**. They occur in these positions.

In the exercise you will learn properties about the angles related to parallel lines.

11.3 exercise

A

1 (a) Name two pairs of alternate angles.

(b) Name four pairs of corresponding angles.

(c) Which angles are interior angles on the same side of the transversal?

2 Two parallel lines are drawn and a transversal RS crosses them.

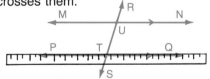

(a) Measure ∠MUT and ∠UTQ. What type of angles are these?

(b) Measure another pair of alternate angles in your diagram. What do you notice?

3 (a) Construct two parallel lines by drawing two lines perpendicular to another line as shown.

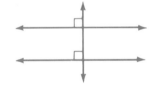

(b) Measure pairs of alternate angles. What do you notice?

(c) Repeat the above steps for other parallel lines.

4 (a) Use both edges of a ruler and construct two parallel lines.

(b) Draw a transversal. Measure pairs of alternate angles.

(c) Repeat steps (a) and (b) for other parallel lines.

5 Repeat the steps in Questions 3 and 4.

(a) Measure the corresponding angles. What do you notice for each pair of parallel lines?

(b) Measure the interior angles on the same side of the transversal. What do you notice about the sum of these angles?

6 Write a summary of your conclusions about the properties of the following angles.

(a) alternate angles

(b) corresponding angles

(c) interior angles on the same side of the transversal.

B Now that you have completed the investigation for parallel lines, you need to use their properties to find missing measures for parallel lines.

▶ The alternate angles are equal.
▶ The corresponding angles are equal.
▶ The interior angles on the same side of the transversal are supplementary.

7 Refer to the diagram.

(a) How are the measures of ∠6 and ∠7 related? What are these angles called?

(b) How are the measures of ∠7 and ∠8 related? What are these angles called?

(c) Using your results from parts (a) and (b), how are the measures of ∠6 and ∠8 related? What are these angles called?

8 Find the missing measures.

(a)   (b)

9 You can combine the earlier geometric properties you learned, with this knowledge of parallel lines. Find the missing measures.

(a)   (b)   (c)

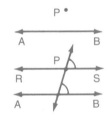

(d)   (e)

10 The properties of angles for parallel lines can be used to construct parallel lines.

(a) You are given a line and a point, as shown. What steps do you need to use to construct RS parallel to AB through the point P?

(b) Draw a point Q and a line, DF. Use the above steps. Construct a line parallel to DF through the point Q.

(c) Draw △EFG. Construct a line through E parallel to FG.

(d) Construct a parallelogram. Construct an altitude of the parallelogram.

11 Find the measures of the angles marked in each figure.

(a)   (b)

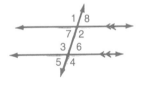

11.4 working with numerical relations

You are already aware of many non-numerical relations from your earlier work with geometry. Relations occur in different ways.

In Jerome's class a record was made of the heights of the students (to the nearest centimetre).

Jacqueline	160 cm
Gerda	153 cm
Manya	163 cm
Jan	162 cm
Francesca	159 cm
Steven	156 cm

The arrow could be used to show a pairing rule.

Manya   163 cm

(The pairing rule is read Manya is 163 cm.

From the table you could write another pairing rule.

Jan   Gerda

(Jan is taller than Gerda

There are other pairing rules that occur in dealing with relations.

"is a brother of"
"is a sister of"
and so on

Pairing rules can also be used to relate numbers.

The pairing rule is "add 2" to the number.

$2 \rightarrow 4$
$3 \rightarrow 5$
$4 \rightarrow 6$

The pairing rule is "square" the number.

$2 \rightarrow 4$
$3 \rightarrow 9$
$4 \rightarrow 16$

The pairing rule in general for the above is shown as
$n \rightarrow n + 2$

The pairing rule in general for the above is shown as $n \rightarrow n^2$ and is read "n maps onto n^2".

To show a numerical relationship such as $n \rightarrow n + 2$, you can use a table of values.

To find the value of an expression, you use a replacement set or **domain**.

$n \rightarrow n + 2$, $n \in W$ (means the values of n are whole numbers.

n	$n + 2$
0	2
1	3
2	4
3	5

value of n ⌐   ⌐ value of $n + 2 = 3 + 2$
                                        $= 5$

From the table of values you could write

$\rightarrow$ (0, 2)
$\rightarrow$ (1, 3)
$\rightarrow$ (2, 4)
$\rightarrow$ (3, 5)

11.4 exercise

A

1 The points earned by some of the soccer clubs are shown.

Everton	35	Middlesborough	29
Ipswich	34	Leeds	27
Stoke	33	Coventry	26
Liverpool	31		

Use each pairing rule. Copy and complete the table.

(a) (Scored more points than)

Liverpool $\rightarrow$?
Stoke $\longrightarrow$?
Leeds $\longrightarrow$?

(b) (Scored two more points than)

Everton $\longrightarrow$?
Stoke $\longrightarrow$?
Middlesborough $\rightarrow$?

2 The points earned in the novice girls' singles skating are shown.

Janet F.	104.06	Linda M.	98.94
Cathy S.	101.39	Cheryl H.	92.02

(a) Suggest a pairing rule for Cathy → Cheryl.

(b) Write the other names which fit the pairing rule in (a).

(c) Why do the following not have the same pairing rule?
Linda → Cathy   Cathy → Linda

3 Allison and Edgar have 3 sons: Peter, Maurice, Waun; and 2 daughters: Lucille and Yvonne. For each pairing rule, find names for ■.

(a) ■ is a brother of ■.   (b) ■ is a sister of ■.

(c) ■ is the mother of ■. (d) ■ is the son of ■.

(e) ■ is the father of ■.

(f) ■ is the daughter of ■.

4 A pairing rule is given by "is a factor of".   3 is a factor of 6
Find two values of ■ for the pairing rule for each of the following.

(a) ■ → 8   (b) ■ → 18   (c) ■ → 24

(d) 3 → ■   (e) 6 → ■   (f) 5 → ■

5 A pairing rule is given by "is a multiple of".   16 is a multiple of 4
Find three values of ■ for the pairing rule.

(a) ■ → 3   (b) ■ → 5   (c) ■ → 7

(d) 25 → ■   (e) 30 → ■   (f) 24 → ■

6 Copy and complete the table of values. Write each pairing rule in words.

(a)
n	$n + 3$
0	
1	
2	
3	

(b)
s	$2s$
0	
1	
2	
3	

7 Copy and complete the tables for the pairing rules. Express each pairing rule in words.

(a) $n \rightarrow 3n + 1$

n	$3n + 1$	Ordered Pair
0	0	(0, 0)
1		
2		
3		

(b) $n \rightarrow 2n + 6$

n	$2n + 6$	Ordered Pair
0		
1		
2		
3		

8 (a) Write three ordered pairs for the relation
$n \rightarrow n^2, \ n \in W$

(b) Write three ordered pairs for the relation
$y \rightarrow 2y + 4, \ y \in W$

(c) Write three ordered pairs for the relation
$p \rightarrow p^2 + 1, \ p \in W$

9 The following ordered pairs of numbers are given for a relation, (1, 2), (2, 4), (3, 6)

(a) Write two more ordered pairs for the relation.

(b) Write the pairing rule by finding the value of ■.
$n \rightarrow ■, \ n \in W$

10 The ordered pairs of numbers, (2, 6), (3, 8), (4, 10), are given for a relation.

(a) Write two more ordered pairs for the relation.

(b) Write the rule by finding the value of ■.
$n \rightarrow ■, \ n \in W$

11 Look for a pattern for these ordered pairs.
(3, 12)   (1, 10)   (4, 13)
(5, 14)   (8, 17)   (2, 11)

(a) Rearrange the ordered pairs so that you can find the relation rule easily.

(b) Write the relation rule by finding the value of ■. $n \rightarrow ■, \ n \in W$

12 For each pairing rule, find 2 pairs of numbers for the missing values.

(a) ■ is 3 more than ■.

(b) ■ is the square of ■.

(c) ■ is less than ■.

(d) ■ is one half of ■.

13 An arrow diagram shows the relation "is 2 more than". What is the pairing rule for each arrow diagram?

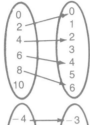

(a)

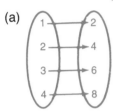

(b)

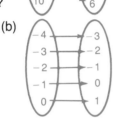

14 Two sets of numbers are shown,

$A = \{-4, -3, -2, -1, 0, 1, 2, 3, 4\}$
$B = \{-2, -1, 0, 1, 2, 3, 4, 5, 6\}$

Construct an arrow diagram from A to B for each of the following pairing rules.

(a) is 2 more than (b) is 4 less than

(c) is one half of (d) is double

(e) is a factor of (f) is a multiple of

C

15 In the Zecchino family, there was Mr. Zecchino, Mrs. Zecchino, Mr. Zecchino's brother Harry, and Mrs. Zecchino's sister Martha. Four sons, David, Januk, Herb, and Bert, as well as three daughters, Cassandra, Karen, and Linda, lived at home with Mr. and Mrs. Zecchino.

(a) How would you interpret the relation rule for this ordered pair? Bert → Januk
Write two more ordered pairs for this relation rule.

(b) How would you interpret the relation rule for this ordered pair? Karen → Herb
Write two more ordered pairs for this relation rule.

(c) How would you interpret the relation rule for this ordered pair? Harry → David
Write two more ordered pairs for this relation rule.

(d) How would you interpret the relation rule for this ordered pair? Martha → Linda
Write two more ordered pairs for this relation rule.

problem-solving: strategy

Often a problem may have more than one answer.

A rectangle has a perimeter of 100 cm. Each side is a whole number of centimetres.

► How many different rectangles can you find that have the same property?

► Do you see a pattern to find *every one* of the rectangles?

problem-solving: puzzler

Copy these 9 dots

● ● ●

● ● ●   Try the other
problem solvers.
● ● ●

How can you draw 4 line segments to cross each dot without lifting your pencil off the paper?

computer tip

The computer will give you the square root of a number. Use this program to check the table of square roots on page 378.

```
10  PRINT "SQUARE ROOT TABLE"
20  INPUT "THE NUMBER IS"; N
30  LET Q = SQR(N)
40  PRINT "THE SQUARE ROOT IS"; Q
50  END
```

11.5 graphs of relations

To show the ordered pairs of the relation, $n \rightarrow 2n$, $n \in W$ you use a table of values.

n	$2n$	ordered pairs
0	0	(0, 0)
1	2	(1, 2)
2	4	(2, 4)
3	6	(3, 6)

To see a picture of this relation, you can draw a graph of the ordered pairs. The ordered pairs are plotted.

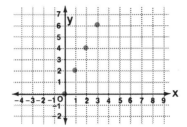

If the above relation is drawn for any number, then you can join the points to draw a line to show the graph.

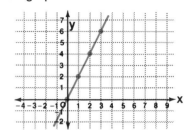

From the graph, you see that the points appear to fall in a straight line pattern. Using this pattern you can use the graph to name other ordered pairs for the relation.

A relation also occurs when you travel. For example, Christie walks to school at a steady rate of two metres per second.

   In 1 s Christie walks 2 m.
   In 2 s Christie walks 4 m.

Time, t in seconds	Distance, d in metres	Ordered pairs
1	2	(1, 2)
2	4	(2, 4)
3	6	(3, 6)
4	8	(4, 8)

You can use the ordered pairs to make a graph of this relation, as shown below.

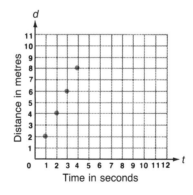

If all distances and times are included, you draw a straight line to show the graph.

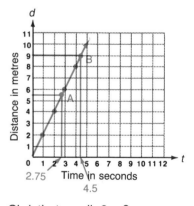

You can use the graph to solve problems.
How far did Christie walk in 2.75 s?
▶ From the graph, the ordered pair provides the answer.

     A(2.75, 5.5)

  2.75 s—⌐   ⌐(5.5 m

Christie walks 5.5 m in 2.75 s.

How long did it take Christie to walk 9 m?
▶ From the graph, the ordered pair (4.5, 9) provides the answer.

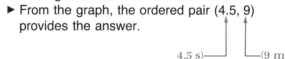

It takes Christie 4.5 s to walk 9 m.

By drawing the graphs of different number relations, you will find many interesting patterns and relationships. The graph of a relation helps you see how the numbers are related.

11.5 exercise

A

1 (a) Copy and complete
    this table of values
    for the relation
    $n \to n + 1, n \in W$.

    (b) Plot the ordered
    pairs from (a) on a
    graph.

n	n + 1
0	
1	
2	
3	

    (c) Use your graph to name
    two other ordered pairs for the relation.

2 (a) Copy and complete
    the table of values
    for the relation
    $k \to k - 1, k \in I$

    (b) Graph the ordered
    pairs found in (a).

k	k − 1
1	
2	
3	
4	

    (c) Use your graph to
    name two other ordered pairs for the relation.

3 (a) Draw the graph of the relation given by
    $n \to n + 1, n \in I$

    (b) Draw the graph of the relation given by
    $n \to n + 1, n$ is any number

    (c) How are the graphs in (a) and (b) alike?
    How are they different?

B

4 A relation is given by $n \to n^2, n \in W$.

    (a) Construct a table of values.

    (b) Use ordered pairs. Draw the graph of the
    relation.

    (c) How does the above graph differ from
    those you have drawn earlier?

5 Use a grid with each axis labelled from 0 to 15.
    Draw a graph of each relation.

    (a) $n \to 3n, n \in \{0, 1, 2, 3\}$

    (b) $n \to 2n, n \in W$

    (c) $n \to 3n - 1, n$ is any number

6 On one field day, the
    relation between
    distance that
    Rosanne ran and the
    time taken is shown
    on the graph.

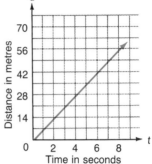

    (a) How far did
    Rosanne run
    in 4 s?

    (b) How far did she
    run in 8 s?

    (c) How long did it take Rosanne to run 35 m?

    (d) How long did it take her to run 63 m?

7 At the same field day a record was made of
    Gino's race.

Time taken (seconds)	0	1	2	3	4
Distance run (metres)	0	5	10	15	20

    (a) Draw a graph of this information.

    (b) Use your graph to find how far Gino ran in
    1.5 s and in 3.5 s.

    (c) Use your graph to find out how long it
    would take Gino to run 50 m.

8 The graph shows the
    relation between the
    distance the spring is
    stretched and the
    mass attached.

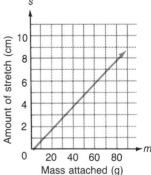

    (a) How much will
    the spring stretch
    if you attach a
    mass of 30 g?

    (b) About how much
    will the spring
    stretch if you
    attach a mass of
    45 g?

square roots: problem-solving strategy

In your study of mathematics, you will often find different ways of solving a problem.

Earlier, you found the square roots of numbers such as $\sqrt{25} = 5$, $\sqrt{64} = 8$.
How do you find the square root of $\sqrt{55}$?

You can use the skills you have just learned for drawing graphs. Draw the graph of the relation $n \to n^2$. *From the graph you can estimate the square root of numbers, such as $\sqrt{55}$.*

From the graph
$\sqrt{55} \doteq 7.5$

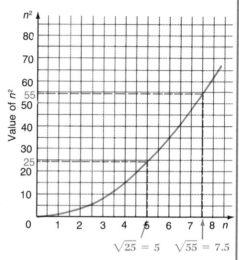

$\sqrt{25} = 5 \qquad \sqrt{55} = 7.5$

Since a graph is not a very accurate way of finding the square root of a number, you need another strategy for finding a square root. Thus, computers are used to calculate square roots to many decimal places. The table below was produced by a computer to show the square roots of numbers rounded to 3 decimal places. From the table you can locate the square root of $\sqrt{55}$ as 7.416.

9 Use the graph to estimate the missing terms in these ordered pairs.

(a) (2.5, ?) (b) (?, 43) (c) (?, 12)

(d) (5.8, ?) (e) (6.6, ?) (f) (?, 22)

10 (a) Estimate a square root for 13.

(b) Why is it difficult to use the graph to find a square root for 13?

11 Use the graph to estimate each square root.

(a) $\sqrt{40}$ (b) $\sqrt{60}$ (c) $\sqrt{5}$

(d) Compare your values to those obtained from the square root table.

12 Use the table to find the square root of these numbers, to 1 decimal place.

(a) 55 (b) 45 (c) 58 (d) 40 (e) 35

(f) 50 (g) 13 (h) 82 (i) 3 (j) 79

13 Use the table of values. Find each square root to 2 decimal places.

(a) $\sqrt{10}$ (b) $\sqrt{58}$ (c) $\sqrt{50}$

(d) $\sqrt{35}$ (e) $\sqrt{20}$ (f) $\sqrt{62}$

You can also use your calculator to find square roots. Use the square root $\boxed{\sqrt{}}$.

square root table

n	$\sqrt{n}$	n	$\sqrt{n}$	n	$\sqrt{n}$	n	$\sqrt{n}$
1	1.000	26	5.099	51	7.141	76	8.718
2	1.414	27	5.196	52	7.211	77	8.775
3	1.732	28	5.292	53	7.280	78	8.832
4	2.000	29	5.385	54	7.349	79	8.888
5	2.236	30	5.477	55	7.416	80	8.944
6	2.450	31	5.568	56	7.483	81	9.000
7	2.646	32	5.657	57	7.550	82	9.055
8	2.828	33	5.745	58	7.616	83	9.110
9	3.000	34	5.831	59	7.681	84	9.165
10	3.162	35	5.916	60	7.746	85	9.220
11	3.317	36	6.000	61	7.810	86	9.274
12	3.464	37	6.083	62	7.874	87	9.327
13	3.606	38	6.164	63	7.937	88	9.381
14	3.742	39	6.245	64	8.000	89	9.434
15	3.873	40	6.325	65	8.062	90	9.487
16	4.000	41	6.403	66	8.124	91	9.539
17	4.123	42	6.481	67	8.185	92	9.592
18	4.243	43	6.557	68	8.246	93	9.644
19	4.359	44	6.633	69	8.307	94	9.695
20	4.472	45	6.708	70	8.367	95	9.747
21	4.583	46	6.782	71	8.426	96	9.798
22	4.690	47	6.856	72	8.485	97	9.849
23	4.796	48	6.928	73	8.544	98	9.900
24	4.899	49	7.000	74	8.602	99	9.950
25	5.000	50	7.071	75	8.660	100	10.000

Turn to page 73, use Newton's Method to find the square root of the above numbers.

11.6 a special relation in right triangles

Everywhere you look you see examples of right triangles. In how many places do they occur?

One property of the right triangle that is useful in solving problems was studied many years ago by Pythagoras, a Greek mathematician. By working with many right triangles he proved an important relation among the three sides. The exercise that follows develops this relation. In the next lesson you will apply the relation to solving problems.

Remember, AB is the **hypotenuse**, and faces the right angle.

11.6 exercise

1 Pythagoras drew a square on each side of a right triangle as shown.

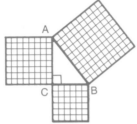

(a) Calculate the area on the square drawn on the hypotenuse AB.

(b) Calculate the area of the squares drawn on the other two sides.

(c) How does the area of the square drawn on AB seem to be related to the areas of the squares drawn on AC and BC?

2 You often use the symbols, a, b, c, to represent the measures of the sides of a triangle.

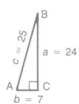

(a) For the triangle, what are the values of a, b, c, a^2, b^2, and c^2?

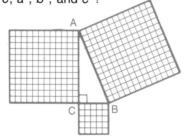

(b) Find the sum $a^2 + b^2$.
How is the value of $a^2 + b^2$ related to the corresponding value of c^2?

3 Bonita's class constructed right triangles and recorded these measures for the sides.

△	a	b	c
1	4.0 cm	3.0 cm	5.0 cm
2	8.0 cm	6.0 cm	10.0 cm
3	6.0 cm	3.0 cm	6.7 cm
4	3.5 cm	2.6 cm	4.4 cm
5	4.8 cm	5.6 cm	7.4 cm

(a) For each triangle calculate $a^2 + b^2$, c^2.

(b) Compare your answers. What do you notice?

4 (a) Construct a right △ABC of your choice.

(b) Measure a, b, and c to the nearest millimetre.

(c) Calculate a^2, b^2, c^2. What relationship do you see among a^2, b^2, and c^2?

(d) Repeat (a), (b), and (c), for other right triangles.

5 Use the results of the previous questions about right triangles. Write a statement about your finding about right triangles.

11.7 applications: Pythagoras and right triangles

Throughout your work in mathematics, you have repeated the steps shown many times.

In the previous section you found that for any right triangle it seems that this result is true.

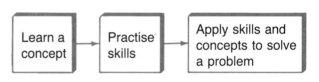

> In any right triangle the square of the length of the hypotenuse is equal to the sum of the squares of the other two sides.

Pythagoras proved that this was indeed true for any right triangle. To this day you call this property the **Pythagorean Relation**.

$a^2 + b^2 = c^2$

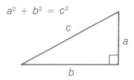

Once you understand the property of right triangles, you apply the skills and concepts to solve problems, as shown in the next example.

Example A 5 m ladder rests against a wall. The foot of the ladder is 2 m from the wall. How far up the wall does the ladder reach? Express your answer to one decimal place.

$\left(\begin{array}{l}\text{Use } a, b, c, \text{to} \\ \text{represent the length} \\ \text{of the sides of } \triangle ABC.\end{array}\right)$

Solution From the diagram, $a = 2$, and $c = 5$ in metres. Since $\triangle ABC$ is a right triangle, you know that

$$a^2 + b^2 = c^2$$
$$2^2 + b^2 = 5^2$$
$$4 + b^2 = 25$$
$$b^2 = 21$$
$$b = \sqrt{21}$$
$$b \doteq 4.583$$

$\left(\begin{array}{l}\text{From the table of square} \\ \text{roots (or your calculation)} \\ \sqrt{21} = 4.583 \text{ (to 3 decimal places)}\end{array}\right)$

Thus, the ladder reaches about 4.6 m up the wall.

11.7 exercise

A Throughout these problems estimate square roots. Use the table of square roots to help you.

1 Find the value of c to 1 decimal place if $c^2 = 69$.

2 Find the value of c to 2 decimal places if $c^2 = 4^2 + 8^2$.

3 Find the missing value in each example. Round off your answers to 2 decimal places.

(a) $c^2 = 6^2 + 4^2$

(b) $12^2 = a^2 + 9^2$

(c) $b^2 + 4^2 = 8^2$

(d) $5^2 + a^2 = 9^2$

(e) $3^2 + 7^2 = c^2$

(f) $4^2 + b^2 = 9^2$

4 Complete the statement of the Pythagorean Relation for each triangle.

(a)

(b)

(c) Calculate the missing lengths in each triangle.

B

5 Calculate the missing length for each right triangle.

(a) (b) (c)

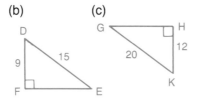

6 Calculate the missing lengths (to 1 decimal place).

(a) (b) (c)

7 Find the missing values. You will need to estimate the square roots to 1 decimal place.

(a) $c^2 = (2.1)^2 + (3.6)^2$

(b) $(4.5)^2 + a^2 = (7.8)^2$

(c) $b^2 + (3.2)^2 = (6.9)^2$

(d) $(4.6)^2 + (6.1)^2 = c^2$

(e) $(3.9)^2 + b^2 = (6.9)^2$

8 Calculate the missing lengths. Round your answers to 1 decimal place.

(a) (b) (c)

 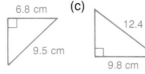

9 Calculate the length of the wire AB.

Estimate first.
Then calculate.

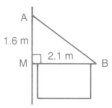

10 To calculate the height of the kite, the base of the triangle is measured. John is standing vertically below the kite. Use the data in the diagram. Calculate the height of the kite.

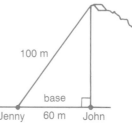

11 (a) Use the measures of this baseball diamond to calculate the length of the throw from home to second base.

(b) Bradley who plays shortstop is between 2nd and 3rd base. Calculate the length of his throw to 1st base.

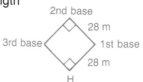

C

12 This is a challenge. The skeleton of a box is shown. What is the longest fishing pole that can be placed in the box?

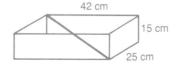

---

computer tip

Use this program to calculate the length of the hypotenuse in a right triangle.

```
10  PRINT "PYTHAGORUS"
20  INPUT A, B
30  LET V = A ↑ 2 + B ↑ 2
40  LET H = SQR (V)
50  PRINT "THE HYPOTENUSE IS"; H
60  END
```

11.8 transformations and co-ordinates

Earlier, you investigated some of the concepts of translations, reflections and turns. You can use the Cartesian plane and ordered pairs to draw the images of figures which have had transformations applied to them.

Translations

The square A'B'C'D' is the image of square ABCD after a translation has been applied to it. By listing the ordered pairs you can find a relation among the vertices of the square.

The second co-ordinates have not changed in value.

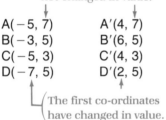

A(−5, 7)   A'(4, 7)
B(−3, 5)   B'(6, 5)
C(−5, 3)   C'(4, 3)
D(−7, 5)   D'(2, 5)

The first co-ordinates have changed in value.

To find the vertices of the square in the image position you use this relation rule.
▶ The first (or x co-ordinate) is increased by 9.
▶ The second (or y co-ordinate) is left unchanged.

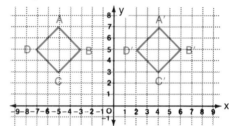

Reflections

Ordered pairs are again used to describe the image position of a square ABCD, after it is reflected about the x-axis.

The image is marked by the figure A'B'C'D'. By writing the corresponding ordered pairs you can find a relation.

Co-ordinates of   Co-ordinates of
square ABCD   square A'B'C'D'
   A(4, 6)   A'(4, −6)
   B(6, 4)   B'(6, −4)
   C(4, 2)   C'(4, −2)
   D(2, 4)   D'(2, −4)

The first co-ordinates remain unchanged.   The second co-ordinates are opposites.

You could write this rule to find the position of figure A'B'C'D'.

▶ The first co-ordinate is unchanged.
▶ The second co-ordinate is the opposite of the original co-ordinate.

For your reflection, you can think of the x-axis as a mirror. The x-axis is thus a reflection line.

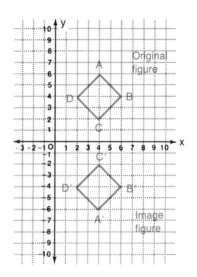

Rotations

△ABC is rotated as shown about the point O. The image △A′B′C′ is drawn.

The measure of ∠COC′ is 90°. You have made a quarter-turn about the point O. You call O the **rotation** or **turn centre**.

You can use the co-ordinates of △ABC to find the co-ordinates of △A′B′C′

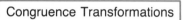
Apply the rotation

A(3, 5) → A′(−5, 3)
B(7, 3) → B′(−3, 7)
C(3, 3) → C′(−3, 3)

For the rotation, the origin is the rotation centre. The angle of rotation is 90° counter clockwise.

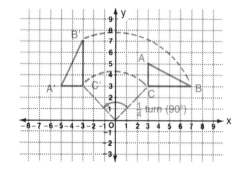

Congruence Transformations

When you apply a translation, reflection, or rotation to a figure, the image is congruent to the original figure. For this reason, translations, reflections, and rotations are called **congruence transformations**.

In the next section, you will study another type of transformation, namely a similarity transformation.

The following is an important strategy for remembering the properties of translations, reflections and rotations. Ask yourself:

▶ What properties do translations, reflections and rotations have in common?
▶ What properties do translations, reflections, and rotations *not* have in common?

11.8 exercise

A In the exercise that follows you need to use your skills with translation, reflection and rotation. Read carefully!

1 A square is moved from its original position to an image position.
  ▶ List the ordered pairs for the original position and the image position.
  ▶ Write a relation rule to relate the co-ordinates
    A → A′
    B → B′
    C → C′
    D → D′

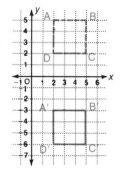

2 In each of the following diagrams, a slide is applied to a polygon. Write a relation rule for each slide. You may find it helpful to list the ordered pairs.

(a)

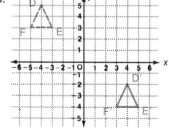

(b)

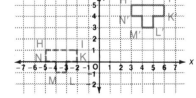

3 A reflection is applied to △ABC about the y-axis as shown.

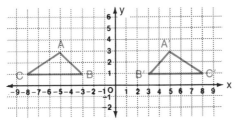

(a) Which points correspond to A, B, and C?

(b) List the ordered pairs for the original figure and the image figure.

(c) Write a relation rule to relate the co-ordinates
A → A′, B → B′, C → C′.

4 In each of the following diagrams, a reflection about a line is applied.

▶ Name the line of reflection.
▶ Write the co-ordinates of the image points that correspond on the original figure.
▶ Write a relation rule for each reflection.

(a) 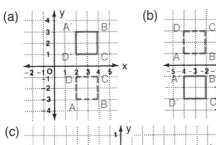 (b)

(c)

5 Copy each of the following figures. The origin is the rotation centre

(a) 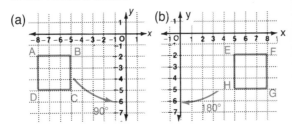 (b)

(c) 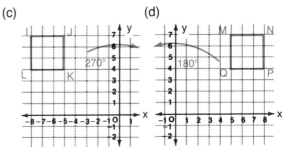 (d)

(e) Write the co-ordinates of the original figure and the image figure for each rotation.

B

6 (a) Use squared paper. Mark the axes. Draw a triangle with co-ordinates
A(−4, −2), B(−5, −4), C(−3, −4)

(b) Use the following relation rule to locate the image of △ABC.

▶ The first co-ordinate is increased by 6.
▶ The second co-ordinate is left unchanged.

(c) Apply the following relation rule to the image triangle you drew in (b).

▶ The first co-ordinate is left unchanged.
▶ The second co-ordinate is increased by 7.

(d) Use △ABC in (a). Apply the following relation rule.

▶ The first co-ordinate is increased by 6.
▶ The second co-ordinate is increased by 7.

(e) Compare your results in (c) and (d). What do you notice about the final image position of △ABC in each case?

7 (a) △ABC has co-ordinates A(−3, 3), B(−7, 1), C(−6, 6). Use the relation rule to find the image of △ABC.

▶ Increase the x co-ordinate by 4.
▶ Decrease the y co-ordinate by 5.

(b) Measure AA′, BB′, CC′. What do you notice?

(c) Give reasons why AA′, BB′, and CC′ appear to be parallel?

8 The fundamental property of a translation is illustrated by Questions 7(b), 7(c). What, in your own words, is the fundamental property of a translation?

9 △ABC is drawn with co-ordinates
$\quad$ A(2, 3)$\quad$ B(−2, 4)$\quad$ C(−5, 0)

(a) Apply the following relation rule and find the image position.

▶ The first co-ordinate is increased by 2.
▶ The second co-ordinate is decreased by 5.

(b) For the figure and its image, measure the

▶ length of corresponding sides
▶ corresponding angles

What do you notice?

(c) Calculate the area of the figure and its image. What do you notice?

(d) The vertices A, B, and C are arranged in clockwise direction. We refer to this direction as the "sense" of the triangle. Compare the sense of the image. What do you notice?

10 (a) △EFG has co-ordinates E(−2, 3), F(−7, 2), G(−5, 5). Plot the triangle.

(b) A reflection is applied to △EFG about the y-axis. Find the image and the co-ordinates of its vertices.

(c) Measure the distances from the points E, F and G to the y-axis. Measure the distances from the points E′, F′, G′ to the y-axis. How do these distances compare?

(d) Decide whether EE′, GG′, and FF′ are perpendicular to the y-axis. Give reasons for your answer.

11 (a) △BCD is given by B(5, 6), C(2, 4), and D(4, 1). Plot the triangle.

(b) A reflection is applied to △BCD about the x-axis. Find the image and the co-ordinates of its vertices.

(c) Measure the distances from the points B,

C, and D to the x-axis. Measure the distances from the points B′, C′, and D′ to the x-axis. How do these distances compare?

(d) Decide whether BB′, CC′, and DD′ are perpendicular to the x-axis. Give reasons for your answer.

12 The fundamental property of a reflection is shown by Questions 10(c), 10(d), 11(c), 11(d). Write, in your own words, the fundamental property of a reflection.

13 (a) A triangle has co-ordinates D(3, 5), E(3, 3), F(6, 3). Draw △DEF.

(b) Find the rotation image if △DEF is rotated 90° clockwise about the origin.

(c) Measure OD, OD′, OE, OE′, OF, OF′. What do you notice?

(d) Measure angles ∠DOD′, ∠EOE′, ∠FOF′. What do you notice?

14 (a) Use squared paper. Draw square ABCD.
$\quad$ A(2, −5)$\quad$ B(4, −3)$\quad$ C(6, −5)$\quad$ D(4, −7)

(b) Find the image of the square after a rotation of 180° counter-clockwise about the origin. Mark the co-ordinates of the vertices.

(c) Measure OA, OA′, OB, OB′, OC, OC′, OD, OD′. What do you notice?

(d) Measure ∠AOA′, ∠BOB′, ∠COC′, and ∠DOD′. What do you notice?

(e) Which pairs of line segments in your diagram have equal measures?

15 The fundamental property of a rotation is shown by Questions 13(c), 13(d), 14(c) and 14(d). Write, in your own words, the fundamental property of a rotation.

16 Based on the results of your work with translations, reflections, and rotations,

(a) list all the properties of translations, reflections, and rotations that you can.

(b) justify each property that you list in (a).

11.9 size transformations: similar figures

In your earlier work with transformations, the original figure and image figures were congruent. These transformations are called congruence transformation.

▶ Figures are **congruent** if they are the same shape and size.
▶ Figures are **similar** if they have the same shape.
  If you enlarge a picture, the figure in the picture and the enlarged picture are similar.

Often, you will see an advertisement giving a discount on photo enlargements.

▶ How are the original and the enlargement alike?
▶ How are they different?

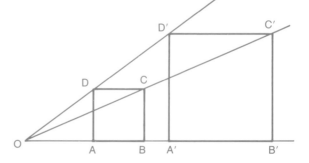

You can use grid or dot paper to make an enlargement. An enlargement factor of 2 is applied to the original figure. Namely, A'D' measures 2 units, and AD measures 1 unit.

The enlargement   A'D' : AD = 2:1
or **scale ratio**
is given by   (length on enlargement)   (length on original)

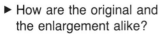

You can apply an enlargement factor of 2 to obtain an enlargement of a figure about a point O as shown in the diagram. The construction lines are shown for each enlargement.

▶ How are the original and the enlargement alike?
▶ How are they different?

The centre of the enlargement, O, is a vertex of the figure
OA' : OA = 2:1

The centre of the enlargement, O, is in the interior of the figure
OA' : OA = 2:1

The centre of the enlargement, O, is outside of the figure.
OA' : OA = 2:1

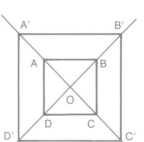

Often in the study of mathematics, the skills you learn in one part apply to another. For example, the skills you learn for enlargements apply to finding reductions. In the diagram, the original figure has undergone a **reduction factor** of $\frac{1}{2}$. The reduction (or scale ratio) is given by

$$\text{A'F'} : \text{AF} = 2:4 \text{ or } 1:2$$

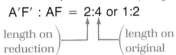

$\overbrace{}^{}$ $\left(\begin{array}{l}\text{length on} \\ \text{reduction}\end{array}\right)$ $\left(\begin{array}{l}\text{length on} \\ \text{original}\end{array}\right)$

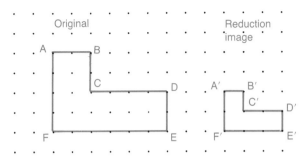

You can use your earlier work with co-ordinates to obtain the image when a size transformation is applied to a figure.

Example △ABC has co-ordinates A(1, 2), B(3, 2), and C(4, 0). Find the image of △ABC if an enlargement factor of 2 is used. The centre of enlargement is the origin.

Solution Draw △ABC. Mark the vertices. Mark the construction lines.

Apply the size transformation. Find △A′B′C′.

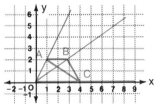 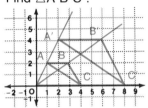

What is the relation among the co-ordinates of △ABC and △A′B′C′?

$A(1, 2) \rightarrow A'(2, 4)$ $B(3, 2) \rightarrow B'(6, 4)$ $C(4, 0) \rightarrow C'(8, 0)$

▶ The enlargement or scale factor is 2.
▶ Each co-ordinate is multiplied by 2.

For the above enlargements and reductions the shape of the figures remain the same, but the size changes. This type of transformation is often called a **size transformation** or **dilatation**.

11.9 exercise

A In the exercise that follows you will explore properties of similar triangles and figures. In the next section you will apply these properties to solve problems.

1 Use each diagram. Make a copy of each. Use the enlargement factor.

(a) 2   (b) 3

    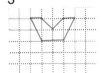

2 For the school advertisement, the school team wants to use the logo. Construct an enlargement of the logo, 5 times larger.

3 For a project, you want to make the size of a map of Newfoundland 10 times as great. Use a grid to construct the enlargement.

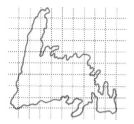

4 An enlargement is applied to △ABC to obtain △DEF.

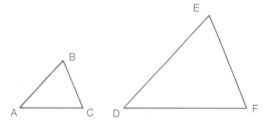

(a) Find the ratios of corresponding sides. What is the enlargement factor?

(b) Measure corresponding angles. What do you notice?

5 An enlargement is applied to square ABCD to obtain square EFGH.

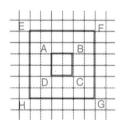

(a) Find the ratios of corresponding sides. What is the enlargement factor?

(b) Measure corresponding angles. What do you notice?

6 A square ABCD is enlarged as shown.

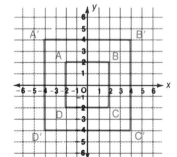

(a) Which points correspond?

(b) Write a relation rule to relate the co-ordinates.

(c) Measure and compare the lengths of the corresponding sides.

AB and A′B′   BC and B′C′
CD and C′D′   DA and D′A′

What do you notice?

7 Two figures are shown. Give reasons why each pair of figures is not similar.

(a)   (b)

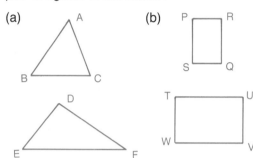

B

8 (a) Copy each figure and construct the following enlargement for each figure.

▶ Use an enlargement factor of 2.
▶ Use the centre of enlargement E.

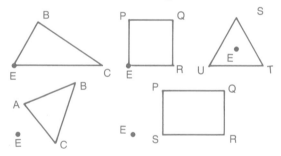

(b) Copy and complete the chart for each figure in (a).

Perimeters of similar figures		Areas of similar figures	
Perimeter of original	Perimeter of image	Area of original	Area of image

Based on your results in the chart, what observations can you make?

9 For each figure,

▶ Make a copy of the figure. Mark the centre of enlargement, E.

▶ Construct the enlargement or reduction for the factor shown. Use the centre of enlargement.

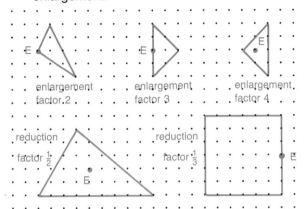

enlargement factor 2   enlargement factor 3   enlargement factor 4

reduction factor $\frac{1}{2}$ reduction factor $\frac{1}{3}$

10 △PQR is similar to △P′Q′R′.

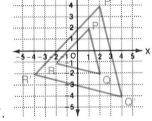

(a) Write the co-ordinates of each vertex of △PQR.

(b) Write the co-ordinates of each vertex of △P′Q′R′.

(c) What is the relation between the co-ordinates of △PQR and those of △P′Q′R′?

(d) What is the enlargement factor?

(e) What are the co-ordinates of the centre of enlargement?

11 The co-ordinates of △XYZ are
X(2, −1) Y(−1, −1) Z(−1, 2)
The co-ordinates of △XYZ are related to the co-ordinates of △X′Y′Z′ by the relation

▶ The first co-ordinate is multiplied by 3.

▶ The second co-ordinate is multiplied by 3.

(a) Find the co-ordinates of △X′Y′Z′.

(b) Graph △XYZ and △X′Y′Z′.

(c) What is the enlargement factor?

(d) What is the centre of enlargement?

12 △ABC is shown on the grid. Construct the image for △ABC for each dilatation.

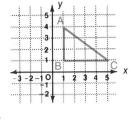

(a) Centre of enlargement (1, 1). Enlargement factor 3.

(b) Centre of enlargement (0, 0). Enlargement factor 4.

13 △EFG is drawn on squared paper so that the points E, F, and G are shown clockwise.
E(−2, 2) F(−5, 2) G(−4, 4)

(a) Find the image of △EFG for the relation rule: double the value of each co-ordinate.

(b) Are the vertices of the image labelled in a clockwise or counter-clockwise direction?

(c) Compare the original and image figures. Which corresponding sides are parallel?

(d) Is the image figure congruent to the original figure? Why?

14 (a) Draw the following rectangle ABCD on squared paper.
A(−3, 4) B(3, 4) C(3, −4) D(−3, −4)

(b) Use this enlargement rule: multiply each co-ordinate value by 3.

(c) Are the vertices A, B, C, D, in a clockwise or counter-clockwise direction? How are the points A′, B′, C′, D′ labelled, clockwise or counter-clockwise?

(d) Is the image figure congruent to the original figure? Why?

15 Use your results in Questions 1 to 14.

(a) List the properties of a size transformation or dilatation.

(b) When a size transformation is applied to a figure,
   ▶ What remains unchanged?
   ▶ What changes?

11.10 solving problems: similar triangles

To solve problems about similar triangles, you use the same strategies you used to solve other problems.

Step 1

Learn the properties of similar triangles. Two triangles are similar if they have the same shape. For similar triangles

▶ corresponding angles are congruent.
▶ ratios of the measures of corresponding sides are equal.

$$\frac{A'B'}{AB} = \frac{B'C'}{BC} = \frac{A'C'}{AC}$$

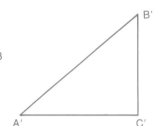

Step 2

Use the properties of similar triangles to find missing measures. △ABC and △DEF are similar. The ratios of the measures of corresponding sides are equal.

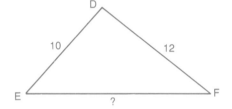

$$\frac{AC}{DF} = \frac{AB}{DE} \quad \text{or} \quad \frac{AC}{12} = \frac{5}{10} \qquad \boxed{\text{Think } \frac{5}{10} = \frac{1}{2} = \frac{6}{12}}$$

Thus AC = 6.

$$\frac{EF}{BC} = \frac{DE}{AB} \quad \text{or} \quad \frac{EF}{8} = \frac{10}{5} \qquad \boxed{\text{Think } \frac{10}{5} = \frac{2}{1} = \frac{16}{8}}$$

Thus EF = 16.

Use the properties of similar triangles to solve problems as shown in the following example.

Example On a hot day, a tower casts a shadow 12 m in length. To find the height of the tower, Joelle used two similar triangles. What is the height of the tower?

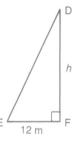

Solution Let h represent the height of the tower, in metres.

$$\frac{DF}{AC} = \frac{EF}{BC}$$

$\left(\begin{array}{l}\text{Think:}\\ \triangle ABC \text{ and } \triangle DEF \text{ are similar.}\\ \text{Thus, corresponding ratios are equal.}\end{array}\right.$

$$\frac{h}{2} = \frac{12}{1} \qquad \boxed{\text{Think } \frac{12}{1} = \frac{24}{2}}$$

$$\frac{h}{2} = \frac{24}{2}$$

$$h = 24 \qquad \text{The height of the tower is 24 m.}$$

Check whether your answer is reasonable.

A

1 △PQR and △STV are similar.

(a) Which pairs of angles correspond?

(b) What is the ratio of corresponding sides?

2 △ABC and △DEF are similar.

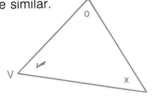

(a) Which pairs of angles correspond?

(b) Write the ratios of corresponding sides.

(c) Write a suitable proportion to find the length of BC. What is the length of BC?

(d) Find the length of DE.

3 For each pair of similar triangles, find the missing measures.

(a)

(b)

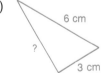

B

4 The height, *h*, in metres, is the altitude of the kite. Find the altitude.

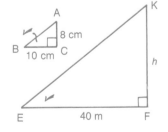

5 To measure the distance across the river, Francis, Michael, Helen, and Bob placed stakes as shown and marked off triangles. Michael located the point E lining up the rock at C and the tree at A.

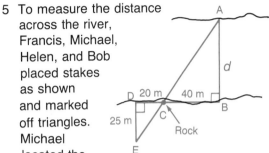

(a) Use the diagram to explain why ∠DCE = ∠ACB.

(b) Why are △ABC and △EDC similar?

(c) Why is $\frac{AB}{ED} = \frac{BC}{DC}$?

(d) Use the proportion in (c) to find the width of the river.

6 Lesley and Jeff made measurements to calculate the width of a gulley. Use the diagram to find the width of the gulley.

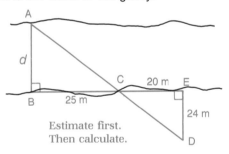

Estimate first.
Then calculate.

7 (a) Sandra and Steven worked together to obtain the measurements shown in the following diagram. Calculate the height of the flag pole.

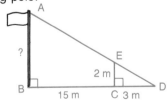

11.11 problem-solving: more than one transformation

You can combine translations, reflections, and rotations to obtain the image of a figure.

Translate the figure. 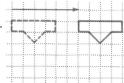   Then reflect the figure.    You can obtain the result another way.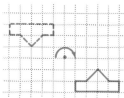

Refer to the diagram at the bottom of the page. In the diagram many different figures are shown. Some are congruent, some are similar. Some figures might be related by a rotation. Some might be related in more than one way.

(a) Decide which figures are related by a translation.

(b) Decide which figures are related by a reflection. Name the line of reflection.

(c) Decide which figures might be related by a

reflection and a translation.

(d) Decide which figures are related by a rotation about the origin.

(e) Decide which figures might be related by a combination of translations, reflections, or rotations.

(f) Decide which figures are related by an enlargement (about the origin).

You may want to copy these diagrams on squared paper and experiment with them.

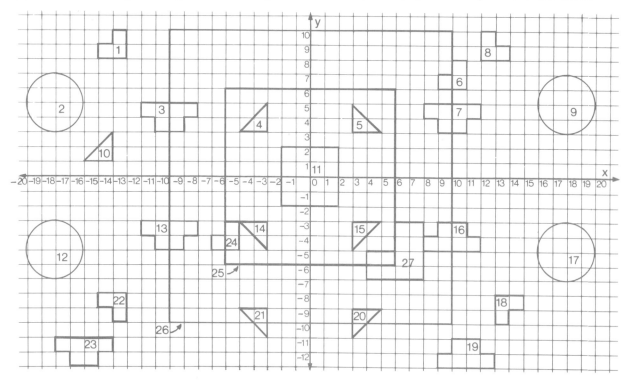

practice and problems: a chapter review

(11.1) 1 What information does each diagram tell you?

(a)

(b)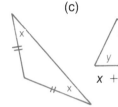

(c)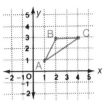

$x + y + z = ?$

(11.2) 2 Find the missing measures.

(a)

(b)

(c)

(11.3) 3 Find the missing measures.

(a)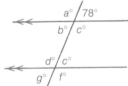

(b)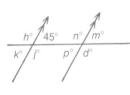

(11.4) 4 (a) Draw the graph of each relation.

$n \rightarrow n + 3, n \in W$

$n \rightarrow n + 3, n$ is any number

(b) How are the graphs alike? different?

(11.5) 5 A pairing rule is given by "is double the value of". Find the missing values.

(a) ▢ → 3   (b) ▢ → 12   (c) 64 → ▢

(11.6) 6 (a) Tanya measured a right triangle with the longer sides 24 cm and 26 cm. What is the measure of the shortest side?

(11.7) (b) A cake pan measures 22 cm by 33 cm. Find the length of the diagonal.

(11.8) 7 Apply, to the figure, △ABC,

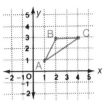

(a) the translation
  ▶ the horizontal co-ordinate is increased by 4.
  ▶ the vertical co-ordinate is decreased by 2.

(b) a reflection about the y-axis

(c) a rotation of 90° clockwise about the origin.

(11.9) (d) an enlargement with factor 3, and enlargement centre (0, 0).

(11.10) 6 From the diagram, Rick was able to find the measure of the height of the trees. What is the height?

skills quiz

This skills quiz reviews your calculations with decimals.

(a) 365 × 23

(b) 56 × 4.6

(c) 12.65 + 14.23

(d) 36.95 − 12.96

(e) 9.83 × 2.5

(f) 343²

(g) $\dfrac{265.20}{6.8}$

(h) 698.75 − 309.86

(i) 146.36 × 12.9

(j) 21.482 ÷ 46

(k) 3634 ÷ 46

(l) 0.565 × 73.9

(m) 2346.96 + 3432.07

(n) 963.2 × 45.5

(o) 247.234 ÷ 37

(p) 59)‾21 476

(q) 1004.3 × 296

(r) 998.76 − 989.87

math is plus: distorted figures

To distort the shape of a figure you can use distorted grids.

Start with this figure.

Use a larger grid to magnify the figure.

Stretch the grid horizontally. You can distort the figure.

Stretch the grid vertically. You can again distort the figure.

---

1 How is each distorted figure obtained?

(a)   (b)

2 For each figure, use the distorted grid. (Make a larger copy of each distorted grid.) Then draw a distorted image of each figure.

(a)

(b)

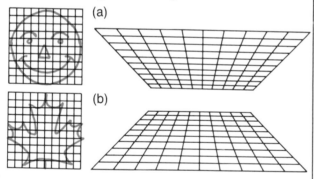

3 Here is a grid you'll like. Use the figure shown. Make a copy of the figure on the distorted grid.

(a)

(b)

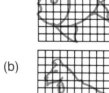 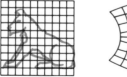

4 (a) Use this figure on the distorted grid. Find its image.

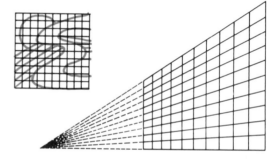

(b) Draw a map of Canada on the distorted grid.

5 Design a distorted grid of your own. Draw the image of each of these figures on your distorted grid.

(a)   (b)

6 Make a copy of each distorted grid in question 3. Draw this figure on each of the previous distorted grids.

12 problem-solving: using equations to solve problems

Translating English to mathematics, solving equations systematic trial, inspection, properties of equations, using equations to solve problems, using algebra, solving inequations, problem solving skills, solving problems and applications

In mathematics, you often develop strategies by solving straightforward problems. Then you apply the strategy to solve more complex problems.

Problem A
You learn a strategy to solve problem A. Probably, you know the answer to this problem already.

> A number increased by 6 is equal to 10. What is the number?

You can use your answer to the problem to check the steps of your method.

Problem B
You can use the strategy you developed to solve problem A, to solve a more complex problem.

> A number is tripled and then increased by 3. Two-thirds of this sum is 36. Find the number.

You then apply your strategy step by step to solve problem B.

The main reason for learning mathematics is to acquire more skills and strategies for solving problems. Many of the thought processes or methods you use to solve a mathematics problem are the same as those that you would use to solve *any* problem. Compare the charts shown for the *Steps For Solving Problems*.

Solving computation problems

Steps for Solving Problems

A Ask yourself:
  I *What information am I asked to find?*
  II *What information am I given?*

B Decide on a method.
  Which operation do I use?

C Do the work.
  Complete the calculation.

D Check your work.
  Use your rounding skills.

E Make a final statement.
  Answer the original problem.

Solving problems about equations

Steps for Solving Problems

A Ask yourself:
  I *What information am I asked to find?*
  II *What information am I given?*

B Decide on a method.
  Use a variable. Translate into symbols.

C Do the work.
  Solve the equation.

D Check your work.
  Verify the root in the equation.

E Make a final statement.
  Answer the original problem.

Solving any problem

Steps for Solving Problems

A Ask yourself:
  I *What information am I asked to find?*
  II *What information am I given?*

B Decide on a method.
  Use the skills you have learned.

C Do the work or results.

D Check your work, or results.

E Make a final statement.
  Answer the original problem.

12.1 first step: translating English into mathematics

To solve word problems, you need to develop skills for translating from English to mathematics and mathematical symbols.

Example 1 Write an expression for a number doubled and then increased by 5.

Solution Let n represent the number.

the number doubled   the number increased by 5

$$2n + 5$$

$\left(\begin{array}{l}2n + 5 \text{ is called a } \textbf{variable} \\ \textbf{number expression.}\end{array}\right.$

To solve certain word problems, you need to write equations or inequations.

Example 2 Translate the following into mathematics.
(a) A number when tripled and increased by 4 is equal to 19.
(b) Five increased by a number is greater than 8.

Solution (a) Let n represent the number.

the number is tripled   increased by 4

$$3n + 4 = 19 \longleftarrow \text{is equal to 19}$$

$\left(3n + 4 = 19 \text{ is called an } \textbf{equation.}\right.$

(b) Let n represent the number.

5 increased by a number

$$5 + n > 8 \longleftarrow \text{is greater than 8}$$

$\left(5 + n > 8 \text{ is called an } \textbf{inequation.}\right.$

12.1 exercise

A

1 Match each English expression in Column A with the mathematical expression in Column B.

Column A	Column B
(a) n doubled	$n - 4$
(b) n increased by five	$2 + n$
(c) n decreased by four	$\frac{1}{4}n$
(d) two more than n	$2n$
(e) three less than n	$n + 5$
(f) one fourth of n	$n - 3$

2 Match each equation below with the correct expression.

A $3n = 7$ B $\frac{n}{3} = 7$

C $n + 3 = 7$ D $n - 3 = 7$

(a) A number n increased by 3 is equal to 7.

(b) A number n decreased by 3 is equal to 7.

(c) A number n multiplied by 3 is equal to 7.

(d) A number n divided by 3 is equal to 7.

3 Classify the following as expressions, equations or inequations.

(a) $j + 4$ (b) $j + 4 = 9$ (c) $j < 3$

(d) $5 + y = 8$ (e) $6r + 1$ (f) $4p > 20$

4 In each of the following,
▶ choose a variable.
▶ then translate into a variable expression.

(a) A number is increased by 2.

(b) A number is doubled.

(c) A number is decreased by 3.

(d) Three is subtracted from a number.

(e) Four is added to a number.

(f) Three fifths of a number is increased by 9.

B

5 Write an English expression for each of the following.

(a) $n + 4$ (b) $h - 4$

(c) $3t$ (d) $t - 3$

(e) $2t + 1$ (f) $2c - 3$

(g) $\frac{2}{3}d$ (h) $k - \frac{1}{5}$

6 Translate each of the following into a mathematical expression.

(a) y is decreased by 8.

(b) Nine is subtracted from k.

(c) z is subtracted from 15.

(d) One-half of n is added to one-third of n.

(e) Three-quarters of x.

(f) Eight times the sum of x and 19.

(g) Three-fifths of the sum of p and q.

(h) Nine more than the product of seven and k.

(i) Two times n is decreased by 12.

(j) One half of s is decreased by a third of 3.

(k) k is doubled.

7 Choose a variable to translate each of the following.

(a) Nine is subtracted from a number.

(b) The sum of a number and 12.

(c) A number is doubled and decreased by 8.

(d) A number is added to itself.

(e) Two-thirds of a number.

(f) A number is divided by 5 and decreased by 4.

(g) A number is increased by 12.

(h) One half of the number is decreased by 8.

C

8 Translate each of the following.

(a) A number is multiplied by 5 and the result is 35.

(b) A number is increased by 1 and the result is 17.

(c) A number is decreased by 7 and the result is 8.

(d) A number doubled is greater than 8.

(e) Twelve is less than one third of a number.

(f) Two-thirds of a number is increased by 5 and the result is 9.

(g) Eighteen is 5 less than some number.

problem-solving: research

In each sentence, ■ represents a Canadian city. Choose one city which makes the sentence true and one city which makes the sentence false.

A ■ is the capital of British Columbia.

B ■ is a city in New Brunswick.

C ■ has a professional hockey team.

D ■ has a professional football team.

E ■ and ■ are cities on Canada's Atlantic Seaboard.

12.2 solving equations: systematic trial

In your earlier work you often estimated an answer to a problem. This estimate told you whether your final answer was reasonable. You can also use your skills with estimating to solve another type of problem. For example:

The cost, C, in dollars, of producing the local magazine is given by

$C = 25 + 2n$

$25 initial cost — n, number of magazines produced

A To find the cost of producing 40 magazines, you substitute $n = 40$ and calculate the cost, C.

$$C = 25 + 2n$$
$$= 25 + 2(40)$$
$$= 25 + 80$$
$$= 105$$

The cost of producing 40 magazines is $105.

B To find how many magazines were produced at a cost of $41, you need to *reverse* the process and find the value of n.

$$41 = 25 + 2n$$

—(What is the value of n?

A replacement value of n that makes the equation true is called a **solution** of the equation.

The process of finding a solution of the equation is called **solving the equation**.

One method of solving an equation is to systematically try different values. First estimate a value. Since the cost is $41, use an estimate for n.

Try $n = 5$.
$$25 + 2n = 25 + 2(5)$$
$$= 25 + 10$$
$$= 35 \neq 41 \quad \text{false}$$

Estimate a greater value.
Try $n = 7$.
$$25 + 2n = 25 + 2(7)$$
$$= 25 + 14$$
$$= 39 \neq 41 \quad \text{false}$$

Now try $n = 8$.
$$25 + 2n = 25 + 2(8)$$
$$= 25 + 16$$
$$= 41 \quad \text{✔ true}$$

The value $n = 8$, is a solution of the equation. Thus the number of magazines produced at a cost of $41 is 8 magazines.

The value 8 is also called a **root** of the equation. Once you have found the root of an equation, a simple check will **verify** your calculations, as shown.

The above method of finding a solution to an equation is called **systematic trial**. It is so called because you systematically try different values for the variable until the solution of the equation is obtained.

Verification. Use $n = 8$.

L.S.	R.S.
41	$25 + 2n$
	$= 25 + 2(8)$
	$= 25 + 16$
	$= 41$

L.S. = R.S.
Thus 8 is a root.

A Throughout this exercise, the replacement set for each variable is the set of integers.

1 For each equation, copy and complete the chart.

(a) $3n - 1 = 14$

Value	True or False
$n = 2$	?
$n = 3$	?
$n = 4$	?
$n = 5$	?

(b) $5n + 1 = 16$

Value	True or False
$n = 0$	?
$n = 1$	?
$n = 2$	?
$n = 3$	?

2 Three values of the variable are shown for each equation. Which is the solution?

(a) $n + 6 = 9$ 1, 2, 3

(b) $2n - 1 = 9$ 4, 5, 6

(c) $3n - 1 = 8$ 3, 4, 5

(d) $3n + 1 = 7$ 1, 2, 3

3 For each equation, choose

▶ 2 numbers that make it false.
▶ 1 number that makes it true.

(a) $n + 5 = 9$ (b) $n - 6 = 2$

(c) $6 - n = 4$ (d) $2n = 20$

(e) $2n - 1 = 15$ (f) $2n + 1 = 25$

B Once you find the solution of each equation, be sure to check (verify) your value.

4 To solve each equation
▶ estimate the solution.
▶ use the method of systematic trial.

(a) $2n + 8 = 12$ (b) $3q - 5 = 4$

(c) $\frac{n}{2} = 8$ (d) $12 - s = 6$

(e) $9m + 3 = 75$ (f) $6d - 12 = 36$

5 (a) Estimate the root of the equation.
$$0.8h - 0.2 = 2.2$$

(b) Use systematic trial to find the root.

6 Solve. Check your answer. Some roots may be decimal numbers.

(a) $3p + 2 = 35$ (b) $100 - 6n = 52$

(c) $4p + 6.2 = 48.2$ (d) $\frac{m}{2} = 3.2$

7 (a) Use the chart. Find the value of each expression.

n	$6n + 2$	$5n + 6$
2	?	?
3	?	?
4	?	?

(b) Use your results in (a). What is the solution of the equation
$$6n + 2 = 5n + 6?$$

(c) Solve the equation $5n - 3 = 3n + 7$

8 The commission, C, in dollars, for selling magazines is shown by the expression $C = 10 + 3n$, where n is the number of magazines.

(a) Solve the equation $46 = 10 + 3n$.

(b) To what problem is the solution in (a) the answer?

C

9 Do you know what a civet is? The solution to the equation $2n + 6 = 36$ tells you the average length of life for a civet. Solve for n.

10 Would you believe that there are mammals that lay eggs? One of them is the platypus. Its life span in captivity is given by the root of the equation, $3n + 18 = 168$. What is the life span of the platypus?

solving equations by inspection

In the previous work, you solved equations using systematic trial. Where possible, you should inspect an equation to check whether you can obtain the solution by simply asking useful questions. To solve the next equation, you need to again ask useful questions. You can solve some equations by the **inspection method**.

You can use the method of inspection to solve an equation when the equation is reasonably simple. But to do so you need to ask useful questions.

Solve
$2n + 3 = 15$

Think: What number added to 3 equals 15?

Compare
$\quad 12 + 3 = 15$
$\quad 2n + 3 = 15$

Now solve
$2n = 12$

Think: What number, multiplied by 2, is equal to 12?
$2 \times 6 = 12$
$2 \times n = 12$ — Compare
Thus $n = 6$

Thus, the solution is $n = 6$.

Check:
L.S. $= 2n + 3 \qquad$ R.S. $= 15$
$\quad = 2(6) + 3$
$\quad = 12 + 3$
$\quad = 15 \quad$ L.S. $=$ R.S. ✔ checks

---

11 What is the solution of each equation?

(a) $g + 12 = 54$ (b) $m - 16 = 98$

(c) $2c = 16$ (d) $\frac{m}{3} = 8$

(e) $16 + k = 24$ (f) $12 = p - 4$

(g) $16 = 4m$ (h) $25 = \frac{k}{5}$

12 For each equation, the first question is shown. Use the question to solve the equation.

(a) $2n + 6 = 8$ (Think: What number, added to 6, is equal to 8?)

(b) $5n - 3 = 12$ (Think: 3 is subtracted from a number and the answer is 12. What is the number?)

(c) $\frac{n}{3} - 4 = 14$ (Think: 4 is subtracted from a number divided by 3 and the answer is 14. What is the number?)

13 To solve each equation, what is the first question to ask yourself? Then solve each equation.

(a) $2p + 3 = 13$ (b) $5p - 1 = 19$

(c) $\frac{p}{2} + 3 = 11$ (d) $\frac{q}{2} - 3 = 3$

(e) $8 + 3p = 23$ (f) $13 = 5 + \frac{q}{3}$

14 Solve each equation. Use the inspection method.

(a) $6y - 3 = 15$ (b) $3 + 4k = 23$

(c) $\frac{y}{3} - 1 = 9$ (d) $2h + 6 = 16$

(e) $8x + 4 = 20$ (f) $12h - 24 = 0$

(g) $34 = 2p + 6$ (h) $3y - 4 = 23$

(i) $2m - 3 = -7$ (j) $2m - 1 = -6$

(k) $2x + 1 = 2$ (l) $8 - y = 6$

15 Find each root. Check your answer.

(a) $4y = 12$ (b) $8 - y = 12$

(c) $2y - 8 = 32$ (d) $30 = 2x + 24$

(e) $\frac{m}{3} = 3.1$ (f) $7t + 11 = 46$

(g) $56 + 2p = 90$ (h) $4p = 6.8$

(i) $2h + 23 = 65$ (j) $3k - 14 = 25$

12.3 solving equations: using properties of addition and subtraction

The method of systematic trial is time-consuming if the roots are decimals or proper fractions. To develop a strategy for solving equations, you need to understand how equations are built.

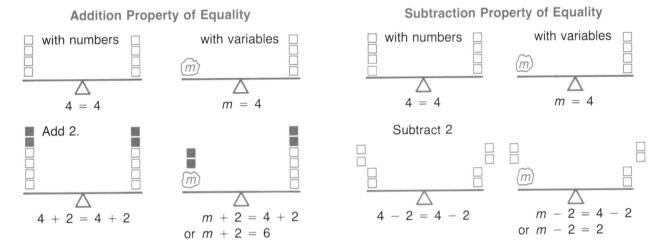

Addition Property of Equality

with numbers

$4 = 4$

with variables

$m = 4$

Add 2.

$4 + 2 = 4 + 2$

$m + 2 = 4 + 2$
or $m + 2 = 6$

Subtraction Property of Equality

with numbers

$4 = 4$

with variables

$m = 4$

Subtract 2

$4 - 2 = 4 - 2$

$m - 2 = 4 - 2$
or $m - 2 = 2$

In the above examples, you have built equations.

To solve the equation you need to reverse the operations or undo the building of the equation.

$$m + 2 = 6$$
$$m + 2 - 2 = 6 - 2$$
$$m = 4$$

$\left(\begin{array}{l}\text{How do you decide} \\ \text{what number and} \\ \text{operation to use?}\end{array}\right)$

$$m - 2 = 2$$
$$m - 2 + 2 = 2 + 2$$
$$m = 4$$

You can build other equations so that they all have the same root. These are called **equivalent equations**.

$m = 24$	$m = 24$	$m = 24$	$m = 24$
$m + 6 = 24 + 6$	$m + 9 = 24 + 9$	$m - 9 = 24 - 9$	$m - 12 = 24 - 12$
$m + 6 = 30$	$m + 9 = 33$	$m - 9 = 15$	$m - 12 = 12$

Example   Solve and verify $m + 8 = 24$, $m \in W$ ◀— The replacement set is W.

Solution   Solve $m + 8 = 24$
$$m + 8 - 8 = 24 - 8$$
$$m = 16$$

Verify   L.S. $= m + 8$ R.S. $= 24$
$$= 16 + 8$$
$$= 24$$

Since L.S. $=$ R.S., then 16 is the root of the equation.

A

1 For each equation, use addition to build an equivalent equation.

(a) $x = 3$　　(b) $y = 5$　　(c) $m = 6$

2 For each equation, use subtraction to build an equivalent equation.

(a) $b = 6$　　(b) $s = 5$　　(c) $r = 4$

3 The equations in each pair are equivalent. How is the second equation built from the first?

(a) $y = 3, y + 9 = 12$

(b) $t = 3, t - 5 = -2$

(c) $x = -1, x + 6 = 5$

(d) $s = 2, s + 9 = 11$

4 Complete the missing step for each solution.

(a)　　　$y + 6 = 15$
　　　$y + 6 - 6 = 15 - 6$

(b)　　　$k - 8 = 23$
　　　$k - 8 + 8 = 23 + 8$

B

5 For each equation, decide on the first step to solve the equation. Then solve.

(a) $y + 8 = 16$　　(b) $k - 3 = 9$

(c) $19 = m - 2$　　(d) $16 = 8 + k$

6 Which equations have been built from $p = 3$?

(a) $p + 6 = 9$　　(b) $p + 8 = 10$

(c) $p - 8 = -5$　　(d) $9 + p = 12$

7 Solve. Check your answers.

(a) $y - 6 = 4$　　(b) $8 + k = 12$

(c) $15 + z = 23$　　(d) $11 = s + 3$

8 Find each solution.

(a) $k + 3 = 12$　　(b) $a - 9 = 9$

(c) $b - 6 = -2$　　(d) $8 = 12 + f$

9 What is the root of each equation?

(a) $s - 3 = 5$　　(b) $5 + t = 18$

(c) $3 = 6 + r$　　(d) $x - 12 = -6$

10 Each equation involves decimals. Solve the equation.

(a) $x + 8.6 = 12.6$　　(b) $6.3 + y = 15.3$

(c) $7.3 = m + 2.5$　　(d) $9.6 + p = 12.5$

11 Solve. Which equations are equivalent?

(a) $8 + k = 17$　　(b) $21 = 12 + k$

(c) $k + 3 = 10$　　(d) $0 = k - 9$

C

12 A plane's ground speed when flying with a tail wind is given by the following formula.

Ground Speed = Air Speed + Tail Wind
$$G = A + T$$

(a) Find the ground speed, G, when $A = 600$ km/h　and　$T = 100$ km/h.

(b) Find A when $G = 900$ km/h and $T = 150$ km/h.

(c) Find T when $G = 450$ km/h and $A = 75$ km/h.

13 When a plane flies into a head wind its ground speed is given by the following formula.

Ground Speed = Air Speed − Head Wind
$$G = A - H$$

(a) Find G when $A = 475$ km/h and $H = 30$ km/h.

(b) Find A when $G = 650$ km/h and $H = 150$ km/h.

12.4 solving equations: using all operations

You can use other operations to build an equation. Similarly, you can use other operations to help you solve equations.

| Multiplication | | | | Division | | |

Building
$x = 16$
$2x = 2 \times 16$
$2x = 32$

$\left(\begin{array}{c} \text{Reverse} \\ \text{the} \\ \text{operation} \end{array} \right)$

Solving
$2x = 32$
$\frac{2x}{2} = \frac{32}{2}$
$x = 16$

Building
$x = 16$
$\frac{x}{2} = \frac{16}{2}$
$\frac{x}{2} = 8$

$\left(\begin{array}{c} \text{Reverse} \\ \text{the} \\ \text{operation} \end{array} \right)$

Solving
$\frac{x}{2} = 8$
$2 \times \frac{x}{2} = 2 \times 8$
$x = 16$

12.4 exercise

A

1 What is the inverse of each operation?

(a) multiply by 3   (b) divide by 6

2 The equations in each pair are equivalent. How is the second equation built from the first?

(a) $y = 3, 2y = 6$ (b) $f = 2, 6f = 12$

(c) $k = 8, \frac{k}{2} = 4$ (d) $q = 24, \frac{q}{6} = 4$

(e) $d = 0, 5d = 0$ (f) $r = -6, \frac{r}{2} = -3$

3 Which equations have been built from $s = 24$?

(a) $\frac{s}{2} = 12$ (b) $\frac{s}{6} = 3$ (c) $2s = 48$

(d) $8 = \frac{s}{3}$ (e) $72 = 3s$ (f) $\frac{s}{12} = 3$

4 Which equations are equivalent to $t = 16$?

(a) $\frac{t}{2} = 8$ (b) $2t = 8$ (c) $48 = 3t$

(d) $2 = \frac{t}{8}$ (e) $5t = 80$ (f) $4 = \frac{t}{4}$

5 For each equation, decide on the first step to solve the equation. Then solve.

(a) $3y = 12$ (b) $\frac{m}{2} = 18$ (c) $25 = 5t$

(d) $16t = 32$ (e) $\frac{v}{4} = 16$ (f) $20 = \frac{t}{4}$

B

6 Solve. Check your answers.

(a) $2m = 30$ (b) $\frac{s}{2} = 8$ (c) $3a = 15$

(d) $16 = \frac{p}{2}$ (e) $24 = 12t$ (f) $18 = \frac{p}{3}$

7 Find the root of each equation.

(a) $3q = 9$ (b) $\frac{r}{5} = 25$ (c) $4t = 16$

(d) $12 = 4k$ (e) $16 = \frac{s}{2}$ (f) $5m = 25$

8 Each equation involves decimals. Solve the equation.

(a) $4k = 6.4$ (b) $\frac{k}{3} = 3.2$ (c) $4k = 5$

9 For each equation decide on what number you should multiply by or divide by to obtain a simpler equivalent equation. Then solve.

$\left(\text{Remember: } \frac{1}{3}a \text{ can be written as } \frac{a}{3} \text{ or as } a \div 3. \right)$

(a) $\frac{a}{3} = 6$ (b) $4a = 24$

(c) $3k = 9 + 12$ (d) $64 = 8y$

(e) $4 = \frac{2}{3}x$ (f) $k \div 6 = 18$

(g) $\frac{4}{5}y = 8$ (h) $20 = \frac{5}{4}m$

12.5 solving equations: more than one step

In your earlier work, you built equations using only one operation.
You can also build equations using more than one operation.

| Building the Equation | Solving the Equation |

Building the Equation

$$n = 3$$
(Multiply by 2.) $2 \times n = 2 \times 3$
$$2n = 6$$
(Add 3.) $2n + 3 = 6 + 3$
$$2n + 3 = 9$$

$\left(\begin{array}{l}\text{To solve the equation}\\\text{you use the inverse}\\\text{operations in the}\\\text{reverse order.}\end{array}\right)$

Solving the Equation

$$2n + 3 = 9$$
(Subtract 3.) $2n + 3 - 3 = 9 - 3$
$$2n = 6$$
(Divide by 2.) $\dfrac{2n}{2} = \dfrac{6}{2}$
$$n = 3$$

To solve an equation, you obtain an equivalent equation which
you can more easily solve by inspection, as shown in the
example.

Example   Find the root of the equation $3y - 8 = 7$.

Solution
$$3y - 8 = 7$$
$$3y - 8 + 8 = 7 + 8$$
$$3y = 15$$
$$\frac{3y}{3} = \frac{15}{3}$$
$$y = 5$$
The root is 5.

$\left(\begin{array}{l}\text{Think: Check your answer.}\\\text{L.S.} = 3y - 8 \quad \text{R.S.} = 7\\\quad = 3(5) - 8\\\quad = 15 - 8\\\quad = 7\\\text{L.S.} = \text{R.S. checks} ✔\end{array}\right)$

To show the steps for building an equation or
solving it, you can use a flow chart.

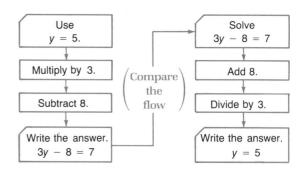

12.5 exercise

A

1 What is the inverse of each operation?

   (a) add 6   (b) multiply by 8

   (c) subtract 4   (d) divide by 3

   (e) add -8 (f) subtract -6

2 For each of the following, how is each step
obtained?

   (a) $3x + 4 = 16$
$$3x + 4 - 4 = 16 - 4$$
$$3x = 12$$

(b)
$$2a - 1 = 5$$
$$2a - 1 + 1 = 5 + 1$$
$$2a = 6$$

(c)
$$3x - 4 = 17$$
$$3x - 4 + 4 = 17 + 4$$
$$3x = 21$$

3 (a) By starting with $x = 2$, Jean built the equivalent equation $5x + 1 = 11$. What did she do?

(b) Build an equivalent equation for each of the following. $m = 3$, $k = 8$

4 For each equation, decide on the first step to solve the equation, then solve.

(a) $2f + 3 = 15$ (b) $5e - 8 = 22$

(c) $6 + d = 12$ (d) $12 - 3g = 6$

B

5 For each equation decide on what number you should add or subtract to each side to obtain a simpler equivalent equation. Then solve.

(a) $2x - 5 = 15$ (b) $12x + 4 = 64$

(c) $14 = x - 2$ (d) $-13 = x + 9$

(e) $3x + \frac{1}{3} = -\frac{2}{3}$ (f) $21 = 4y + 5$

6 Which equations have been built from $p = 36$?

(a) $3 + 2p = 75$ (b) $2p - 3 = 69$

(c) $\frac{p}{2} + 8 = 20$ (d) $\frac{p}{3} - 6 = 6$

7 Solve. Check your answers.

(a) $2y - 13 = 25$ (b) $24 = 3x - 3$

(c) $\frac{y}{3} + 2 = 8$ (d) $2x + \frac{1}{3} = \frac{2}{3}$

8 What is the root of each equation?

(a) $3p - 6 = 30$ (b) $6 + \frac{k}{4} = 10$

(c) $9 + 3m = 15$ (d) $\frac{y}{6} + 8 = 14$

9 These equations involve decimals. Find the root of each equation.

(a) $x + 4.5 = 7.6$ (b) $9.8 + y = 12.6$

(c) $0.3x = 12$ (d) $96 = 0.12y$

(e) $0.2x + 4.5 = 4.9$ (f) $0.4y - 3.6 = 12.8$

10 Construct an equation to show the results of each flow chart.

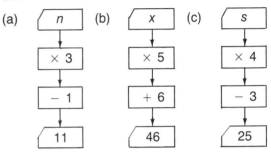

(a) n (b) x (c) s

$\times 3$ $\times 5$ $\times 4$

$- 1$ $+ 6$ $- 3$

11 46 25

11 Solve each equation. Use a reverse flow chart. Which equations are equivalent?

(a) $3k + 4 = 13$ (b) $2 + 3h = 14$

(c) $\frac{m}{3} + 5 = 6$ (d) $\frac{n}{6} + 3 = 9$

12 The perimeter of a rectangle is given by $P = 2l + 2w$.

(a) Find P if $l = 6$, $w = 3$.

(b) Find l if $w = 8$, $P = 24$.

(c) Find w if $l = 16$, $P = 48$.

13 The cost, C, in dollars, of producing the posters is $C = 15 + 8n$, where n is the number of posters.

(a) Find C if $n = 36$.   (b) Find n if $C = 79$.

C

14 Quite often the solution in one part of a problem is needed in another. Replace ■ with the solution of the previous equation. What is the value of t?

(a) $3n - 2 = 13$ (b) $■k + 3 = 13$

(c) $3r - ■ = 10$ (d) $\frac{3t}{■} + 15 = 18$

12.6 solving problems: using equations

To solve any problem, including problems with variables, you follow steps you have used before for solving other problems. To solve a problem you must translate accurately from English to mathematics. You need to translate the problem into an equation using symbols.

Example 1   When a number is doubled and increased by 5, the answer is 23. What is the number?

Solution   Let n represent the number.   (A)

A number doubled   increased by 5   is equal to 23

$$2n + 5 = 23 \quad \text{(B)}$$
$$2n + 5 - 5 = 23 - 5$$
$$2n = 18$$
$$\frac{2n}{2} = \frac{18}{2} \quad \text{(D)}$$
$$\text{(C)} \quad n = 9$$

Check: Double 9 = 18
Add   5   5
The answer is   23
✓ checks

(E)   The number is 9.

> **Steps for Solving Problems**
>
> A Read the problem carefully. Ask yourself:
>   I What information am I asked to find?
>   II What information am I given?
> B Decide on a method.
>   Choose a variable and translate.
> C Do the work.
>   Solve the equation.
> D Check your work.
>   Check or verify the answer in the original problem.
> E Make a final statement.
>   Answer the original problem.

To solve some problems you need to understand the meaning of special words as shown in the next example.

Example 2   The sum of 3 *consecutive* whole numbers is 36. Find the 3 numbers.

5, 6, 7 are consecutive numbers.
$n, n + 1, n + 2$ are consecutive numbers.

Solution   Let n represent the first number, then $n + 1$ represents the second number, and $n + 2$ represents the third number.

$$n + n + 1 + n + 2 = 36$$
$$3n + 3 = 36$$
$$3n + 3 - 3 = 36 - 3$$
$$3n = 33$$
$$\frac{3n}{3} = \frac{33}{3}$$
$$n = 11$$

Think
$n + n + n = 3n$

Check: 11, 12, 13 are 3 consecutive numbers.
$11 + 12 + 13 = 36$ ✓ checks

The three consecutive whole numbers are 11, 12, 13.

12.6 exercise

A Throughout the exercise, the replacement set for the variables is the whole numbers or integers.

1 Translate the following into symbols. Use *n* as a variable for the number.

  (a) one half a number is increased by 2.

  (b) 3 times a number is added to 2.

  (c) The sum of a number and 6 is doubled.

  (d) A number decreased by 3 is then multiplied by 4.

  (e) Divide the sum of a number and 2 by 3.

2 The variable *h* represents a number. Write in words what each of the following represent.

  (a) $h + 5$ (b) $3h$ (c) $h - 3$

  (d) $2h + 1$ (e) $3h - 2$ (f) $h + 2h$

3 Solve and verify.

  (a) $x + 6 = 8$ (b) $22 - k = 13$

  (c) $8 = \frac{2}{3}m$ (d) $k - 2 = -2$

  (e) $2m - 1 = -13$ (f) $k + k = 8$

  (g) $k \div (-3) = -9$ (h) $2m - 1 = 13$

B Remember: Check your answer in the original word problem.

4 Solve each problem.

  (a) A number is multiplied by 6 and the result is 48. Find the number.

  (b) When a number is added to itself the result is 72. Find the number.

  (c) A number increased by 8 is equal to 108. Find the number.

  (d) One-half of a number decreased by 6 is equal to 3. Find the number.

  (e) Seven times a number, plus 4, equals 60. What is the number?

5 Solve. (Be sure to make a final statement.)

  (a) Phoebe is 3 a older than Burk. The sum of their ages is 55. How old are they?

  (b) Mathew is half as old as Alan. If the sum of their ages is 54, find their ages.

  (c) Next year Victoria will be twice as old as Louis and the sum of their ages will be 42. Find their ages today.

6 Solve each problem.

  (a) A number is decreased by 6 and then this result is divided by 2. The result is 15. Find the number.

  (b) A number is divided by 16 to obtain 3. Find the number.

  (c) A third of a number increased by 16 is 23. Find the number.

7 Find the missing numbers.

  (a) The sum of three consecutive whole numbers is 129. Find the numbers.

  (b) The sum of three consecutive integers is -27. Find the integers.

  (c) The sum of three consecutive even numbers is 144. Find the numbers.

8 During a school election, 625 votes were cast. Melanie received 75 more votes than Peter. How many votes did each receive?

9 Pierre and Marie have newspaper routes. Marie's weekly earnings are 3 times Pierre's weekly earnings. Together they make $11.00. How much does each earn in a week?

Check whether your answer is reasonable.

C

10 In a triangle, one angle is three times as large as the smallest. The remaining angle is 30° greater than the smallest. Find the measures of the angles. Classify the triangle.

12.7 applying algebra: solving equations

Skills and concepts you learn in arithmetic extend to skills in algebra, such as the distributive property.

Arithmetic	Algebra
$3(5 + 2)$	$3(x + 2)$
$= 3 \times 5 + 3 \times 2$	$= 3 \times x + 3 \times 2$
$= 15 + 6$	$= 3x + 6$
$= 21$	

Distributive property
▶ How are they alike?
▶ How are they different?

$(5 + 2)3$	$(x + 2)3$
$= 5 \times 3 + 2 \times 3$	$= x \times 3 + 2 \times 3$
$= 15 + 6$	$= 3x + 6$
$= 21$	

You can apply the distributive property when solving an equation.

Example 1 Solve $3(x + 2) = 12, x \in W$.

Solution

$$3(x + 2) = 12$$
$$3x + 6 = 12$$
$$3x + 6 - 6 = 12 - 6$$
$$3x = 6$$
$$\frac{3x}{3} = \frac{6}{3}$$
$$x = 2$$

Check
L.S. $= x(3 + 2)$ R.S. $= 12$
$= 3(2 + 2)$
$= 3(4)$
$= 12$
L.S. = R.S. checks ✓

To solve some equations, special skills in algebra are developed.

In algebra $y + y + y + y$ becomes $4 \times y$ or $4y$

$4y$ is called a **term**. The terms $5y$ and $4y$ are called **like terms**.

This number is called the **numerical coefficient**.

Like terms have the same letter or **literal coefficient**.

To add like terms, you can use your understanding of what a term is.

$4y$ means $y + y + y + y$
$5y$ means $y + y + y + y + y$
$4y + 5y$ means $\underbrace{y + y + y + y}_{4y} + \underbrace{y + y + y + y + y}_{5y} = 9y$

To add or subtract like terms each time in this way is time-consuming so the distributive property is used.

$4y + 5y = (4 + 5)y$
$= 9y$

$6y - 3y = (6 - 3)y$
$= 3y$

What's Algebra?

To most people the word suggests a mysterious study of symbols and letters. This study of symbols and letters has gone on for thousands of years. People have posed problems and each time they confronted a problem that was difficult to solve, they invented more mathematics. As early as 1650 B.C. in the Rhind Papyrus (a collection of ancient writings), the following problems written in Greek occur.

> A quantity, its $\frac{2}{3}$, its $\frac{1}{2}$, and its $\frac{1}{7}$ added together becomes 33. What is the quantity?

On the surface, the problem appears as an arithmetic problem. If you look up the meaning of arithmetic in the dictionary you will find this definition.

- The science of computing with numbers by the operations of addition, subtraction, multiplication, and division.

To solve many problems you need to go beyond arithmetic. You use algebra. In the same dictionary this meaning of algebra is given.

- The branch of mathematics that treats quantity and the relations of numbers in the abstract, where calculations are performed by means of letters and symbols.

The word *algebra* is believed to have originated from the title of an Arabic publication, which appeared as

Al-jebr-w'al-muqabâlah

The meaning of Al-jebr in Arabic is "the reunion of broken parts, bone setting". Over the years, the early mathematicians passed on these early mathematical writings from one generation to the next and eventually these ideas found their way to the Western World. Eventually, the word *al-jebr* became the name used to study this powerful branch of mathematics, called algebra.

It has been said that the impact of algebra on the study of mathematics exceeds the impact of computers on today's society.

The skill of adding or subtracting like terms is referred to as *collecting like terms*. As in your study of arithmetic, once you learn a skill you apply the skill. The same procedure is used in your study of algebra as shown in the example.

Example 2   Solve and verify $4y - 5 = 2y + 3$.

Solution

Solve

$$4y - 5 = 2y + 3$$
$$4y - 5 + 5 = 2y + 3 + 5$$
$$4y = 2y + 8$$
$$4y - 2y = 2y - 2y + 8$$
$$2y = 8$$
$$\frac{2y}{2} = \frac{8}{2}$$
$$y = 4$$

Thus, $y = 4$ is the solution. ←

Verify

L.S. $= 4y - 5$
$= 4(4) - 5$
$= 16 - 5$
$= 11$

R.S. $= 2y + 3$
$= 2(4) + 3$
$= 8 + 3$
$= 11$

L.S. $=$ R.S.

An important nature of mathematics is the following. Often the development of mathematics occurs when people solve new problems they are confronted with. To solve the problem, suitable skills are invented to obtain the solution.

12.7 exercise

A

1 Write each of the following as one term.

(a) $y + y$

(b) $y + y + y$

(c) $k + k + k + k$

(d) $m + m + m + m + m$

(e) $x + x + x + x + x + x + x$

2 Find the answer. Complete each step.

(a) $2k + 3k$
$= (2 + 3)k$
$= ?$

(b) $3p + 4p$
$= (3 + 4)p$
$= ?$

(c) $5x + 3x$
$= (?)x$
$= ?$

(d) $2y + 6y$
$= (?)y$
$= ?$

3 Simplify each of the following.

(a) $2x + 4x$

(b) $6x + 3x$

(c) $4y + 5y$

(d) $2y + 7y$

(e) $3k + k$

(f) $k + 5k$

(g) $2p + 8p$

(h) $5s + 6s$

(i) $3d + 9d$

(j) $2r + 3r + 6r$

(k) $3s + 5s + s$

(l) $4t + t + 6t$

(m) $5k + k + k$

4 Find each answer. Find the missing part.

(a) $6k - 3k$
$= (6 - 3)k$
$= ?$

(b) $9y - 5y$
$= (9 - 5)y$
$= ?$

(c) $8m - 3m$
$= (?)m$
$= ?$

(d) $12p - 9p$
$= (?)m$
$= ?$

5 Simplify each of the following.

(a) $8x - 3x$

(b) $4y - 2y$

(c) $9k - 3k$

(d) $3k - k$

(e) $5y - y$

(f) $12k - 10k$

(g) $9p - 6p - p$

(h) $7p - 3p + p$

(i) $8k + 3k - 4k$

(j) $9s - 2s + 3s$

6 Expand.

Expand means to multiply.
$3(x + 2) \rightarrow 3x + 6$

(a) $3(k + 3)$

(b) $2(s - 2)$

(c) $5(k - 3)$

(d) $8(m + 5)$

(e) $3(2k + 2)$

(f) $5(3k - 2)$

7 Simplify.

(a) $3k + 2k$ (b) $5y - 2y$ (c) $2(y - 3)$

(d) $6(k + 5)$ (e) $2(3p + 1)$ (f) $4k + 2k + k$

(g) $8s - 2s + s$ (h) $5(2r - 3)$

(i) $3(2k + 1 + 3)$ (j) $5(5k - 3k)$

(k) $5p - 3p + 2p$ (l) $4(2k + 3k)$

8 Evaluate each of the following, use $x = 3$.

(a) $3x + 2x$ (b) $8x - 5x$

(c) $3(x - 2)$ (d) $5(2x - 1)$

(e) $2(5x - 2x)$ (f) $3(2x - x + 8)$

B

9 Equivalent expressions give the same value. Use $n = 5$. Which expressions are equivalent?

(a) $8n + 2n$ (b) $6n - 2n$

(c) $9n - 3n + n$ (d) $2(4n - 2n)$

(e) $3n + 2n - n$ (f) $5n - 2n + n$

10 Solve.

(a) $y + 3 = 8 + 9$ (b) $3 + m = 8 - 6$

(c) $2k - 8 = 3 + 11$ (d) $3p - 2 = 19 - 12$

11 Solve.

(a) $2x + 3x = 25$ (b) $6p - 4p = 8$

(c) $13 - 11 = 8y - 7y$ (d) $12 + 8 = 4k - 2k$

12 (a) What is the first step required to simplify the equation $6y - 3y - 3 = 18$?

(b) Solve the equation. Check your answer.

13 Solve.

(a) $5y + 3y + 8 = 24$ (b) $2y - 8 + 3y = 17$

(c) $6y - 4y + 2 = 12$ (d) $8y + 6 - 3y = 26$

14 (a) What is the first step required to simplify the equation $6(p - 3) = 12$?

(b) Solve the equation. Check your answer.

15 Solve.

(a) $3(k + 1) = 12$ (b) $2(p - 3) = 7 + 5$

(c) $25 = 5(t - 3)$ (d) $4(k + 3 + 2) = 16$

16 Solve. Verify your answers.

(a) $12k - 2k = 110$ (b) $48 = 5y + 3y$

(c) $7(y - 5) = 49$ (d) $s + 3s - s = 36$

(e) $38 = 8k + 2 + k$ (f) $2p + 4 = 15 + p$

(g) $3y - 5 = 2y + 15$ (h) $3y + 6 = y + 12$

17 Solve.

(a) $8k + 3k = 22$ (b) $12k - 3k = 63$

(c) $12p - 6p + p = 84$ (d) $3p + 4p - 6 = 15$

(e) $2(p - 1) = 12$ (f) $6m - 20 = 2m$

(g) $6 + 5m = 7m$ (h) $3(2k + 5) = 15$

(i) $3y + 5y - 24 = 0$ (j) $48 = 8(t + 3)$

(k) $7y + 1 = 4 + 4y$ (l) $4k + 8 = 3k + 22$

(m) $16 = 4(y - 5)$ (n) $5y - 2 = 28 - y$

18 Each equation involves decimals. Solve.

(a) $4.5t + 1.5t = 18$ (b) $1.7h - 0.45h = 5$

(c) $2.5k - 8 = 1.5k$ (d) $3.6p + 2 = 1.6p$

(e) $3.5m - 2 = 1.5m + 6$

(f) $4(0.5s + 1) = 8$

(g) $8(0.2m - 2) = 0.6m$

(h) $3(1.5k - 1) = 1.5k + 9$

---

problem-solving: strategy

To solve a problem, often you can try an easier similar problem.

How many triangles are in the figure?

Hint: Try this pattern of triangles. How many triangles are in each diagram?

problem solving: using diagrams

To solve earlier problems you often used a diagram to plan
the solution. When solving problems with equations often it is
helpful to record the information given in a problem in a
diagram. Then use your skills with algebra to solve the problem.

Example The length of a rectangle is twice as long as the
width. If the perimeter is 180 cm, find the
dimensions.

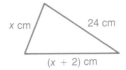

Solution Let w represent the width of the rectangle in
centimetres. Then the length of the rectangle, in
centimetres, is $2w$.

$\left(\text{Record the information on a diagram.}\right)$

$$2w + w + 2w + w = 180 \quad \left(\begin{array}{l}\text{Write the equation from}\\\text{the facts in the diagram.}\end{array}\right)$$
$$6w = 180$$
$$\frac{6w}{6} = \frac{180}{6}$$
$$w = 30$$

Check:
2 lengths = 120 cm
2 widths = $\underline{60}$ cm
180 cm

The length is 60 cm, the width is 30 cm.

---

19 For each diagram, write an expression for the
perimeter.

(a)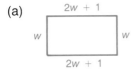

(b)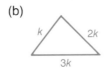

20 A rectangle has length k metres and width
$k - 2$ metres.

(a) Draw a diagram to show the information.

(b) Write an expression for the perimeter.

21 A triangle has sides w, $w + 2$ and $2w - 1$, in
centimetres. Draw a diagram to show the
information in the problem.

22 (a) The perimeter of
the square is 48 m.
Find the
dimensions.

(b) The perimeter of
the rectangle is
80 cm. Find the
dimensions.

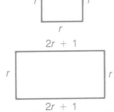

23 (a) A rectangle has length, in centimetres, of g
and width, in centimetres, of $g - 3$. If the
perimeter is 30 cm, find the dimensions.

(b) The perimeter of a square is 36 m. Find its
dimensions.

(c) The perimeter of a rectangle is 40 cm. The
width is 5 cm. Find the dimensions.

24 Find the length of each
side of the triangle if
the perimeter is 62 cm.

25 The length of a rectangle is 3 times the width. If
the perimeter is 128 m, find the dimensions of
the rectangle.

26 The length of a rectangle, decreased by 1 cm,
equals the width of the rectangle. If the
perimeter is 102 cm, find the dimensions of the
rectangle.

27 A ribbon is 72 cm long. It is cut into 2 pieces so
that one is $\frac{1}{3}$ the length of the other. Find the
length of the pieces.

12.8 extending skills: solving inequations

Earlier, you solved inequations and then you drew their graphs. You can now extend the skills you learned with algebra and solving equations to solving inequations. Compare these solutions.

> Remember, number sentences that use the symbols $<, >, \leq, \geq$ are called *inequations*.

Example Find the solution set.

(a) $3y + 2 \leq 8, y \in W$

(b) $3k + 2 > 2k + 6, k \in I$

Solution

(a) $3y + 2 \leq 8, y \in W$
$3y + 2 - 2 \leq 8 - 2$
$3y \leq 6$
$\frac{3y}{3} \leq \frac{6}{3}$
$y \leq 2$

Use $y \in W$. The solution set is $\{0, 1, 2\}$.

(b) $3k + 2 > 2k + 6, k \in I$
$3k + 2 - 2 > 2k + 6 - 2$
$3k > 2k + 4$
$3k - 2k > 2k - 2k + 4$
$k > 4$

Use $k \in I$. The solution set is $\{5, 6, 7, 8, \dots\}$.

12.8 exercise

A Use the skills you developed in Section 12.7.

1 For each inequation, choose

▶ one whole number that makes it true.

▶ one whole number that makes it false.

(a) $d + 5 < 11$ (b) $2n > 5$

(c) $\frac{1}{2}n > 5$ (d) $15 + m < 10$

2 Solve each inequation, $k \in W$.

(a) $k > 3$ (b) $k \leq 4$ (c) $8 \geq k$ (d) $k + 1 < 5$

3 Complete each step. Solve the inequation, $y \in I$.

(a) $3y + 2 > 8$
$3y + 2 - 2 > 8 - 2$
▬▬▬▬▬▬▬▬

(b) $3(m - 2) \leq 6$
$3m - 6 \leq 6$
▬▬▬▬▬▬▬▬

B

4 The solutions to the following may require more than one step. Solve.

(a) $k + 6 - 3 \geq 8, \ k \in W$

(b) $m - 8 > 5 + 3, \ m \in I$

(c) $s - 5 < 5, \ s \in I$

5 Find each solution set. The variables are whole numbers.

(a) $3b + 1 > 10$ (b) $3 + 2y < 11$

(c) $2(k - 1) \geq 3$ (d) $4(m + 2) \leq 24$

6 Each variable represents integers. Solve.

(a) $3k + 2k \geq 10$ (b) $8p + 3 < 5p$

(c) $2t - 3 > t + 5$ (d) $2(t - 5) > 8$

7 Find the solution sets. Variables are integers.

(a) $n + 3 < 12$ (b) $m + 1 > 5$

(c) $t - 3 \leq 8$ (d) $t - 4 \geq 5$

(e) $3m - 1 < 11$ (f) $t + 2t \leq 18$

(g) $9y + 4 \geq 5y + 12$ (h) $6a - 3 < 16 - 2a$

8 Translate the following into symbols then solve. The replacement set is W.

(a) k is doubled and is less than 6.

(b) m is increased by 4 and is less than or equal to 8.

test for practice

1 Translate each of the following into symbols.

  (a) Three is added to w.

  (b) k is greater than 2.

  (c) q is decreased by 4.

2 Choose a variable, then translate into symbols.

  (a) A number is doubled and increased by 7.

  (b) A number divided by 5 and decreased by 3 is equal to 11.

3 For the equation $2n - 9 = 21$, find a value that makes the sentence true and one that makes it false.

4 Solve each equation by systematic trial.

  (a) $z + 1.8 = 5.3$ (b) $2.8 + 4t = 17.6$

5 Solve each equation by inspection. Verify your answer.

  (a) $3w - 4 = 17$ (b) $32 - 2r = 10$

6 Use the equation $3n + 4 = 25$.

  (a) Construct a flow-chart for building the equation.

  (b) Construct a reverse flow chart to solve the equation.

7 Solve each equation. Verify your solution.

  (a) $3y - 4 = 53$ (b) $3(m + 1) = m + 9$

8 Find an expression for the perimeter.

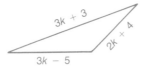

9 (a) Find the solution set $m + 3 < 5$, $m \in I$.

  (b) A number when multiplied by 4 and increased by three is the same as 39. Find the number.

maintaining skills

These questions review computations throughout your earlier work. Find the value of ■ in each question. The questions are in no special order.

  (a) The value of $2^3 + 3^2$ is ■.

  (b) If the radius of a circle is 36 cm, then the area to 1 decimal place is ■. (Use $\pi \doteq 3.14$.)

  (c) If $k = 3$, $m = -4$, then $k^2 + m^2 + km$ equals ■.

  (d) $\dfrac{2}{3} = \dfrac{8}{■}$ (e) $\dfrac{3}{■} = \dfrac{5}{15}$

  (f) The lowest common denominator of $\dfrac{1}{2}$, $\dfrac{3}{4}$, and $\dfrac{1}{3}$ is ■.

  (g) $-9 + 3 - 4 - 6 - 2 + 8$ equals ■.

  (h) If $k = 5$ then $k^2 + k - 2$ equals ■.

  (i) $416\ 934 \div 231$ equals ■ to 2 decimal places.

  (j) $(-3)(-2)(-6) = ■$.   (k) $(-12) - (-3) = ■$.

  (l) 4.9659 rounded off to the nearest hundredth is ■.

  (m) $12\frac{1}{4} - 3\frac{2}{5}$ equals ■. (n) $4\frac{4}{5} \div 2\frac{2}{5}$ equals ■.

---

computer tip

A very important method of solving equations is an **iterative method**. The computer tries different values of the variable and isolates the approximate value of the root. Try this program. You will see approximately what the root of this equation is.

$6x + 2 = 3x + 3$

```
10  PRINT "SOLVING EQUATIONS"
20  FOR X = -4 TO 4 STEP .25
30  LET L = 6 * X + 2
40  LET R = 3 * X + 3
50  LET F = L - R
60  PRINT "VALUES ARE"; F, X
70  NEXT X
80  END
```

If the value of F = 0, then the corresponding value of X is the root. When F is close to the value of zero, then X is near the root. What is the approximate root of the equation?

looking back: a year end review

An important step in problem solving is to decide which skills you need to use. For this reason, these problems are not placed in any special order.

1 (a) Find the remainder when the difference of 298 and 139 is divided by 33.

   (b) Find the remainder when the sum of 496 and 1835 is divided by 232.

   (c) Find the product when the difference of 2986 and 1378 is multiplied by 496.

2 One of the largest airliners in the world is the Boeing 747C which can carry 490 passengers. If the town of Caledonia has 23 520 citizens, how many planes would be needed to fly them to Europe?

3 Theresa wanted to make a square pen for her dog. If she had 24 m of fencing, find the dimensions of the dog pen.

4

New rule for mixtures won't drive you nuts

OTTAWA: — The Consumer Affairs Department announced yesterday any mixture of nuts sold after Dec. 1 next year will have to contain at least 5 per cent, by mass, of each nut identified in the mi˖

In a premium brand bag of mixed nuts, cashews are 12.5% of the mass and filberts are 8.5%. Find the amount of cashews and filberts in a mixture having a mass of 96 g.

5 (a) Collect data about how you spend your time on Saturdays.

   (b) Draw a graph of your results for four Saturdays.

   (c) Why would the information you collected be useful to a person who wants to build a roller skating plaza.

6 A rectangular field requires 214.8 m of fencing. The shortest side measures 48.6 m. Find the area of the field.

7 Ted Lindsay is the all-time penalty leader in the National Hockey League. He has the worst record, with 1808 penalty minutes in 17 seasons.

   (a) About how many minutes in penalties did he have each season?

   (b) What assumption did you make in finding your answer in (a)?

8 (a) Construct a triangle whose sides are congruent to

   _____ a   _____ b

   _____ c

   (b) What measures do you need to calculate the area of the triangle in (a)?

   (c) Find the area of the triangle. (Round off your answer to one decimal place.)

   (d) Compare your answer in (c) to those of other students. Why do your answers vary?

9 (a) In a right triangle, the measure of an angle is 38°. Find the measure of the remaining angle.

   (b) Construct a parallelogram whose largest angle is 120° and whose sides are all congruent.

10 In New Orleans you will find the world's largest dome, the Louisiana Superdome. The outside diameter of the dome is 207.3 m. Calculate the outside circumference of the dome (to 1 decimal place).

11 John's father borrowed $150 from the bank at a rate of interest of $9\frac{3}{4}$%/a. He agreed to pay back the loan and the interest owed 1 a later. How much should John's father make out the cheque for?

12 Find the missing terms.

(a) $\frac{k}{10} = \frac{7}{14}$ (b) $\frac{2}{6} = \frac{m}{15}$ (c) $\frac{6}{15} = \frac{8}{p}$

(d) $\frac{12}{r} = \frac{9}{15}$ (e) $\frac{15}{20} = \frac{b}{24}$ (f) $\frac{8}{w} = \frac{10}{15}$

(g) $\frac{25}{30} = \frac{15}{k}$ (h) $\frac{u}{18} = \frac{5}{30}$ (i) $\frac{21}{7} = \frac{t}{9}$

13 Calculate the area of each stamp. Express your answer to the nearest square millimetre.

(a)

4.5 cm

8.6 cm

(b)

3.8 cm

3.1 cm

14 Estimate first, then calculate.

(a) 3.2×4.8 (b) $4.6 + 3.8$

(c) $4.45 \div 5$ (d) $6.8 - 3.9$

(e) $9.83 + 3.62$ (f) $(4.8)^2$

(g) 3.21×4.9 (h) $82.79 \div 17$

(i) $14.26 - 3.98$ (j) $14.29 + 18.63$

(k) $2326.62 \div 34$ (l) 6.83×4.26

(m) $136.29 - 49.86$ (n) $3767.4 \div 78$

(o) $38.96 + 28.1 + 36.936 - 28.9$

15 Cereal is kept in a large rectangular container which measures
3.65 m × 2.95 m × 1.25 m

(a) How many boxes measuring 17 cm × 5 cm × 23 cm can be filled from this container of cereal?

(b) What assumption did you make in finding your answer in (a)?

16 Rogatien Vachon, a hockey goalie, improved his performance. At one time his "goals against" average was 2.80, and now it is 1.39. By how much has this average decreased?

17 (a) The area of a parallelogram is 65 cm². Find the length of the base if the height is 13 cm.

(b) The base of a parallelogram is 4.2 m. Find the height if the area is 23.1 m².

18 Find each missing term.

(a) $3 : 9 : 6 = 1 : k : 2$

(b) $1 : m : 4 = 3 : 6 : 12$

(c) $m : 18 : 9 = 4 : 6 : 3$

(d) $12 : 8 : s = 3 : 2 : 5$

19 The perimeter, P, for a triangle is given by
$$P = a + b + c$$
Find the missing sides.

	a	b	c	P
(a)	163 cm	212 cm	?	571 cm
(b)	?	19.6 m	17.2 m	55.3 m
(c)	1.96 km	?	2.41 km	7.92 km

20 The measures of two angles in a triangle are 48° and 36°.

(a) Calculate the measure of the remaining angle.

(b) What type of triangle is this?

21 The marks obtained by students on a test are recorded on a stem and leaf plot.

Use the stem and leaf plot.

ones {
```
        4
        9
        4 2 3
        1 6 5 5 2
        8 2 8 8 1 1
        2 3 4 3 3 2 3
```
}
tens 3 4 5 6 7 8 9

(a) Predict the value of the mean.

(b) Calculate the average.

(c) How do your answers in (a) and (b) compare? How close were you to the predicted value?

(d) Find the range of the data. How is the range helpful in determining whether the average is helpful to know?

math is glossary

This glossary is a quick reference for the meanings of various words or phrases that you need to do mathematics. In places where a word or phrase requires further explanation, you are referred to the Index to find specific pages in the text in which the diagrams and examples provide more information.

Throughout the text, many Math Tips suggest that you compile your own list of words and their meanings. Your *list of words* together with the *Math Is Glossary* and the *Index* will be very helpful to you not only to study mathematics, but also to solve problems.

acute angle: an angle with a measure less than 90°.

acute triangle: a triangle in which each angle has a measure less than 90°.

adjacent angles: angles sharing a common vertex, a ray and with no intersection of interior points

alternate angles: refer to the index.

altitude: the perpendicular distance between a base and the opposite vertex. AE is the altitude to side BC.

angle: the figure formed by two rays with a common end point.

approximate number: the number obtained by rounding a number.

arc: a part of a curve; for a circle, part of its circumference.

area: the number of square units needed to cover a surface.

associative property: if 3 or more numbers are added or multiplied, the numbers can be combined in any order;
e.g. $4 + (6 + 5) = (4 + 6) + 5$,
$4 \times (6 \times 5) = (4 \times 6) \times 5$

average: the average of numbers is found by calculating their sum and then dividing by however many there are of them; e.g. average of 4, 6, 8, 2, 3 is
$(4 + 6 + 8 + 2 + 3) \div 5$

axes (singular, axis): the intersecting number lines or scales on a graph.

axis of symmetry: see *line of symmetry*.

---

bar graph: a diagram that uses bars to display data or information.

base (of a polygon): any side may be referred to as a base; in a triangle, the base is usually the side to which the altitude is drawn.

base (of a power): the number that is the repeated factor in a power, e.g. in 2^3 the base is 2; see also *power*.

biased sample: a sample in which not every member has an equal chance of being selected.

bisect: to separate a geometric figure into two congruent parts.

bisector (of an angle): a ray or line that bisects the angle into two congruent angles.

bisector (of a line segment): a line that bisects the line segment into two congruent parts; see also *perpendicular bisector* of a line segment.

branches: see *stem* and *leaf plot*.

---

broken line graph: a graph that displays data by means of points joined by line segments.

---

capacity: the amount of substance a container can hold; see also *litre* and *cubic units*.

Cartesian co-ordinates: see *co-ordinates*.

centimetre: one hundredth of a metre; 100 cm = 1 m; see also *metre*.

central angle: an angle with its vertex at the centre of a circle. ∠AOB is a central angle.

centre: the point in the middle of a figure.

centre (of a circle): the point that is an equal distance from any point on the circumference.

chord: a line segment that joins two points on a curve; for a circle, a chord joins any two points on the circle.

circle: a closed curve such that all points on the curve are the same distance from the centre; see also *centre* of a circle.

circle graph: a diagram that uses a circle to display data or information.

circumference: the distance around a circle; see also *perimeter*.

commission: fee paid to sale persons based on amount of sales

common denominator: a number that is a common multiple of the denominators; *lowest* common denominator is a number that is the *lowest* common multiple of the denominators; see also *common multiple* and *lowest common multiple*.

common factor (of numbers): a number that is the factor of each number; 3 is a common factor of 6 and 9; see also *factor*.

common multiple: a number that is the multiple of two or more numbers, e.g. 20 is a common multiple of 2 and 5; see also *multiple*.

commutative property: if 2 numbers are added or multiplied, the operations can be done in any order;
e.g. $4 \times 5 = 5 \times 4$ or $5 + 4 = 4 + 5$.

compasses (pair of): an instrument used for drawing circles.

complementary angles: angles for which the sum is 90°.

composite number: a number with 3 or more factors; see also *factor*, *prime number*.

congruence transformations: transformations in which the original and image figures are congruent.

congruent figures: figures that have the same size and shape.

co-ordinates: an ordered pair of numbers that shows the position of a point on a grid; also referred to as Cartesian co-ordinates; see also *grid*.

corresponding angles: refer to the index.

cube: a polyhedron with 6 congruent square faces; see also *polyhedron, congruent*.

cubic units: units used for the measure of volume and capacity; see also *litre*.

---

data: facts or information.

decagon: a polygon with ten sides; see also *polygon*.

decimal number: a number written in the decimal system; the digits 0, 1, 2, 3, 4, 5, 6, 7, 8, 9 are used to record decimal numbers; decimal numbers, including decimal fractions, are often referred to as decimals.

degree (Celsius): a unit for measuring temperature; 45°C means a temperature of 45 degrees Celsius.

degree (measure of an angle): a unit for measuring angles; 45° means 45 degrees; 1° is the measure of $\frac{1}{360}$ of a complete turn.

denominator: in the fraction $\frac{2}{3}$, the number 3 is the denominator; the denominator tells the number of equal parts into which a whole has been divided; also used to refer to the second term of a ratio.

diagonal: a line segment that joins two vertices in a polygon that are not adjacent; AC is a diagonal.

diameter: a line segment with end points on a circle and containing the centre.

digit: a symbol used to record numbers; the symbols 0, 1, 2, 3, 4, 5, 6, 7, 8, 9 are used to record decimal numbers.

dilatation: a transformation that creates similar figures.

dimensions: the measure of the sides of a figure.

discount: the amount by which a price is reduced; refer also to *rate of discount* in the index.

distributive property: a property of numbers illustrated by
$3 \times (5 + 4) = 3 \times 5 + 3 \times 4;$
$3 \times (5 - 4) = 3 \times 5 - 3 \times 4;$

dividend: see *division*.

divisible: a number is divisible by another number if the remainder is zero; see also *division*.

division:

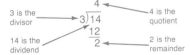

divisor: see *division*.

dodecagon: a polygon with twelve sides; see also *polygon*

dodecahedron: a polyhedron with twelve faces; see also *polyhedron*.

---

edge: see *polyhedron*.

equation: a mathematical sentence that shows equality; the symbol = is used; e.g. 4 + 5 = 9 is an equation; refer also to the index.

equiangular triangle: a triangle with all sides of equal size; a triangle with 3 lines of symmetry.

equivalent decimals: decimal numbers that name the same number.

equivalent fractions: fractions that name the same number.

equivalent equations: equations that have the same solution.

equivalent ratios: ratios that name the same lowest-terms ratio.

estimate: refer to the index.

even number: a whole number that has 2 as a factor.

expanded form: a decimal number is written in expanded form, $421 = 4 \times 100 + 2 \times 10 + 1$; expanded form shows the place value of each digit.

exponent: a number that shows how many times the base is used as a factor; e.g. for 2^3, the exponent is 3.

---

face: see *polyhedron*.

factor: any natural number that evenly divides a number.

factor tree: a diagram used for finding the prime factors of a number; see also *prime factor*.

flip: refer to *reflection* in the index.

flow chart: an organizational method to show a sequence of instructions or steps to find an answer.

formula: a rule or equation used to find the value of one variable when the remaining variables are known.

fraction: a number that represents a part of a whole; common fractions are shown by numerals, such as $\frac{2}{3}$, $\frac{3}{4}$, and so on; decimal fractions are shown by numerals such as 0.4, 0.68, and so on.

frequency: the number of times some event or item occurs.

frequency table: a diagram used to record the number of times some event or item occurs; see also *frequency*.

---

gram: a unit of mass.

graph: a display of information or data using a pictorial method; see also *bar graph, circle graph, broken line graph, pictograph, stem-leaf plot*.

greatest common factor: the greatest factor common to 2 or more numbers; see also *factor*.

grid: a pattern of lines or dots; see also *Cartesian co-ordinates*.

---

hectare: a unit of measure for measuring area, usually land. One hectare is equal to 10 000 m².

height: see *altitude*.

heptagon: a polygon with seven sides; see also *polygon*.

hexagon: a polygon with six sides; see also *polygon*.

hexahedron: a polyhedron with six faces; see also *polyhedron*.

horizontal axis: the horizontal number line drawn to show Cartesian co-ordinates.

Icosahedron: a polyhedron with twenty faces; see also *polyhedron*.

image: the figure produced by a transformation; see also *transformation*.

improper fraction: a fraction in which the numerator is greater than the denominator.

inequality signs: the symbols used for inequality are listed: not equal to $\neq$; less than $<$; greater than $>$; less than or equal to $\leqslant$; greater than or equal to $\geqslant$.

inequation: a mathematical sentence that shows inequality; e.g. $3 < 4, 5 > 3$.

input: a number used to replace a variable.

inspection method: a method used to solve an equation; refer to the index.

integer: one of the numbers $\ldots, -3, -2, -1, 0, +1, +2, +3, \ldots$

interior angles: refer to the index.

intersecting lines: lines that have a point in common.

intersection point: the point common to intersecting lines.

inverse operation: addition is the inverse operation of subtraction; multiplication is the inverse operation of division, and so on.

isosceles triangle: a triangle with two sides of equal size; a triangle with 1 line of symmetry.

---

kilogram: a unit of mass shown by the symbol kg

kilometre: a unit of distance shown by the symbol km

kite: a polygon as shown.

---

legend: the description of the symbols in a pictograph.

line of reflection: see *line of symmetry*.

line of symmetry: a line that divides a figure into two congruent parts; also referred to as *axis of symmetry*, or *line of reflection*, or *mirror line*.

line segment: part of a line with two end points.

line symmetry: a figure has line symmetry if it has a line of symmetry.

litre: a unit of volume, often used to indicate the measure of the contents of a container; refer also to the index.

lowest common denominator: the lowest common multiple of two or more denominators; see also *common denominator*.

lowest common multiple: the smallest number that is a multiple of two or more numbers; see also *common multiple*.

lowest terms: a fraction or ratio for which the numerator and denominator have only the number 1 as a common factor.

---

magnitude: size.

mapping: a correspondence of points,

mass: the amount of substance or matter in an object; see also *gram*, *kilogram*.

mathematical expression: a combination of numbers and symbols; e.g. $4 + 3, 8 \times 3$.

mathematical sentence: a statement expressed in numbers and symbols, e.g. $4 + 3 = 7, 8 \times 3 = 24, 4 < 5$

mean: see average.

median: the middle value of the data.

metre: a unit of length; refer to the index.

midpoint: the point on a line segment that divides it into two equal lengths.

milligram: a unit of mass.

millilitre: a unit of volume or capacity.

millimetre: a unit of length.

mirror line: see *line of symmetry*.

mixed number: a number that has a whole part and a fraction part; e.g. $1\frac{3}{4}$.

mode: the member of the data that occurs most frequently.

multiple: a multiple of a number is a product of the number and a whole number.

---

natural number: one of the numbers 1, 2, 3, 4, . . . ; they are called counting numbers.

negative integer: one of the integers $-1, -2, -3, \ldots$

net: a pattern or arrangement of polygons to construct a polyhedron.

net price: see *selling price*.

numerator: in the fraction $\frac{2}{3}$, the number 2 is the numerator; the numerator shows how many equal parts there are; see also *denominator*.

---

obtuse angle: an angle that measures more than $90°$ but less than $180°$.

obtuse triangle: a triangle with an obtuse angle.

octagon: a polygon with eight sides.

octahedron: a polyhedron with eight faces; see also *polyhedron*.

odd number: a whole number that does not have 2 as a factor.

opposite integers: the numbers $+2$ and -2 are opposite integers.

ordered pair of numbers: a pair of numbers in which the order is important; used to represent Cartesian co-ordinates of a point. refer also to the index.

order of operations: a set of rules to follow when evaluating expressions; refer to the index.

order of rotational symmetry: see *rotational symmetry*; refer to the index.

origin: the point at which the horizontal and vertical axes meet.

outcome: the result obtained in an experiment, etc.

---

parallel lines: two lines in the same plane that do not have any point in common.

parallelogram: a quadrilateral with opposite sides parallel; see also *quadrilateral*.

pentagon: a polygon with five sides; see also *polygon*.

per annum: the interest rate given in terms of one year.

percent: a number of parts per 100.

perimeter: the distance around a closed figure; for a circle, its circumference.

perpendicular bisector: a line that bisects a line segment and meets it at a right angle.

perpendicular lines: two or more lines that meet at right angles.

perspective drawing: a drawing which makes a figure appear three dimensional.

pictograph: a diagram that displays data or information using pictures.

pie graph: see *circle graph*.

place value: refer to the index.

plane of symmetry: a flat surface that acts like a mirror in reflecting one half of the shape onto the other half.

polygon: a closed figure made of line segments.

polyhedron: a three-dimensional figure with faces that are polygons.

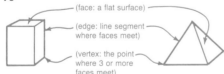

positive integer: $+1, +2, +3, \ldots$ are positive integers.

power: a power, such as 2^3, is expressed using a base and exponent.

pre-image point: the point to which a transformation is applied.

prime factor: a factor of a number that is a prime number; see also *prime number*.

prime number: a number that has only 1 and itself as factors. It has exactly two factors.

principal or positive square root: the positive square root.

principal: the money deposited into or borrowed from a bank.

prism: refer to the index. These figures are prisms.

probability: a number that shows how likely it is that an event will happen; it is defined as the number of favourable outcomes divided by the total number of outcomes.

proper fraction: a fraction for which the numerator is less than the denominator.

proportion: an equation that shows the equality of two ratios.

protractor: an instrument used to measure angles; refer also to the index.

Pythagorean relation: in any right triangle the square of the length of the hypotenuse is equal to the sum of the squares of the length of the other two sides.

pyramid: refer to the index. These figures are pyramids.

These faces are congruent triangles

The base is a polygon.

---

quadrant: one of four regions formed by two intersecting perpendicular lines.

quadrilateral: a polygon with four sides; see also *polygon*.

quotient: see *division*.

---

radius: half of the diameter of a circle; a line segment that joins the centre of a circle to any point on the circle.

range: the difference between the greatest and least value of data.

rate: refer to the index.

rate of commission: rate at which commission is paid.

ratio: a comparison of two numbers.

rational number: a number that can be expressed as the quotient of two integers, provided the divisor is not zero.

ray: a part of a line with one end point.

reciprocals: two numbers are said to be reciprocals if their product is 1; e.g. $\frac{2}{3}$ and $\frac{3}{2}$ are reciprocals $\frac{2}{3} \times \frac{3}{2} = 1$.

rectangle: a quadrilateral with opposite sides equal and angles that measure $90°$; see also *quadrilateral*.

reflection: refer to the index; see also *flip* in the index.

reflectional symmetry: see *line symmetry*.

reflex angle: an angle with measure between $180°$ and $360°$.

regular polygon: a polygon with all sides and all angles equal.

regular polyhedron: a polyhedron with faces that are congruent regular polygons; see also *polyhedron*.

remainder: see *division*.

root: the solution to an equation.

repeating decimal: a decimal fraction in which the digits in the decimal repeat e.g., $\frac{3}{11}$ = 0.272 727 . . . written as $0.\overline{27}$ or $0.2\dot{7}$.

replacement method: a method used to solve an equation.

rhombus: a parallelogram with all sides equal.

right angle: an angle that measures 90°.

right bisector: see *perpendicular bisector*.

right triangle: a triangle with a right angle.

rotation: refer to the index.

rotation angle: the amount and direction of the rotation.

rotation centre: the centre about which an object is rotated.

rotational symmetry: a figure that fits onto itself more than once during one complete rotation is said to have *rotational symmetry*. The number of times it fits onto itself during one complete rotation is its order of rotational symmetry.

rounding off: refer to the index.

sample: a part of a group or population that is studied in order to predict information about the entire group or population.

scale: see *similar figures*.

scale drawings: see *similar figures*.

scale ratio: ratio of corresponding sides in similar figures.

scalene triangle: a triangle with all sides of unequal length.

scientific notation: a method of writing large and small numbers using powers of ten.

selling price: amount of money the customer pays after a discount.

shell: a three-dimensional figure of which the interior is empty.

side: a line segment of a polygon.

similar figures: figures that are the same shape but not always the same size; the scale drawing of a figure is similar to the original figure. The lengths on an enlargement or reduction of a figure are an enlargement or reduction of the corresponding lengths in the original figure. The ratio of the distance on the scale drawing to the actual distance is called its scale.

similarity transformations: transformations for which the original and image figures are similar (dilatations).

size transformation: see *dilatation*.

skeleton: a three-dimensional figure that shows its framework.

slide: refer to the index; see also *translation*, *slide arrow*.

slide arrow: an arrow that shows the distance and direction of a slide; see also *slide*.

solid: a three-dimensional figure that is not hollow.

solution: a number or numbers that make a mathematical sentence true.

solve: the process of finding a solution.

square number: a number that can be expressed as a base to the second power, e.g. $36 = 6^2$.

square root: a number which when multiplied by itself produces the given number.

stem-leaf plot: a diagram that is used to display data or information; refer to the index.

straight angle: an angle that measures 180°.

substitution: to replace the variable with a numerical value.

supplementary angles: angles for which the sum is 180°.

surface area: the total area of all the faces of a three-dimensional object.

symmetry: see *line symmetry*, *rotational symmetry*.

systematic trial: a method used to solve an equation; refer to the index. see *solving equations*.

tally chart: a diagram that is used to display data or information by means of strokes and bars.

terminating decimal: a decimal which does not repeat.

tetrahedron: a polyhedron with four faces; see also *polyhedron*.

tiling pattern: a pattern composed of one or more congruent tiles that cover a surface with no spaces left and no tiles overlapping.

tonne: a unit of mass.

transformation: a translation, reflection or rotation; the term transformation is also used to refer to slides, flips, and turns; refer to the index.

translation: refer to the index; also refer to *slide*.

transversal: a line that intersects two or more other lines.

trapezoid: a quadrilateral with one pair of parallel sides; also often called a trapezium, see also *quadrilateral*.

triangle: a polygon with three sides; see also *polygon*.

turn: refer to the index; also refer to *rotation*.

unit: a standard quantity of measure, e.g., a metre is a standard unit of length.

unit rate: a rate for which the second term is one.

variable: a symbol used to represent a number or numbers.

vertex: the common point of two rays of an angle; the point where two sides of a polygon meet; the point where three or more faces of a polyhedron meet.

vertical axis: the vertical number line drawn to show Cartesian co-ordinates.

verification or verify: the process of checking your solution.

volume: the amount of space occupied by a three-dimensional figure; measured in cubic units, such as cubic centimetres and in litres.

whole number: one of the numbers 0, 1, 2, 3, . . .

Index